PHYSICAL PRINCIPLES OF CHEMISTRY

OTHER BOOKS IN CHEMISTRY

General Chemistry (Second Edition)
Linus Pauling

A Laboratory Study of Chemical Principles (Second Edition)
Harper W. Frantz

College Chemistry (Third Edition)
Linus Pauling

College Chemistry in the Laboratory, No. 1
Lloyd E. Malm and Harper W. Frantz

College Chemistry in the Laboratory, No. 2
Lloyd E. Malm and Harper W. Frantz

General Chemistry Workbook: How to Solve Chemistry Problems (Second Edition)
Conway Pierce and R. Nelson Smith

Introductory Quantitative Chemistry
Axel R. Olson, Charles W. Koch, and George C. Pimentel

Chemistry of the Covalent Bond
Leallyn B. Clapp

A System of Chemical Analysis
Ernest H. Swift

Chemical Thermodynamics: A Course of Study (Second Edition)
Frederick T. Wall

Principles of Organic Chemistry (Second Edition)
T. A. Geissman

The Hydrogen Bond
George C. Pimentel and Aubrey L. McClellan

Structure and Change: An Introduction to the Science of Matter
G. S. Christiansen and Paul H. Garrett

Essentials of Chemistry in the Laboratory
Harper W. Frantz and Lloyd E. Malm

Qualitative Elemental Analysis
Ernest H. Swift and William P. Schaefer

Fundamental Experiments for College Chemistry
Harper W. Frantz and Lloyd E. Malm

Tables of Experimental Dipole Moments
A. L. McClellan

Selected Experiments in Organic Chemistry
George K. Helmkamp and Harry W. Johnson, Jr.

Experimental Biochemistry
John M. Clark, Jr., Editor

The Architecture of Molecules
Linus Pauling and Roger Hayward

PHYSICAL PRINCIPLES OF CHEMISTRY

R. H. COLE *Brown University*

J. S. COLES *Bowdoin College*

W. H. FREEMAN AND COMPANY

SAN FRANCISCO AND LONDON

Preface

THIS TEXT was written to meet the need for a modern physical chemistry logically ordered in terms of present-day chemical and physical concepts and in terms of the preparation of present-day students. It is based upon a syllabus first used in the sophomore physical chemistry course of the Brown University chemistry program. It has also proved a challenging text for college juniors and seniors taking physical chemistry in the normal sequence. Some students entering college will have had precollege work in chemistry, mathematics, and physics of such quality that they can undertake the study of physical chemistry according to this text as freshmen. We assume a good secondary school course in chemistry, a year of college physics, or an advanced second year of high school physics, and an acquaintance with differential and integral calculus. Since the students at Brown begin organic chemistry as freshmen, a considerable number of the examples chosen use organic compounds.

The order of presentation is unusual in beginning with an introductory account of atomic and molecular theory, followed by examination of the gaseous, solid, and liquid states of matter, before taking up such traditional subjects as thermodynamics, equilibria, and kinetics. This order was dictated by our belief that an elementary knowledge of molecular structure and kinetic theory is invaluable background for proper understanding of thermodynamics. It has a further advantage that early chapters do not require extensive use of the calculus, which permits students to take mathematics at this level concurrently.

The authors are convinced of the value of problems, both as a test of understanding and as incentive to apply principles to new situations. Students will find time to work but a small fraction of the more than 600 problems available. If, however, they find these a test and a challenge, the purpose of the problems will have been achieved.

Some readers may wonder at the elementary considerations of Chapters 1 and 2. Many college students take for granted the physical existence of atoms and molecules, without appreciating the strength (or weakness) of the evidence. In our brief review we hope to suggest the efforts by which this evidence was secured; at the same time, some of the elementary methods and calculations for the determination of atomic and molecular weights can be stated concisely. For those who have already studied these subjects, these chapters are a brief review to ensure that they are familiar with such concepts and problems. Elementary texts with fuller presentations are easily available for those whose background has been weak.

In part, the content of earlier chapters has been prepared to accommodate students who may not have had any general chemistry course in college. This material can be quickly skimmed by college juniors or seniors in courses taken in the normal sequence. Similarly, some parts of the chapters dealing with equilibria, solutions, and ionic reactions include greater detail than the usual physical chemistry textbook. This is because a knowledge of qualitative or quantitative analysis is not a prerequisite for the study of this text. In addition, it permits such students to undertake directly courses on instrumental methods of analysis which assume previous mastery of ionic equilibrium calculations.

As is always the case, the authors are obviously indebted to many others—first of all to the many workers and writers in chemistry and physics who have preceeded them. We should acknowledge especially the contributions of many past and present members of the Department of Chemistry at Brown University who took part in the countless discussions out of which the Brown Plan and the general outlines for this book were conceived: Charles A. Kraus, Paul C. Cross, Donald F. Hornig, Leallyn B. Clapp, Robert P. Epple, William W. Russell, and others. We want explicitly to recognize with our thanks the work of Professor Donald J. Denny of Hamilton College and that of Professor Bayes M. Norton of Kenyon College in the preparation of many of the problems. We also acknowledge the labors of students who undertook to work all of the problems. They found many errors and suggested many improvements; we are grateful for all their contributions.

We are particularly indebted to our families for their patience, forbearance, and encouragement.

September, 1964   R. H. COLE
                                                       J. S. COLES

Contents

Introduction   ix

CHAPTER

1. Evidence for the Existence of Atoms and Molecules   1
2. The Determination of Atomic and Molecular Weights   11
3. Fundamental Particles. Electrons and Nuclei   23
4. Matter and Radiation   39
5. Quantum Principles and Atomic Structure   54
6. Molecular Constitution   101
7. The Solid State   142
8. Equations of State of Gases   178
9. Kinetic Theory. Boltzmann's Equation   216
10. Heat Capacities and Molecular Energies of Gases   246
11. Some Properties of Liquids and Solutions   273
12. The First Law of Thermodynamics   323
13. Thermochemistry   353
14. The Second Law of Thermodynamics. Entropy and Chemical Potential   382
15. Equilibrium in Gas Reactions   418
16. Heterogeneous and Solution Equilibria   462
17. Electrochemical Reactions and Galvanic Cells   512
18. Ionic Conductance in Solution   570
19. Ionic Reactions in Solution   607
20. The Phase Rule and Some Applications   644
21. Surface Chemistry   688
22. Chemical Kinetics   727

INDEX   782

Introduction

PREVIOUSLY you have studied the chemistry of compounds whose molecules are composed of atoms joined by covalent bonds, and you have become familiar with the chemistry of compounds made up of carbon, hydrogen, oxygen, and a limited number of other elements. You have also studied "chemistry" in two other garbs, namely, in your mathematics and physics courses, both of which are as essential to chemistry as the test tube and the Bunsen burner. The study of mathematics has provided you with a language by which ideas and concepts that are difficult to express in words may be expressed in symbols and equations. You know a most powerful system of shorthand; how much easier it is to write "dy/dx" than "the rate of change of y with respect to x"! You will find that many of the principles of physics that you have learned will be equally useful as principles of chemistry.

In the present work, we shall study the physical principles of chemistry, and shall make frequent application of concepts of physics to chemical properties and problems. We shall express as many of these ideas as possible in the language of mathematics, so as to give them precision and quantitative meaning.

Our discussions will begin with the consideration of the blocks from which matter is built—atoms and molecules—the evidence for their existence, their structure, and the means by which we have obtained our present ideas concerning their structure. We shall then study the way in which these atoms and molecules interact with one another to make up the various forms of matter: solids, gases, and liquids. In order to understand, however, the properties of the three states in which matter may exist, and the transitions from one state to another, we require a knowledge of the energy relationships that exist in material systems. Many of these relationships must be considered on a statistical basis as the net result of forces between enormous numbers of molecules. These relationships involve enthalpy, entropy, and other functions that are included in the logical development of thermodynamics. This background will enable us to go on to study mixtures of matter, in the form of solutions, and then, later, the electrical properties of these systems, homogeneous and heterogeneous equilibrium, and chemical kinetics.

Your understanding of the physical principles of chemistry will enable you to use them in the further study of inorganic and organic chemistry. The thorough study of all the elements beyond the first row in the periodic table is in many ways more complex, and in some respects simpler than that of the elements you have already studied. Thus, complex interrelations compose the science of inorganic chemistry. Although inorganic chemistry has existed as a segment of chemistry for a long time, there is still much more that is unknown about it than is known.

Your study of the physical principles of chemistry will be challenging, for you will have to use and integrate information and techniques from several different courses in understanding these concepts. At the same time you will have to understand the extension and application of the content of physical chemistry to other courses. You will also obtain much practice in the application of quantitative ideas to chemical problems, and in so doing you will solve many examples that will test your understanding of the principles involved, and your ability to apply them.

Chapter 1

Evidence for the Existence of Atoms and Molecules

AMONG THE MOST basic chemical concepts is the idea that matter is composed of atoms and molecules. In spite of its fundamental importance—because it is so essential to the explanation of chemical reactions as well as to the whole of chemistry—beginning students must often accept this concept without critically evaluating the experimental evidence on which it is based.

It is highly important that the grounds for the existence of atoms and molecules and the manner in which the atomic and molecular hypothesis is supported be clearly understood. These supporting data fall into two classes: the older evidence (principally chemical), which became known in the first half of the nineteenth century, and the modern evidence, obtained mainly during the present century.

A third type of confirmation lies in our ability to determine actual values that we can assign as atomic or molecular weights to chemical substances. This is confirming evidence in the sense that these could not be determined unless discrete chemical units such as atoms and molecules do exist.

1.1. The Older Evidence for the Existence of Atoms and Molecules

Dalton, in 1808, and before him, Higgins, in 1789, proposed an atomic theory for the structure of matter. (Previously, Leucippus and Democritus, in the fifth century B.C., had propounded an atomic theory, and later in the sixteenth and seventeenth centuries, Galileo, Newton, and others held that matter was composed of discrete particles.) Their suggestions were considered quite radical, however, and were not accepted immediately, although they are readily accepted today. In fact, in the twentieth century, William Ostwald, one of the leading early physical chemists, expressed his own doubt of the validity of the atomic theory.

Dalton's name is associated with the atomic theory because he was able to support his argument with quantitative experimental data. He advanced four main postulates: (1) an atom is the smallest particle of an element that can exist (this does not necessarily imply that atoms are not made up of still smaller particles); (2) as many different kinds of atoms exist as there are different elements; (3) the atoms of a given element are alike in every respect; (4) individual molecules of a given compound contain the same number of atoms of each of the different elements that make up the compound.

Our present-day knowledge of isotopes (different forms of the same element having the same atomic number but different atomic weights) modifies the second and third of Dalton's postulates. But although there may be more than one kind of an atom for a given element, their differences in chemical properties are almost always too small to be significant. Further, the isotope ratio is almost always constant in naturally occurring elements; hence the average atomic weight is practically constant.

Dalton thus believed that for any sample of a particular pure substance (element or compound) the ultimate particles of which it is composed are alike in size, mass, and shape; that chemical reactions involve no change in the atoms other than their rearrangement; and that the combination of atoms to form molecules is always in the ratio of small whole numbers, as represented in molecular formulas XY, X_2Y, and so on.

The evidence available to Dalton when he proposed the atomic hypothesis was both meager and subtle, but the introduction of his four postulates at the beginning of a great era of quantitative work in chemistry was opportune, and a large amount of experimental work not only supported but was made amenable to explanation by the atomic hypothesis. The data available to Dalton may be summarized by the following empirical laws.

The Law of Conservation of Mass

For any chemical or physical change, the total mass of the substances produced must be equal to that of the substances entering into the change. For all ordinary chemical reactions or processes, both mass and energy are independently so nearly conserved that any deviation from the law of conservation of mass is negligible. Even in nuclear reactions, in which large amounts of energy (ΔE) may be released, the change in mass (Δm) as given by Einstein's equation $\Delta E = \Delta m\, c^2$ (where c is the velocity of light), is still very small. For example, in the Hiroshima atomic bomb, which released 8.4×10^{20} ergs (on the basis of the statement that the energy released was equivalent to the explosion of 20,000 tons of TNT), the difference between the mass of the uranium 235 and the mass of the fission products was less than one gram.

b. The Law of Definite Proportions

In any sample of a particular compound, the elements of which it is composed are present in a definite and constant ratio by weight. In water, for example, hydrogen and oxygen are always present in the ratio 1.008:8 by weight (the numbers given, 1.008 for hydrogen, and 8 for oxygen, are those that have been arbitrarily assigned as the equivalent weights of these elements). Beginning in 1961, the values assigned for the entire scale of atomic, molecular, and equivalent weights have been determined relative to an agreed value for C^{12} of exactly 12. Previously two scales were used: the chemical scale based upon an arbitrarily assigned value of 16.0000 as the atomic weight of "ordinary" oxygen (a mixture of O^{16}, O^{17}, and O^{18} as it occurs in nature), and the physical scale, in which the value 16.0000 was assigned the O^{16} isotope. Values of atomic weights on the chemical scale were 0.027% less than those on the physical scale. The conversion factor between the C^{12} scale now accepted and the O^{16} (physical) scale is

$$1 \text{ unit } (C^{12} = 12) = (1.000317917 \pm 0.000000017) \text{ units } (O^{16} = 16)$$

The reciprocal is $0.999682184 \pm 0.000000017$, and may be used as a factor to convert masses given on the O^{16} scale to the C^{12} scale.

The Law of Multiple Proportions

If two elements unite to form two or more different compounds, the weights of one element—combining with a fixed weight of the second element to form the different compounds—will always be in the ratio of small whole numbers.

As an example, consider water, which is composed of 88.8% oxygen and 11.2% hydrogen. Another compound of hydrogen and oxygen is hydrogen peroxide, which contains 94.1% oxygen and 5.9% hydrogen. For water, 7.94 grams of oxygen will combine with one gram of hydrogen; for hydrogen peroxide, 15.9 grams of oxygen will combine with one gram of hydrogen. Within the accuracy of the figures, the ratio 7.94:15.9 is equal to 1:2, a ratio of small whole numbers.

The law of multiple proportions was first proposed by Dalton, and his atomic hypothesis partially prompted its proposal.

The Law of Combining Weights

In all the compounds of a given element, the weight of that element may be represented by some number known as its combining weight, or by a simple multiple of that number.

In terms of present knowledge, the combining weight of an element is equal to the atomic weight of the element, or some integral fraction thereof. We know that the combining weight of an element used in earlier times often corresponds to the equivalent weight as defined today.

At the beginning of the nineteenth century there was considerable uncertainty as to which multiple of the combining weight for a given element corresponded to its atomic weight. For that reason, combining weights were often used in place of atomic weights.

The Law of Combining Volumes

In a reaction involving gases, the volumes of gaseous reactants or gaseous products measured under the same conditions of temperature and pressure are always in the ratio of small whole numbers.

The following equations represent several reactions which exemplify this law.

carbon (solid) + oxygen (gas) → carbon monoxide (gas)
1 volume → 2 volumes

nitrogen (gas) + hydrogen (gas) → ammonia (gas)
1 volume + 3 volumes → 2 volumes

carbon (solid) + oxygen (gas) → carbon dioxide (gas)
1 volume → 1 volume

The fact for some reactions that the volume of the products is greater than that of the reactants, for some less, and for some the same, was incomprehensible prior to the complete understanding of the Dalton theory.

Dalton could not agree that this law, discovered by Gay-Lussac, supported the atomic theory. To Berzelius, however, it suggested that equal volumes of gases contain equal numbers of atoms. The final theoretical consequence was *Avogadro's hypothesis*—equal volumes of gases under the same conditions of temperature and pressure contain equal numbers of *molecules*. It was the lack of distinction between atoms and molecules of gaseous elements that caused Dalton to reject Gay-Lussac's law as inconsistent with his theory. (We know now that one gram-molecular weight of any gas occupies 22.4 liters of space under standard conditions and contains 0.602×10^{24} molecules.)

Faraday's Laws of Electrolysis

The two laws were first proposed by Michael Faraday in the 1830's.

1. The weight of a substance produced or consumed during electrolysis at either electrode will be directly proportional to the quantity of electricity passing through the electrolytic cell.

2. The weights of different substances used or produced by a given quantity of electricity will be proportional to their respective equivalent weights.

On the basis of more recent work, these may be summarized as follows: 96,519 coulombs (one faraday) of electricity during electrolysis will produce or consume one gram equivalent weight of a substance at each electrode of an electrolytic cell.

1.2. Modern Evidence for Atoms and Molecules

Even if we reason from our extensive present-day knowledge of atoms and molecules, the evidence for their existence just cited is indirect and not free from possible ambiguity. It is no wonder that many of Dalton's contemporaries found it hard to accept the atomic theory.

Drawing a sharp line between the older evidence and modern evidence is difficult, but if that line is conceptual rather than temporal, the modern evidence for the atomic theory may be said to include that based principally upon physical considerations, theoretical or experimental, rather than chemical. This evidence became significant about the middle of the nineteenth century—when a variety of experiments suggested that the old concept of the continuity of matter might be faulty.

Kinetic Theory of Gases

One of the first bits of modern evidence was the kinetic theory of gases (developed in Chapter 9). By assuming that a gas is composed of molecules moving for the most part independently of each other, it is possible quantitatively to account for the various empirical gas laws: Charles's law—that the volume of a gas will vary directly with the absolute temperature if the pressure is held constant; Boyle's law—that the pressure of a gas varies inversely with the volume at constant temperature; the equation of state for a perfect gas—

$$PV = nRT,$$

where P is the pressure, V the volume, n the number of moles, R the universal gas constant, and T the absolute temperature; Graham's law—that the rate of diffusion of a gas is inversely proportional to the square root of its molecular weight. The success of the assumption of the kinetic-molecular hypothesis in quantitatively accounting for the observed behavior of gases described by the above laws, as well as by others not listed, is excellent evidence for the existence of atoms and molecules.

X-ray Diffraction

Further, more recent evidence for atoms and molecules comes from X-ray diffraction. An X-ray diffraction pattern is obtained when a beam of X-rays, which are electromagnetic radiations of very short wavelength (about 10^{-8} cm), is scattered by a crystal placed in the beam. The resulting diffraction patterns may be quantitatively accounted for by assuming that the crystal by which these X-rays are diffracted is made up of atoms, ions, or molecules in orderly arrangements (Chapter 7). The success of this assumption is strong evidence in support of the existence of atoms and molecules.

Electron Diffraction

Evidence to be presented in Chapter 5 will demonstrate that a beam of accelerated electrons will have associated with it a wave motion analogous to that associated with the photon for ordinary light.

For some beams of electrons, the wavelengths are about equal to those of X-ray beams. Electron beams differ from X-rays, however, in that their penetrating power is much lower. Although they are stopped by crystalline materials of any ordinary thickness, they are scattered by gaseous substances, and the diffraction patterns so obtained may be explained by assuming molecules in the gas, composed of atoms acting as diffracting centers. Thus by using X-ray and electron diffraction, actual three-dimensional models of molecules and atoms and crystals may be constructed.

Mass Spectrograph

Just as the optical spectrograph, familiar from the study of physics, separates a beam of light into its components of different wavelengths, so does a mass spectrograph separate an atomic or molecular beam into its components of different masses.

There are several different forms of the mass spectrograph, which is discussed in Section 3.6, and illustrated in Fig. 3.4. In general, an ion beam is formed by vaporizing the substance under investigation and then ionizing the gaseous particles by bombardment with electrons from a hot filament. The ion beam so formed is then accelerated between two electrically charged plates, deflected by transmission through a magnetic field, and focused on a detection device, such as a photographic plate. As the beam is deflected, the heavier particles are not affected to as great an extent as the lighter ones, and thus the separation on the basis of mass is made. The different isotopes of a given element may in this way be separated and identified, and similar techniques may be used in analysis of organic materials, particularly hydrocarbons, which are difficult to analyze by ordinary methods.

The assumption of atoms, isotopes, and molecules makes it possible to interpret unambiguously the results obtained through the use of the mass spectrograph.

The Electron Microscope

With an optical microscope using visible light, there is a theoretical limit of about 1500 diameters for maximum magnification, owing to the wavelength of the visible light used. Upon the realization of the wave nature of the electron in 1925, and with the subsequent developments in focusing electron beams by means of electrostatic and magnetic lenses, the construction of an electron microscope capable of magnification up to 100,000 diameters was made possible. While the limit of resolution with the electron microscope is still too great to permit the observation of individual atoms, it is sufficiently small that photographs of naturally occurring protein molecules, such as the "bushy stunt" virus, give a good impression of the grosser features of size and shape of these very large molecules.

Atomic and Molecular Structure

Prior to the end of the nineteenth century, it was believed that atoms were ultimate particles and could not be further subdivided. In 1876, R. Angus Smith suggested that atoms were not necessarily indivisible, and by 1889 J. J. Thomson speculated that electrons were contained in atoms. Further developments in atomic structure and the contributions of line spectroscopy in this field will be considered in Chapter 5. Other equally pertinent evidence of similar nature may be found in the discovery of various fundamental particles, such as the electron, proton, neutron, positron, neutrino, and mesons. The practical use of atomic and molecular beams in laboratory experiments (and even in production processes) must also be considered as substantiating evidence.

In addition to atomic structure, the results of the study of molecular structure have provided almost indisputable evidence for the existence of atoms and molecules. The study of molecular structure by means of band spectroscopy and infrared and Raman spectroscopy, together with X-ray and electron diffraction, permits a detailed description of molecules, including the assignment of the distances, orientations, and valence-bond forces between the atoms within a molecule.

Avogadro's Number

From a knowledge of the charge on the electron, and independently from X-ray data, it has been shown that there are 0.602×10^{24} atoms in one gram atomic weight of any element, or 0.602×10^{24} molecules per gram molecular weight of any compound. This allows the determination of the absolute mass of any given atom or molecule.

The Periodic Table

The orderly consecutive arrangement of the elements in the periodic table according to an experimentally obtained parameter of atomic structure (the atomic number) is in itself evidence supporting the existence of atoms. It would be difficult to conceive why there should be such regular similarities and variation in the properties of the elements as arranged in the periodic table were that arrangement not rationally determined in terms of actual elemental atoms.

Atomic and Molecular Weights

While it seems scarcely necessary to belabor the point by further presentation of evidence for the validity of the atomic theory, one final and different attack lies in our ability to assign atomic and molecular weights. It is, of course, conceivable that some other hypothesis might be presented which would account for the experimental data that has been interpreted in terms of the assignment of atomic and molecular weights. Careful sifting of all supporting data, however, indicates that the ability to determine atomic and molecular weights must be considered as evidence that there are such particles as atoms and molecules. Methods by which atomic and molecular weights may be determined are discussed in Chapter 2.

Suggested Readings

The history of the early development of chemistry has been told in numerous places. A very readable account of its subject is given in *Discovery of the Elements*

(6th ed.) by M. E. Weeks, edited by H. M. Leicester (Journal of Chemical Education, Easton, Pa., 1956). A treatise with a monumental store of information in its four volumes—of some 800 pages each—is *A History of Chemistry* by J. R. Partington (Macmillan, New York, 1960). Some of the classic early developments in atomic theory are described in *Case Histories in Experimental Science*, edited by J. B. Conant (Harvard, Cambridge, 1950).

Chapter 2

The Determination
of Atomic and
Molecular Weights

THE RAPID ADVANCES in our understanding of the nature of matter came as the subject of chemistry became quantitative. Similarly, our understanding of the principles and ideas of the preceding chapter will be more complete after we have used them in a quantitative fashion. It is appropriate, therefore, that some examples of the quantitative data from which such principles were derived be studied, as well as some examples of the quantitative application of those principles.

2.1. Law of Definite Proportions

This law states that for all samples of a particular compound substance the elements composing that substance are present in a fixed, and constant ratio by weight.

A sample of chromyl chloride (sometimes called chromium oxychloride) was found by analysis to contain 33.6% by weight of chromium,

11

20.6% of oxygen, and 45.8% of chlorine. From the law of definite proportions, we know that every sample of chromyl chloride contains 0.336/0.206 g of chromium per gram of oxygen. If a sample of chromic oxychloride contains 6.83 g of oxygen, the number of grams of chromium (x) and chlorine (y) contained therein can be calculated. Thus

$$x = \frac{0.336}{0.206} \times 6.83 \text{ g} = 11.13 \text{ g of chromium}$$

and similarly

$$y = \frac{0.458}{0.206} \times 6.83 \text{ g} = 15.18 \text{ g of chlorine}$$

(In this example, as in most of the examples and problems in this book, the number of significant figures included has been limited to the number which can be calculated by a 10-inch slide rule. When greater precision than can be obtained on the slide rule is needed, it will usually be apparent from the problem.)

2.2. Law of Multiple Proportions

If two elements unite to form two or more different compounds, the weights of one element—combining with a fixed weight of the second element to form the different compounds—will always be in the ratio of small whole numbers.

This law need not be limited to a series of compounds composed of two elements, but applies equally well if three or more elements form a number of different compounds. For example, carbon, hydrogen, and oxygen combine to form the compounds listed below, with the corresponding percentage compositions.

Compound	Carbon	Hydrogen	Oxygen
Formaldehyde	40.0%	6.7%	53.3%
Methanol	37.5%	12.5%	50.0%
Formic acid	26.1%	4.3%	69.6%
Oxalic acid	26.7%	2.2%	71.1%

Taking one gram of hydrogen as a fixed weight of one of the elements, the weights of the others combining with it to form these four compounds may be found by simple arithmetic.

Compound	Wt. of Hydrogen (g)	Wt. of Element Combining with 1 g of Hydrogen	
		Carbon (g)	Oxygen (g)
Formaldehyde	1.00	5.97 (2)	7.96 (2)
Methanol	1.00	3.00 (1)	4.00 (1)
Formic acid	1.00	6.07 (2)	16.2 (4)
Oxalic acid	1.00	12.1 (4)	32.3 (8)

The ratios of the weights of either carbon or oxygen combining with a fixed weight of hydrogen to form the different compounds is the ratio of small whole numbers (shown in parentheses), within the limits of the precision of the figures given.

2.3. Law of Combining Weights

In all compounds of a given element, the relative weight of that element may be represented by some number known as its combining weight, or by a simple multiple of that number. Table 2.1 gives the names and compositions of a number of compounds which illustrate this relationship.

TABLE 2.1.   *Composition of Several Compounds*

Compound	Composition by Weight						
	CARBON	HYDROGEN	CHLORINE	OXYGEN	PHOSPHORUS	NITROGEN	MAGNESIUM
Carbon tetrachloride	6.005		2 × 35.46				
Methyl chloride	2 × 6.005	3 × 1.008	35.46				
Methylene chloride	6.005	1.008	35.46				
Methanol	6.005	2 × 1.008		8.000			
Phosphorus oxychloride			3 × 35.46	2 × 8.000	30.98		
Carbon dioxide	6.005			2 × 8.000			
Hydrogen chloride		1.008	35.46				
Phosphoric acid		3 × 1.008		8 × 8.000	30.98		
Hydrogen cyanide	2 × 6.005	1.008				14.008	
Ammonia		3 × 1.008				14.008	
Phosphorus trichloride			3 × 35.46		30.98		
Phosphorus pentachloride			5 × 35.46		30.98		
Methyl magnesium chloride	2 × 6.005	3 × 1.008	35.46				2 × 12.16
Magnesium chloride			35.46				12.16
Magnesium oxide				8.000			12.16
Methyl amine	2 × 6.005	5 × 1.008				14.008	
Nitrous anhydride				3 × 8.000		14.008	
Water		1.008		8.000			
Hydrogen peroxide		1.008		2 × 8.000			
Chlorine dioxide			35.46	4 × 8.000			

The composition data of Table 2.1 reduce to a set of self-consistent numbers, and, as pointed out in Chapter 1, are good supporting evidence for the atomic hypothesis. It is of interest to note here that the atomic concept, of itself, has not been mentioned in the preceding illustrations, nor has knowledge of the chemical formulas of the compounds been at all necessary. In spite of this, it is apparent that some concept of a particle nature can simply and consistently explain the evidence.

2.4. Law of Combining Volumes

In a reaction involving gases, the volumes of gaseous reactants and gaseous products measured under the same conditions of temperature and pressure are always in the ratio of small whole numbers.

An example of a reaction following this law is

$$\text{nitrogen} + \text{hydrogen} = \text{ammonia},$$

in which the relative volumes are

| 1 liter | + | 3 liters | → | 2 liters |

Explanation of the volume change is not possible unless one assumes that in some manner the molecules of nitrogen and hydrogen must be capable of division by some number, and that the several subparticles so formed combine to form molecules of ammonia. In this case, the simplest assumption—recalling Avogadro's hypothesis that equal volumes of gases under the same conditions of pressure and temperature contain equal numbers of molecules—is that the molecules of nitrogen and hydrogen are divisible by two, and that they combine in the ratio 1:3 to form ammonia, with twice the number of ammonia molecules as there were nitrogen molecules. This, of course, means that there must have been at least 2 subparticles (atoms) from each nitrogen molecule.

2.5. Calculations Utilizing Atomic Weight Tables

By use of tables giving values for atomic weights, a number of types of calculations can be made. Several of these will be illustrated below.

Calculation of Percentage Composition from the Formula

Knowing the formula for ethanol to be C_2H_5OH, the percent of carbon, hydrogen, and oxygen can be determined by using a table of atomic weights.

$$
\begin{array}{lll}
2\ C & 2 \times 12.01 & = 24.02 \\
6\ H & 6 \times 1.008 & = 6.05 \\
1\ O & 1 \times 16.000 & = \underline{16.00} \\
\text{Formula weight} & & 46.07
\end{array}
$$

Thus the composition will be

$$\% \text{ of C} = \frac{24.02}{46.07} \times 100\% = 52.2\%$$

and

$$\% \text{ of H} = \frac{6.05}{46.07} \times 100\% = 13.1\%$$

and

$$\% \text{ of O} = \frac{16.00}{46.07} \times 100\% = 34.7\%$$

Conversely, if the composition of a compound is known, the atomic ratios of its constituents may be determined. One hundred grams of a compound of 80% of carbon and 20% of hydrogen would have

$$\frac{80}{12.01} = 6.66 \text{ g atomic weights of carbon}$$

and

$$\frac{20}{1} = 20 \text{ g atomic weights of hydrogen}$$

(Note that the percentage compositon has been assumed as the relative number of grams of each element. Thus, if the analysis is given directly in grams, those values can be divided by the corresponding atomic weights, without resorting to the percentage composition.)

The atomic ratio of hydrogen to carbon would be

$$\frac{20 \text{ g atomic wts of hydrogen}}{6.66 \text{ g atomic wts of carbon}} = 3$$

and the simplest formula for the compound is CH_3. Without further information, the formula could equally well be C_2H_6, C_3H_9, $\cdots$, C_nH_{3n}, with no way of selecting the correct formula.

If information is available by which the approximate molecular weight of the compound can be determined, a choice can be made, since the corresponding weights would be 15, 30, 45, $\cdots$, $15n$. In this case, the compound is gaseous, and it is known that one mole (one gram molecular weight) of any gas occupies a volume of approximately 22.4 liters under standard conditions (0°C and 760 mm pressure). From a determination that 100 ml of the gas weigh 0.13 g at standard conditions, one mole should weigh $22,400/100 \times 0.13$ g $= 29.2$ g. Thus the molecular weight must be 30 rather than 15, 45, or any other multiple of 15, and the correct formula for the compound is C_2H_6.

In the above example, it was unnecessary to obtain more than approximate values either for the atomic ratio or the molecular weight, since the atomic theory requires that all values be integral multiples and the approximations are always rounded off to the nearest integer. Also, once the formula is determined with a table of precise values of atomic weights at hand, the exact molecular weight is easily obtained, even though only approximate values are available from laboratory data.

2.6. Law of Dulong and Petit (Atomic Heats)

For some elements the product of the atomic weight by the specific heat in calories per gram degree Centigrade is equal approximately to the value 6.3 cal/mole °C. (This product is called the atomic heat.)

As an example, the specific heat of aluminum is 0.0214 cal g^{-1} °C^{-1}, and the approximate value of the atomic weight estimated from this relation is $6.3/0.0214 = 29.4$. (The actual value is 27.0.) Although this rule has been valuable in the past, notable exceptions are known, and it is not a safe guide, unless corroborated by other evidence.

2.7. Use of Chemical Methods

As previously demonstrated, when the composition is known, an atomic ratio can be calculated. Chemical methods of analysis are also useful in determining equivalent weights, from which, together with knowledge of the valence or the approximate atomic weight, the exact atomic weight can be calculated. The equivalent weight of an element is defined as that weight which will combine with or displace 1.008 g of hydrogen, 35.46 g of chlorine, or 8.00 g of oxygen.

When 5.394 g of aluminum is burned, 10.194 g of the oxide is formed. From this, it is seen that 5.394 g of aluminum combine with 4.800 g of oxygen, and that $x = (5.394/4.800) \times 8 = 8.99$ g of aluminum will combine with 8.00 g of oxygen. The equivalent weight of aluminum is therefore 8.99, and its atomic weight must be some integral multiple of this number.

From the approximate atomic weight of 29.4 for aluminum found by the law of Dulong and Petit (Section 2.6), it is apparent by inspection that the exact atomic weight of aluminum is $3 \times 8.99 = 26.97$, since

this is the integral multiple of the equivalent weight most closely corresponding to the approximate atomic weight. It is apparent that the
valence of aluminum in this oxide is 3.

2.8. Law of Isomorphism

If two different compounds occur in the same crystalline form, they
are said to be isomorphous. Isomorphous compounds which have similar
chemical properties generally can be represented by analogous formulas.
Therefore, knowing the formula for one of a series of isomorphous compounds and the composition of others, the atomic weights of the element
substituted in a second compound can be calculated.

As an example, potassium sulfate and rubidium sulfate are isomorphous compounds. The former has the formula K_2SO_4; the latter contains 64.0% rubidium. It is desired to find the atomic weight of
rubidium. Since the compounds are isomorphous, one assumes the
formula for rubidium sulfate to be Rb_2SO_4. The fraction of rubidium
present is given by

$$\frac{2x}{2x + 96} = 0.640$$

where x is the atomic weight of rubidium, 96 is the formula weight of
the sulfate ion, and 0.640 is the fraction of rubidium present. Solving the
equation gives $x = 85.48$ as the atomic weight of rubidium. This is but
one type of example where the law of isomorphism can be used.

2.9. Atomic Weights from the Mass Spectrograph

By means of the mass spectrograph (see pp. 33–34) direct comparisons of atomic mass can be made, relative to the standard for the old
physical atomic weight scale of the oxygen isotope of atomic weight 16
having atomic weights of 16.0000 ($O^{16} = 16.0000$). (See Section 1.1 for
relation to present standard, $C^{12} = 12$.) On the former chemical atomic
weight scale, natural-occurring oxygen—a mixture of isotopes of atomic
weights 16, 17, and 18—was assigned the atomic weight of 16.0000. From
the isotope ratios ($O^{16}/O^{18} = 503 \pm 10$ and $O^{18}/O^{17} = 4.9 \pm 0.2$), the
conversion factor 1.000274 can be calculated for use as a multiplier to
convert atomic weights on the former chemical scale to atomic weights
on the former physical scale. To avoid confusion, the term mass number,
the integer nearest a given atomic weight, is often used to identify a

given isotope. For example, the hydrogen isotope of atomic weight (physical scale) 1.00813 has the mass number 1; deuterium (at wt 2.01472) has mass number 2.

Mass spectrographic data for magnesium give the following isotope weights (physical scale) and abundances:

$$Mg^{24} \qquad 23.99300 \qquad 77.4\%$$
$$Mg^{25} \qquad 24.99462 \qquad 11.5\%$$
$$Mg^{26} \qquad 25.99012 \qquad 11.1\%$$

By taking the sum of the products of the isotopic weight by the abundance, and multiplying by the conversion factor from the physical and chemical scale, the atomic weight is obtained.

$$
\begin{aligned}
23.99300 \times .774 &= 18.5737 \\
24.99462 \times .115 &= 2.8744 \\
25.99012 \times .111 &= \underline{2.8859} \\
\text{Sum} &= 24.3340
\end{aligned}
$$

At wt (chemical scale) $= 24.3340/1.000274 = 24.3275$, which may be compared with the accepted value 24.32.

2.10. Atomic Weights from X-ray Data

Modern X-ray diffraction techniques give data of high precision concerning dimensions of a unit cell of a crystal and the arrangement and number of atoms in each unit cell. As discussed in Chapter 7, a unit cell of a crystal is the smallest repeating unit from which a large crystal can be constructed by stacking unit cells as building blocks.

If the volume of the unit cell of an elementary crystalline substance and the number of atoms contained in the cell are known, the atomic weight of the element can be calculated from a knowledge of the density of the crystal and Avogadro's number.

The unit cell of silver is a face-centered cube, 4.078 Å on each edge, and there are 4 atoms per unit cell. The density of silver is 10.50 g cm^{-3}. Using Avogadro's number $N_0 = 0.6024 \times 10^{24}$, the atomic weight of silver can be calculated as follows. From unit cell data, the volume per silver atom is

$$\frac{(4.078)^3 \times (10^{-8})^3 \text{ cm}^3}{4} = 16.96 \text{ cm}^3 \times 10^{-24}$$

The volume of one gram atomic weight of silver (Avogadro's number of silver atoms) is

$$\frac{0.6024 \times 10^{+24} \times 4.078^3 \times 10^{-24} \text{ cm}^3}{4} = \frac{0.6024 \times 4.078^3 \text{ cm}^3}{4}$$

The weight of Avogadro's number of atoms is

$$\text{gram atomic weight} = \frac{0.6024 \times 4.078^3}{4} \text{ cm}^3 \times 10.50 \text{ g cm}^{-3}$$

$$= 107.5 \text{ g}$$

The calculated atomic weight of silver is 107.5 (to the precision of the given numbers, as compared with the accepted value of 107.88.

Problems

2.1. A crystalline substance containing 23.41% cesium and 4.75% aluminum was found to be isomorphous with potassium alum, $K_2SO_4Al_2(SO_4)_3 \cdot 24H_2O$. Calculate the atomic weight of cesium, assuming the atomic weight of aluminum to be 26.97.

2.2. Potassium selenate contains 35.77% selenium and is isomorphous with potassium sulfate, K_2SO_4. Calculate the atomic weight of selenium.

2.3. Chromic oxide contains 68.4% of chromium. What is the atomic ratio for the compound?

2.4. If 14.18 g of chlorine combine with 11.00 g of iron, whose specific heat is 0.115 cal g^{-1} deg^{-1} C^{-1}, what is the exact atomic weight of iron?

2.5. Analysis of a gaseous oxide of carbon yields 72.7% of oxygen and 27.3% of carbon. (a) What is the simplest formula for the compound? (b) If 210 mg of the oxide occupy 105 ml at standard conditions, what is the molecular formula?

2.6. What is the percentage composition of methyl ethyl ketone?

2.7. One gram of sodium is burned in the air to produce 1.7 g of sodium oxide. (a) What is the simplest formula for the oxide? (b) What is the composition of the oxide in percent?

2.8. From the compositions of the compounds given in the table (p.20), show that there is a law of combining weights.

Compound	Percent of Elements Present in Compound					
	CHLORINE	MERCURY	SULFUR	OXYGEN	IRON	NITROGEN
Mercuric chloride	26.2	73.8				
Mercuric sulfide		86.2	13.8			
Mercuric oxide		92.6		7.4		
Mercurous chloride	15.0	85.0				
Mercurous sulfide		92.6	7.4			
Mercurous oxide		96.2		3.8		
Sulfur dichloride	68.9		31.1			
Sulfur dioxide			50.1	49.9		
Sulfur trioxide			40.1	59.9		
Sulfur monochloride	52.5		47.5			
Ferric chloride	65.6				34.4	
Ferric oxide				30.1	69.9	
Ferrous chloride	56.0				44.0	
Ferrous oxide				22.3	77.7	
Nitric anhydride				74.1		25.9
Nitrogen tetroxide				69.6		30.4
Nitrous anhydride				63.2		36.8
Nitric oxide				53.4		46.6
Nitrous oxide				36.4		63.6

2.9. Five hundred milliliters of chlorine monoxide gas decompose to yield 500 ml of chlorine gas and 250 ml of oxygen gas under the same conditions of pressure and temperature. (a) Show that this is in agreement with the law of combining volumes. (b) Devise an atomic-molecular explanation for the observed data.

2.10. Trichloromethyl silane and dichlorodimethyl silane are composed of 8.09% carbon, 2.04% hydrogen, 18.9% silicon, and 71.0% chlorine, and 18.6% carbon, 4.65% hydrogen, 21.8% silicon, and 54.9% chlorine, respectively. By means of these figures, demonstrate the law of multiple proportions.

2.11. The four compounds in the table below are composed of carbon and hydrogen with the composition shown.

Compound	% Carbon	% Hydrogen
Methane	75.0	25.0
Acetylene	92.3	7.7
Ethylene	85.7	14.3
Ethane	80.0	20.0

Demonstrate that these data are in agreement with the law of multiple proportions.

2.12. A sample of calcium cyanamide was analyzed and found to contain 30.9 g of calcium, 9.25 g of carbon, and 21.6 g of nitrogen. Another sample was found to contain 14.3 g of carbon. (a) How much calcium was present in this second sample? (b) What was the total weight of the second sample?

2.13. Phosphoric acid is known to contain 3.08% by weight of hydrogen, 31.6% of phosphorus, and 65.3% of oxygen. Another sample of phosphoric acid was found to contain 7.74 g of hydrogen. How many grams of phosphorus and oxygen were also contained therein?

2.14. Calculate the atomic weight of tungsten, using the mass spectrographic data given, and compare with the accepted value.

Isotope	Abundance (%)	Atomic Mass
W^{180}	0.14	179.947
W^{182}	26.29	181.948
W^{183}	14.31	182.950
W^{184}	30.66	183.951
W^{186}	28.60	185.954

2.15. Tetranitromethane has a density of 1.63 g cm^{-3} as a solid and crystallizes in the cubic system, with the length of the edge of a unit cube equal to 9.2 Å and 4 molecules per unit cell. Using Avogadro's number, calculate the molecular weight and compare with the known molecular weight.

2.16. Aluminum crystallizes with a face-centered cubic unit cell with 4 atoms and an edge length of 4.04 Å. The density of aluminum is 2.70 g cm^{-3}. Calculate the atomic weight.

2.17. From the abundance ratios for the isotopes of oxygen given in Section 2.7, calculate the conversion multiplier used for the formerly different chemical and physical atomic weight scales. Assume the masses of the three isotopes to be precisely 16, 17, and 18. (By appropriate use of algebra, this may be calculated to six decimal places, doing all multiplying on a slide rule.)

2.18. From the following data, calculate the atomic weight of oxygen.

Isotope	Abundance (%)	Atomic Mass
O^{16}	99.7587	15.9949
O^{17}	0.0374	16.9991
O^{18}	0.2039	17.9992

Compare with the published value.

2.19. The natural radioactive decay of radium results in emission of helium nuclei (α-particles). By counter techniques, 10 mg of radium are found to give off these particles at a rate of 1.38×10^9 per second. After a year, the amount of helium produced is 0.00158 cm^3 at STP. The atomic weight of helium is 4.0026; calculate Avogadro's number.

2.20. When oxygen is removed from air, as by passage over red-hot copper, the remaining gas has a density 0.5% greater than that of nitrogen prepared chemically from pure compounds. This difference was first observed by Ramsey in the 19th century, and led to the discovery of argon. Assuming that the difference is due entirely to argon (atomic weight 39.9), what is the percentage of argon in air?

2.21. When a sample of an unknown substance weighing 0.2200 g was burned in a closed bomb with an excess of oxygen, 0.6179 g of CO_2 and 0.1264 g of water were formed. What is the empirical formula of the substance, assuming it contained only carbon, hydrogen, and oxygen?

Suggested Readings

The great historical importance for atomic theory of chemical methods for determining atomic weights is well illustrated in the references to Chapter 1. A very readable discussion of molar quantities is found in the paperback *The Mole Concept in Chemistry*, by W. J. Kieffer (Reinhold, New York, 1962). Values of physical constants recommended by a committee of the National Academy of Sciences–National Research Council in 1963 are tabulated in the magazine *Physics Today*, February, 1964, p. 48.

Chapter 3

Fundamental Particles. Electrons and Nuclei

THE RECOGNITION of the atomic nature of matter was followed more slowly by the further recognition that atoms were themselves composed of other elementary particles, and by a realization of the importance of the electrical properties these constituents were found to possess. In this chapter we shall be concerned with the evidence for these elementary particles, with their fundamental properties of mass and charge, and with the magnitudes of the constants describing these properties.

3.1. The Electron

Evidence for the elementary particle we today call the electron began to accumulate in forceful fashion over the period from 1880 to 1910. The experiments in these years were for the most part qualitative in nature, and they derived from observations of electrical effects.

23

Stoney in 1874 advanced the postulate of discrete elementary charges by inference from Faraday's laws of electrolysis (Section 1.1). These laws stated that equivalent quantities of electrical charge passing through an electrolytic solution correspond to chemically equivalent amounts of substances deposited or dissolved at the two electrodes. (Faraday had appreciated the implications of this law and related results many years earlier but had not ventured as definite an explanation.) In 1881 Helmholtz had advanced a similar explanation, and in 1891 Stoney proposed the name "electron" for this elementary electrical particle.

About this time J. J. Thomson carried out a classic series of experiments, as a result of which he is usually credited with "discovery" of the electron. Thomson found that a gas subjected to a beam of X-rays would conduct electricity and that this property of conductivity could be removed in a number of ways, such as by passing the gas between a pair of charged plates. His explanation was that the conduction was due to the existence of charged particles within the gas. When the gas was passed between the plates, the positive and negative particles were attracted to the negative and positive electrodes, respectively, and the ability to conduct was lost.

Sir William Crookes, in the 1870's and 1880's, devised the forerunner of today's cathode ray tube. He found that application of a high electrical potential across two electrodes contained within a glass bulb which had been evacuated to low pressure resulted in the emission of charged particles from the negative electrode (cathode).

A number of properties of these particles were observed. When the "ray" from the cathode struck a chemical substance coated on the bulb, fluorescence resulted. A thick metal plate interposed in the beam cast a shadow, but sufficiently thin sheets of metal could be penetrated. A small paddle wheel suitably placed in the path could be made to revolve in the fashion to be expected of an impinging jet of material particles.

Crookes also studied the influences of electric and magnetic fields on the effects he had discovered. Passage of the beam between two oppositely charged metal plates resulted in a deflection toward the positive plate, thus indicating a negative charge associated with the ray itself. Passage through a magnetic field resulted in a deflection at right angles to both the path and the field, giving rise to a circular arc path for the beam while it was in the field. (see Fig. 3.1). The result was just that predicted by the law governing the force on a conductor carrying an electric current through a magnetic field. The various effects were all consistent

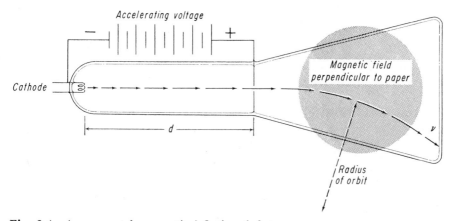

Fig. 3.1. *Arrangement for magnetic deflection of electrons.*

with the interpretation that the beam consisted of negatively charged particles of small mass moving with high velocity. The evidence indicated that these particles could be the electrons postulated by Stoney and others.

3.2. The Properties of the Electron

If the existence of the electron were to be reliably established, it was important to determine its properties more quantitatively. From the available evidence, it was clear that values for the mass of the electron (m) and charge on the electron (e) were necessary parts of a complete description. But the magnitudes of both are so small that special methods for their determination are necessary. The electron mass (m), now known to be 9.107×10^{-28} g, was hopelessly small for conventional weighing, whether of an individual electron or of a countable number of electrons. In fact, the first accepted value was the result of experiments which determined combinations of m with other quantities, notably the electronic charge, e.

Pioneer experiments leading to determination of charge and the ratio of mass to charge were carried out by J. J. Thomson. Descriptions of various methods which result in values for the ratio m/e will be found in elementary physics textbooks. [See, for example, F. W. Sears and M. W. Zemansky, *College Physics* (Addison-Wesley, Reading, Mass., 3rd ed., 1960, pp. 617 ff.)]

It will be recalled that the two basic phenomena employed in such determinations are the forces exerted on the moving electron by electrostatic and magnetic fields. In a uniform electric field E, an electron of charge e experiences a force eE. If it starts from rest, it will accelerate and, after traveling a distance d, acquire a definite velocity v. The magnitude of v must satisfy the requirement that the work done equal the increase in kinetic energy. Hence we can write

$$eEd = \tfrac{1}{2}mv^2$$

In this equation, only E and d can be directly measured by the experimenter, and we can thus determine only the combination of quantities

$$\frac{mv^2}{2e} = Ed \qquad (3.1)$$

If now the experiment is elaborated by adding a known constant magnetic field H, through which the electrons must pass, the beam of electrons will be acted on by a force $F = Hev$ at right angles both to the direction of motion and the field H. This causes a centripetal acceleration equal to v^2/r, where r is the radius of the circular path that results, while the speed v remains constant. By Newton's second law, $F = ma$, and we have

$$Hev = \frac{mv^2}{r}$$

By the proper design of the apparatus, both H and r can be measured and we can calculate the ratio

$$\frac{mv}{e} = Hr \qquad (3.2)$$

Comparing the results of the combined experiment (Eqs. 3.1 and 3.2) shows that we can calculate either v or the ratio m/e. The value of v depends of course on the size of the apparatus and the strength of the applied electric field. The fundamental constant m/e obtained from the relation

$$\frac{m}{e} = \frac{(Hr)^2}{2Ed} \qquad (3.3)$$

should, however, be independent of the experimental conditions. This is found to be so, and the value obtained by methods employing the principles outlined is

$$\frac{m}{e} = 1.8962 \times 10^{-18} \text{ g esu}^{-1} = 5.6847 \times 10^{-9} \text{ g coulombs}^{-1} \quad (3.4)$$

3.3. Charge on the Electron

A direct measurement of the electronic charge e is important both in its own right and also to permit calculation of m by use of the value for m/e obtained from electric and magnetic field measurements (Eq. 3.4). The first accurate measurement of the electronic charge, by R. A. Millikan, is now one of the classic experiments of physics. This work is described in detail in Millikan's own account and in many physics textbooks.

In his experiments Millikan succeeded in ionizing small oil droplets and then measuring their rates of rise and fall under the forces of a reversible electric field and of gravity. He found that these rates could be explained only if the tiny droplets carried electric charges which were always integral multiples of a discrete quantity of charge. Assuming that this charge was that of the electron, a number of which were added to or taken from the oil drops by the ionizing effect of X-rays or radium, Millikan obtained the value $e = 4.77 \times 10^{-10}$ esu (1.59×10^{-19} coulombs).

A necessary complication of Millikan's experiment was calculation of the effect of the frictional resistance of air on the speed of rise or fall of the oil drops. An incorrect value for the viscosity of air used in this calculation made his original determination of the electronic charge low. This error was not discovered until more than 25 years after Millikan's original work; meanwhile the low result was commonly accepted as a reliable value.

The original determination of the charge on the electron, its acceptance and use for so many years without question, and the ultimate redetermination and discovery of the error and its source is an excellent illustration of the manner of scientific work. Millikan's work was invaluable to the development of modern chemistry and physics, and was both pioneering and unique. With a continually developing science, new techniques and refinement of techniques became available, and in the middle thirties, X-ray determinations of the dimensions of unit cells in crystalline substances provided the opportunity of a check of the value of the charge on the electron independent of previous determinations.

It was in 1928 that a discrepancy was observed in the determination of the wavelength of X-rays by diffraction from the face of a crystal and diffraction from a ruled grating. The former determination was dependent on the spacings of atoms in a crystal, in which Avogadro's number was used. The accepted value for Avogadro's number was, in turn, dependent upon Millikan's value for the charge on the electron. The determination from the ruled grating, on the other hand, depended upon a direct measurement of the distance between the parallel scratches made mechanically.

So thoroughly accepted was Millikan's work, that for several years the source of the discrepancy was sought in the spacing of the ruled grating rather than elsewhere. Finally it was suggested that the process could be reversed, and that e could be calculated from X-ray data.

As described in Section 2.10, from X-ray data we obtain the number of atoms (n) in the unit cell and its volume (v) and hence the number of atoms per unit volume, n/v. Dividing by the density (ρ) and multiplying by the gram atomic weight (w) gives the number of atoms per gram atomic weight, which is Avogadro's number. From the electrical charge per gram equivalent weight (the Faraday, F), which is Avogadro's number of charges, the value for the charge on the electron can be obtained as

$$e = \frac{F}{nw/v\rho} = \frac{Fv\rho}{nw}$$

From such X-ray data, the charge, e, was calculated to be

$$(4.8025 \pm 0.0004) \times 10^{-10} \text{ esu}$$

which was significantly higher than Millikan's value. In an attempt to find the cause of the discrepancy, all of Millikan's data were reexamined. It was finally determined that the value used for the viscosity of air was too low, and when later, more accurately determined values were used, good agreement between the two determinations of the electronic charge was obtained.

The accepted value for the charge on the electron is today

$$e = (4.8022 \pm 0.0001) \times 10^{-10} \text{ esu}$$

$$= 1.602 \times 10^{-19} \text{ coulombs}$$

When combined with the value of m/e from Eq. 3.4, one obtains for the electron mass the value

$$m = (9.1072 \pm 0.0003) \times 10^{-28} \text{ g}$$

A realization of the smallness of these quantities is important for a proper perspective on the scale of atomic phenomena. A mass of 10^{-27} g is easily recognized to be far too small to weigh. The small size of the electronic charge can be appreciated on recalling that the enormously larger figure of 96,519 coulombs of charge is associated with one gram equivalent of chemical reaction at an electrode in electrolysis. The student can by a simple calculation verify for himself that the number of electrons associated with this amount of electrolysis is 0.602×10^{24}, Avogadro's number. To appreciate the magnitude of this figure, consider that if—when life first appeared on earth about a million years ago—some creature had been able to count electrons, and counted them at the rate of 5 each second, 24 hours a day, 365 days a year, by today that superhuman creature would have counted only one-trillionth of the electrons equal in electrical charge to one faraday of electricity.

3.4. Size of the Electron

No actual measurement of the physical size of an electron has been made. An estimate of its effective size is in fact not a result to be taken literally, but rather is an indication of a distance of approach, less than which an electron cannot be considered to act as a mass point. Such an estimate can be made by considering the energy an electron would have if it were a charged spherical body and comparing this result with the energy corresponding to its mass according to Einstein's equation $E = mc^2$. The electrostatic energy for the hypothetical process of building up a charge e on a sphere of radius r is $e^2/2r$, and if this is assumed equal to the mass equivalent value mc^2, one obtains

$$r = \frac{e^2}{2mc^2} = 1.4 \times 10^{-13} \text{ cm}$$

This figure is smaller by a factor 10^5 than the distances characteristic of atom spacings in molecules and crystals. The size of the electron is so small that for chemical purposes it may be disregarded. At the same time, the energy mc^2 is too large for the electron to be a reasonable constituent of positively charged nuclei, as we shall see in Section 3.6.

3.5. The Atomic Nucleus

The study of atomic nuclei had its beginnings in Becquerel's observation of radioactivity in 1895, when he noticed that a photographic plate placed near an uranium salt was affected as though exposed to light. Investigation showed three types of radiation emanated from substances containing uranium. Originally these were noncommittally labeled α, β, γ rays; but further study of the effects of electric and magnetic fields showed that they were respectively positively charged particles with a mass equal to that of the helium nucleus, negatively charged electrons, and a penetrating uncharged radiation similar to X-rays.

The availability of a natural source of positively charged helium ions was a great boon to Rutherford and his associates. Within a short time they completed a series of classic experiments which culminated in the postulate of the nuclear atom. A wealth of experimental data supported this postulate.

Rutherford and Soddy, following up the work of Lenard, performed experiments in which they passed α and β particles through gases and through thin metallic foils, and determined their courses by the scintillations resulting from their impact upon a fluorescent zinc sulfide screen. They found that gases of high atomic weight were less transparent to radiation than gases of lower atomic weight. β particles were found to penetrate further into the gas than α particles, but were more easily deflected and consequently pursued a more tortuous path. In the case of thin metal foils, α particles were generally found to pass through them and emerge in much the same direction as their incident path, with small deflections. Occasionally, however, one of the particles would suffer an unexpectedly large deflection. This led Rutherford to visualize an atom as consisting of a relatively small and compact positive nucleus surrounded by a large space containing a cloud of negatively charged electrons. Bombarding β particles, being light and of the same charge as the electrons surrounding atomic nucleus, would be easily deflected, while α particles, heavy and positively charged, would pass unaffected by the electrons and only suffer a directional change when passing close to a small nucleus.

The Rutherford Scattering Experiment

If we assume that the deflections of the α particle are caused by coulombic repulsion due to interaction with a positively charged nucleus, we can find the force of repulsion by using Coulomb's Law $F = qq'/r^2$, where q and q' are the charges on the interacting bodies and r is the distance between them. If Z is the number of positive charges on the nucleus, then Ze is the total nuclear charge. For the helium nucleus (α particle), $Z = 2$, the charge is $2e$, and

$$F = \frac{Ze \times 2e}{r^2} \quad \text{or} \quad F = \frac{2Ze^2}{r^2}$$

The magnitude of this repulsive force is seen to vary inversely with the square of the distance r, and hence only for very small distances of approach to the nucleus will the α particle suffer any considerable change in direction. It is a straightforward problem in mechanics to calculate the angle through which an α particle will be deflected. (The mathematics is in fact very similar to that in the problem of the path of a comet passing near a planet, the only essential difference being that the gravitational force is attractive while the electrical force for like charges is repulsive.) As an example of the results obtained from such a calculation, the α particles from radium, with a speed of approximately 1.5×10^9 cm/sec (1/20th the speed of light) must pass within a distance of 3×10^{-12} cm of a nucleus with charge $Z = 79$ (gold) to be deflected by $90°$.

Very few of the α particles traveling through a thin foil as shown in Fig. 3.2 will come so close to a nucleus, and only on rare occasions

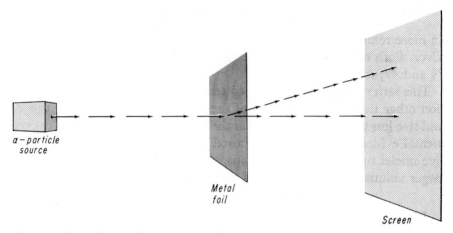

Fig. 3.2. *Scattering experiment on α-particles.*

will large deflections be registered as scintillations on the zinc sulfide screen. By assuming that one distance of approach was as likely as any other, Rutherford was able to calculate the cumulative effect of all nuclei in the foil in scattering particles at different angles as a result of the Coulomb forces of repulsion. This scattering formula for the fraction g of the total number of particles which are found in a ring of angular width $d\theta$, as shown in Fig. 3.3, has the form

$$g = \frac{4\pi n Z^2 e^4}{(MV^2)^2 \tan\left(\frac{\theta}{2}\right) \sin^2\left(\frac{\theta}{2}\right)} \qquad (3.5)$$

where n is the number of scattering nuclei of atomic number Z which are in or behind one square centimeter of surface of the foil, and M and V are the mass and velocity of the impinging α particles.

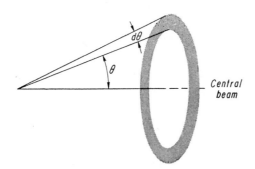

Fig. 3.3. *Ring of angular width dθ at scattering angle θ.*

By the simple but tedious process of counting numbers of particles scattered into rings of different radii, Rutherford and his associates were able to calculate g for various angles θ and verify that Eq. 3.5 does describe the variation of g with angle. Having established this, they then used Eq. 3.5 to calculate Z for the nuclei of the atoms in the foil. The result for gold foils was $Z = 79 \pm 2$. In more refined later experiments Chadwick found $Z = 46.3 \pm 0.7$ for silver. Both of these results agree beautifully with the correct values of 79 and 47, respectively.

This series of experiments on scattering had no consistent interpretation other than the assumption of the existence of nuclei of charge Ze and size less than 10^{-13} cm, and on the basis of such quantitative experimental evidence Rutherford proposed that atoms consist of small, massive nuclei surrounded by electrons, which collectively occupy a much larger volume than do the nuclei themselves.

Wavelengths of Characteristic X-rays

Further evidence for the nuclear atom was found from consideration of the wavelengths of characteristic X-rays emitted by targets bombarded with electrons. Mosely discovered in 1914 that these wavelengths varied with but a few exceptions in a regular fashion with the atomic numbers of successive elements. The six exceptions to regular progression corresponded to what are known now to have been the six undiscovered elements—hafnium, rhenium, technetium, prometheum, astatine, and francium. All have since been discovered. Mosely recognized the fundamental importance of the atomic numbers with relation to the character of the X-ray radiation, and hypothesized correctly that the atomic number represented the size of the nuclear charge. This is discussed in greater detail in Chapter 5.

3.6. Nuclear Masses

With the recognition of the planetary nature of an atom, described as a nucleus of charge Ze surrounded by electrons each of charge e but of mass far smaller than that of the nucleus, determinations of atomic masses with high precision by electromagnetic methods became possible. The necessary experiments are very similar in their principles to those already described for measurements of m/e for electrons. Positive ions are first formed by removal of an electron from the neutral atom, accelerated to a suitable velocity by an electric field, and then deflected in a magnetic field. From the magnitudes of the resulting deflection and the known fields responsible for it, values of M/e for the charged particle can be deduced. The apparatus, called a mass spectrometer, must employ higher fields than are required in the similar experiments for electrons because of the greater inertia of the heavy ions of a mass nearly equal to that of the neutral atom. A sketch of the elements of one type of mass spectrometer is shown in Fig. 3.4.

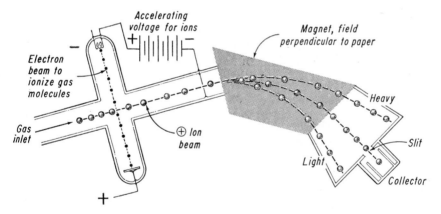

Fig. 3.4. *Production, acceleration, and deflection of ions in a mass spectrograph.*

By suitable refinement, high precision in mass determination is possible, and the value $m = 1.6731 \times 10^{-24}$ g for the mass of the hydrogen atom (isotope 1) has been obtained. This value is some 1836 times that of the electron, indicating that, as was already surmised less directly, nearly all of the mass of an atom is in the nucleus.

As previously discussed in Chapter 1, physical mass measurements are referred to the carbon isotope of mass 12.0000 by definition. Exact determinations of the masses of other nuclei are of much importance to an understanding of nuclear forces and stabilities because of the large energies associated with small mass differences according to the Einstein relation $E = mc^2$.

The importance of relative isotope abundances for precise atomic weights of elements as they naturally occur has led to much work in determining these values. Mass spectrometers such as the one shown in Fig. 3.4 are adapted to this purpose by adding a suitable ion collector at the final point of their path and measuring the current flow corresponding to the rate at which ions reach this collector. The ratio of currents for different ions is then a measure of their relative abundance.

Another application of the mass spectrometer is for analysis of molecular or submolecular species in an unknown sample or a reaction mixture. If these can be ionized, the presence of the various ions can be detected and their various amounts determined by bringing them successively "into focus" at the collector and measuring the ion currents. Oftentimes a large organic molecule undergoing ionizing bombardment in the mass spectrometer will be split into a number of smaller segments or ions. The mass numbers and abundance ratios of these breakdown products are unique for given substances, and lead to a valuable method of analysis of complex materials. From such data, too, we can learn much about the structural elements of new compounds.

3.7. Sizes of Nuclei

From his scattering experiments and Coulomb's Law, Rutherford was able to conclude that α particles approach the nuclei as closely as 10^{-12} cm. This order of distance, which is far smaller than interatomic distances of the order of 10^{-8} cm, must be an upper limit on the size of nuclei. No direct means of length or volume measurement exist for particles this small, and indirect evidence must be employed.

The scattering and absorption of neutrons by nuclei indicate that to a bombarding neutron a nucleus is a target of at most 10^{-24} square centimeters in area. (This area of 10^{-24} cm^2 has been termed "as big as a barn," and this size—taken as a unit of nuclear cross section—a "barn.") Theories of α particle decay lead to similar values, and accordingly a figure of 10^{-12} cm is the order of magnitude of nuclear diameters. The size of the nucleus increases with nuclear mass and is approximately given by the expression

$$\text{radius of nucleus (cm)} = 1.5 \times 10^{-13} Z^{1/3} \qquad (3.6)$$

where Z is the atomic number.

For the purpose of discussing the motions of electrons around nuclei, the dimensions of nuclei are negligibly small, and we may note that they are also so small that electrons cannot be confined in them without supplying enormous energies. As estimated in Section 3.4, the radius of an electron is of the order 10^{-13} cm, which would seem about right for it to fit. However, the energy mc^2 is ten times the experimental energy changes found for nuclear processes involving addition or removal of elementary nuclear particles. On this basis and a variety of other evidence—Chadwick's discovery of the neutron in particular—the older picture of nuclei as composed of protons and electrons has been discarded in favor of a structure composed of protons and neutrons. The protons determine the atomic number Z by their total charge, while the atomic weight depends on both the number of protons and the number of neutrons (plus the much smaller contribution from extranuclear electron masses).

Problems

3.1. Coulomb's Law of force between two charges of magnitude q_1 and q_2 a distance r apart is given by $F = Aq_1q_2/r^2$, where A is a constant with magnitude and dimensions depending on the system of units used. In the cgs system, A is made dimensionless and given the value one, thereby defining the electrostatic unit of charge (esu). What are the dimensions of q in terms of mass, length, and time?

3.2. (a) In the normal hydrogen atom, the nucleus has a positive charge numerically equal to the electronic charge. What is the electrical force of attraction between the nucleus and electron when they are separated by a distance of 0.54×10^{-8} cm? (The value 0.54×10^{-8} cm is a characteristic distance of separation, as discussed in Chapter 5.) (b) Compare the answer to (a) with the force between two charges of 1 esu each, which are 10 cm apart.

3.3. An oil drop of density 0.80 g cm^{-3} and radius 10^{-4} cm captures an ion with two electronic charges. Calculate the potential difference in volts between two plates 2.54 cm apart which will keep the drop stationary. (Remember that 1 esu of potential is equal to 300 v.)

3.4. The Faraday is the quantity of charge carried by Avogadro's number of electrons or by one gram equivalent of ions. Calculate the value of the Faraday in electrostatic units and in coulombs. (The coulomb is the unit of charge in the practical system and has a magnitude such that 1 coulomb = 2.996×10^9 esu.)

3.5. The unit of current in the practical system is the ampere and corresponds to a flow of 1 coulomb per second. (a) Ion and electron currents in discharge tubes are typically of the order of a few microamperes. A current of 1 micro-ampere $(10^{-6}$ ampere) corresponds to how many electrons per second? (b) Sensitive current-measuring devices (electrometer circuits) can detect currents of 10^{-14} amperes or less. How many electrons per second flow would there be for a current of 10^{-14} amperes?

3.6. A current of 1.00 amperes flows through a wire across which a potential difference of 10.0 volts is applied. (a) How much energy must be supplied per second in ergs to maintain the flow? (b) How many seconds must the current flow to dissipate 300 calories as heat? (1 calorie = 4.19×10^7 ergs.)

3.7. An electron initially at rest is accelerated in a field of 100 v cm^{-1}. (a) What are its speed and kinetic energy after traveling 5.0 cm? (b) How long did the electron take to travel this distance? (c) If the field is suddenly reversed in direction at this point, how much further will the electron travel before reversing its direction? before losing half its speed?

3.8. An electron is accelerated through a potential difference of 2000 v. It then enters a magnetic field of 20 oersteds perpendicular to its path. (The oersted is the electromagnetic unit of field strength H, and is equal to 0.334×10^{-9} esu of field strength.) What is the radius of its circular path while in this field?

3.9. What electric field must be applied perpendicular to both the electron path and magnetic field in Problem 3.8 in order to make the electron travel in a straight line?

3.10. In one form of mass spectrometer for study of positive ions, the ions must travel in a semicircle of radius 10.0 cm from the point where it enters the magnetic field in order to reach the target or detector. If singly charged Li^7 ions (atomic weight = 7) are first accelerated through a potential difference of 300 v, what magnetic field must be applied for them to impinge on the detector?

3.11. Naturally occurring lithium contains about 6% of Li^6 (atomic weight = 6). For the conditions of Problem 3.10, what field is necessary if singly charged Li^6 ions are to reach the detector?

3.12. A mass spectrometer is used to discriminate between the singly positive charged O^{16} ion and the ion C^{12}H$_4^+$, the masses of which on the physical scale are 15.99491 and 16.03130. If the O^{16} ions travel in an orbit in the magnetic field of the spectrometer of radius 15.0 cm, how much different is the radius for C^{12}H$_4^+$ ions?

3.13. An alpha particle moving with a speed of 10^9 cm/sec approached a stationary nucleus of atomic number $z = 47$ on a direct collision path. Calculate the distance of closest approach. (Hint: At this distance, the alpha particle will have potential energy in the electrostatic field of the nucleus equal to its initial kinetic energy.)

3.14. Sodium chloride (molecular weight $= 58.45$) has a density of 2.16 gm/cm³. Using the approximate formula for nuclear radii in the text, estimate the fraction of the volume occupied by the nuclei in a sample of solid sodium chloride.

3.15. The resolution of a mass spectrograph can be defined in various ways; it is a measure of the instrument's ability to distinguish ions of the same charge and different mass. Using Eqs. 3.1 and 3.2, discuss how the resolution of a spectrograph varies with the ion mass if the orbit radius and ion accelerating potential are fixed.

3.16. The Millikan oil-drop experiment can be performed by measuring the speed of fall v_1 under gravity of an oil drop with attached ions of charge q and then the speed of fall v_2 of the same drop when a field E is applied in opposition to gravity. In each case, the retarding force from viscosity of the air is given by F (viscous) $= -6\pi\eta rv$, where η is the coefficient of viscosity, r the radius of the drop, and v the velocity of the drop. Show that the speeds v_1 and v_2 satisfy the equations

$$6\pi\eta rv_1 = mg$$
$$6\pi\eta rv_2 = mg - qE$$

where m is the mass of the drop.

3.17. In performing his experiment, Millikan observed drops which acquired additional charges, and hence new speeds with and without the field E. (a) Show that the use of the values of these speeds makes possible a determination of the ratio of the new charge q' to the original charge q without a knowledge of either the mass or radius of the drop. (b) What other data are then necessary to determine q and q' separately?

3.18. Consider a square plane layer of charged nuclei 10^{-8} cm apart, against which a beam of alpha particles is directed at right angles. If any one particle must pass within 3×10^{-12} cm of a nucleus to be deflected by more than $90°$, what fraction of the particles in the beam will undergo such deflections?

3.19. Discuss the difference in the scattering pattern predicted by Rutherford's equation if protons were used instead of alpha particles.

3.20. Show that Eq. 3.1 is dimensionally consistent, i.e. that the units on the two sides of the equation are the same when expressed in the fundamental units of mass, length, and time.

Suggested Readings

An excellent elementary account of the development of atomic theory is given in *Introduction to Atomic Physics* (2nd ed.) by O. Oldenberg (McGraw-Hill, New York, 1954); another is *Atomic Physics* by G. P. Harnwell and W. E. Stephens (McGraw-Hill, New York, 1955).

Good accounts of classic experiments on elementary particles are given in *The Particles of Modern Physics* by J. D. Stranathan (Blakiston, Philadelphia, 1943). A text dealing with properties of nuclei is *Introductory Nuclear Physics* by D. Halliday (Wiley, New York, 1950).

Chapter 4

Matter and Radiation

STUDIES of how electric and magnetic fields affect and are affected by matter have long been one of the most important sources of information about atoms and molecules. Many, if not most, of the advances in our understanding of the theory of matter have had their origin in such studies. In the preceding chapter, we have considered special examples of this, in the use of steady fields for charge and mass determinations.

Of even greater importance is the information obtained by studying the effects of radiation on matter. In this chapter we will consider some of the characteristic properties of radiation as a preliminary to discussing some of the effects.

4.1. Radiation

The recognition of light as one form of electromagnetic radiation we owe to Maxwell, who in 1864 presented his celebrated field theory as a result of long and careful consideration of Faraday's work on electromagnetic induction. In Maxwell's theory, the basic laws by which electric and magnetic waves are governed in traversing space were formulated in a very general way.

From Maxwell's work and further studies of new forms of radiation as they were discovered, it is known today that radio waves, microwaves used in radar, infrared heat radiation, visible light, ultraviolet light, X-rays, and γ-rays are all forms of electromagnetic radiation. Like other periodic wave phenomena, these are waves which can be characterized by a velocity v at which they are propagated, a wavelength λ between points of the same phase, and a frequency ν at which successive waves pass any particular point. These three quantities are not independent, being related by the formula $v = \nu\lambda$, familiar to the student from his study of elementary physics.

In passing through a vacuum, all electromagnetic waves travel with a speed $v = c = 2.99793 \times 10^{10}$ cm/sec; this is one of the fundamental physical constants. This quantity has most often been determined by measuring the speed of visible light, as by Michelson and many others, but recently precision determinations have been made employing microwaves. In passing through various substances, the velocity of propagation of electromagnetic waves depends on the substances and the kind of radiation, but it is always less than c. The radiation may also be absorbed and dissipated, even so strongly that its wave properties are not apparent.

The primary distinguishing feature of different types of electromagnetic radiation is the frequency, which is determined by the nature of the exciting source of the radiation. A representation of the frequencies

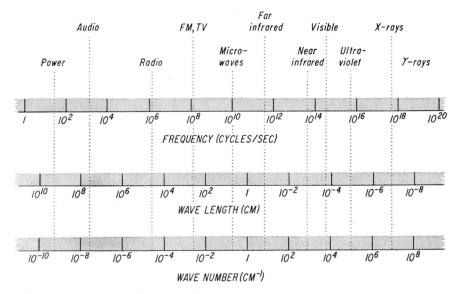

Fig. 4.1. *Range of the electromagnetic spectrum.*

of various kinds of radiation is given in Fig. 4.1. It should be noted that a scale in powers of ten is used for frequency, to permit the entire electromagnetic spectrum to be shown in a reasonable space. Two other scales are also shown, one giving the corresponding wavelengths ($\lambda = c/\nu$) and the second giving the wave numbers ($\bar{\nu} = 1/\lambda$ cm^{-1}), discussed below.

4.2. Systems of Units

With the extended range of wavelength and frequency of electromagnetic waves, a system of units of convenient size for one part of the spectrum would be awkwardly large or small in other regions. As a result, several different units of sizes convenient for particular problems have come into common usage. The more important such units which will be encountered in further reading follow.

Units expressing frequency

Cycles/sec, or cycles sec^{-1}.
  Abbreviated c/s.
  Often expressed merely as cycles.
  Used to describe power and low-audible frequencies.

Kilocycles/sec or kilocycles sec^{-1}.
  Abbreviated kc/sec, kc/s, kcs, kc sec^{-1}.
  Equals the number of thousands of cycles/sec; for example, 2 kc/s = 2000 cycles/sec.
  Often expressed merely as kilocycles.
  Used for audio frequencies as in sound waves, and for broadcast band radio frequencies.

Megacycles/sec or megacycles sec.
  Abbreviation Mc/sec, Mc/s, Mc sec^{-1}.
  Often expressed merely as megacycles.
  Equals the number of millions of cycles/sec; for example, 1.5 Mc/s = 1500 kc/s = 1.5 × 10^6 c/s.
  Useful for television or frequency modulation frequencies.

Wave number.
  Abbreviated $\bar{\nu}$ or cm^{-1}.
  This is not strictly a frequency, but is a reciprocal wavelength, $1/\lambda$. It is equal to ν/c, and is the number of waves per centimeter in free space.
  Convenient for describing infrared waves of frequency 10^{11} to 10^{13} cycles sec^{-1}, because such frequencies on being divided by $c = 3 \times 10^{10}$ cm sec^{-1} yield the much more convenient numbers 3.3 cm^{-1} to 333.3 cm^{-1}.

Units expressing length

Micron, abbreviated μ.
   A length of one-millionth of a meter, 10^{-4} cm.
   Used for wavelengths of infrared (IR) radiation, and for expressing linear
   dimensions of small particles.

Ångström, abbreviated Å or A.
   A length of 10^{-8} cm.
   Used for wavelengths of light waves, ultraviolet, X-rays, and for atomic
   dimensions.

X units, abbreviated XU.
   A length of 10^{-11} cm.
   Used in work in X-rays and γ-rays.

4.3. Sources and Detection of Electromagnetic Radiation

The characteristic wavelengths and frequencies have a very direct relation in many cases to the way in which radiations of various kinds are produced and to the way in which they interact with matter. As shown in Fig. 4.1, there are many types of radiation other than the light which is visible to the human eye; consideration of the electromagnetic spectrum places these in a proper relation to one another.

The approximate range of the visible region of the spectrum is 4100 Å to 7000 Å, and radiation within this range can be detected by the human eye, photographic plates, or photoelectric cells. While the different types of radiation being discussed are essentially the same, the eye is sensitive only in this very limited region specified.

In the region of longer wavelengths—beyond the infrared—we find the section called Hertzian or radio waves. Short Hertzian waves have a wavelength of about 10^7 Å, or 0.1 cm, and the radar bands range upward from roughly 1 cm. Beyond radar are the "regular" radio waves, in which we find the frequencies of commercial broadcasting stations—AM, FM, and TV.

Thus the electromagnetic spectrum includes wavelengths from X-rays of $\lambda = 10^{-8}$ cm up to radio broadcast bands of several hundred meters. The origins of these various waves are important because radiation of every wavelength has some important application in chemistry. Some originate in nature and some in the laboratory through man-made devices. Visible waves, ultraviolet, infrared, and certain X-rays (or radiation corresponding to X-rays) can be found in nature. All types of radiation discussed here may be artificially produced, such as visible light from an ordinary incandescent bulb. Radio waves are perhaps thought to be exclusively man-made, but the static caused by lightning heard on radio demonstrates that these, too, can be of natural origin.

In the interaction of radiation with matter, there is an interesting and significant correspondence in order of magnitude between the wavelength of the radiation and the dimension of the object with which it is interacting. As examples, we may note that the wavelengths of television waves, 3 m, are of the order of the size of TV antennas; visible light, with $\lambda \cong 10^{-4}$ cm, is scattered by dust particles of similar dimensions; X-rays, with $\lambda \cong 10^{-8}$ cm, are scattered in a characteristic fashion by crystals with similar distances of their interatomic spacings. More examples of such relations, some of a very fundamental nature, will appear in chapters which follow.

One of the more interesting aspects in the study of the electromagnetic spectrum is the means by which various wavelengths may be detected. Photographic plates can be used to detect X-rays or radiation in the extreme ultraviolet as well as in the visible and infrared. Devices such as Geiger counters may be employed for X-rays. In the visible range the human eye is a very sensitive detector. Instruments such as thermocouples, thermistors, and bolometers will detect infrared radiation. Beyond the infrared, radio receivers may be used.

For certain wavelengths, glass cannot be used in the optical system utilized for the detection and measurement of radiation because of its absorption in those wavelengths. Ordinary glass, for example, absorbs so strongly in the ultraviolet (U.V.) that prisms and lenses of glass are opaque, and some other substance, often quartz, must be used in U.V. optics. In the infrared, certain crystalline substances such as potassium bromide are sufficiently transparent to be used in lenses and prisms. As will be seen later, it is extremely important to be able to measure wavelengths and frequency accurately because these are the necessary data for powerful methods in the exploration of atomic and molecular structure. (See Harrison, Lord, and Loofbourow, *Practical Spectroscopy*, a practical text which covers these matters with a minimum of theoretical discussion.)

As may be surmised from this discussion, matter and radiation affect each other in characteristic ways. These interactions are the basic tools with which many fundamental properties of each have been studied. The two examples presented in Sections 4.4 and 4.5 have been historically important in evolving theories of the constitution of matter;

they are particularly significant in showing the quantum properties of both matter and radiation.

4.4. Black-body Radiation

Any body not at the absolute zero of temperature is continually emitting radiation and receiving it from other bodies. Because radiation is an electromagnetic phenomenon, these processes can come about only by changes in the motion of the electrically charged elementary particles of which the body is composed. It was recognized in the 19th century that—when they were not complicated by reflection, scattering, or transparency—the processes of emission and absorption were independent of the particular physical and chemical constitution of the body. Instead, these processes were found to depend only on the frequency of the radiation and the temperature of the body studied. An understanding of this very general behavior is a necessary preliminary to study of the effects of radiation, which depend greatly on the physical and chemical properties of different substances.

Stefan-Boltzmann Law

The dependence of the total energy radiated by a completely absorbing surface (a black body) on the temperature is expressed by the Stefan-Boltzmann equation, which states that the energy emitted is equal to the product of a constant, σ, and fourth power of the absolute temperature:

$$E = \sigma T^4 \tag{4.1}$$

Stefan observed this relationship empirically in 1879, and Boltzmann later was able to derive it theoretically from energy considerations. The Stefan-Boltzmann constant, σ, is equal to 5.69×10^{-5} ergs cm^{-2} (centigrade degree)$^{-4}$ sec^{-1}. As examples, a surface 1 cm^2 in area at 1°K would emit 5.69×10^{-5} ergs of energy per second, and 15.4 ergs per second at 300°K. For real, imperfectly black, bodies the temperature exponent may approximate 5, but less energy is radiated, especially at low temperatures.

Dependence of Energy Radiated on Frequency

A bar of metal when heated glows dull orange or red at 400–500°C. In the neighborhood of 600–700°C its color becomes yellow, and at perhaps 1400°C it is white hot. Thus there is a shift from the red to the blue end of the spectrum, and hence to higher frequencies, as the temperature of the emitting body becomes higher. This spectral distribution of radiant energy is of immediate concern in the understanding of the phenomena of radiation.

Measurements of the distribution of energy from a black body accumulated from 1879 on, and are described by a quantity called the emissivity E_ν. This is defined as the rate at which energy in a narrow frequency band $d\nu$ between frequencies ν and $\nu + d\nu$ is emitted from unit area of a surface. The way in which E_ν depends on frequency ν and absolute temperature T of the radiating surface is shown for black bodies in Fig. 4.2. A little consideration of these results shows their agreement with what has been said previously: at higher temperatures the total energy radiated increases rapidly, and although spread over a wide range of frequency the predominant radiation is of higher frequencies.

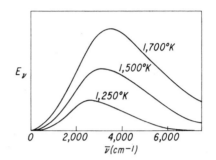

Fig. 4.2. *Emissivity E_ν of a black body at three temperatures as a function of frequency (expressed in wave numbers).*

Failure of Classical Theory

Because these emissivity curves are the same for any body, provided only that it is sufficiently black, their explanation became a basic problem for physicists. The classical theory for objects that are in thermal equilibrium requires that oscillating particles have an average energy of amount kT, where Boltzmann's constant k has the value 1.38×10^{-16} erg (centigrade degrees)$^{-1}$ and T is the absolute temperature (discussed further in Chapter 9). By assuming that these small oscillators were capable of exchanging energy with their surroundings as radiation emitted in any amount and at all frequencies, it was possible to show that E_ν should depend on frequency and temperature according to the equation

$$E_\nu \, d\nu = \frac{2\pi\nu^2 kT}{c^2} \, d\nu \qquad (4.2)$$

where c is the velocity of electromagnetic waves (3×10^{10} cm sec^{-1}).

Although derived for the oscillator model of the radiating particles, the result is independent of the detailed process, and so is a completely general result for thermal equilibrium.

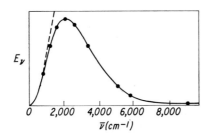

Fig. 4.3. *Emissivity E_ν at 1070°K. Circles from data of Paschen; solid curve, Planck's equation; dashed curve, classical equation.*

Unfortunately for the classical theory, this equation, the Rayleigh-Jeans law, was in only partial agreement with experiment. The nature of the difficulty is illustrated by radiation of a black body at 1000°K, in Fig. 4.3. The points are experimental results of several observers, the dashed curve is the prediction of Eq. 4.2. The agreement, while good at low frequencies, becomes increasingly poor at higher frequencies.

The equation requires that at lower frequencies radiation should result in diminished energy, and that the energy emitted should become infinitely large as the frequency of radiation increases. If this were actually the case, it would lead spontaneously to a gigantic explosion, which has been referred to as the "violet catastrophe." Since we have not suffered this "violet catastrophe," the Rayleigh-Jeans law does not accurately represent radiation phenomena at short wavelengths. Too, infinitely large energies radiated because of infinitely short wavelength are contrary to the Stefan-Boltzmann equation, a relationship which is in complete agreement with experimental evidence. This can be seen from the fact that the area under the curve representing E_ν as a function of frequency is the total energy emitted. The dashed curve in Fig. 4.3 has an infinite area under it if all frequencies are considered, and so contradicts the result of Stefan and Boltzmann, which shows that the true curve must have a finite area corresponding to the actual finite total energy emission.

This intolerable state of affairs could not be blamed on experimental error, nor could any mistake in working out the theory be found, *once its initial assumptions were granted.* Something more fundamental was involved, and the nature of the difficulty was first recognized by Max Planck in 1899.

The Planck Radiation Law

Planck had been concerned for some time with the problem, and first found, simply as a matter of describing the data, that the curves for E_ν were fitted within experimental error by a modification of the Rayleigh-Jeans equation of the form

$$E_\nu \, d\nu = \frac{2\pi k T}{c^2} \left(\frac{h\nu/kT}{e^{h\nu/kT} - 1} \right) \nu^2 \, d\nu \qquad (4.3)$$

The parenthetical factor is Planck's modification, and by choosing the constant h to have a value of about 6.5×10^{-27} erg seconds he found that the equation was an excellent representation of emissivity as a function of both temperature and frequency. This is illustrated by the fit of the solid curve in Fig. 4.3, calculated from Eq. 4.3. There is today no doubt of its essential correctness. Planck's ingenuity in devising the equation was helped by certain other results: the Stefan-Boltzmann law, the knowledge that the Rayleigh-Jeans equation held at low frequencies, and a relation developed by Max Wien showing that the frequency ν_{max} of the maximum value of E_ν varied directly with the absolute temperature. The interested student will find that all these less general results can be deduced from Eq. 4.3 by straightforward algebra and calculus.

Planck's Quantum Hypothesis

Planck was not satisfied with what at first was merely "curve fitting," nor is it likely that his work would have been taken very seriously by others in the absence of some fundamental explanation. In his own words, "Even if this radiation formula should prove to be absolutely accurate it would after all be only an interpolation formula found by happy guesswork, and would thus leave one rather unsatisfied. I was, therefore, from the day of its origination, occupied with the task of giving it a real physical meaning, and this question led me, along Boltzmann's line of thought, to the consideration of the relation between entropy and probability; until after some weeks of the most intense work of my life clearness began to dawn upon me, and an unexpected view revealed itself in the distance."

Planck's really far-reaching contribution was his finding that his equation could be derived if one assumed that the oscillating charges could emit radiation only in discrete unit portions of energy, rather than in any continuously varying amount, as assumed in deriving the Rayleigh-

Jeans law. These unit packages of radiated energy are called *quanta*, and Planck found that to derive his equation each quantum had to be assigned an energy hv. By allowing only amounts of energy hv, $2hv$, or any other multiple of hv to be radiated at a frequency v—but *not* amounts $\frac{1}{2}hv$, $3.7hv$, or any other nonintegral value—the necessary modifications of classical theory led to precisely the result we have given as Eq. 4.3.

In this sketch of the problem of black-body radiation and its solution by Planck, for brevity we have had to omit most of the details of the underlying theory. It is not to be expected of the reader that he will understand the problem fully from what has been described, or that he will remember the exact forms of the equations presented. He should, however, realize that Planck's step of quantizing the emission of radiation from material bodies was the key to solving a basic problem which otherwise was inexplicable. If Planck's hypothesis had gone no further, its success for radiation, which was a rather special case, would probably have seemed curious rather than important. Further evidence of its importance, however, was soon forthcoming.

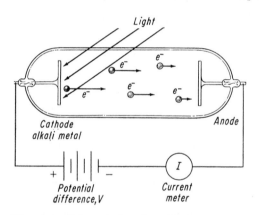

Fig. 4.4. *Schematic drawing of arrangement to produce and study photoelectric effect. Electrons leaving the cathode in the direction of the anode lose speed when the anode is more negative (as illustrated) than the cathode.*

4.5. Photoelectric Effect

Hertz and others had found before 1900 that radiation striking a metal surface caused the surface to lose electrical charge under certain conditions. It was soon recognized and demonstrated that the surface lost its charge by emitting electrons, and that the energy required for their emission had to be obtained at the expense of the incident radiation. When the phenomenon was investigated more systematically with careful attention to cleanliness of the metal surfaces, and using monochromatic light, simple regularities were found which were not to be explained by the classical principles of the time.

The scheme of measurements to show the effects is sketched in Fig. 4.4. The metal surface to be investigated is placed in an evacuated bulb, together with a second electrode to collect electrons emitted from the first surface when it is illuminated by light of frequency selected by an optical system of prisms and slits. Electrons set free from the cathode surface by the incident light flow to the collector anode, and can be measured as a current in the external battery circuit. By changing the applied potential difference between the cathode and anode, it is possible to find the largest negative potential difference against which electrons will flow. With more elaborate arrangements based on the same principle, certain general results were obtained.

1. On decreasing the frequency of light, the emitted electrons could be stopped by lower retarding potentials (that is, the collector did not need to be as negative to prevent electron emission), implying that the maximum energy with which the electrons were emitted from the surface decreased.

2. At a given potential, there was a lower limit of frequency of the impinging radiation below which no electrons were emitted.

3. With increasing light intensity, the *number* of electrons emitted increased, but not the retarding potential to stop them (that is, the energy with which they were emitted was unaffected).

The failure of light below a certain frequency to emit electrons at all and the failure of greater intensity of illumination to produce faster electrons (higher energy electrons) were both incompatible with classical assumptions as to the energy absorption—and, furthermore, with classical theory of electrons in metals. (See Chapter 5.)

Einstein's Hypothesis

Einstein realized that the observations were explicable if Planck's hypothesis were extended to the quantization of both the impinging radiation and its absorption by an electron in the metal. He postulated first that radiation of frequency v was quantized, each unit bundle or packet containing an amount of energy ϵ given by Planck's condition

$$\epsilon = hv \qquad (4.4)$$

The second key step was to assume that each electron ejected from a metal first absorbed *exactly* one quantum of energy hv, no more and no less. In order to leave the surface, a definite minimum energy E_0 is first required. The electron is finally emitted with a net kinetic energy, $\frac{1}{2}mv^2$. The fastest electrons will have a kinetic energy $\frac{1}{2}mv_{max}^2$, where v_{max} is their velocity, which must then be given by

$$\tfrac{1}{2}mv_{\max}^2 = E - E_0 = h\nu - E_0 \qquad (4.5)$$

The maximum energy can best be measured indirectly by finding the retarding potential V_s, which will stop them because they lose energy eV_s equal to $\tfrac{1}{2}mv_{\max}^2$, and hence never reach the collector. This "stopping potential" should then be given by

$$V_s = \left(\frac{h}{e}\right)\nu - \frac{E_0}{e}$$

Very careful experiments by Millikan, using different metals and light of different frequencies, verified this equation; furthermore, h/e was found to be 1.374×10^{-17} erg sec esu^{-1} from the variation of V_s with frequency ν. By using $e = 4.802 \times 10^{-10}$ esu, the value of h is calculated to be 6.598×10^{-27} erg sec, in good agreement with the spectroscopic value of 6.624×10^{-27} erg sec, using $c = 2.99776 \times 10^{10}$ cm/sec. (It will be noted that only the combination h/e is determined, just as in particle deflection experiments only m/e is determined.)

The agreement of Einstein's explanation with experiment is important as an independent verification of Planck's hypothesis. It further shows that electrons absorb only single quanta, the unit amount of energy in radiation.

Problems

4.1. The following table lists several characteristic electromagnetic effects, with a frequency, wavelength, or wave number in a unit commonly used in the given part of the spectrum. Complete the entries in the table for all units of expression.

Effect	Frequency (cycles/sec)	λ (cm)	λ (Å)	λ (μ)	$\bar{\nu}$ (cm^{-1})
AC power	60	—	—	—	—
Radio broadcast	10^6	—	—	—	—
Radar (microwave)	—	3	—	—	—
Thermal radiation (room temp.)	—	—	—	10	—
Vibrations of HCl molecule	—	—	—	—	3000
Mercury line	—	—	4358	—	—

4.2. Colloidal particles have dimensions much larger than molecules, but smaller than particles with properties of bulk matter. They can often be studied by wavelengths of radiation comparable with their dimensions. What is the wavelength of radiation comparable to particles 1μ in diameter? What are the wave number and frequency? In what part of the electromagnetic spectrum does this radiation occur?

4.3. The index of refraction (n) of a liquid is defined as the ratio of the speed of light in vacuum to the speed in the liquid. Light of frequency 5×10^{14} sec^{-1} in vacuum passes into a liquid. What is its wavelength in vacuum? In the liquid? What is its frequency in the liquid? Assume $n = 1.39$.

4.4. Regularly spaced particles or obstacles show diffraction effects when radiation has a wavelength comparable with the distance between adjacent units. If these are scratches on a glass plate, spaced 10^{-4} inches apart, what is the wavelength and in what part of the spectrum does it lie? If the spacing is of atoms in a crystal which are 2×10^{-8} cm apart, in what part of the spectrum will radiation give diffraction effects?

4.5. Calculate the energy of one quantum of radiation at a wavelength 6000 Å in ergs and in calories (1 calorie $= 4.19 \times 10^7$ ergs). How many such quanta have a total energy of 1000 calories? How many X-ray quanta of wavelength 0.5 Å have this energy?

4.6. Acetone vapor can be decomposed by ultraviolet light (photochemical reaction), giving ethane and other products. When light of wavelength 3000 Å is used, 40 joules of energy absorbed by the vapor results in decomposition of 10^{-4} moles of acetone. How many quanta on the average are absorbed per molecule decomposed? (1 joule $= 10^7$ ergs.)

4.7. The energy required to dissociate nitric oxide into atoms is 123 kcal/mole (1 kcal $= 1000$ calories). If this energy is to be supplied by single molecules absorbing one quantum of radiation, what is the minimum frequency of the radiation? Where is this in the spectrum?

4.8. Show that the Planck radiation formula (Eq. 4.3) is dimensionally consistent. (E_ν has dimensions of energy/cm^2.)

4.9. (a) A completely absorbing body 100 cm^2 in area is held at a temperature of 300°K (27°C). How much energy must be supplied per second (in ergs and in calories) to maintain this temperature? (b) What would be the answers to (a) were the temperature to be 900°K?

4.10. On a graph sketch a curve showing how the number of electrons (as ordinate) emitted from a photosensitive surface varies with the frequency of radiation (as abscissa), the intensity of this radiation striking the surface being held constant. Sketch another curve for a higher (and constant) intensity of radiation.

4.11. The table below gives some of Millikan's data from his original photo-electric measurements (*Phys. Rev.*, 7:355, 1916). The voltages (V) listed are potential differences just sufficient to prevent electron current for light at the different wavelengths given. Use these data to make a plot, which should be a straight line of slope h/e by Einstein's theory; determine the slope from the graph and calculate Planck's constant (h) from the slope.

λ (Å)	5461	4339	4047	3650	3126	2535
V (volts)	+0.520	−0.380	−0.915	−1.295	−1.487	−2.045

4.12. The value of E_0 in Eq. 4.5 is 4.00 eV for a particular metal. (a) What is the minimum frequency of light quanta which will just remove electrons from the metal surface, the emitted electrons possessing no kinetic energy? (b) What is the minimum frequency if a retarding potential of 1.00 V is applied?

4.13. In the text it is stated that Planck's formula (Eq. 4.3) reduces to the classical Rayleigh-Jeans result (Eq. 4.2) at sufficiently low frequencies—i.e., where $h\nu$ is much less than kT. Show that for $h\nu \ll kT$, the statement is correct. (Hint: The exponential e^x can be expressed as the power series $e^x = 1 + x + x^2/2 + \cdots$. Use this mathematical result and the condition that $h\nu/kT$ is much less than one.)

4.14. The text states that the Planck formula when integrated over all frequencies predicts that the total energy radiated by a black body is proportional to T^4 as in the Stefan-Boltzmann equation—i.e., that

$$\int_0^\infty E_\nu \, d\nu = \text{constant} \times T^4$$

(a) Show that this must be true by expressing the integral as a function of the dimensionless variable $x = h\nu/kT$ times a factor independent of frequency ν. The resulting integral cannot be evaluated simply, but any integral of the form $\int_0^\infty F(x) \, dx$ with x a number must be a dimensionless number. (b) If the numerical value of the integral is A, verify that the Stefan-Boltzmann constant σ is given by

$$\sigma = \frac{2\pi k^4}{c^2 h^3} A$$

4.15. When electrons are accelerated through a potential difference V, the minimum wavelength $\lambda_{\min}$ of X-rays produced when they strike a target is related to V by an expression of the form

$$\lambda_{\min} = \frac{\text{constant}}{V}$$

(a) Derive this equation and an expression for the constant in terms of fundamental constants. (b) For λ in Ångströms and V in volts, this formula was for some time taken to be $\lambda_{\min} = 12345/V$, but this has changed because of more accurate values of the fundamental constants. Use present values to obtain the value which must be used in place of 12345.

4.16. The emission of X-rays from a metal surface bombarded with electrons is referred to as the "inverse photoelectric effect" if the kinetic energy of the electrons is completely converted to energy of X-ray quanta. (a) Write an equation relating the potential difference V through which the electrons are accelerated to the maximum frequency ν_m of X-rays emitted, and show that measurements of V for different frequencies ν_m can be used to obtain h/e. (b) Use the experimental data below, due to Duane and Hunt (*Phys. Rev.*, **6**:166, 1915), to calculate a value of h/e:

λ (Å)	0.307	0.318	0.345	0.371	0.425	0.486
V (volts)	39,150	37,950	34,900	32,250	28,400	25,000

4.17. (a) Demonstrate that the frequency of maximum energy density in black-body radiation is proportional to the absolute temperature, by showing that this frequency (ν_m) satisfies the equation

$$3\left[\exp\left(\frac{h\nu_m}{kT}\right) - 1\right] = \frac{h\nu_m}{kT}\exp\left(\frac{h\nu_m}{kT}\right)$$

(b) Verify that this equation has the solution

$$\nu_m = \frac{2.83kT}{h}$$

Suggested Readings

Most textbooks on atomic physics discuss the material of this chapter, including the references for Chapter 3. Other discussions are given in *Physical Chemistry* by E. A. Moelwyn-Hughes (Pergamon, New York, 1957) and *Physical Chemistry* (3rd ed.) by W. J. Moore (Prentice-Hall, Englewood Cliffs, N.J., 1962).

Max Planck's Nobel Prize address, *The Origin and Development of the Quantum Theory* (Oxford, 1922), describes the thoughts and efforts which led to his quantum hypothesis.

Chapter 5

Quantum Principles and Atomic Structure

IN THE PRECEDING chapter we have seen how phenomena of electromagnetic radiation and the emission of photoelectrons from metallic surfaces presented problems on the atomic scale for which explanations based upon the classical physics of particles were inadequate. In both cases, only a very limited understanding of the constitution of atoms was necessary for some appreciation of the quantum explanations postulated by Planck and Einstein. In this chapter we shall review suggestive evidence that quantum effects are important in atomic structure, and describe the major developments in quantum theory applied to atoms.

5.1. The Spectrum of Hydrogen

For our present purposes the simplest of atomic systems will serve: the hydrogen atom, composed of a singly charged nucleus (the proton) and one planetary or exterior electron. Atomic hydrogen is not a stable substance at room temperature (hydrogen usually occurring in molecular form), but it can be easily formed by an electric discharge through rarefied hydrogen gas.

When the light emitted by such a discharge is separated according to wavelength with a prism or grating, a series of sharp bright lines is observed in the visible region, and by means of photographic techniques this series was found to extend into the ultraviolet and infrared, as indicated in Fig. 5.1.

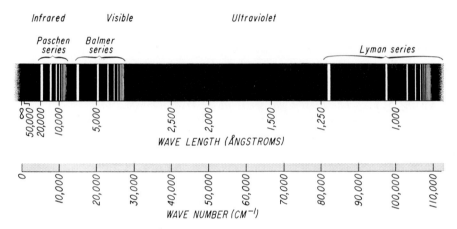

Fig. 5.1. *Schematic emission spectrum of atomic hydrogen. Higher series than the Paschen series* (n = 3) *have been omitted to avoid overlapping.* [*After Herzberg.*]

That only a limited number of sharp lines can be found, rather than a continuous smear of light of all wavelengths, of itself suggests a quantized character of the process in the atom by which light is emitted. Equally striking is the regularity of the frequencies at which the lines occur. Balmer in 1885 was impressed by this, and found that he could represent the frequencies of four lines in the visible region by a very simple formula. Later, the more general but almost equally simple Rydberg equation was found, by which all of the Balmer lines, as well as those of other series, could be represented. This formula has the form

$$\nu \; (\text{c/s}) = \frac{c}{\lambda} = Rc \left(\frac{1}{n_1^2} - \frac{1}{n_2^2} \right) \qquad (5.1)$$

where c is the speed of light, n_1 and n_2 are integers (now called quantum numbers) starting with unity, and n_2 is necessarily the larger integer if ν is to be positive. R is the Rydberg constant, which for hydrogen is 109,677.59 cm^{-1}. Expressing frequency in cycles/sec in this spectral region results in numbers too large for convenience, and either wavelengths or the wave numbers defined in Section 4.2 are used in preference to frequencies. The wave number corresponding to a frequency (ν) of Eq. 5.1 is given by

$$\bar{\nu} = \frac{\nu}{c} = \frac{1}{\lambda} = R\left(\frac{1}{n_1^2} - \frac{1}{n_2^2}\right) \tag{5.2}$$

The various frequencies predicted for a fixed n_1 and variable n_2 ($> n_1$) are called series, because each such set is a regular progression from the highest frequency for the series to lower values. These various sets are named in honor of their discoverers; some frequencies of the first four sets are listed in Table 5.1.

TABLE 5.1. *The First Four Series in the Hydrogen Spectrum.*

n_1	Name of Series	n_2	$\bar{\nu}$ (cm^{-1})	λ (Å)
1	Lyman	2	82,259	1216
	(Ultraviolet)	3	97,491	1026
		4	102,823	972
		5	105,291	950
2	Balmer	3	15,233	6563
	(Visible)	4	20,564	4861
		5	23,032	4340
3	Paschen	4	5331	18,756
	(Near infrared)	5	7799	12,821
		6	9139	10,939
4	Brackett	5	2468	40,500
	(Infrared)	6	3808	26,300

Although the number of significant figures is large, the values listed do not do full justice to the data or to the accuracy of the Rydberg formula in predicting the observed values. The agreement between the formula and experiment is to within one part per million. Only measurements of extraordinary precision are adequate to show the slight differences and also to demonstrate that the lines have fine structure—that is, are groups of very closely spaced lines—and so are not completely described by the formula.

5.2. The Bohr Atom and the Hydrogen Spectrum

The forerunner of present-day quantum theory was Niels Bohr, who in 1913 postulated a model for the hydrogen atom which initiated the development of modern quantum mechanics. Although his model has been superseded by newer postulates based upon data not available to Bohr, we will discuss his model because of its simplicity and its importance for our present concepts of atomic structure.

Bohr's Frequency Condition

Bohr first assumed a quantum condition for the emission or absorption of radiation of frequency v: namely, that this corresponded to a change in energy of the atom of amount hv. Second, he assumed that for the atom only definite quantized values for its energy were possible. These had to be such as to satisfy the celebrated *Bohr frequency condition* for emission: that

$$hv = E_{\text{initial}} - E_{\text{final}}$$

where E_{initial} and E_{final} are the energies before and after the quantum is emitted.

Quantization of Angular Momentum and the Bohr Formula

Bohr then imposed the seemingly arbitrary condition that the only allowed energies of the atom were those for which the electron traveled in a closed orbit about the nucleus with an angular momentum equal to an integral multiple of $h/2\pi$. By this requirement—and further, by not allowing the moving electron to radiate energy (a further violation of classical ideas)—Bohr could calculate the possible energies or orbits of different radii from the corresponding kinetic energy of rotation and the application of Coulomb's law for the force between two electrically charged particles.

The Bohr formula for the energy obtained from these considerations is derived in elementary physics texts. For an atom in which the angular momentum of the electron is $nh/2\pi$, where $n = 1, 2, 3, \cdots$ is the principal quantum number, the corresponding energies E are given by

$$E = -\frac{2\pi^2 me^4}{h^2}\frac{1}{n^2} \tag{5.3}$$

The frequency for a transition from a state or level of energy corresponding to n_2 to a state corresponding to n_1 (of lower energy) is then

$$\nu = \frac{1}{h} \left(E_{\text{initial}} - E_{\text{final}} \right)$$

$$= -\frac{2\pi^2 me^4}{h^3} \frac{1}{n_2^2} - \left(-\frac{2\pi^2 me^4}{h^3} \frac{1}{n_1^2} \right)$$

or

$$\nu = \frac{2\pi^2 me^4}{h^3} \left(\frac{1}{n_1^2} - \frac{1}{n_2^2} \right) \tag{5.4}$$

If this result is compared with Eq. 5.1, it is seen that the theory gives
exactly the Rydberg formula and predicts that the Rydberg constant
is expressed in terms of fundamental constants by the equation

$$R = \frac{2\pi^2 me^4}{h^3 c}$$

A correction must be made to allow for the fact that the nucleus is not
stationary while the electron revolves about it, but in actuality must
itself move if the center of mass is at rest. By considering the mutual
rotation around the common center of mass, the so-called reduced mass,
μ, of the electron is obtained:

$$\mu = \frac{mM}{m + M}$$

where m is the electronic and M the nuclear mass. Substituting the
reduced mass for the mass of the electron, we obtain the corrected formula for the Rydberg constant:

$$R = \frac{2\pi^2 e^4}{h^3 c} \frac{mM}{m + M} \tag{5.5}$$

Since R is dependent upon the mass of the nucleus, it is to be expected
that the value of R will vary from one element to another. For elements
of high atomic weight the values of R change only slightly because M
is large and nearly the same; for lighter elements the difference is more
noticeable. Thus the Rydberg constant for hydrogen is 109,677.59 cm^{-1};
for helium it is 109,722 cm^{-1}; for an element of infinitely great atomic
weight, 109,737.323 cm^{-1}. Using the corrected formula (Eq. 5.5), it has
been possible to calculate Rydberg constants which agree almost exactly
with those obtained experimentally from spectral studies.

5.3. Ionization of Hydrogen Atoms

We may consider the mechanism of the formation of a line in the emission spectrum of hydrogen to be as follows. Enough energy is imparted to normal molecular hydrogen by some means of excitation, such as an electrical discharge, to dissociate the molecules and produce atoms with electrons in various energy levels. Thus some electrons will be in higher states than in the normal atom. An excited electron may now fall back to its original state, with a resultant loss of energy. This energy appears as a line in the emission spectrum. For hydrogen, if the level to which the electron falls is represented by the quantum number $n_1 = 1$, the emitted energy lies in the ultraviolet range, and the spectral line is a member of the Lyman series. Other electrons, absorbing other possible amounts of energy, are excited to different levels, and may return to any available level.

A photograph of the spectrum of a given series shows a group of lines whose successive members appear closer and closer together, finally converging at a sharp limit. Beyond this series limit is an area of continuous radiation. The bunching of the lines near the series limit cor-

responds to the increasingly diminishing energy, indicated by Fig. 5.2. The series limit itself represents the energy necessary to ionize an atom; that is, to move an electron from the lowest energy state to a state where $n = \infty$. It corresponds to the ionization potential. Since the ease of removal of electrons is a measure of chemical reactivity, the ionization potential is of considerable interest to chemists. The energy of ionization for hydrogen may be calculated by substituting 1 for n_1 and ∞ for n_2 in the energy difference formula. This gives

Fig. 5.2. *Copy of Balmer series spectrum of atomic hydrogen as photographed with a prism spectrometer.* [*After Herzberg.*]

$$E_{\text{ioniz.}} = Rhc \qquad (5.6)$$

which is 2.14×10^{-11} ergs per molecule (using Eq. 5.4 for R) or 13.54 electron volts. The ionization energy may also be found from the observed wave number of the series limit, $\bar{\nu}_\infty$:

$$E_{\text{ioniz.}} = hc\bar{\nu}_\infty \qquad (5.7)$$

5.4. Other Ions with a Single Electron

The simple postulates made by Bohr for the hydrogen atom are readily applied to other one-electron atomic systems—for example, the He^+ ion and the Li^{+2} ion. In such a system, one has a nucleus of charge Ze, where Z is the atomic number, and the energy formula 5.3 is modified to read

$$E_{\text{initial}} = -\frac{2\pi^2\mu Z^2 e^4}{h^2}\frac{1}{n^2} \tag{5.8}$$

where μ is the reduced mass. This formula is often written in terms of the Rydberg constant $R \ (= 2\pi^2\mu e^4/h^3 c)$ as

$$E_{\text{initial}} = -hcRZ^2\frac{1}{n^2} \tag{5.9}$$

The frequencies of observed lines are from Bohr's conditions:

$$\nu = RcZ^2\left[\frac{1}{n_1^2} - \frac{1}{n_2^2}\right] \tag{5.10}$$

The primary difference between the H-atom spectrum and the He^+-ion spectrum results from the factor Z^2, which makes analogous frequencies for He^+ four times larger. The slightly larger Rydberg constant (because μ is larger when M is the mass of the helium nucleus) causes a further small increase. Both predictions have been accurately verified. Similar studies have been made of Li^{+2}, Be^{+3}, and other one-electron ions.

Fig. 5.3. *Emission spectrum of sodium. The lines have been separated according to sequences. In actual photograph the four sequences would be superposed on a single strip.*

5.5. Spectra of Multi-electron Atoms

The simplicity and regularity of the hydrogenlike spectra is lost to some extent in many-electron atoms, but definite regularities are still apparent in their more complicated spectra. A familiar and relatively simple example is found in the spectrum of sodium and the other alkali metals with but a single valence electron. Four distinct series of frequencies have been recognized in the spectrum.

By assuming that each such line represents transitions between two states differing in energy by $E_2 - E_1 = h\nu$, a diagram of energy levels has been constructed capable of accounting for these series. This energy-level diagram for sodium is shown in Fig. 5.4, together with the corresponding one for hydrogen.

Differences between energy levels in the diagram should by Bohr's postulate correspond with observed spectral lines. In order to arrive at a consistent scheme for making the number of possible transitions between energy levels equal to the number of lines observed, however, it was necessary to impose a *selection rule* restricting the transitions possible. In the diagram of Fig. 5.4 this rule limits allowed frequencies of emission or absorption to transitions between energy levels in adjacent columns.

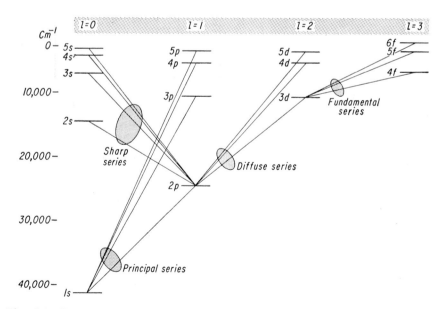

Fig. 5.4. *Energy level diagram for sodium.*

The existence of such selection rules is a characteristic property governing radiation, by atoms and molecules alike.

Bohr was able to formulate a basis for predicting such selection rules by his famous *correspondence principle*. This requires that when small changes in properties are involved, the predictions of quantum theory must approach those of classical mechanics. Application of this reasonable principle to Bohr's mechanics of atoms was not always easy, and extensions of it to more complex atoms met with increasing difficulties and arbitrariness in formulating more and more rules of quantization.

More detailed investigation of spectral lines also indicated greater complexities than could be readily comprehended within the framework of the original theory. Closer examination of alkali metal spectra, for example, shows that the spectral lines shown in Fig. 5.3 as single, broad lines are actually closely spaced pairs of lines (doublets). These could be split into even more lines when the atoms emitted or absorbed light while in a magnetic electrostatic field. Even the simple spectrum of atomic hydrogen has revealed a fine structure of its lines, as already mentioned, when examined closely by special refined techniques.

5.6. Development of Quantum Mechanics

The initial success of Bohr's theory stimulated extensions to more complicated systems, but increasing difficulties were encountered which forced continued re-examinations of the theory. These led ultimately to a fundamental new formulation of quantum principles in 1926 by Schrödinger and Heisenberg. This development, sufficiently completed for most purposes of chemistry by 1931, resulted in the postulates of present-day quantum mechanics. That Bohr's theory has been superseded by these later developments does not diminish his accomplishment: theories develop by evolution, and the basic frequency condition and stationary energy states envisaged by Bohr remain valid today, as does the fundamental significance of quantized angular momentum.

The definite electron orbits suggested by Bohr are replaced in the newer theory by a statistical description, but this theory is merely a further evolution founded on classical ideas, so modified and broadened as to be adequate for motions on the atomic scale. Prior to our elementary consideration of quantum mechanics, however, we must understand something of the wave properties of an electron.

5.7. The Wave Nature of the Electron

   Prince Louis de Broglie (1924), thinking of the dualistic nature—wave and particle—of light, postulated that electrons might partake of the nature of waves as well as of particles, as previously discussed. If the assumption is made that there is a wave property associated with the motion of the electron about the nucleus of an atom, then it is not unreasonable to require an integral number of wavelengths in an "orbit" in order that the waves remain in phase and not destroy one another.
   The principle is illustrated in Fig. 5.5, where two circular orbits

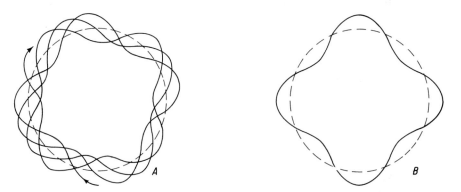

Fig. 5.5. *Interference and reinforcement of wave amplitudes.*

are shown and two possible circular wave paths are superimposed upon them. For the path in *a*, there is some nonintegral number of waves corresponding to a single circumference. In *b* there is an integral number of waves equal to the circumference, so that successive waves are precisely superimposed on previous wave paths. It is readily seen that unless the condition of *b* obtains, the successive waves not exactly in phase will at frequently recurring intervals be 180° out of phase, and destruction will result, leaving nothing to describe the electron motion.

De Broglie's Relation

For a circular orbit of radius *r*, the succession will reinforce rather than cancel if the wavelength λ satisfies the condition

$$\lambda = 2\pi r/n \tag{5.11}$$

where n is an integer only: $n = 0, 1, 2, 3, \cdots$. Bohr's expression for the quantization of angular momentum,

$$mvr = \frac{nh}{2\pi} \tag{5.12}$$

may be multiplied by Eq. 5.11 to yield

$$\lambda = \frac{h}{mv} \tag{5.13}$$

for the wavelength associated with an electron.

The same relationship may be obtained independently of the Bohr hypothesis of circular orbits from the fundamental equations of relativity and quantum theory,

$$E = mc^2 \tag{5.14}$$

and

$$E = h\nu \tag{5.15}$$

Equating,

$$h\nu = mc^2 \tag{5.16}$$

If c/λ is substituted for ν, then

$$\lambda = \frac{h}{mc} \tag{5.17}$$

where mc is the momentum of a photon. If the velocity (v) of a particle other than a photon is substituted for c, this equation is the same as Eq. 5.13.

When de Broglie first hypothesized his wavelength-momentum relation $(\lambda = h/mv)$ for elementary particles in 1924, its basis was a highly speculative one. De Broglie felt more or less intuitively that material particles could most easily have the quantum character required by the Bohr theory if there were at the same time some sort of wave property associated with them. Many ingenious constructions of this sort have come to nothing, but it was not long before experiments showed that de Broglie's result was fundamentally related to observable properties of electrons.

Electron Diffraction

Davisson and Germer of the Bell Telephone Laboratories (1927) and several investigators in England, that same year, found experimental evidence for the wave nature of the electron. Davisson and Germer, studying the interaction of electron beams with the surface of a nickel crystal, surmised that a crystal surface, which because of the spacing between crystal units can act as a diffraction grating for X-rays, might behave in the same fashion for a beam of electrons. They found that an electron beam does, in fact, obey Bragg's law; certain definite angles of incidence produce strong reflections and others produce weak reflections, in exactly the same manner as with X-rays. At angles where reflection occurs, the electron waves reinforce each other, but at angles where reflection does not occur they are out of phase.

The English group approached the problem differently. G. P. Thomson and A. Reid passed a beam of electrons through extremely thin gold foil and obtained interference rings where the electrons struck a photographic plate behind the foil. Such interference phenomena are, of course, characteristic of wave motion. The quantitative prediction of the spacings of these diffraction rings by associating the wavelength $\lambda = h/mv$ to the electrons striking the foil with velocity v was accurately verified by these experiments, and further confirmed de Broglie's hypothesis for such free electrons.

All particles may be said to have associated with them a wavelength which may vary from 0.1 Å for an electron moving with one-fifth the velocity of light to 2×10^{-24} Å for a baseball moving at 2500 cm/sec. The fact that such wave properties as diffraction are not a noticeable characteristic of common objects is due to the extreme shortness of these wavelengths. (The student will remember from his study of light in physics that the short wavelength of visible light has a dominant role in determining the conditions for observing diffraction effects.)

5.8. Wave Function and the Uncertainty Principle

If the de Broglie wave is to have any relevance to the electron, its amplitude at any point must bear some relation to the electron's being at that point. The significance of the de Broglie waves in so describing an electron was first exploited by Schrödinger and developed by him into his formulation of the wave equation.

As in other wave phenomena, the amplitude of the electron wave function is less significant than the square of the amplitude. The intensities of sound and electromagnetic waves, for example, measure the energy carried by the wave disturbance, and are proportional to the square of the amplitude of the wave function describing the motion. In a somewhat similar fashion, Max Born postulated that the probability of finding an electron at any point is proportional to the square of the amplitude of the associated wave function. This amplitude is usually abbreviated Ψ or ψ, and so the probability of the electron being at a point is by this hypothesis proportional to the value of Ψ^2 at that point.*

Schrödinger's great contribution lay in his formulating a set of principles from which to calculate what the wave functions must be under different circumstances. These principles are embodied in the celebrated wave equation, which contains the real basis for predicting atomic and molecular constitution. Before considering the consequences of these principles and the approximate solutions which have been obtained for the motions of electrons in atoms and molecules, some attention needs to be paid to implications of Schrödinger's association of the wave intensity with the electron's position.

Indeterminacy of Position and Momentum

At first sight, the association of particles with waves appears to have quite unfortunate consequences. If an electron is to have single definite momentum, it must be described by a wave of a single definite wavelength. If we represent this as a simple sine wave, the wave function and its square at any instant would look as shown in Fig. 5.6. A truly

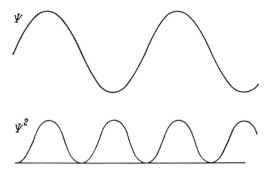

Fig. 5.6. *Amplitude of Ψ and intensity Ψ^2 of a free electron wave.*

monochromatic wave has no beginning or end, and since all its loops are equivalent, there is no way of localizing the electron at any one. What is more, the wave travels with a definite speed corresponding to the momentum, $mv = h/\lambda$, and over a period of time any one point is the same as any other with respect to the peaks passing by. Thus there

---

* Usually, ψ is used with reference to an individual electron, and Ψ is used with reference to an organized system of electrons.

is no way of assigning any preferred position to an electron described by a single value of momentum (and hence energy).

If the electron is to be located more exactly, a bounded wave function of some sort must be used to describe its probable location—in other words, the wave may not extend indefinitely but must have appreciable amplitude only in a small region. Two possible patterns of this kind are sketched in Fig. 5.7. Neither of these can be described as a simple

Fig. 5.7. *Bounded wave functions.*

wave of a single wavelength with which a correspondingly definite momentum can be associated by de Broglie's equation. The finite wave train can be partially described by the spacing of the loops, but something must also be said about the limits. The square pulse has no periodicity at all of the sort associated with simple wave motion, but only a beginning and end.

These and other waves can, however, be represented as the *sum* of groups of simple periodic waves of *different* wavelengths, in somewhat the same way that a sound of complex wave form can be built up of a series of pure tones. Only certain such tones in harmonic relation (fundamental and overtones) are necessary to describe a sustained note, as produced by a musical instrument, but one of short duration which is not repeated must be constructed from an infinite number and one of very short duration has no single principal pitch associated with it at all. Similarly, the wave functions sketched must, to be of finite extent and not repeated, be represented by simple waves of many wavelengths, and there will be a corresponding spread in the momentum values associated with them.

Heisenberg's Uncertainty Principle

The two examples just discussed suggest that it is impossible to associate both a precise position and a precise value for the momentum of a particle if it is to be represented by a wave function. An increasing precision in defining the one makes the other less accurately defined. This conclusion cannot be escaped if one is to describe the wave behavior of electron diffraction and other experiments, and is expressed by *Heisenberg's uncertainty principle:* the products of the uncertainties in position Δx and momentum Δp may not be zero, but must have a value of order of magnitude of Planck's constant h. An exact equation for this product can only be written if one specifies in some definite way exactly how the uncertainties Δp and Δx are to be gauged. This can be done in various ways, but the important conclusion for our purposes is that any reasonable definition gives $\Delta p \, \Delta x \cong h$. (The symbol $\cong$ means "is approximately" or "is of order.") The uncertainty values satisfying this relation are insignificant for objects of ordinary dimensions. A baseball with uncertainty of 10^{-8} cm in position can be regarded as adequately located for most purposes. Its uncertainty in momentum is then $\Delta p \cong h/10^{-8} = 6 \times 10^{-19}$ erg sec/cm $= 6 \times 10^{-19}$ gm cm/sec. Since the mass of a baseball is about 150 g, its uncertainty in speed (Δv) is $\Delta v = \Delta p/m = 4 \times 10^{-21}$ cm/sec, which is far smaller than the error in measuring the speed of a baseball. On the atomic scale, however, the situation is very different. An electron with uncertainty of 1×10^{-8} cm in position is not very well located in an atom of radius approximately 2×10^{-8} cm. At the same time its speed is quite imprecise, as we have $\Delta v = 6 \times 10^{-19}/9 \times 10^{-28} = 6.7 \times 10^8$ cm/sec, an uncertainty equal to 2% of the speed of light.

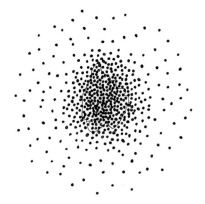

Fig. 5.8. *Time exposure of electron distribution around a point, as for the electron in the 1s state of a hydrogen atom.*

Statistical Nature of the Wave Function

The use of a wave function to describe an electron's motion thus has inherent limitations, and the wave intensity gives only a statistically precise description. In other words, the value of the wave intensity Ψ^2 in a particular region gives the probability of finding the electron in that region. The nature of this limited prediction is usefully visualized as follows. A whole series of actual positions of an electron are represented by dots. Some thousands of dots accumulate to give a pattern, as in Fig. 5.8. The value of Ψ^2 in any region, being a measure of the probability, is proportional to the number of dots in this region, and thus

represents a *probability density*. For millions of dots, one obtains an illusion
of a continuous cloud of varying density and the value of Ψ^2 describes,
so far as we now know, precisely the variations in density of the cloud,
but does not and cannot give the precise sequence of electron motions
producing the result.

5.9. Schrödinger Equation

In the preceding section it was stated that Schrödinger was able to
formulate a set of rules for finding the wave functions describing the
observable properties of electrons and more complicated systems of
elementary particles. In doing this he was confronted by the necessity
of harmonizing quantum and wave properties—found when phenomena
on the atomic scale were explored—with the results of classical mechanics, which were successful for determining the motions of larger scale
systems.

The laws of classical mechanics have their most general expression
in equations of momentum and energy. The properties of wave phenomena, such as vibrations of a string or the fluctuations in pressure
and density characterizing a sound wave, are predicted from a differential equation expressing changes in motion with time and position.
These results may well have suggested to Schrödinger the direction to
take in devising a more general wave mechanics, but the Schrödinger
equation is no more *derived* from the more limited classical laws of
mechanics and waves than Newton's laws are derived from the special
case of a freely falling body.

The differential equation which the wave function ψ for a particle of
mass m is assumed to satisfy is

$$-\frac{h^2}{8\pi^2 m}\left(\frac{\partial^2\psi}{\partial x^2} + \frac{\partial^2\psi}{\partial y^2} + \frac{\partial^2\psi}{\partial z^2}\right) + V\psi = E\psi \qquad (5.18)$$

In this equation, V is the potential energy of the particle at the point
(x, y, z), which might for example represent the distance of an electron
of mass m from a positively charged nucleus. The quantity E in the
equation is the total energy of the particle and it is characteristic of the
equation that only for special values of E can solutions be found for ψ
which have physically meaningful properties.

The nature of the allowed solutions and the corresponding values of
E vary with the form of the potential energy V. For a free particle which
has no forces acting, V is the same everywhere and the solutions for ψ

correspond to a simple traveling wave. For a particle confined in a definite space, such as a molecule of a gas in a box or the delocalized electrons in an aromatic ring, standing waves fitting the box or ring are possible. In a hydrogen atom, the potential energy represents the electrostatic energy $-e^2/r$ of the electron and proton a distance r apart, and characteristic energies and wave functions are obtained, as discussed in the next section.

The Schrödinger equation is often called the wave equation because, like equations for light waves and vibrations of strings, it involves second derivatives of the wave function ψ. The analogy is not sufficiently close to be emphasized unduly, but it is not hard to show that the equation can be satisfied by functions of the same kind used to describe other wave motions.

A wave traveling in the x direction with frequency ν and constant wavelength λ can be described by a sine function:

$$\psi = A \sin \left(2\pi\nu t - \frac{2\pi x}{\lambda} \right) \qquad (5.19)$$

This should correspond to a free particle for which $V = 0$ and therefore should satisfy Eq. 5.18 with $V = 0$:

$$-\frac{h^2}{8\pi^2 m} \frac{\partial^2 \psi}{\partial x^2} = E\psi \qquad (5.20)$$

Differentiating the ψ of Eq. 5.19 twice gives

$$\frac{\partial^2 \psi}{\partial x^2} = -\left(\frac{2\pi}{\lambda} \right)^2 A \sin \left(2\pi\nu t - \frac{2\pi x}{\lambda} \right)$$

$$= -\left(\frac{2\pi}{\lambda} \right)^2 \psi \qquad (5.21)$$

Substitution in Eq. 5.18 gives, on noting that y does not depend upon x,

$$\frac{h^2}{2m\lambda^2} \psi = E\psi \qquad (5.22)$$

and the energy is $E = h^2/2m\lambda^2$. But this is exactly the energy of a particle with the momentum $p = h/\lambda$ of de Broglie's relation, since this gives $E = p^2/2m =$ kinetic energy of a particle with momentum p. The reader can easily verify that a standing wave

$$\psi = A \sin (2\pi\nu t) \sin \left(\frac{2\pi x}{\lambda} \right) \qquad (5.23)$$

also satisfies the equation with the same significance of $\lambda = h/p$.

The wave aspect of such free particles thus is associated with energy in a very direct way. For problems in which V is not constant the wavelength λ does not have as simple a significance, but there is a fundamental relation to the classical equation of energy. A particle classically satisfies the equation Kinetic Energy + Potential Energy (V) = Total Energy (E). In terms of momentum components p_x, p_y, p_z this equation of conservation of energy is

$$\frac{1}{2m} [p_x^2 + p_y^2 + p_z^2] + V = E \tag{5.24}$$

The wave equation (Eq. 5.18) can be written for comparison as

$$\frac{1}{2m} \left[-\frac{h^2}{4\pi^2} \frac{\partial^2 \psi}{\partial x^2} - \frac{h^2}{4\pi^2} \frac{\partial^2 \psi}{\partial y^2} - \frac{h^2}{4\pi^2} \frac{\partial^2 \psi}{\partial z^2} \right] + V\psi = E\psi \tag{5.25}$$

The wave equation thus associates terms in V and E of the classical equation of energy with the wave function ψ. A corresponding similarity for momentum terms is achieved if $-(h^2/4\pi^2)(\partial^2/\partial x^2)$ rather than p_x^2 is associated with ψ, and the differential equation satisfied by the wave function results from this replacement. A similar process is used in constructing the wave equation for more complicated systems of many particles from the energy equation of classical mechanics.

To complete the usefulness of the wave equation, other fundamental rules for finding suitable solutions and for calculating such observable properties as average momenta are required. The complete set of rules will not be given here, because they are properly stated against a background of advanced mechanics and theory of differential equations, which is not expected of the reader. There are two, however, which are easily seen to be reasonable and will be useful in discussion of the results obtained by solving the equation.

The first kind of requirement is that proper solutions for a wave function must give only one value of ψ^2 at any one point. This is certainly not only reasonable but essential if this value of ψ^2 is to be associated with reality rather than just mathematical possibility. Only wave functions for definite quantized energies can satisfy this requirement.

The second requirement is that the integral of ψ^2 over all possible points in space shall be finite and equal to unity:

$$\int_0^\infty \psi^2 \, dV = 1 \tag{5.26}$$

V here representing the volume. This rule, too, is eminently sensible on remembering the stipulation that the value of ψ^2 for a quantum state is a measure of the probability of finding the system it describes in that state. Integrating over all possibilities thus should lead to the finite value of unity, as the system must be found *somewhere*. Imposing this requirement on a mathematical expression is called a *normalization condition*. A corollary is evident—that otherwise possible solutions for ψ must be excluded if they cannot be normalized, because they assume impossibly large values over finite regions.

With these conditions and others dictated by the nature of particular problems, only certain special functions remain as possible solutions and these functions are the ones which are significant in predicting the possible normal states of atoms and molecules.

5.10. Hydrogenlike Wave Functions

The simplest atomic system, hydrogen, is one for which simple and accurate energies and wave functions can be determined. The results for the related problem of an electron of charge $-e$ and nucleus of atomic number Z with its total nuclear charge $+Ze$, are essentially as simple. They will also be discussed in order to show the influence of nuclear charge on the energy and the electron charge distribution.

Energy Levels

The allowed energies for satisfactory solutions of the wave equation for a nucleus of charge Ze and an electron are the same as the result of Bohr's theory, Eq. 5.8:

$$E = -\frac{2\pi^2\mu Z^2 e^4}{h^2}\frac{1}{n^2} \tag{5.27}$$

The quantum number n, called the principal quantum number, may have only integral values ($n = 1, 2, 3, 4, \cdots$). This results directly from the solution of the wave equation; otherwise the wave function ψ would have two or more values at a given point, or else fail to remain finite for all distances at which the electron might be from the nucleus.

The agreement of Eq. 5.27 with experiment has been discussed in Sections 5.1 and 5.2 and it remains to consider now the properties of the allowed wave functions (ψ) corresponding to the different possible energies.

The Ground State

The state for $n = 1$ has the lowest energy and is the state in which atomic hydrogen is most frequently found. The wave function and derived charge distribution are of a simple form. It is found that for $n = 1$

$$\psi = \text{constant} \times e^{-Zr/a_0},$$

where r is the distance of the electron from the nucleus. The quantity a_0 has the same value as the radius found by Bohr for the first orbit of his theory, or

$$a_0 = \frac{h^2}{4\pi^2 m e^2} \qquad (5.28)$$

The concept of a specific orbit of definite radius is lost in the newer theory, but a_0 still retains significance as a measure of the size of the probability distribution for the electron's position. The normalization requirement already discussed shows that the constant must have the value $(1/\sqrt{\pi})(Z/a_0)^{3/2}$, and the wave function for the lowest state is therefore

$$\psi = \frac{1}{\sqrt{\pi}} \left(\frac{Z}{a_0}\right)^{3/2} e^{-Zr/a_0} \qquad (5.29)$$

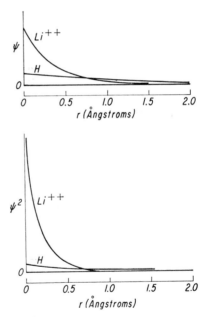

Fig. 5.9. *Variation of amplitude ψ and intensity ψ^2 for 1s electrons in H and Li^{++}.*

The significance of this result can be illustrated in a number of ways. One could calculate values of ψ for various values of r, and then make a pattern of dots in *three-dimensional space*, with the number of dots per unit volume in proportion to the value of ψ^2, as in Fig. 5.8. (Only a projection of such a pattern can be reproduced on the printed page, and the reader must imagine such a projection as shown in Fig. 5.8 extended throughout space.)

A quantitative way of representing the behavior required by Eq. 5.29 is to plot the values of ψ or ψ^2 against distance r, as is done in Fig. 5.9.

The values have been plotted for both $Z = 1$ and for a doubly ionized lithium atom with $Z = 3$, to show the effect of nuclear charge. It is seen that the charge distribution is concentrated for higher charge, as would be expected from the increased electrostatic attraction between the electron and the nucleus. A less quantitative representation, which is useful for visualizing the charge distribution, is to draw contour surfaces representing constant values of ψ or ψ^2, as shown in Fig. 5.10.

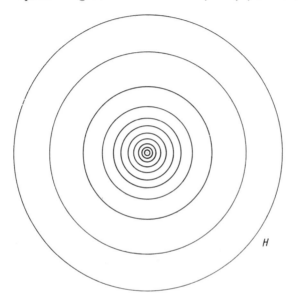

Fig. 5.10. *Contour lines of equal probability for 1s electrons in H and Li^{++}.*

These various graphic or schematic representations each have individual usefulness and limitations, and all are helpful when visualizing the wave functions for the higher energy states which we next consider.

The First Excited State

For the first excited state, with $n = 2$, there are, if but one electron is considered, four possible wave functions, all possessing the same energy. Of these four, one has spherical symmetry like the wave function for $n = 1$; such functions with spherical symmetry are described as s functions. The counterparts of the drawings for the 1s state* are shown in

---

* The arabic number refers to the numerical value of the principal quantum number, n. The lower case letter (which will be s, p, d, or f) identifies the particular wave function for the given value of n.

Fig. 5.11. Comparing those drawings for the 2*s* state with the one for the 1*s* state shows that there are now two distinct regions of appreciable charge density (ψ^2) and that at the larger distances ψ is negative. The solution for ψ, which is readily verified to have these properties, is

$$\psi(2s) = \frac{1}{4\pi^2}\left(\frac{Z}{a_0}\right)^{3/2}\left(2 - \frac{Zr}{a_0}\right)e^{-Zr/2a_0} \qquad (5.30)$$

The three remaining functions in this state are called 2*p* functions. They are equivalent to one another and show a new feature: the electron charge distribution is no longer spherically symmetrical but is concentrated about an axis passing through the nucleus, as shown in Fig. 5.12a. Because of this, plots of ψ and ψ^2 as a function of *r* must be made for some particular direction in space—for example, along the axis about which charge is concentrated, as shown in Fig. 5.12b.

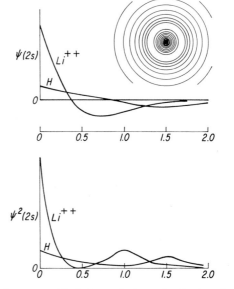

Fig. 5.11. *Variation of ψ and ψ^2 for 2s electrons in H and Li^{++}.*

If there are no external influences on an electron in this 2*p* state, one orientation of the axis of charge symmetry is as good as any other. It can be shown, however, that the wave function $\psi(2p)$ for *any* orientation of this axis can be constructed as a sum of suitable proportions of *three* such functions with their axes in mutually perpendicular directions. These three are thus in the relation shown in Fig. 5.13. By identifying the axes as *x*, *y*, and *z*, these functions are designated $\psi(2p_x)$, $\psi(2p_y)$, $\psi(2p_z)$.

The distinctive difference between *p* functions and *s* functions can be seen in another way by considering the paths indicated by broken lines in Fig. 5.13. For any closed path in the plane through the nucleus, the value of ψ changes from plus to minus. There is thus one complete cycle corresponding to one wavelength of a standing wave per round trip, rather than no wave at all for an *s* function. This difference in character

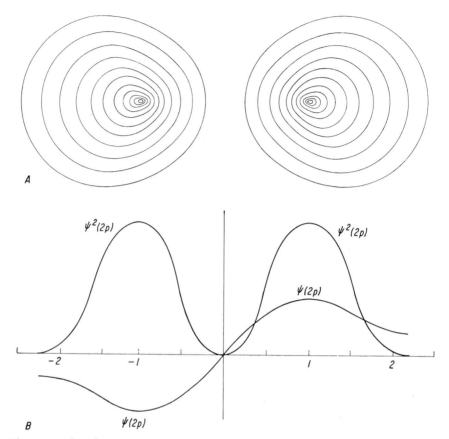

Fig. 5.12. (Top) *Electron distribution for a 2p electron as represented by contours. The pattern in space is dumbbell-shaped.* (Bottom) *Variation of ψ and ψ^2 along the symmetry axis for a 2p electron state.*

is described by the *angular momentum quantum number l*, which has the value $l = 1$ for a p function, and $l = 0$ for an s function. The existence of three p states, no one of which can be obtained by combinations of the other two, is recognized by the *magnetic quantum number m*, which can have any positive or negative integral value not larger than l. For $l = 1$, m can therefore be 1, 0, and -1, corresponding to three p states, while for $l = 0$, m can only be zero, corresponding to the one s state.

High Energy States

Still more energy states are possible for $n = 3$. One 3s state occurs which is spherically symmetrical, as for $n = 1$ and $n = 2$, but with three re-

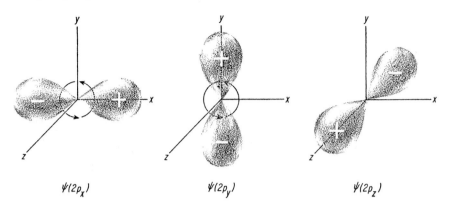

$\psi(2p_x)$ $\psi(2p_y)$ $\psi(2p_z)$

Fig. 5. 13. *Shape and relative configurations of the three 2p orbitals.*

gions of charge concentration. Three $3p$ states are possible with quantum number values $n = 3$, $l = 1$, and $m = 1, 0,$ or -1. The symmetry about an axis in $3p$ states occurs as it did for $n = 2$ also, but the dependence of ψ on distance is more complicated, just as is the analogous dependence for s states.

The distinct types of wave functions and charge distribution are referred to as orbitals; the two so far considered are thus conveniently called s and p orbitals. In using this term, however, we must keep in mind that quantum theory does not allow any such narrow and specific description of an electron's motion as the word "orbit" implies.

A distinctly new kind of wave function occurring for $n = 3$ is the d wave function. The symmetry of this type of function can be represented by a sort of double dumbbell, as shown in Fig. 5.14. Just as

Fig. 5.14. *Shape of a 3d orbital.*

for the p functions, no one orientation of this double dumbbell is preferred, but any orientation can be constructed by adding together combinations of certain arbitrarily oriented orbitals. Five arbitrary d-orbital orientations are required in order to construct all possible d orbitals (compared with p orbitals) and their relative orientations are shown in Fig. 5.15. The reader should verify that the sixth orbital in parentheses at the extreme right, which at first

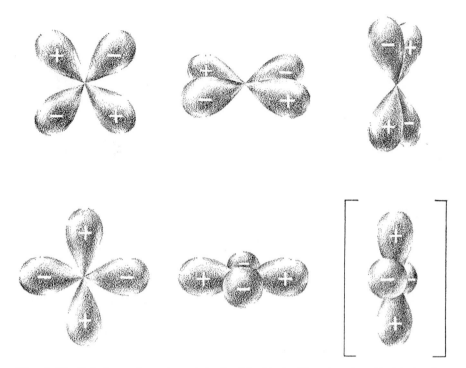

Fig. 5.15. *Relative configurations of the five 3d orbitals. Note that the orbital in brackets is the result of adding the two illustrated to its left.*

sight seems appropriate and necessary, can be constructed by adding together the two to the left of it, and so is not necessary for the construction of any other orbital.

For a *d* function, a closed path in the plane of the nucleus has two alternations in the sign of ψ, and hence two wavelengths for a closed path. The corresponding *l* value is $l = 2$, and there are five *m* values of $+2$, $+1$, 0, -1, -2, representing the existence of five *d* states or orbitals.

The Classification of Allowed States

The allowed wave functions for $n = 1$, 2, 3 follow a regular and systematic progression. This progression continues for larger values of *n* according to certain rules.

1. Only integral values of the principal quantum number *n* are permitted: $n = 1$, 2, 3, $\cdots$.

2. The angular momentum quantum number l may have positive integral values within the limitation $l = n - 1, n - 2, \cdots, 0$.

3. For a given l, integral values of magnetic quantum number m from $m = -l$ to $m = +l$ are permitted (a maximum of $2l + 1$ values are possible).

4. Each different allowed combination of the three quantum numbers corresponds to a distinct quantum state.

For $n = 4$, the allowed values of l are thus 0, 1, 2, 3. As before, the values 0, 1, and 2 represent s, p, and d states. The wave functions for $l = 3$ are called f orbitals, and there are $2l + 1$ or 7 such orbitals. Similar deductions apply for $n = 5$ and for higher n values, but the possible states of higher angular momentum which are permitted are of less importance for most chemical problems than the ones here discussed.

The sequence of principal quantum numbers with increasingly large subgroups of the quantum numbers l and m, shown in the chart of Fig. 5.16, is suggestive of the regularities of the sequence of elements if it is supposed that addition of Z electrons to a nucleus of charge Ze results in filling successive quantum states. That

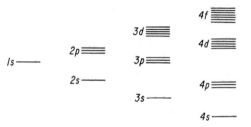

Fig. 5.16. *The sequence of orbitals for increasing values of the principal quantum number n.*

such a filling must occur is a consequence of the Pauli *exclusion principle* but in order to arrive at the actual structure of the periodic table, we must consider one further quantum property and quantum number for an electron, which will be called the *electron spin*.

5.11. The Exclusion Principle and Electron Spin

When two or more electrons are near an atomic nucleus, the Schrödinger equation to be solved for the description of the atomic properties becomes more complicated than for a single electron. This is because the total energy of the system is determined both by the attraction of the nucleus for each electron, and by the mutual repulsion of the electrons. The accurate wave functions are necessarily more complicated than those for a hydrogenlike atom with one electron, since they must necessarily describe several electrons. However, the most important single force turns out to be that of nuclear attraction.

That the forces between electrons are smaller than the nuclear attraction is seen to be reasonable if it is remembered that electrons in hydrogenlike orbitals occupy considerable volume surrounding the nucleus; hence on the average they will not be as close to one another as they are to the nucleus. If the nuclear attraction is the dominant force, one would expect that electrons added to nuclei of large charge would all go into the $1s$ or similar states which would allow them to be close to the nucleus. Constructing larger atoms according to this hypothesis, however, gives no explanation of the periodicity of the sort found in the periodic table, which is suggestively similar to the sequence of hydrogen atom states of larger principal quantum numbers and higher energies. In addition to nuclear attraction, some other factor must therefore be involved.

The Pauli Exclusion Principle

The resolution of the difficulty just described cannot be found in the solutions of Schrödinger's equation, but lies in the existence of a fundamental principle first stated by Pauli in 1926. This *exclusion principle* requires that no two electrons of an atom can have all of their quantum numbers the same. Two electrons with the same value of principal quantum number, n, must therefore have differing values of at least one other quantum number. For $n > 1$, either of the two further quantum numbers, l and m, can be different, and therefore permit a larger number of electrons in the higher quantum states.

The requirement of the exclusion principle thus makes it necessary that the electrons successively added to form the heavier atoms go into higher quantum states. However, even this does not accord with the chemical knowledge of the elements, and which has been systematized in the periodic table. It is recalled that there are two elements, hydrogen and helium, in the first row of the table; in the second there are eight, lithium, beryllium, boron, carbon, nitrogen, oxygen, fluorine, and neon; in the third are eight, the final one being another rare gas, as in the first and second rows; in the fourth are eighteen, concluding with a rare gas.

With but the three quantum numbers n, l, and m, it is impossible to reproduce the observed periodicities of the elements in terms of their electron orbital wave functions. For example, if $n = 1$, then l and m must both be zero, and in accordance with the Pauli principle, there could be but one electron with $n = 1$, and hence the first "shell" would be completely filled. For $n = 2$, only four electrons would be possible: $l = 1$ and $m = 1$, 0, or -1; $l = 0$ and $m = 0$. For $n = 3$, only nine electrons would be permitted: five states with $l = 2$, three with $l = 1$, and one with $l = 0$.

Corresponding to these quantum numbers, hydrogen would be the only element in the first row of the periodic table; the second row would contain but four elements, starting with helium and ending with boron; the third would contain a maximum of eight, starting with carbon and ending with aluminum. This is impossible in terms of chemical evidence: hydrogen and boron would be associated with filled "shells" and hence should be inert, whereas actually they are quite reactive; helium and carbon would both be expected to exhibit monovalent cationic properties by losing one electron in reacting, whereas their observed properties are quite otherwise.

In terms of the older concept of completed "shells," it is with helium rather than hydrogen that the first shell is completed, and it is with the progression of eight elements to neon that the second shell is completed. The sequence for these two rows thus provides just twice the number of atoms permitted on the basis of the three quantum numbers so far described and the exclusion principle.

The Pauli principle can thus lead to a prediction of periodic properties by requiring that orbitals of larger quantum number be used, corresponding to a series of shells, but with the quantum numbers so far considered this principle fails to give the right periodicity.

Electron Spin

The remaining difficulty in associating the periodic table with allowed quantum states suggests the existence of some further property of electrons by which two electrons may have their three orbital quantum numbers respectively with the same values. To satisfy the Pauli principle as well requires that this further electron property, usually called the electron spin, be described by a fourth quantum number, called the *spin quantum number*, s. (This s is not to be confused with an s electron with $l = 0$.) In the Schrödinger form of quantum mechanics the spin quantum number is associated with intrinsic magnetic properties of the electron.

This association is similar to the magnetic behavior relative to the orbital motion of an electron. The orbital angular momentum of an electron describes a motion about the nucleus in which the circulating electron, through the motion of its electrical charge, has an associated magnetic field, like a tiny magnet. The *magnetic moment* of this orbital motion is quantized in definite relation to the angular momentum, and is described in magnitude by the value of the angular momentum quantum number, l, and in direction by the magnetic quantum number, m.

In a somewhat analogous fashion, the spin quantum number describes the magnetic moment which is intrinsic to the electron completely independent of the orbital motion. This number may have either of the two possible values $+\frac{1}{2}$ and $-\frac{1}{2}$, corresponding to parallel or antiparallel magnetic moments. The intrinsic magnetic moment can be visualized as associated with a corresponding intrinsic spin momentum, which is the counterpart of angular momentum of orbital motion. Too literal a significance should not be attached to this picture, as a more far reaching quantum theory developed by Dirac leads to wave equations which make no explicit mention of electron spin as such, but do require the four quantum numbers n, l, m, s for proper solutions, together with the values $\pm\frac{1}{2}$ for s.

The electron spin with two possible spin quantum numbers fits logically with the experimentally determined order of chemical properties represented by the periodic table, as suggested above and as discussed more fully in the next section. This evidence is by no means the only confirmation of the place of electron spin in a proper description of atoms, and in fact was not the primary evidence leading to the original proposal of the concept.

As with so much atomic theory, the original clues came from observed atomic spectra, and Uhlenbeck and Goudsmit in 1925 first proposed the concept of electron spin largely on the basis of the number and spacings of spectral lines, such as the observed double lines for sodium at 5890 and 5896 Å. The postulate proved immediately fruitful in explaining atomic spectra, particularly as affected by applied external magnetic fields (note the magnetic property of electron spin), and it has since been invoked successfully for understanding many other properties.

The order of presentation in this section should not leave the reader with the impression that the chemical evidence in the periodic table led to the Pauli principle and then electron spin. The historical order was in fact discovery of spin, followed by the Pauli principle and realization of the elegant and simple constructions that could be made in harmony with the chemical evidence previously organized in the periodic table.

The important consequences for chemistry of electron spin are associated with the possibility of providing *pairs* of electrons with the same orbital properties, and this pairing is of fundamental importance in the periodic table and in chemical bonding.

5.12. The Periodic Table

From the preceding discussion, the following requirements *must* be satisfied by electrons in an atom.

1. No two electrons in an atom may have all four quantum numbers (n, l, m, and s) alike (Pauli principle).
2. The possible values of quantum numbers are restricted:

   n may have values $n = 1, 2, 3, \cdots$.

   l may have integral values from 0 to a maximum of $(n - 1)$. (Hence n in all for a given n.)

   m may have integral values from $-l$ to $+l$. [$(2l + 1)$ in all for a given l.]

   s may have two values ($+\frac{1}{2}$ or $-\frac{1}{2}$), and *two* electrons with these two values fill one orbital described by a given set of values for n, l, and m.

The *order* in which the various orbitals will be filled by the electrons added around the nucleus in a given element is not rigidly prescribed. The choice actually made must be the one which gives the entire group of electrons the minimum total energy. For the heavier elements this choice is governed by a rather delicate balance of opposing effects. A detailed examination of all the competing factors would require a discussion of the theory of atomic spectra too lengthy to be undertaken here. However, two factors are important and readily appreciated.

1. States of higher principal quantum number have higher energy and larger orbitals for the same angular momentum quantum number l than states with lower principal quantum numbers.

Thus the energy is lower and the charge more concentrated near the nucleus for a $1s$ state than for a $2s$ state. Similarly, a $2p$ state has a lower energy than a $3p$ state. This order of energy and orbital size is like that for the solutions of the wave equation for the hydrogen atom, and is obviously consistent with the larger attractive force of the nucleus when the electron is close to it.

2. States of higher angular momentum quantum numbers have higher energies when the principal quantum numbers are the same.

Thus the 2s state ($l = 0$) has lower energy than 2p states ($l = 1$), and similarly the order for $n = 3$ is $3s < 3p < 3d$. This effect of charge symmetry does not appear for the one-electron atom hydrogen, as the 2s and 2p states have the same energy. When other electrons are present, however, the more extended orbitals with larger l have higher energies, corresponding to increased effects of mutual electron repulsion. Another way of visualizing these differences is in terms of the "shielding" of the nucleus by the other electrons of charge opposite to the nucleus, which will reduce the attraction of an electron when it is further from the nucleus.

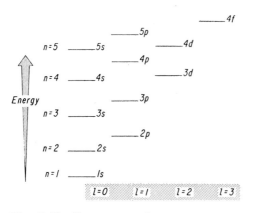

Fig. 5.17. *Energy states of atoms.*

The factors governing which of two levels with n and l *both* different will have lower energy are less simple, and are not as readily deduced either by qualitative arguments or reasonably simple calculations. More detailed study has shown, however, that the order of energies is the one indicated in Fig. 5.17.

Lighter Elements

With the arrangement shown, it is possible to follow the building up of electron structure in many electron atoms by placing electrons in the lowest and successively higher states, as required by the Pauli principle. The one electron of hydrogen and the two of helium go into the 1s orbital, which is indicated by writing the electron configurations as $(1s)$, $(1s)^2$, the superscript 2 indicating the number of electrons in the particular state.

With filling of the $(1s)$ orbital, further electrons added must go into states with $n = 2$, with higher energy than the $(1s)$ state for the given value of Z. [Notice that energy of the $(1s)$ state is lower for larger Z because of the larger nuclear charge.] The electrons of the second-row elements (lithium to neon) successively fill the $(2s)$ and $(2p)$ states for $n = 2$. One can easily verify from Fig. 5.17 that the electron configurations are:

Li	Be	B	C	N	O	F	Ne
$(1s)^2$	$(1s)^2$	$(1s)^2$	$(1s)^2$	$(1s)^2$	$(1s)^2$	$(1s)^2$	$(1s)^2$
$(2s)$	$(2s)^2$	$(2s)^2$	$(2s)^2$	$(2s)^2$	$(2s)^2$	$(2s)^2$	$(2s)^2$
		$(2p)$	$(2p)^2$	$(2p)^3$	$(2p)^4$	$(2p)^5$	$(2p)^6$

This process can be continued in the same way for the next eight elements, of the third row, as the electrons fill the $3s$ and $3p$ orbitals successively. The configurations of phosphorus and argon, for example, evidently are:

$$\text{P:} \quad (1s)^2 \, (2s)^2 \, (2p)^6 \, (3s)^2 \, (3p)^3$$
$$Z = 15$$

$$\text{A:} \quad (1s)^2 \, (2s)^2 \, (2p)^6 \, (3s)^2 \, (3p)^6$$
$$Z = 18$$

For the next element, potassium, with 19 electrons, the last electron cannot from the rules given be assigned definitely to the $4s$ orbital or to one of the $3d$ orbitals. The assignment from spectroscopic and chemical evidence is that instead of further filling the only available orbitals of the $n = 3$ shell, the $(4s)$ state is occupied in preference. Similarly, the last two electrons for $Z = 20$, calcium, are $(4s)^2$ rather than $(3d)^2$.

After calcium, however, the $4p$ orbitals are less stable than the unfilled $3d$ orbitals, and for the ten *transition* elements the added electrons begin to fill the five $3d$ orbitals.

This progression is regular with the exceptions of chromium and copper. For $Z = 24$, chromium has *five* $3d$ electrons and *one* $4s$ electron, and for $Z = 29$, copper has not nine but *ten* $3d$ electrons, and not two but *one* $4s$ electron. The fact that the $4s$ orbital is less stable than the last $3d$ orbital to be filled suggests not only the closeness in energy and delicacy of balance but also the *stability associated with a completed subshell.* (In this case, the $3d$ orbitals.) The differences in physical and chemical properties of these transition metals are thus largely associated with the partial occupation of the inner $3d$ subshell—"inner," since for the transition elements the $(4s)$ shell with larger n is occupied by two electrons, with the exceptions of chromium and copper. Further addition of electrons after occupation of the $3d$ states is made by filling the $4p$ orbitals. This subshell is complete with the particularly stable inert gas krypton $(Z = 36)$, which completes the fourth row in the periodic table.

The process of constructing the periodic table so far described is summarized in the tabulation of electron configuration for the elements, given in Table 5.2. Tables 5.3 and 5.4 also include the structures of heavier elements to $Z = 96$, which will now be considered.

TABLE 5.2.   *Electron Structures of Lighter Elements (to $Z = 36$).*

Atomic Number	Element	Number of Electrons							
		(1s)	(2s)	(2p)	(3s)	(3p)	(3d)	(4s)	(4p)
1	H	1							
2	He	2							
3	Li		1						
4	Be		2						
5	B			1					
6	C	(1s) filled		2					
7	N		(2s) filled	3					
8	O			4					
9	F			5					
10	Ne			6					
11	Na				1				
12	Mg				2				
13	Al					1			
14	Si			(2p) filled		2			
15	P					3			
16	S				(3s) filled	4			
17	Cl					5			
18	Ar					6			
19	K							1	
20	Ca							2	
21	Sc						1	2	
22	Ti						2	2	
23	V						3	2	
24	Cr					(3p) filled	5	1	
25	Mn						5	2	
26	Fe						6	2	
27	Co						7	2	
28	Ni						8	2	
29	Cu						10	1	
30	Zn						10	2	
31	Ga								1
32	Ge								2
33	As						(3d) filled	(4s) filled	3
34	Se								4
35	Br								5
36	Kr								6

TABLE 5.3. *Electronic Structures of Heavier Elements (Z = 37 to Z = 72).*
[(1s) to (4p) states are all filled and hence are omitted.]

Atomic Number	Element	Number of Electrons							
		(4d)	(4f)	(5s)	(5p)	(5d)	...	...	(6s)
37	Rb			1					
38	Sr			2					
39	Y	1		2					
40	Zr	2		2					
41	Nb	4		1					
42	Mo	5		1					
43	Tc	6		1					
44	Ru	7		1					
45	Rh	8		1					
46	Pd	10		None					
47	Ag			1					
48	Cd			2					
49	In				1				
50	Sn	(4d) filled			2				
51	Sb				3				
52	Te				4				
53	I			(5s) filled	5				
54	Xe				6				
55	Cs								1
56	Ba								2
57	La					1			
58	Ce		1						
59	Pr		2		(5p) filled				
60	Nd		3						
61	Pm		4						
62	Sm		5						
63	Eu		6						
64	Gd		7						
65	Tb		8						
66	Dy		9						
67	Ho		10						
68	Er		11						
69	Tm		12						
70	Yb		13						
71	Lu		14			1			
72	Hf		14			2			2

TABLE 5.4. *Electron Structures of Heaviest Elements* ($Z = 73$ to $Z = 103$).
[(*1s*) to (*5p*) states are all filled and hence are omitted.]

Atomic Number	Element	Number of Electrons									
		(5d)	(5f)	···	(6s)	(6p)	(6d)	···	···	···	(7s)
73	Ta	3			2						
74	W	4			2						
75	Re	5			2						
76	Os	6			2						
77	Ir	9			None						
78	Pt	9			1						
79	Au	10			1						
80	Hg	10			2						
81	Tl	(5d) filled			(6s) filled	1					
82	Pb					2					
83	Bi					3					
84	Po					4					
85	At					5					
86	Rn					6					
87	Fr											1
88	Ra											2
89	Ac							1				
90	Th		1									
91	Pa		2									
92	U		3									
93	Np		4									
94	Pu		5									
95	Am		6			(6p) filled					
96	Cm		7									(7s) filled
97	Bk		8									
98	Cf		9									
99	E		10									
100	Fm		11									
101	Md		12									
102	No		13									
103	Lw		14					1				2

Building Up of Heavier Elements

The progression of filled levels with increasing number of electrons beyond $Z = 36$ can be seen from Tables 5.3 and 5.4 to follow the same principles. The filling of $4d$ states in competition with $5s$ has irregularities of the sort already found with copper, and the filling of $4f$ states is postponed until the $5p$ and $6s$ states are filled and there is one $5d$ electron.

The sequence from $Z = 58$ to $Z = 72$ is thus one in which the outer electron configuration for $n = 5$ and $n = 6$ remains the same, and only the occupation of inner $4f$ states changes. This is reflected in the great chemical similarity of this rare earth series, as would be expected from the primary importance of the outermost electrons in governing chemical properties.

For the elements beyond $Z = 72$, one again finds the competition of s and d states, this time for $6s$ and $5d$. The $6p$ states fill regularly after the $5d$ states are filled and the $5f$ states are occupied only after the two $7s$ and one $6d$ electron states are filled.

The stability of these heavier elements against disintegration into smaller products decreases rapidly with increasing atomic number. Until the age of nuclear studies and nuclear fission, the last element listed in the periodic table was uranium, with $Z = 92$. The radioactive elements beyond $Z = 92$ have since been produced by nuclear reactions, and their properties have been studied by ingenious methods devised for their investigation, to cope with the short times between their production and decay.

Assignments of States in Unfilled Subshells

In the filling process discussed, the electrons have been assigned to various p, d, or f states without specifying which of the various individual p, d, or f orbitals possible are actually occupied. That more than one combination is possible if the number of electrons is less than the maximum for the given state can easily be seen by considering the simplest elements for which the question arises—those of the second row.

In boron, the one $2p$ electron can occupy any one of the three $2p$ orbitals, but since these are all equivalent, there is no distinction between the possibilities. In carbon, however, the two electrons could either occupy one orbital with opposed spins or two orbitals with spins either parallel or opposed. Similarly, in nitrogen, the three $2p$ electrons could singly occupy all three states without spin restriction, or two states by pairing in one of the opposed spins. Oxygen lacks two electrons of a complete $2p$ subshell, and the two vacancies could both be in one orbital or singly in two orbitals. The case of fluorine resembles boron in the sense that the single electron *vacancy* could be in any one of the three equivalent orbitals, just as the single *electron* of boron could be in any orbital.

The question of which states are actually occupied in carbon, nitrogen, and oxygen has been settled by studies of their spectra, especially as affected by magnetic fields. The use of magnetic fields is decisive because the orbital and spin magnetic moments are affected in a way depending on their relative alignment. The results of the studies have led to simple rules, known as *Hund's rules*, by which the occupations can be determined. Hund's first rule for equivalent orbitals is that electrons prefer to avoid each other as much as possible by occupying different orbitals. This is a reasonable result, simply because the like charges of two electrons results in repulsion, which is larger when they occupy the same orbital. The second rule is that two electrons occupying different orbitals will prefer parallel rather than opposed spins.

These rules do not hold without exception, but they do predict the electron configurations correctly for the lighter elements, which will be of primary interest in the further discussions later. When applied to the second-row elements, they predict correctly the *p* electron configurations diagramed here.

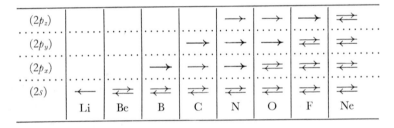

In the diagram the presence of an electron in *p* orbitals is indicated by an arrow, the direction of the arrow showing the orientation of the spin. The particular orbital chosen is arbitrary in the absence of a magnetic field, or other external factor rendering one direction *x*, *y*, or *z*, different from the others.

5.13. Charge Distributions and Energies of Atoms and Ions

In preceding sections, the process of completing successive shells and subshells of electrons in atoms has been discussed, but the extent and energies of the resulting charge distributions have not been considered in any detail. Some of the characteristic and important features can now be described.

Charge Densities of Completed Shells and Subshells

For all atoms other than hydrogen, solutions of the wave equation are complicated and become increasingly so with increasing number of electrons. Various approximate methods have been developed, however, for calculating the wave function ψ, from which the densities ψ^2 at various distances from the nucleus can be obtained.

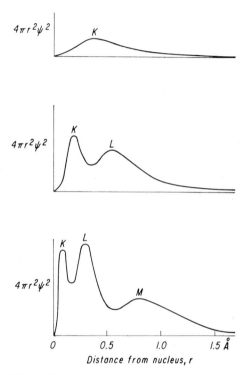

The results of such calculations are shown for helium, neon, and argon in Fig. 5.18. The quantity plotted as a function of distance r from the nucleus is the so-called radial density $4\pi r^2\psi^2$ rather than ψ^2, because the probability of finding an electron in a range between r and $r + dr$ increases with the value of r. The factor $4\pi r^2$ is just the area of a sphere of radius r, and the number of electrons which would be found in a shell of thickness dr is proportional to the volume $4\pi r^2$ dr of this shell rather than just to dr.

Fig. 5.18. *Electron densities of noble gases. Note the peaks corresponding to electron "shells."*

The striking characteristic of these curves is the separation of electron density into quite distinct regions. For helium there is just one region, corresponding to the filled shell for $n = 1$, often called the K shell; this description comes from X-ray nomenclature, to be discussed shortly. For neon and argon there are two and three regions corresponding to the addition of electrons in the L ($n = 2$) and M ($n = 3$) shells.

The reader will recall that while s states have spherical symmetry, this is not true of individual p and d states; hence he may properly wonder if it is allowable to describe the L and M shells by a spherically symmetrical function as plotted in Fig. 5.18. This description is legitimate for filled shells because the superposition of *all* allowed p and d

orbitals when all are occupied is spherically symmetrical. This is not hard to show from the p, d, and other orbital functions for hydrogen, and the sketch in Fig. 5.19 for densities of p_x, p_y, and p_z functions suggests how their superposition does give a spherical distribution.

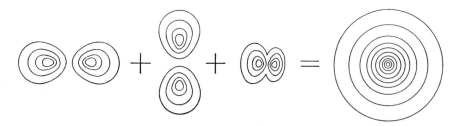

Fig. 5.19. *Addition of p electron densities to form a spherical charge distribution.*

The electron density pattern is thus rather clearly similar to the more sharply defined charge shells of the primitive quantum theory discussions. Because of the weighting factor $4\pi r^2$, the total areas under the curves are equal to the numbers of electrons for the different atoms. It is easily seen that the areas under the different regions are also in the general proportions of the numbers of electrons in the K, L, and M shells, or as two, eight, and eight. The segregation into separate regions is not complete, of course, and electrons with different n do have overlapping charge distributions, but there is a real significance to considering K, L, M, and other shells as successively larger and more diffuse. In the same way, it is not strictly possible to assign a unique figure as *the* radius of any atom, but the sizes are characteristically of the order of one to two Ångström units (10^{-8} cm).

Nuclear Charge and "Electron Shielding"

The electron density plots in Fig. 5.18 show clearly that the sizes of atoms increase only slowly with increasing number of electrons, and that the inner shells in fact become more concentrated. The decreased radii of K and L shells are simply understood if it is remembered that the attracting nuclear positive charge is larger for neon ($Z = 10$) than for helium ($Z = 2$). For the innermost shell the full nuclear charge is effective in attracting the K electrons and the wave function is large at smaller distances. For one-electron atoms or ions with a nuclear charge Ze, the $1s$ wave function is

$$\psi(1s) = \frac{1}{\sqrt{\pi}} \left(\frac{Z}{a_0}\right)^{3/2} e^{-zr/a_0} \tag{5.31}$$

where $a_0 = 0.54$ Å is the Bohr radius. For larger Z, $\psi(1s)$ is large at smaller distances r, corresponding to the increased nuclear attraction. The contraction is not as large as would be estimated by the equation, because the repulsion of the other $1s$ electron if present is not considered, but the nuclear effect represented by Z is much the more important.

The electrons in outer shells do not affect the inner shells greatly, for the same kind of reason that gravitational forces decrease in the interior of the earth and are zero at the center. That is, the resultant electrical force of an outer shell of charge on charges inside it adds to zero by cancellation of oppositely directed forces. The electrons of inner shells do, however, *shield* the effect of nuclear charge on outer shell electrons— that is, they partly compensate the nuclear charge for these electrons. As a result, the attraction is less than that by the bare nucleus, and the shells are not contracted as much as are the inner shells. These simple explanations are important factors in the result, and are seen to account for the general features of the different density curves.

Sizes of Ions

For simplicity, only the results for the three simplest noble gases have been compared. It is interesting to go a little further by comparing the sizes of ions with the same numbers of electrons as the inert noble gas atom. Thus the effect of nuclear charge can be compared for these sequences:

  2 electrons: He ($Z = 2$), Li$^+$ ($Z = 3$)
  10 electrons: F$^-$ ($Z = 9$), Ne ($Z = 10$), Na$^+$ ($Z = 11$)
  18 electrons: Cl$^-$ ($Z = 17$), Ar ($Z = 18$), K$^+$ ($Z = 19$)
  36 electrons: Br$^-$ ($Z = 35$), Kr ($Z = 36$), Rb$^+$ ($Z = 37$)

Instead of drawing radial density curves as above, the convenient visualization of the charge clouds (used before in Section 5.10) is employed in Fig. 5.20.

The importance of nuclear charge is evident, and characteristically has the effect that the monovalent cations are distinctly smaller than the isoelectronic anion. This effect is pronounced enough that Rb$^+$ with $Z = 37$ is smaller than Cl$^-$ with $Z = 17$, despite the fact that Cl$^-$ lacks the outer shell of 18 electrons of Rb$^+$.

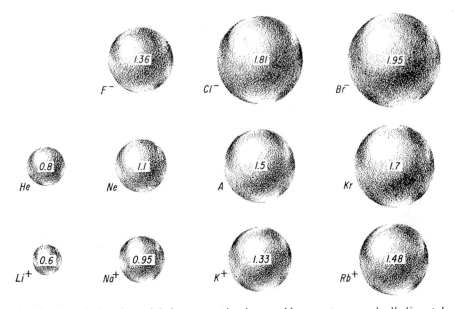

Fig. 5.20. *Relative sizes of halogen negative ions, noble gas atoms, and alkali metal positive ions.*

It is possible to assign fairly definite ionic radii from various experimental evidence, such as their distances of separation in ionic crystals (see Chapter 7), and a list of radii chosen to give reasonable average agreement with various kinds of estimates is given below. The radii of noble gas atoms have not been defined as accurately, and so the values given are to fewer significant figures.

Radii of Atoms and Ions

		F^-	1.36	Cl^-	1.81	Br^-	1.95	I^-	2.16
He	0.8	Ne	1.1	Ar	1.5	Kr	1.7	Xe	1.9
Li^+	0.60	Na^+	0.95	K^+	1.33	Rb^+	1.48	Cs^+	1.69

It should *not* be thought that these ion sizes are properly descriptive of the state of these simple ions in solution, especially aqueous solution. This is because simple ions are known to be heavily hydrated or solvated with a quite definite sheath of solvent molecules. The extent and exact nature of such solvation depends on both ion and solvent, but an important factor differentiating positive and negative ions in this respect is precisely the size difference. (Other factors are discussed in Chapters 11 and 17.) Ion sizes also play an important role in stereochemical considerations of possible structures of compounds and solids.

5.14. X-ray Diffraction and Atomic Number

With an elementary understanding of atomic structure, it is now possible to consider Moseley's law and its relation to structure.

In 1912 von Laue suggested that X-rays were electromagnetic waves of short wavelength and that they should be diffracted by crystalline substances, much as light is diffracted by a grating. Thus X-rays could be separated into their constituent wavelengths, and might be recorded as lines on a photographic plate. Various investigators began to study the spectrum of X-radiation, produced by bombarding electrons against targets of different materials, and then diffracted by passage through a crystal. It was found that the same grouping of lines was obtained for all the elements tested, differing only in wavelength from one element to another. A typical X-ray spectrum for an elementary substance is shown in Fig. 5.21. (Actually, each K line is further divided into doublets, so K_α is composed of two lines, K_{α_1} and K_{α_2}.)

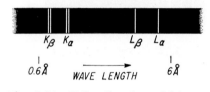

Fig. 5.21. *X-Ray lines for molybdenum.*

Moseley observed that the displacement of X-ray lines in going from one element to another is related to the atomic number of the elements according to

$$\sqrt{\nu} = K(Z - s) \qquad (5.32)$$

where K and s are constants for a particular line and Z is the atomic number. A plot of $\sqrt{\nu}$ for a particular line in an X-ray series against atomic number yields a straight line, of a slope that is dependent upon the line chosen. At the time of Moseley's work, not all the elements known today had been discovered, and breaks in these straight lines would indicate missing elements. (Six breaks were noted by Moseley according to his compilation of atomic numbers. The elements corresponding to these breaks—hafnium, rhenium, technetium, prometheum, astatine, and francium—have all since been discovered.) Moseley hypothesized that Z represented the size of the nuclear charge. This was later confirmed by other evidence, such as scattering experiments.

The origin of these X-ray spectra can be explained in terms of the possible electron states of an atom. Figure 5.22 shows a series of energy levels in an atom, the letters K, L, M, N, and so on, representing quantum states of $n = 1, 2, 3, 4$, as before. Assume that enough energy can be introduced into the atom to expel an electron from the lowest energy level ($n = 1$, the K level). This leaves a vacant space in the K level into which electrons from higher states can drop. If an electron from, say, the L level fills the original vacancy, a hole is left in the L level which can be filled by an electron from a still higher state.

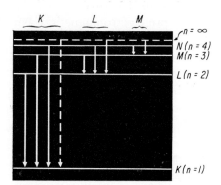

Fig. 5.22. *Energy levels and transitions for X-Ray lines.*

This situation differs from that of the emission of lines in the visible spectrum because the transitions involved in X-ray emission are between energy levels *deep within* the atom. Here, under the influence of a nucleus carrying a considerably greater positive charge than the core of the hydrogen atom, the energy differences are very much larger. Consequently, the frequencies are greater in the X-ray spectrum than in the visible spectrum and the wavelengths are shorter—of the order of a single Ångström unit.

The transition from L to K gives rise to the K_1 line in the X-ray spectrum of the emitting element. If the original K vacancy is filled by an M electron, the K_2 line results. A space filled in the L level causes the emission of one of the L series of X-rays, the particular frequency depending upon the origin of the filling electron. The difference in energy between the K_1 and K_2 lines for an element is equal to the energy of the L_1 line.

That the frequencies of these characteristic X-ray lines increases so strongly with atomic number shows directly how much more tightly inner shell electrons are bound to nuclei of large Z. The energy difference $h\nu$ of a given X-ray line from Eq. 5.12 depends on Z as

$$h\nu = hK^2(Z - s)^2 \qquad (5.33)$$

and hence roughly as the square of the atomic number. Thus, for hydrogen, a transition from $n = 2$ to $n = 1$ is at a wavelength $\lambda = 1215$ Å, while the analogous transition in molybdenum ($Z = 42$) is at 0.62 Å.

For different lines of the K series, $s = 1$ and K^2 is found to be given by the Rydberg formula; thus

$$K^2 = hcR(z - 1)^2\left(\frac{1}{1} - \frac{1}{n^2}\right) \qquad (5.34)$$

This is just the frequency expression for a transition from $n = n$ to $n = 1$ of a hydrogenlike atom with nuclear charge $Z = 1$. The value $Z - 1$ thus represents the amount by which the effect of nuclear charge Z is reduced by the "screening" which results from the other $1s$ electron of the K shell.

Problems

5.1. What are the highest frequencies for each of the four hydrogen spectral series listed in the text? What are the corresponding wavelengths in Ångströms?

5.2. An electron revolves at constant speed around a proton, considered fixed in space at a distance r_0 from it. What is the electrostatic potential energy of this system? (Consider the potential energy equal to zero at infinite separation.) What is the kinetic energy of the system?

5.3. The electrostatic force between proton and electron in Problem 5.2 can be equated to the mass of the electron times its centripetal acceleration $[m(v^2/r_0)]$. Show that the total energy of the system (kinetic plus potential) is equal to $-e^2/2r_0$.

5.4. With the result from Problem 5.3 and the Bohr condition that the angular momentum $(I_\omega = mvr)$ is an integral multiple of $h/2\pi$, derive the Bohr energy formula.

5.5. Show that the quotient $2\pi^2 me^4/h^2$ has units of energy.

5.6. What is the value of the reduced mass for the electron-proton system (hydrogen atom)? What is the limiting value of this quantity as the mass of the nucleus increases?

5.7. Calculate the amount of energy released when 1 mole of electrons and protons combine to form hydrogen atoms in the lowest energy state. Consider the electrons and protons to be at infinite separation and zero relative velocity in the initial state.

5.8. For each spectral series of the hydrogen atom there is a corresponding series for the He^+ ion. Are the lines closer together or farther apart in the case of He^+? Neglecting the reduced mass effect, what is the ratio of corresponding frequencies?

5.9. What is the ionization energy of the He^+ ion? the Li^{++} ion? Express the results in electron volts, ergs per molecule, and calories per mole.

5.10. The first member of the sixth spectral series ($n_1 = 6$) of atomic hydrogen has been observed in the infrared (Humphreys, *J. Research Natl. Bur. Standards,*

50:1, 1953) between 12.25 μ and 12.50 μ. What wavelength does the Rydberg formula predict for this line?

5.11. At approximately what wavelength would you expect to find the K_1 line for uranium? What energy change does this correspond to in electron volts? in calories per mole?

5.12. What are the relative sizes of the isoelectronic H atom, He$^+$ ion, and Li^{+2} ion in their ground states?

5.13. What are the electron configurations for manganese, platinum, uranium? (Example: Phosphorus, $1s^2 2s^2 2p^6 3s^2 3p^2$.)

5.14. A 22-caliber rifle bullet has a mass of 2 g. If it travels at a velocity of 800 feet/sec, what is the wavelength associated with it?

5.15. An electron moving at a velocity of 2×10^9 cm/sec has what wavelength associated with it? What is the velocity of an alpha particle with the same wavelength?

5.16. What is the wavelength associated with an electron accelerated from rest through a potential difference of 100 V? What is the momentum of a photon of wavelength 1000 Å?

5.17. Since the ground state of the hydrogen atom has spherical symmetry, we can write $\psi^2\, dv = \psi^2 4\pi r^2\, dr$. Show that the function $4\pi r^2 \psi^2$ reaches a maximum at $r = a_0$, the Bohr radius. How do you interpret this result?

5.18. Using the condition $\int \psi^2\, dv = 1$, show that the normalization constant for the ground state of the hydrogen atom is given by

$$\frac{1}{\sqrt{\pi}} \left(\frac{Z}{a_0}\right)^{3/2}$$

and hence the wave function is

$$\psi(1s) = \frac{1}{\sqrt{\pi}} \left(\frac{Z}{a_0}\right)^{3/2} \exp\left(-\frac{Zr}{a_0}\right)$$

5.19. What is the probability that the electron in the ground state of the hydrogen atom will be found at a distance from the nucleus greater than twice the Bohr radius?

5.20. The three hydrogenlike $2p$ wave functions satisfying the Schrödinger equation are:

$$\psi(2p_x) = \frac{1}{4\sqrt{2\pi}} \left(\frac{Z}{a_0}\right)^{3/2} \exp\left(-\frac{Zr}{2a_0}\right)\frac{Zx}{a_0}$$

$$\psi(2p_y) = \frac{1}{4\sqrt{2\pi}} \left(\frac{Z}{a_0}\right)^{3/2} \exp\left(-\frac{Zr}{2a_0}\right)\frac{Zy}{a_0}$$

$$\psi(2p_z) = \frac{1}{4\sqrt{2\pi}} \left(\frac{Z}{a_0}\right)^{3/2} \exp\left(-\frac{Zr}{2a_0}\right)\frac{Zz}{a_0}$$

where x, y, z are cartesian coordinates of distance from the nucleus. Show that superposition of the squares of the three functions gives a function of the distance r only and hence spherical symmetry.

5.21. Using the $\psi(2p_x)$ and $\psi(2p_y)$ functions of Problem 5.20, show that the sum of the squares of these two functions has axial symmetry around the z-axis.

5.22. There are $(2l + 1)$ quantum states for each value of l (neglecting electron spins), and the quantum number l can take any value from $l = 0$ to $l = n - 1$. Derive a formula which gives the total number of quantum states for any given value of n. How does the inclusion of electron spin affect this formula?

5.23. An electron is confined to move in a box whose x dimension is 1 cm. How closely can we measure its velocity in the x direction?

5.24. The box of Problem 5.23 has a hole of diameter 10^{-5} cm in one wall perpendicular to the x direction. The thickness of the wall is large compared with the hole diameter. What is the uncertainty in the momentum perpendicular to the x direction of electrons leaving the box through this hole?

5.25. A beam of electrons is incident on a slit perpendicular to its axis. The width of the slit is 10^{-3} mm. After an electron has passed through the slit, what is the uncertainty in its momentum parallel to the slit?

5.26. In the experiment of Problem 5.25, if a photographic plate was placed 100 cm behind the slit, parallel to its axis, and if the velocity of electrons incident on the slit was 10^8 cm/sec, what would be the expected width of the line on the plate?

5.27. The elements of the first transition series, from scandium to nickel, form compounds that are highly colored. They also show a strong tendency to variable valence. Explain this behavior on the basis of their electron configuration.

5.28. Copper, silver, and gold each have their outermost electron in an s orbital with the remainder of the electrons in filled inner shells. They are not classed as alkali metals, however, as their chemical behavior is quite different. Discuss this in terms of the energy levels of the two types of atoms.

5.29. Numerous experiments (electrical conductivity, diffusion, etc.) have shown that the Ag^+ ion is much more mobile in the AgCl crystalline lattice than is the Cl^- ion. Discuss this behavior in terms of the electron configuration and relative sizes of the two ions.

Suggested Readings

An elementary discussion is given in the paperback *Electronic Structure, Properties, and the Periodic Law* by H. H. Sisler (Reinhold, New York, 1963). Somewhat more advanced treatments are given in *Physical Chemistry* by E. A. Moelwyn-Hughes (Pergamon, New York, 1959) and *Physical Chemistry* (3rd ed.) by W. J. Moore (Prentice-Hall, Englewood Cliffs, N.J., 1962).

Two classic treatises at an advanced level are available in paperback editions: *Quantum Principles and Line Spectra* by L. Pauling and S. A. Goudsmit (Dover, New York, 1963) and *Atomic Spectra and Atomic Structure* by G. Herzberg (Dover, New York, 1944).

Chapter 6

Molecular Constitution

THE ONLY ATOMS whose structures have been precisely described by quantum mechanics are those simplest ones at the beginning of the periodic table. It is therefore not surprising that precise theories of the structures of molecules containing two or more atoms present still greater difficulties.

Certain approximate concepts of interatomic bonding are familiar from the chemical behavior of molecules. Examples are electrovalence, in which the primary binding forces are electrostatic forces operating between oppositely charged particles, and covalence, in which atoms are held together by the sharing of electrons. The idea of directed chemical bonds, as exemplified by the tetrahedral bonds of carbon, will also be recalled. The usefulness of these concepts in chemistry is too obvious to require discussion or justification here, and it is therefore important to have some understanding of their basis in quantum principles.

In this chapter the application of quantum principles to molecular structure is considered, especially the ways in which they lead to useful descriptions of the nature of chemical bonds. The kinds of experimental information obtained from observations of molecular spectra will be described, and the usefulness of this information in describing, understanding, and predicting molecular properties will be illustrated.

101

6.1. Approximate Treatments of Molecular Structure

The study of the structure of atoms, discussed in Chapter 5, has shown that mathematical difficulties prevent obtaining exact solutions for the electron densities and possible energies of any but the simplest atoms. At the same time, however, approximate results can be obtained, and consideration of characteristic features of the wave functions and quantum states leads to a very satisfactory description of the essential properties of atoms and the structure of the periodic table.

Even the simplest molecule is inherently a more complex system than an atom, because by definition it comprises two or more atomic nuclei about which the electrons achieve the best charge distribution. The true wave equation, which properly must include all energies of interaction exactly, is so complicated that accurate solutions require formidable efforts. In order to make progress it has therefore usually been necessary either to consider smaller parts of the complete problems, or to make simplifying approximations that permit a solution of less accuracy with a moderate amount of effort.

Unfortunately, the simplest approximations do not give very accurate results, and fairly respectable results require much tedious mathematics. In this introductory account, it is not appropriate to become involved in these mathematical complications; hence only the less refined but more readily visualized approaches will be outlined. These necessarily lack the precision we would like, but they do enable us to describe important features of valence, chemical bonds, and molecular energies in a manner which brings out clearly the quantum origins of chemical properties.

Synthesis of a Molecule from Atoms

Because the characteristic quantum properties of atoms are well understood and calculable with fair accuracy, it is natural to attempt the description of electrons in molecules in terms of the properties of the constituent atoms. Several ways of undertaking a mathematical construction, or "paper synthesis," of a molecule from its atoms can be imagined. These will first be described in a general way, and then considered in more detail for the simplest diatomic molecule, molecular hydrogen, in order to illustrate the essential ideas.

One approach is to consider the constituent atoms initially so far removed that they are distinct, and then allow them to come together until their electron charges mutually affect each other. A second approach first places the bare nuclei in their final positions, after which the charge distributions and wave functions resulting from the addition of the electron complement of each nucleus are determined. A third imagines the nuclei superimposed on one another to form a compound atom with all the electrons around the coincident nuclei. The nuclei are then pulled apart until the best redistribution of electrons around them is obtained.

If all these imaginary processes could be calculated with sufficient accuracy, they would all give the same supposed correct final result. Usually none are susceptible to such accurate calculation, but each separately brings out important aspects of the true process when done in a manageable way. Moreover, an appreciation of the quantum nature of chemical bonding which would not otherwise be possible can be gained from these approximate methods.

6.2. Atomic Orbital Method

In the method of atomic orbitals, the approach of bringing together well-separated atoms is adopted. For the simplest case of hydrogen, we therefore start with two hydrogen atoms, each with one $(1s)$ electron in the lowest energy state, whose spins need have no relation to one another. The wave function Ψ_{12}, describing the charge distribution for electron 1 about nucleus A and electron 2 about B, is

$$\Psi_{12} = c[\psi_A(1)\psi_B(2)] \tag{6.1}$$

This equation states that the combined probability function for both electrons is the product of the separate functions for electron (1) of atom A and electron (2) of atom B. The constant c is included to make it possible to normalize Ψ_{12}, that is, to make equal to unity the value of the integral of Ψ_{12}^2 over all possible electron positions.

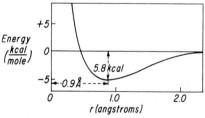

Fig. 6.1. *Coulomb energy of hydrogen molecule plotted against separation* r *of the nuclei.*

As the atoms approach each other, however, the mutual interaction forces between them become important. If it is assumed that even so the charge distribution changes but little, then the energies of electron and nuclear Coulomb forces can be calculated from the positions of the charges given by Eq. 6.1. The change in total energy from all these forces obtained in this way is plotted in Fig. 6.1.

From this curve it will be seen that the Coulomb energy first decreases as each electron comes into the attractive field of the other approaching nucleus, but then increases when the repulsion of the two nuclei begins to be more important. The position of minimum energy is the best one possible for the charge distribution represented by Eq. 6.1 and is therefore the best approximation it can give for the structure of the stable H_2 molecule. The internuclear distance for minimum energy is about 0.9 Å, and is reasonably close to the known bond length of 0.74 Å, but the calculated difference between the energy of the stable molecule and the energy of two separated hydrogen atoms is far too small. This difference, called the binding energy, is calculated in this manner to be 5.8 kcal/mole, but the value determined experimentally is 110 kcal/mole.

Heitler and London in 1927 pointed out the most serious error in the model just described: electron (1) is associated with atom A and electron (2) with atom B at all times, even in the stable molecule. But the electrons in an actual hydrogen molecule have no numbers marked on them, and there is no way of distinguishing one from the other in the molecule. Electron (1) really has an affinity for nucleus B equal to that which it has for nucleus A. The wave function $\psi_A(2)\psi_B(1)$ with the electrons exchanged on the nuclei would obviously be just as wrong, but a combination allowing for both possibilities equally would not discriminate in favor of either. Either of two such combinations—called valence bond orbitals—could be written:

$$\Psi_+ = c_+[\psi_A(1)\psi_B(2) + \psi_A(2)\psi_B(1)]$$
$$\Psi_- = c_-[\psi_A(1)\psi_B(2) - \psi_A(2)\psi_B(1)]$$

(6.2)

where c_+ and c_- are constants chosen to normalize Ψ_+ and Ψ_-. It is obvious that the combination Ψ_+ is unchanged if electrons (1) and (2) are interchanged. The combination Ψ_- changes sign if this is done but the electron density Ψ_-^2 is no different and so the charge distribution is the same. [The reader can easily verify this by squaring Ψ_- and then interchanging the labels (1) and (2).]

Which of the two functions Ψ_+ and Ψ_- is better can be determined by repeating the energy calculations for the two different functions. The results are shown in Fig. 6.2 and it is seen that the *symmetric* function Ψ_+ (unchanged by exchanging electrons) gives a stable molecule. The *antisymmetric* function Ψ_- (sign reversed on exchanging electrons) gives an unstable molecule, because this representation predicts a higher energy than the energy of the separate hydrogen atoms for all values of distances between the nuclei. It will be seen also that the predicted binding energy of 73 kcal/mole using the symmetric function is much closer to the experimental value of 110 kcal/mole than the value 5.8 kcal/mole obtained from the wave function Ψ_{12}, but the agreement is still far from perfect.

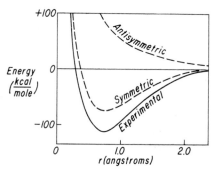

The fact that the electron charge distribution represented by Ψ_+ corresponds to a stable molecule is connected in a very fundamental way with electron pairing and the Pauli principle. The wave function Ψ_+ is equivalent for electrons (1) and (2), which therefore must have equiva-

Fig. 6.2. *Experimental energy of hydrogen molecule, and calculated energies using atomic orbitals.*

lent orbitals. Hence to satisfy the Pauli principle the spins must be anti-parallel or *paired*. The more stable charge distribution for Ψ_+ and paired spins is shown by the contour maps of Ψ_+ and Ψ_- in Fig. 6.3. The reason

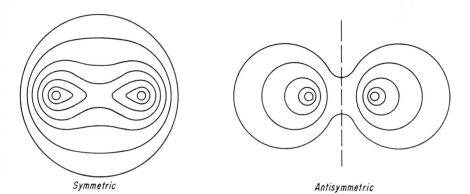

Symmetric   Antisymmetric

Fig. 6.3. *Electron density contours from Heitler-London wave functions for the hydrogen molecules.*

for the pairing is *not* that electrons have a special affinity for pairing as such or for each other (two electrons always repel), but because the orbital resulting in lowest energy considering *all* the electrostatic forces between the nuclei and electrons is possible only when a combination of orbitals permitted by opposed spins is used.

The extra stability of Ψ_+ as compared to Ψ_{12} or Ψ_{21} is often described as the *exchange energy* corresponding to the symmetric wave function. The term "exchange" is a useful one for identification purposes, but it should not be taken to represent an actual process of electrons having lower energy because they exchange positions within the molecule. The situation is rather that by allowing the orbitals for electrons (1) and (2) to be equivalent with respect to *both* nuclei, the energy is less than if they are artificially kept nearer to one or the other nucleus. This is surely reasonable. This extra stability, described as exchange energy, is thus a representation of the amount by which the description of a real molecule in terms of the separate atoms is inaccurate.

The atomic orbital method thus gives a moderately satisfactory description for hydrogen. It is not always this successful, as in some cases it equally well predicts stable combinations between atoms which in reality do not react to form molecules of such combinations.

6.3. The Molecular Orbital Method

The importance of treating the two electrons in H_2 on an equivalent basis with respect to the two nuclei suggests that a desirable approximation would be to describe each electron by a wave function derived from the consideration of *both* nuclei in their final positions from the beginning. This model, which thus makes use of *molecular orbitals*, corresponds for hydrogen to the synthesis of the molecule by placing each electron in an orbital around the two bare separated nuclei, such that the completed molecule has the lowest energy possible. The method is usually approximate because simple rather than exact orbitals are used, and because the forces between the electrons are not accurately calculated.

Hydrogen Molecule-ion

The simplest system of two nuclei to which the molecular orbital approximation can be applied is the hydrogen molecule-ion H_2^+, in which there is only one electron for the two nuclei H_A and H_B. An approximate molecular orbital Ψ for this electron is obtained by assuming it to be the sum or difference of the $(1s)$ atomic orbitals of these nuclei:

$$\Psi_+ = \psi_A(1) + \psi_B(1)$$
$$\Psi_- = \psi_A(1) - \psi_B(1)$$

where ψ_A and ψ_B are atomic $(1s)$ orbitals around nuclei A and B. If the

Coulomb or total energy of this system of one electron and the two hydrogen nuclei is calculated for each of these distributions, Ψ_+ and Ψ_-, the energies for various internuclear distances, r, are as shown in Fig. 6.4. The symmetrical orbital $\psi_A(1) + \psi_B(1)$ leads to a lower energy and hence greater stability than the antisymmetric one $\psi_A(1) - \psi_B(1)$. This greater stability corresponds to a characteristic difference in the electron charge densities Ψ_+^2 and Ψ_-^2, which are

$$\Psi_+^2 = \psi_A^2(1) + \psi_B^2(1) + 2\psi_A(1)\psi_B(1)$$
$$\Psi_-^2 = \psi_A^2(1) + \psi_B^2(1) - 2\psi_A(1)\psi_B(1)$$

(6.3)

The electron is equally distant from the two nuclei on a plane halfway between them, and hence on this plane $\psi_A = \psi_B$. Then Ψ_+^2 is evidently larger than ψ_A^2 or ψ_B^2, but Ψ_-^2 must be zero. At other points between the nuclei, Ψ_- is not zero but it is small, and at points well on one side or the other the effect is not important because either ψ_A or ψ_B is small. Thus the antisymmetric function describes an electron that avoids regions between the nuclei, while the symmetric one describes an electron that does not, as indicated in the contour maps of Fig. 6.3. Two arguments make reasonable the result that the charge distribution of the symmetric func-

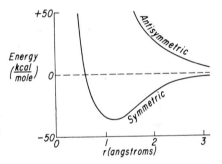

Fig. 6.4. *Energy of hydrogen molecule ion* H_+^2 *calculated from molecular orbitals. The zero of energy is for H and* H^+ *an infinite distance apart.*

tion is one of lower energy. First, the electron is attracted by both nuclei when between them. Second, the electron then also partly shields the like charged nuclei from one another, thus reducing their mutual repulsion.

Resonance

The stability of the symmetric orbital model of the H_2^+ ion, as compared to a separated proton and hydrogen atom, is the simplest example of an effect frequently described as *resonance*. In the description by either electron orbital Ψ_+ or Ψ_- of the ion, the electron charge density is of necessity equally distributed about each nucleus and is more stable than the charge distribution of the extreme structures $H_A H_B^+$ or $H_A^+ H_B$, with the electron belonging to nucleus A or B respectively.

The actual density, to which Ψ_+^2 is an approximation, must also have the symmetry which corresponds to sharing of the electron equally between the two nuclei. This effect is sometimes described as a resonance between the two atomic situations where the electron is first on A and then on B; the decrease in energy of the actual symmetrical distribution relative to the energy of either of the two possible atomic situations is called the resonance energy.

It is important to recognize this added stability of actual symmetrical electron densities compared to those of atomic or ionic structures. While it is convenient to have a name such as resonance energy in referring to this energy difference, false impressions can result if the connotation of the word "resonance" is taken too literally.

In the present case of the H_2^+ ion, the sharing of the electron between the two nuclei is inherent in the true state of the ion, and not to be described as a chemical tautomerism of actually existing and chemically separable species $H_A H_B^+$ and $H_A^+ H_B$. The resonance energy is rather a recognition that the true state is not a simple mixture of the starting approximations, but a more stable arrangement which still retains some of the features of conventional structures.

Molecular Orbitals for the Hydrogen Molecule

The hydrogen molecule differs from the molecule-ion just considered only in having two valence electrons rather than one. As a result, there are Coulomb forces on both electrons in the electric field of the two nuclei, and also the mutual repulsive force between the electrons, which of itself would keep the electrons apart.

As a first approximation it can be supposed that both electrons have molecular orbitals like those of the H_2^+ ion:

$$\Psi(1) = c_1 [\psi_A(1) + \psi_B(1)]$$
$$\Psi(2) = c_2 [\psi_A(2) + \psi_B(2)]$$

$\Psi(1)$ being the orbital for electron 1, and $\Psi(2)$ for electron (2). The complete wave function for both electrons is the product $\Psi_{MO} = \Psi(1)\Psi(2)$. After rearranging terms this product can be written as

$$\Psi_{MO} = c_1 c_2 [\psi_A(1)\psi_B(2) + \psi_A(2)\psi_B(1)] + c_1 c_2 [\psi_A(1)\psi_A(2)]$$
$$+ c_1 c_2 [\psi_B(1)\psi_B(2)] \quad (6.4)$$

A characteristic difference between the molecular orbital and the Heitler-London atomic orbital approximation is evident if this result is compared with the wave function Ψ_+ in Eq. 6.1. Except for the constant, the first term in Eq. 6.4 is just the same as the symmetric valence bond orbital Ψ_+ and so represents covalent bond character, but there are also two further terms. The product $\psi_A(1)\psi_A(2)$ represents a probability of finding both electrons (1) and (2) in the orbital ψ_A of nucleus A, and so corresponds to an ionic bond $H_A^- H_B^+$; similarly, the last product is one for which both electrons are associated with nucleus B, with the structure $H_A^+ H_B^-$.

The two extra terms in the molecular orbital approach thus represent the possibilities of partial ionic character for the electron structure of the molecule. In hydrogen, or any other molecule with two identical nuclei, the contributions of each of the two terms must be equal. For molecules where the nuclei are different, this will no longer be so, and the molecular orbital treatment will yield a larger product $\psi_A(1)\psi_A(2)$ for the more electronegative nucleus, A. In this way, the molecular orbital approach can express the partial ionic character of bonds in such diatomic molecules as HF, HCl, CO, and NO.

For H_2, calculations of the lowest energy possible from molecular orbital wave functions result in a value which is 3.6 ev (84 kcal/mole) less than the combined energies of two hydrogen atoms, which is about 1.1 ev (25 kcal/mole) too small compared with the experimental value.

It is thus clear that neither of the starting approximations—valence bond or molecular orbital—gives results of great accuracy, but both lead quite directly to characteristic features of chemical bonds. Much better calculations for hydrogen than the relatively simple but crude ones discussed here can be made, but with greater labor. A classic calculation by James and Coolidge resulted in wave functions sufficiently good to give a value for the binding energy of molecular hydrogen which agrees with the observed value to within the estimated experimental error of about one part in five thousand.

Equally good calculations can doubtless be made for other molecules at the expense of great time and effort. Much is being done to devise more efficient methods and the best approximations consistent with a given amount of effort. Even so, the more refined calculations are necessarily tedious for any system of more than one nucleus and its associated electrons, and the increased mathematical complexity makes the characteristic features of chemical bonding less discernible. Rather than follow such developments further, we shall instead examine the ways in which simple models similar to those discussed can give an approximate account of important features of chemical valence.

6.4. Bond Orbitals of Polyatomic Molecules

Models similar to those described for the hydrogen molecule have been developed for more complex molecules by the work of many chemists and physicists. The simplest form of such extensions is to represent the bonding of pairs of atoms in the molecule by separate bond orbitals, in the same way that the bonding of the pair of hydrogen atoms in a hydrogen molecule has been represented. To do this, the inner shell electrons of the original atoms are usually assumed to remain localized around their respective nuclei, and only atomic orbitals and "bonding" electrons of the outer shells are considered to take part in bond formation.

In the previous discussion of the hydrogen molecule, the importance of pairing electrons according to the symmetric wave function describing the stable covalent bond was evident. A similar importance is often assumed for other molecules in pairing electrons in overlapping atomic orbitals of lower energy. This can be justified to a certain extent by approximate arguments. The valence bond orbitals leading to stable arrangements of atoms are therefore chosen from atomic orbitals for the two adjacent nuclei, which can overlap to give a large combined function in the vicinity of the nuclei; this function can then accommodate two electrons with paired spins and results in low energy.

Diatomic Molecules

The simplest example of the atomic orbital treatment, that for hydrogen, has already been considered. The atomic orbitals of lowest energy available are $(1s)$ functions, and the electron pair bond is constructed from these, giving the electron configuration of Fig. 6.3.

The next simplest conceivable molecule with two like atoms is He_2. In atomic helium, however, the $(1s)$ orbital is already filled with two electrons. Thus, as two helium atoms are brought together, the Pauli principle does not permit overlap of these filled orbitals, and close approach of two helium atoms is possible only if one or more electrons go into higher orbitals, a process requiring energy. Hence the repulsive forces between He atoms, and instability of He_2 molecules, are reasonable results from the atomic orbital model.

The halogen molecules F_2, Cl_2, and I_2 all have quite similar covalent bonds, but these must be described somewhat differently than in the case of the hydrogen molecule. This is because the unfilled atomic states are p orbitals containing a single electron (in chlorine, $3p$ orbitals). These orbitals are directional, and only by bringing them together in the proper orientation can the resulting molecular valence orbital be large as the result of overlapping of the atomic p orbitals. This is shown in Fig. 6.5,

Fig. 6.5. *Formation of a σ type bonding orbital from two atomic p orbitals.*

which also makes evident the symmetry of the charge distribution around the line joining the two nuclei. A similar symmetry is found in the bond formed from atomic orbitals, although the bond shape is different. Bonds with this symmetry are called *σ bonds*.

Hydrogen and Alkali Halides

Other types of diatomic molecules which can be represented by pairing single atomic orbitals, each with one electron, are hydrogen and alkali halides with the formula MX, where M is hydrogen or an alkali metal, Li, Na, K, $\cdots$, and X is a halogen, F, Cl, Br, $\cdots$; for these molecules, an s orbital and p orbital may be combined. Purely covalent bonding between the two atoms can be described by the Heitler-London type of wave function, but this does not give a very good representation of the molecule when, as in the present case, one of the two atoms is significantly electronegative with respect to the other. The difference is better described by a wave function of the form discussed in Section 6.3, which can give a better approximation to the true charge distribution because of the additional ionic terms.

The bonding orbitals of the various halides are thus most simply described by adding to the covalent wave function an ionic function $\psi_X(1)\psi_X(2)$, the best combination containing a higher percentage of the ionic term if the difference in electronegativity of the two atoms is large. The relative amounts thus represent the *ionic character* of the bond.

A characteristic feature of the ionic contribution when the atoms are different is the existence of a *dipole moment* of the molecule. This is defined as the summation over all charges, both electron and nuclear, in the molecule of the product of each charge by its distance from any one conveniently defined point in the molecule—the position of one nucleus, for example. Evidently, atoms have no dipole moment because the electrons spend as much time on one side of the nucleus as another, and the product of the equally likely positive and negative distances by the equal electron charges gives an average sum of zero. For a molecular bond with ionic character, however, this is not true, as the bonding electrons spend more time near the electronegative atom. In the completely ionic structure the metal atom has lost the one valence electron, which after transfer produces a completely filled outer electron shell of the halogen. The dipole moment is then equal to the product of the net positive charge of the metal ion times its distance from the halogen nucleus, if this nucleus is chosen as the reference point. (If the metal nucleus had been chosen as origin, the resulting product of the one-electron net negative charge of the negative ion times its distance from the metal nucleus would give the same answer, since the distance is measured in the opposite direction.)

The completely ionic structure is indicated by the drawing at the left in Fig. 6.6. Dipole moments calculated from the charge of the ion

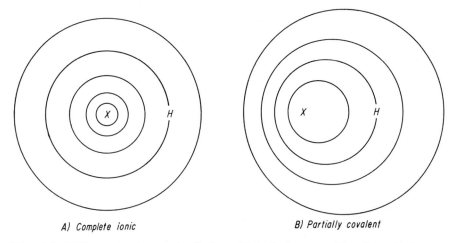

A) Complete ionic   B) Partially covalent

Fig. 6.6. *Difference in electron distribution with ionic character of bonding orbital.*

$(e = 4.8 \times 10^{-10}$ esu$)$ times a nuclear distance (of the order 1 or 2×10^{-8} cm) have the magnitude of a small number times 10^{-18} esu cm. For convenience, dipole moments are expressed in Debye units, or debyes; one Debye unit equals 10^{-18} esu cm, and the symbol μ is usually employed to denote a dipole moment. The actual dipole moments of molecules can be determined in the laboratory in various ways (see Chapter 11).

TABLE 6.1.   *Actual and "Ionic" Dipole Moments of Hydrogen and Alkali Halides.*

Formula	r (Å)	Dipole Moments (μ) Calculated (ionic)	Debye Units Experimental
HF	0.92	4.4	1.9
HCl	1.27	6.1	1.1
HBr	1.41	6.8	0.9
HI	1.61	7.7	0.4
KF	2.55	12.2	7.3
KCl	2.67	12.8	10.6
CsF	2.35	11.3	7.9
CsCl	2.90	13.9	10.5

Experimental values for a number of halides are listed in Table 6.1, and compared with those calculated for complete ionic character from the nuclear separation r.

Comparison of the calculated ionic and measured moments shows that even the extreme case of cesium fluoride, formed from the most electropositive and electronegative elements, cannot be considered wholly ionic. For hydrogen fluoride the ionic character measured is considerably less than that calculated, and for the other hydrogen halides an even greater portion of the bonding is covalent, being the more so when the difference in atom electronegativities is small.

Thus for bonds of the sort considered here, ionic effects must be considered, but they are usually secondary to the covalent type of bond in which the bonding electrons are shared more equally by the two nuclei. The difference in bonding electron distribution from ionic character is suggested by the drawings of Fig. 6.6.

Nitrogen and Oxygen

The other examples of diatomic molecules to be considered in this discussion are nitrogen and oxygen, both of which have more than one unfilled orbital available for bonding.

The electron configuration of the nitrogen atom is $(1s)^2$ $(2s)^2$ $(2p_x)$ $(2p_y)$ $(2p_z)$; there are thus three $2p$ orbitals with one electron each. If two N atoms are brought together, as indicated in Fig. 6.6, the $(2p_x)$

electrons can pair in a σ bond, but a different type of valence bond must be considered for the other four electrons. If the two $(2p_y)$ orbitals overlap there results a favorable bond, called a π *bond*, in which the electron density is concentrated both above and below the line between the nuclei, as shown in Fig. 6.7. A similar π bond in front of and behind

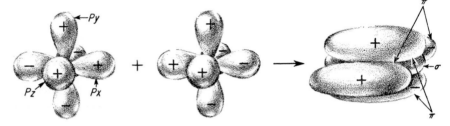

Fig. 6.7. *Formation of one σ and two π bonds from atomic p orbitals.*

this line results from overlap of $2p_z$ orbitals; the bond theory thus can naturally represent the nitrogen triple bond as the result of one σ and two π bonds.

The case of oxygen represents something of a stumbling block for the simple valence bond theory. The oxygen atom has the normal configuration $(1s)^2$ $(2s)^2$ $(2p_x)^2$ $(2p_y)$ $(2p_z)$. A σ bond overlaps p atomic functions better than does a π bond, so one of each would be expected from the overlapping of the $2p_y$ and $2p_z$ orbitals. This conforms with the usual description of oxygen as having a double bond, but it does *not* show without further discussion why two electrons in oxygen actually have their spins *parallel* rather than paired and hence antiparallel. (The existence of parallel spins is shown experimentally by the magnetic moment and paramagnetism of molecular oxygen.) This difficulty suggests the limitations and potential dangers of using the simplest approximate methods for these considerations.

Valence Bonds in Water and Ammonia

Valence bond arguments applied to many polyatomic molecules lead very simply to models with a satisfactory resemblance to the actual structures. References to some of the books dealing with this extensive subject are listed at the end of the chapter, but a few simple examples of such molecules should be given here.

Consider again the two unfilled $2p$ orbitals of oxygen. Each can form a σ bond with an unfilled orbital of two other atoms. If these unfilled orbitals are from hydrogen atoms the resulting model for H_2O is as shown in Fig. 6.8. The predicted bond angle is 90°, since the $2p$ orbitals

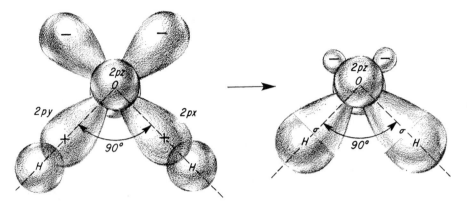

Fig. 6.8. *Use of p orbitals of oxygen to form two σ bonds with hydrogen atoms.*

of oxygen are symmetrical about axes at right angles to one another. This is consistent with the known triangular structure

rather than a linear one, H—O—H, but the 90° angle is in only rough agreement with the true one, known to be about 105°.

This difference—and similar inaccuracies in predicting values of other properties of the molecule, such as its dipole moment—must be ascribed to the neglect of significant interactions by the oversimplified treatment. One such important omission is the mutual repulsion of the two protons bonded to the oxygen. In H_2S and H_2Se, the bonds have less ionic character (compare the dipole moments: $\mu_{(H_2O)} = 1.86$ debye, $\mu_{(H_2S)} = 1.2$ debye; $\mu_{(H_2Se)} = 0.7$ debye) and as might be expected, the bond angles are 92° and 90°+, thus approaching the bond orbital value of 90°.

For nitrogen, its three unfilled atomic p orbitals can be combined with the $1s$ orbitals of three hydrogen atoms, whether as bond orbitals of the Heitler-London type or as molecular orbitals involving the nitrogen with each hydrogen atom. The predicted and actual structures of ammonia, shown in Fig. 6.9, are in agreement that the molecule is a pyramid with nitrogen at the apex upon a triangular base of hydrogens; however, much as in the case of water, the bond angles in the real molecule are larger than the 90° angles predicted by the model.

These examples show how the simple process of devising the bond orbitals in molecules by using unfilled orbitals of atoms to form the bond often leads to models with considerable resemblance to the actual structures of molecules. The process has its pitfalls, some of which have been suggested, in that too simple a description of molecules with several

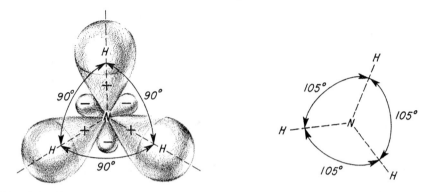

Fig. 6.9. *Three σ bonds with p orbitals of nitrogen, and the actual pyrmidal structure of ammonia.*

nuclei and many electrons of necessity over-simplifies, or neglects entirely, significant electrical forces. This is a fault of the assumptions made, rather than of any inherent limitations of the theory when it is more accurately used. Even with their inaccuracies, however, the results of the simple approximations are a great contribution toward a proper appreciation of the real underlying reasons for valence forces.

6.5. Hybrid Orbitals of Carbon

The reader will probably have noticed that in the discussion of bonding orbitals no mention has so far been made of the valences of carbon. This is obviously a subject of first importance, and the whole usefulness of valence bond or molecular orbital treatments would be seriously suspect if these treatments could not give reasonable interpretations of the characteristic bonding behavior of carbon.

At first sight, the bonding orbitals in atomic carbon do not appear to offer much basis for an explanation of the single, double, and triple bonds of organic chemistry. The normal electron configuration, $(1s)^2$ $(2s)^2$ $(2p_x)$ $(2p_y)$, leaves two p orbitals with single, unpaired electrons, and a third p orbital empty. The preceding discussions would lead to a prediction of two bonding orbitals by pairing of the two $2p$ electrons with bonding electrons of other atoms. This covalence of two obviously does not correspond at all with the four equivalent bonds of carbon so thoroughly established by the chemistry of the enormous number of known carbon compounds.

The reason for this failure of the simple model is that the electron configurations for the lowest energy of isolated atoms are not necessarily close to those in a stable molecule. If a different charge distribution permits more and stronger bonds with other atoms, then the resulting molecule will have greater stability, and the electrons will be in a more favorable situation with respect to all the charges present in the molecule than would be the case if the atomic charge distribution were more closely preserved.

Tetrahedral Bonding and Hybridization

A possible means of making more bonding electrons available in carbon lies in raising one of the two $(2s)$ electrons to the empty $(2p_z)$ orbital, thus giving an excited carbon atom with the configuration $(1s)^2 \, (2s)$ $(2p_x) \, (2p_y) \, (2p_z)$. This would give *four* where there previously were two unpaired electrons. A considerable price in energy must be paid for this, and the energy of this excited state of the atom is higher than that of the ground state by about 4 electron volts (96 kcal/mole). However, this investment does make possible subsequent decrease in electron energy by forming four rather than two bonds with other atoms.

By the "promotion" of one $(2s)$ electron to the empty $(2p)$ level, three of the unfilled orbitals are equivalent $(2p)$ levels, which should have bonding angles of approximately $90°$ as in ammonia, but the fourth $(2s)$ level is distinctly different. If the formation of methane (CH_4) by bonding of carbon with four hydrogen atoms is considered, the use of these orbitals results in the prediction of an unsymmetrical molecule with one hydrogen forming a different bond than the other three equivalent ones having $90°$ bond angles.

For methane it is known, however, that *all* the bonds are exactly equivalent, and the angles between bonds all have the tetrahedral angle of $109°28'$. This equivalence can only be realized in the model by a further modification of the charge distribution around the central carbon atom to produce four equivalent orbitals. This further change can be accomplished by an allowable construction of four new orbitals as suitable combinations of the one $(2s)$ and three $(2p)$ orbitals, as first shown by Pauling.

Pauling found that four orbitals, identical except for direction, can be obtained as four different sums of contributions from the (2s) and all three (2p) states, a process called hybridization. Each of the four

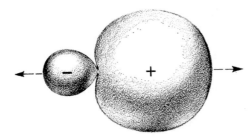

hybrid orbitals has a symmetry of the form shown in Fig. 6.10 and resembles somewhat a one-sided *p* orbital with one oval charge distribution much larger than the other. The four orbitals possible have just the tetrahedral angles of 109°28′ between their axes, and so the complete set of orbitals is arranged as shown in Fig. 6.11. This final atomic valence state

Fig. 6.10. *Angular dependence of an sp³ hybrid orbital (one of four tetrahedrally inclined orbitals).*

described by four hybrid orbitals requires still more energy than the excited state, but is preferred for the molecule provided sufficiently stronger bonds are then possible. That this will happen cannot be proved

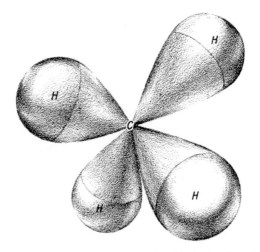

Fig. 6.11. *Set of four tetrahedrally inclined sp³ orbitals forming four σ bonds with hydrogens.*

without detailed calculation, but it is a reasonable result if one considers that *all* of the hybrid orbitals are directional and permit considerable overlap with orbitals of bonded atoms.

With the *sp³ hybridization* just described (the label derives from the fact that one *s* and three *p* orbitals are used for the four hybrid combinations) the four tetrahedral bonds of methane result simply from pairing one electron in each hybrid orbital with a ($1s$) electron of a hydrogen atom, as shown in Fig. 6.11. Similar pairing can be used to describe carbon single bonds with atoms of other elements, including other carbon atoms, to give such molecules as substituted methanes and more complex hydrocarbons.

Trigonal Bonding: sp^2 Hybridization

The complete hybridization of an s orbital with three p orbitals is not the only possibility for the carbon atom. Another is to leave one p orbital unchanged, and hybridize the s orbital with the two remaining p orbitals, as shown in Fig. 6.12. Since all three orbitals are to be equivalent and must lie in the plane of the two p orbitals used, the angle between them is one-third of 360°, or 120°. Another possible model for bonding then results if one electron is assigned to each of these orbitals, and one to the original p orbital at right angles to them.

This trigonal sp^2 *hybridization* is the key—in "valence bond language"—to the carbon double bond and, with regard for the equivalence of carbon atoms, to the benzene ring structure.

Fig. 6.12. *Three trigonal sp^2 hybrid orbitals. The third p orbital (not used) lies above and below the paper.*

Considering first an aliphatic double bond, two trigonally hybridized carbon atoms are supposedly brought together in the relative arrangement of Fig. 6.13. Union of the two in this arrangement results in the overlap of one trigonal orbital from each atom to form a σ type bond, and also in the overlap of the unhybridized p orbital from the two atoms to form a π type bond.

The second overlap will be most effective if the p orbitals are closely adjacent, and the remaining trigonal orbitals will be in one plane, as shown, when this is true. Thus in such a molecule as ethylene (C_2H_4)

the bond is strong only if the two carbons and four hydrogens are all coplanar. Otherwise the advantage of energy from overlapping will be lost; the model thus accounts nicely for the rigidity of the carbon double

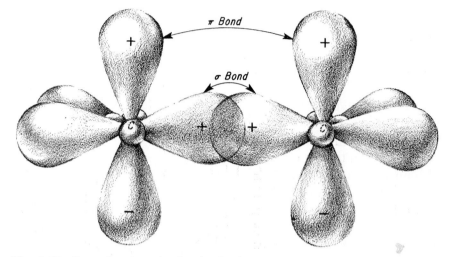

Fig. 6.13. *Formation of a σ bond and π bond.*

bond and the true planar arrangement of bonded atoms. This restriction does not occur in the single sp^3 bond, as in ethane (C_2H_6), for example, which would thus be expected to be much more flexible. This is indeed known to be true from a variety of experimental evidence.

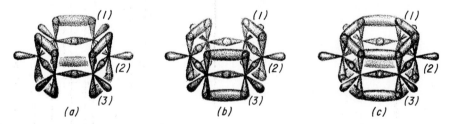

Fig. 6.14. *Bonding in the benzene ring. The σ bonds are formed by sp^2 hybrid orbitals. (a) and (b) show Kekulé structures with π bonds from p orbitals, (c) shows ring orbitals from π orbitals.*

For the bonding of carbon atoms in the benzene ring, this joining of trigonal and *p* bonds is only part of the explanation. The angle of 120° between trigonal bonds is exactly the value found in the geometry of a hexagonal ring, as shown in Fig. 6.14. Once the trigonal orbitals are joined, however, there is difficulty in deciding how to pair the *p* electron orbitals. Either of the two illustrated possibilities exists, but there is really no difference between them except in the numbering of the carbon atoms. Actual carbon atoms have no such numbers, and so there is no reason to ascribe any real meaning to the difference of the drawings. What is more, the atoms are all equivalent, and there is no real reason for the p electron of atom (2) to pair more with one neighbor (1) than the other (3).

The artificiality of these separate structures is resolved in valence bond theory by supposing that the actual wave function corresponds to an equal mixture of the two. This amounts to allowing the p electron of any one carbon to be shared with overlapping orbitals of both neighbors, these likewise sharing electrons with their own neighbors, and so on around the ring. In molecular orbital language, each of the six p electrons occupies orbitals extending completely around the ring, as shown in Fig. 6.14.

The effect, whether described as resonance of valence bond structures or delocalization of electrons into ring orbitals, leads to greater freedom and lower electron energies than with separate, more confined orbitals. The stability of the benzene ring is often described by a *resonance energy*— a term which describes the fact that the energy of the actual electron structure is less by an amount equal to the resonance energy than the energy of reference structures derived from valence bond electron-pair orbitals or other models. There exists a variety of experimental evidence —from heats of dissociation, electronic spectra, and magnetic properties, for example—that this freedom for large orbitals is a real and important property of electrons in conjugated bond and ring systems.

Digonal *sp* Hybridization

The least extensive hybridization is of one s and one p orbital to form two sp or digonal orbitals with axes at an angle of 180°, as shown in Fig. 6.15. With the combination, two of the original three p orbitals remain. Two carbon atoms so hybridized can, on proper orientation as they approach, form one σ bond from sp orbitals and two π bonds from the original p atomic orbitals. The resulting *triple bond* has electron charge density of cylindrical symmetry about the bond line (since charge density varies as ψ^2 and the p_y, p_z functions added and squared have the same value regardless of direction about this line). This is the valence bond representation of the triple bond as in acetylene (C_2H_2), which is thus predicted to have the four atoms all on one line (since the two

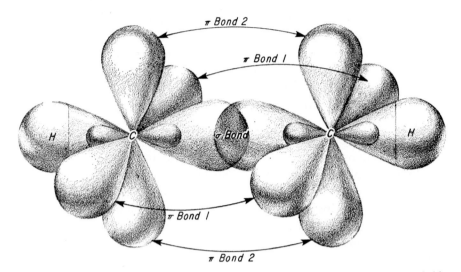

Fig. 6.15. *Formation of triple bond in acetylene. The bond is formed from* sp *hybrids, as are the two C*≡*H bonds; the two π bonds are formed from unhybridized p orbitals.*

hydrogens bond with the remaining two *sp* orbitals which make an angle of 180° with the *sp* orbitals of the triple bond).

Summary Comparison.

The properties of the orbitals characteristic of carbon for various degrees of hybridization are compared in Table 6.2.

TABLE 6.2. *Hybrids of s and p Orbitals.*

Hybrid Type	Bond Angle	Number of Hybrids	Other Orbitals
sp^3	109.5°	4 tetrahedral	None
sp^2	120°	3 in plane	one p, at right angles to plane
sp	180°	2 in line	two p, both at right angles to line

6.6. Other Examples of Hybrid Orbitals

The importance of hybrid orbitals for the bonds formed by carbon is so great that these bonds were singled out for particular discussion. It should not be supposed that the examples discussed are the only ones of importance, or that the concept is not pertinent to other molecules or to other than *s* and *p* orbitals. The range of applications is very large, and has been the subject of many accounts in scientific articles and books. Even a reasonably complete summary would take too much space to be included here, and the reader interested in following the subject further will find more specialized and extensive discussions in the list of references at the end of the chapter. Before turning to other subjects, however, a few examples will be discussed briefly to illustrate both the variety of molecular structures in which hybridization is a useful description, and also to illustrate the fact that the approach is qualitatively rather than quantitatively accurate.

Hydrogen Halides

The atomic orbital picture of hydrogen halides, described in Section 6.4, required the combination of the hydrogen (1*s*) orbital and a *p* orbital of the halogen, with the addition of ionic terms to represent the ionic character. Detailed calculations on this model, however, show that unreasonably large ionic contributions are required to reproduce experimental values of dipole moments. This difficulty can be avoided if the bond-forming orbital of the halogen atom is taken to be one of the two digonal *sp* hybrids which can be constructed from the *s* orbital and the

unfilled *p* orbital. One electron in this hybrid orbital of the halogen pairs with the hydrogen electron, and two unshared electrons fill the other *sp* orbital, as shown in Fig. 6.16. The electrons in this nonbonding orbital then give rise naturally to the ionic character without excessive ionic terms. This hybrid representation is

Fig. 6.16. *Hybrid orbital representation of hydrogen halides: a σ bond to hydrogen (1s) orbital is formed with one sp hybrid, a pair of electrons fills the other.*

probably a better approximation to the actual structure than the pairing of the unfilled *p* orbital previously discussed, but neither is exact.

The Water and Ammonia Molecules

Other examples in which models based on hybrid orbitals give different representations of bonds are the molecules H_2O and NH_3. In the water molecule, sp^3 hybridization of oxygen orbitals can be assumed, with two of the four tetrahedral orbitals filled with paired electrons, and the other two, with one electron each, available for bonding with the hydrogen atoms, as shown in Fig. 6.17. This leads to a tetrahedral bond angle of 109°+, and the actual figure of 105° is thus between this value and the 90° angle between pure p bonding orbitals. The other difference is in the concentration of negative charge in the unshared hybrid orbitals. The true charge distribution is intermediate in character, and the difference of the two models illustrates the approximate nature of both. The reader can easily construct for himself the similar situation in NH_3 and compare with the p-bond picture previously discussed.

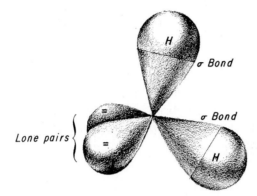

Fig. 6.17. *Hybrid orbital representation of the water molecule. The sp^3 hybrids form σ bonds with hydrogen, the others contain "lone pair" electrons.*

Many other hybrids can be devised by use of possible combinations of s, p, d, and even f atomic orbitals. The mere possibility of such hybrids does not mean they are important, and deciding whether any such hybrids actually come close to existing molecular charge distributions requires further calculations. One may not reasonably use unfilled orbitals of too high energy and expect the resulting situation to be necessarily more stable than other conceivable ones. In any case it is not to be expected that the possible orbitals are more than approximations made in the interest of a simple picture presenting significant elements of the truth.

Use of d Orbitals in Hybridization

Despite the many uncertainties in the approximations, hybrid orbitals often give a very satisfactory interpretation of structures not easily described by unaltered orbitals of the isolated atoms, as will be illustrated by examples of hybrids employing d orbitals.

Orbitals of different types than the s and p combinations discussed so far are needed to understand the structures of a number of complex inorganic molecules and ions. In some fourfold coordination complexes,

tetrahedral bonds are found and can be accounted for by sp^3 hybrids—
for example $Ni(CO)_4$—but other arrangements are also possible. For
example, both the $Ni(CN)_4^{--}$ and
$Pt(CN)_4^{--}$ ions in solid compounds are planar, as shown in
Fig. 6.18. This can be accounted
for by hybridization of orbitals
of the doubly negative Ni^{--} ion,
which before hybridization has
the configuration derived as

$$Ni \qquad (3d)^8 \ (4s)^2$$
$$Ni^{--} \quad (3d)^{10} \ (4s)^2$$

By promoting one $3d$ and one
$4s$ electron to the two $4p$ orbitals
of comparable energy, four singly
populated orbitals result: $(3d)$,
$(4s)$, and $(4p_x)$, $(4p_y)$, or alternatively, $(4p_z)$ as a p orbital. If these

Fig. 6.18. *Use of sp^2d hybrids to form four coplanar equivalent bonds.*

are hybridized, four sp^2d orbitals can be constructed by combination,
as shown in Fig. 6.18.

As would be expected for equivalence of orbitals lying in one plane,
the four orbitals are equally
spaced to give bond angles of
90° in the plane. This prediction for these ions was made
before their actual planar structures were verified by experiment.

Sixfold hybrid orbitals can
also be constructed from combinations of s, p, and d orbitals
to account for such sixfold
coordination complexes as
$Co(NH_3)_6^{+++}$, which has the
configuration shown in Fig.
6.19. The cobaltic ion Co^{+++}
differs from the cobalt atom
by loss of two $(4s)$ electrons
and one $3d$ electron:

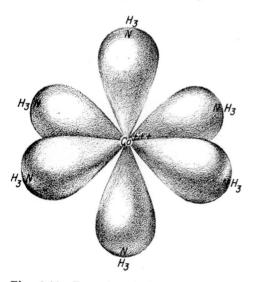

Fig. 6.19. *Formation of six hybrid sp^3d^2 orbitals.*

$$\text{Co} \qquad (3d)^7 \ (4s)^2$$

$$\text{Co}^{+++} \qquad (3d)^6$$

If each nitrogen is supposed to give up a single electron for bond formation (a dative bond), the six lowest energy orbitals which can be filled
are two $(3d)$, one $(4s)$, and three $(4p)$. It proves possible to make six
suitable mixtures of them which are all equivalent and directed as
shown in Fig. 6.19. The electrons donated leave six NH_3^+ groups with
singly occupied orbitals for bonding to the six sp^3d^2 hybrids. The electron
configurations of the nitrogens then probably correspond to sp^3 hybridization as in the ammonium ion (NH_4^+) or as for carbon in methane
(CH_4), with the fourth bond to cobalt rather than hydrogen.

6.7. Molecular Spectra

Much of our information concerning the lengths and orientation of
bonds in molecules is obtained by studying both the frequencies at which
radiation is absorbed or emitted by the compound and the relative
amounts of energy absorbed at these different frequencies. Molecular
spectra observed with visible light or in the near infrared differ qualitatively from atomic spectra in that they consist of bands instead of lines,
as shown in Fig. 6.20. Each band begins with a sharp "band head,"

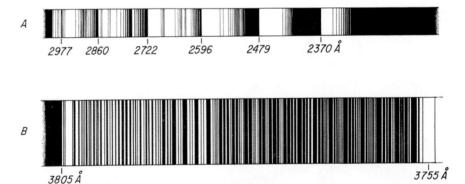

Fig. 6.20. (A) *Absorption bands of N_2 and NO in the ultraviolet.* (B) *Fine structure of
the 3805 Å band of N_2 as seen with high dispersion.* [*After G. Herzberg, Spectra of
Diatomic Molecules, 2d ed. (D. Van Nostrand, Princeton, 1950)*].

which gradually becomes increasingly lighter and more diffuse. The
reason for the existence of these bands, which are really collections of
lines, lies in the existence of molecular energy levels analogous to the

energy states of the atom. Different amounts of quantized energy resulting from both the rotation of the molecule and the vibration of the atoms composing it are associated with each energy level.

The situation for molecular spectra differs from that for simpler atomic spectra in that the motions of the atomic nuclei play more important and specific roles in determining the energy relationships and the primary effects observed are no longer evidence of quantized changes in electronic energy states alone. While electronic changes are important in molecules as well as in atoms, the presence of two or more nuclei with their associated electrons also gives rise to the emission and absorption of energy, which depend on relative motions of the nuclei—classified as rotations and vibrations. Fortunately, these characteristically molecular processes can usually be discussed as effects distinct from those associated with changes in electronic state. This simplification was justified by Born and Oppenheimer and shown by them to result from the much greater masses of nuclei as compared to electrons.

Rotation

A molecule composed of more than one nucleus is capable of rotation about any of several axes, each rotation possessing an associated rotational energy. If such rotation results in net displacement of charge, classical electromagnetic theory leads one to expect emission or absorption of radiation of the same frequency as that of the rotation.

Fig. 6.21. *Rotations of a diatomic molecule about axes perpendicular to the molecular axis (line joining the two nuclei).*

A diatomic molecule (or any linear molecule) may rotate end over end like a dumbbell about any axis of rotation perpendicular to the molecular axis, and passing through the center of gravity, as shown in Fig. 6.21. For nonlinear and other polyatomic molecules, the situation is complicated by the fact that the rotational axis is not necessarily perpendicular to any of the fixed interatomic axes within the molecule.

Vibrations

A second characteristic process of absorption of radiation by molecules is the result of vibrations (oscillations) of the atomic nuclei centered upon their mean positions. The combination of electrical forces between nuclear and electronic charges in conjunction with the inertial forces of the nuclear masses is analogous to a purely mechanical system of masses interconnected by springs. If the vibrations of the electrical system result in net displacement of positive and negative charges during the motion, radiation should be emitted.

Classically one would associate the frequency of the light absorbed with the frequency of a particular mode of vibration; such characteristic frequencies are in fact found in the pure vibrational spectrum. For a diatomic molecule only one such frequency is observed (characteristically in the infrared region of the spectrum), while for more complicated molecules more modes of motion and consequently a number of corresponding frequencies are possible.

Electronic Transitions

The absorption of a relatively large amount of energy by a molecule gives rise to an electronic transition to an excited state, the energy absorbed resulting in a different electron orbital arrangement. A smaller amount of energy absorbed produces a change in the vibrational energy, and a still smaller amount manifests itself as a change in the rotational energy of the molecule. Electronic transitions are nearly always accompanied by a variety of both vibrational and rotational changes. Similarly, vibrational transitions, involving greater energies than rotational transitions, can have rotational changes associated with them. As might be expected, lines due purely to rotation are possible in the low-energy region of the spectrum, being found in the far infrared.

The change in energy, ΔE_e, due to an electronic transition is of the order 5 ev, corresponding to a wavelength region in the ultraviolet (5 ev energy represents a wavelength of 2500 Å). Superimposed on each of the two electronic levels involved in the energy change are vibrational levels, for which the vibrational quantum number, v, can take on the values 0, 1, 2, 3, 4, $\cdots$. The energy associated with the transition from one vibrational level to the next within the same principal quantum state is roughly 0.1 ev, the corresponding wavelength being 20 μ.

Consider again the transition from one electronic energy level to another. The original state might be one of any number of vibrational states within a given electronic level, and the final state might be any of several vibrational levels within a second electronic level. The resulting spectrum contains a series of closely spaced lines, the number of which is governed by certain selection rules restricting the states between which transitions are possible. If a spectrograph of low resolving power is used, the lines on the spectrum obtained are so closely spaced as to give the appearance of a band; the separation of lines is in the neighborhood of 1–30 cm^{-1}.

Vibration-Rotation Spectra

For each vibrational level of energy, a molecule may exist in any one of a series of rotational levels designated by another quantum number J. The energy difference (ΔE_J) between rotational levels in a single vibrational level varies from one molecule to another, but is of the order 0.005 ev, or a wavelength of some 200 μ as compared with the shorter wavelengths such as 20 μ for vibrational changes. Transitions between rotational states in different vibrational levels result in a fine structure for vibrational lines, just as the bands due to electronic transitions show fine structure lines resulting from vibrational changes.

Examination of the rotation spectra as a constituent of bands in the 2500 Å region is often impractical. Instead, the portion of the spectrum most simply analyzed is in the far infrared, at wavelengths of around 200 μ or more. Here the energy is just sufficient to cause rotational changes without electronic or vibrational transitions. (The vibrational-rotational spectrum appears in the near infrared, because these wavelengths correspond to vibrational changes.)

The study of molecular spectra has done much to elucidate the structure of molecules. Because of the complexity of the band spectra of polyatomic molecules, the most complete studies have been made of diatomic molecules, and much remains to be done with more complicated molecules. Without going into the theory itself, we shall consider some of the elementary results of the theoretical treatment of the simplest molecules.

6.8. Rotational Energies of Simpler Molecules

For linear molecules, the rotational lines are very simply described: they occur at evenly spaced intervals. Often only a few of the possible rotational lines are observed because of the experimental problems in the far infrared and centimeter wavelength regions where they are characteristically found. Until the advent of microwave methods evolving from radar development, these regions were accessible only with difficult and crude techniques. Even with present-day techniques the experimental problems are not wholly solved for all regions of interest.

In the microwave region, results of extraordinary precision can be obtained, as shown by the results of Table 6.3 for observed absorption frequencies of carbonyl sulfide (OCS).

TABLE 6.3.   *Rotational Frequencies of Carbonyl Sulfide.*

Frequency (Mc/s)	24,325.92	48,651.7	60,814.7
Transition in quantum number J	$1 \longrightarrow 2$	$3 \longrightarrow 4$	$4 \longrightarrow 5$

(Note that frequency of 30,000 Mc/s corresponds to a wavelength of 1 cm, as compared to radio wavelengths of meters.)

The second frequency is double the first to a precision of a few parts per million and the third is half again larger to similarly good precision. These frequencies are described to this accuracy by the simple formula

$$\nu = 12162.96 J' \tag{6.5}$$

where J' is an integer: $J' = 1, 2, 3, \cdots$.

The quantum theory of rotational energy predicts that for linear molecules a sequence of energy states or levels can exist with energies E_{rot} given by

$$E_{rot} = \frac{h^2}{8\pi^2 I} J(J+1) \tag{6.6}$$

with the requirement that the quantum number J be integral. The quantity I appearing in the formula is the moment of inertia of the linear molecule about an axis perpendicular to the axis of the molecule. For a diatomic molecule, it is equal to the sum of the masses of the nuclei, each multiplied by the squares of their distances from the center of the mass:

$$I = m_1 r_1^2 + m_2 r_2^2$$

If $d = r_1 + r_2$ denotes the nuclear separation (bond length), then—since $m_1 r_1 = m_2 r_2$ (by definition of center of mass)—I can also be written

$$I = \frac{m_1 m_2}{m_1 + m_2} d^2 \tag{6.7}$$

A selection rule also results from the theory: J can only change by one unit in absorption or emission of radiation. The absorption lines observed for OCS corresponds to the transition $J \longrightarrow J+1$, and the frequencies predicted are

$$\nu = \frac{h}{8\pi^2 I}\left[(J+1)(J+2) - J(J+1)\right] = \frac{2h}{8\pi^2 I}(J+1) \quad (6.8)$$

Comparing with the experimental formula, Eq. 6.5, it is seen that the two agree if $J' = J + 1$, and if

$$\frac{2h}{8\pi^2 I} = 12162.96 \text{ Mc/s}$$

Since h is known, the moment of inertia can be calculated, giving $I = 1.3975 \times 10^{-38}$ g cm². For a diatomic molecule a knowledge of I would be enough to determine the nuclear separation, since the nuclear masses are known and only a single interatomic distance is involved. For three atoms, more information is needed. We shall not go into details of how this can be obtained—in some cases by making the same measurements with substituted isotopic atoms; for example, in carbonyl sulfide, S^{34} might replace S^{32}.

The reader may wonder why a molecule like OCS was selected as an example, rather than some simpler or more familiar one such as H_2, N_2, NO. There are two reasons: first, homonuclear diatomic molecules like N_2 exhibit no absorption because their symmetry results in no *net* charge displacement on rotation; second, because the frequencies of many simple molecules are unobligingly in difficult experimental regions, fewer frequencies have been observed.

After techniques for millimeter wavelengths were developed, frequencies of lighter diatomic molecules could be observed. Thus Gillian, Johnson, and Gordy in 1950 found absorption by the $J = 0$ to $J = 1$ transition in carbon monoxide ($C^{12}O^{16}$) at the frequency $\nu = 115,270$ Mc/s. For this transition, one can therefore calculate

$$I = 2h/8\pi^2\nu = 0.145 \times 10^{-38} \text{ gm cm}^2.$$

Using this value for I and the atomic masses of C^{12} and O^{16} in Eq. 6.6 gives the bond length:

$$d^2 = I\frac{(m_1 + m_2)}{m_1 m_2} = 0.145 \times 10^{-38}\frac{12 + 16}{12 \times 16}0.602 \times 10^{24}$$

$$= 1.274 \times 10^{-16} \text{ cm}^2$$

and hence

$$d = 1.13 \times 10^{-8} \text{ cm}$$

With more accurate values of atomic masses and calculations, the value $d_0 = 1.13079 \times 10^{-8}$ cm is obtained.

The important conclusions for our present purpose are: (1) rotational energies are quantized, a result which holds good in more complicated ways for polyatomic molecules in general; (2) rotational energies are much smaller than for changes in electronic and vibrational states; (3) the fact that adequate theory gives significant information about interatomic distances. These distances (bond lengths) are characteristically of the order 10^{-8} cm, a few Ångströms, as shown by Table 6.4, giving

TABLE 6.4.   *Bond Lengths.*

Molecule	Bond	Distance (Å)
H_2	H—H	0.75
O_2	O—O	1.20
Cl_2	Cl—Cl	1.98
C_2H_6	C—C	1.54
C_2H_4	C=C	1.34
C_2H_2	C≡C	1.22
N_2O	⎰N—N	1.126
	⎱N—O	1.191
SO_2	S—O	1.433
OCS	⎰O—C	1.1647
	⎱C—S	1.5576

a number of such distances. Some were determined from rotational spectra, others from rotational structure of vibrational spectra.

6.9. Vibrations of Diatomic Molecules

Values for the vibrational energy of a diatomic molecule may be obtained by considering a model with the two atomic masses at either end of a coiled spring. The restoring forces are thus assumed proportional to the displacement of the nuclei from their equilibrium position (the harmonic oscillator approximation). The allowed energies of vibration, E_{vib}, predicted by quantum theory for such an oscillator are very simple in form:

$$E_{vib} = h\nu_0(v + \tfrac{1}{2}) \qquad (6.9)$$

Here v is the vibrational quantum number which may have integral values only: $v = 0, 1, 2, \cdots$, and ν_0 is a constant determined by the charge distribution and nuclear masses of the molecules. A selection rule limits the observable frequencies by the requirement that v can change only by one unit in emission or absorption of radiation. This leads to the simple result that the allowed frequencies in absorption (transition $\longrightarrow v + 1$) must satisfy only

$$\nu = \frac{1}{h}\left[h\nu_0(v + 1 + \tfrac{1}{2}) - h\nu_0(v + \tfrac{1}{2})\right] = \nu_0$$

Thus only a single frequency equal to ν_0 is predicted, which in classical theory would be simply the vibration frequency of the oscillation itself. In quantum theory, however, the frequency of absorption is associated with transitions between adjacent energy states (levels).

The value of the frequency ν_0, while specific to the molecule concerned, does not give direct and simple information about molecular structure. Certain characteristic relations of its magnitude to the masses of constituent nuclei in diatomic molecules may be noted. If one of the two atoms is hydrogen, ν_0 is much higher than if both are heavy atoms, and for the singular case of molecular hydrogen ν_0 is considerably higher still, as shown in Table 6.5.

TABLE 6.5.   *Vibration Frequencies of Diatomic Molecules.*

Molecule	H_2	HCl^{35}	HBr	HI	Cl_2	I_2
$\bar{\nu}_0$ (cm^{-1})	4405	2989	2650	2231	565	214

These differences provide valuable information about the electronic charge distribution which acts as the "spring" linking the nuclear masses and charges. The values of vibration frequency also have important effects in determining the heat capacities of gases (see Chapter 10).

Rotational and vibrational energies are additive, so the energy evolved in a rotational-vibrational change is

$$\Delta E = (v - v')h\nu_0 \pm \frac{h^2}{4\pi^2 I}J' \qquad (6.10)$$

The value of J' must be an integer which is one or greater, as the reader can readily show from Eq. 6.6 and the selection rule that J can only change by one when radiation is emitted or absorbed. For this reason there is no spectral line corresponding to ν_0 itself. Equally spaced lines for $J = 1, 2, 3, \cdots$, occur on either side of the gap corresponding to the missing ν_0 line.

It should be noted that the values ν_0 listed for the symmetrical molecules H_2, Cl_2, I_2 were not observed from pure vibration spectra, as such molecules cannot emit or absorb radiation by changes in vibrational state that result in no net charge displacement. If, however, electronic changes take place concurrently, this restriction no longer obtains. The absorption in such electronic vibration spectra can be analyzed to determine ν_0 and also give evidence of multiple vibrational energy states with nearly the even spacing predicted by Eq. 6.9. That the actual spacing is not exactly even is not surprising if we remember the idealized assumption about the "harmonicity" of force due to the charge distribution that was made to obtain Eq. 6.9. Real molecules could hardly be expected to be quite this obliging about the nature of the forces opposing vibration—especially for large amplitudes bringing the nuclei quite near one another.

6.10. Vibrations of Polyatomic Molecules

The theory of molecular vibrations becomes more complicated when more nuclei are involved, but fortunately the observed vibrations can often be classified into a limited number of distinct types. These different types can be appreciated from an examination of a few simple molecules.

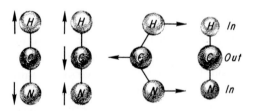

Fig. 6.22. *The four modes of vibration of a linear triatomic molecule: the two at left are stretching, the two at right are equivalent bending vibrations.*

In the case of a linear triatomic molecule such as HCN or N_2O, four different classes of relative nuclear displacements are possible, as illustrated in Fig. 6.22. The two on the left involve *stretching* (and compressing) bonds, while the two on the right correspond to changes in the bond angle—described as *bending* of the bonds. Two such bending vibrations for displacements in perpendicular directions are necessary to construct a bending vibration in any possible plane, but the frequency is the same because there is no difference in the charge distribution with direction around the bond line—that is, there is cylindrical symmetry.

Similar modes of vibration are found in nonlinear triatomic molecules

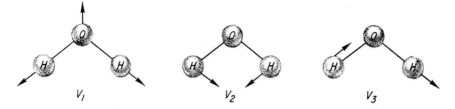

Fig. 6.23. *The three modes of vibration of a nonlinear triatomic molecule.* V_1 *and* V_3 *are stretching vibrations,* V_2 *is a bending vibration.*

such as H_2O and H_2S; these are shown in Fig. 6.23. Of the three modes, those labeled V_1 and V_3 involve changes in bond length, and hence are stretching vibrations, while V_2 is a bending vibration which changes the bond angle.

A third type of vibration is illustrated by ethane. In addition to stretching and bending of the various bonds (there are 20 different possibilities), twisting the two methyl groups around the C—C single bond, as in Fig. 6.24 is possible without changing bond lengths or angles. Motions of this kind are described as *hindered rotation* or *torsional vibrations*. Whether the two groups rotate almost freely or are constrained to small displacements about a position of lowest energy depends on the strength and directional dependence of the forces between the groups.

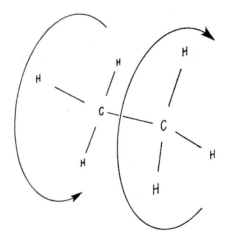

Fig. 6.24. *Hindered relative rotation of* CH_3 *groups about the C—C bond in ethane.*

Number of Modes and Selection Rules

The reader may have wondered whether there exists any basis for predicting the number of possible kinds of vibration from the structure and number of atoms of the molecule. There is a simple rule which does this, and it is readily established.

A molecule with n atoms can be located in space if $3n$ coordinates are known (3 for each nucleus). Instead of using the three position coordinates for each nucleus, it is desirable to use coordinates of the center of mass of the molecule, as defined in ordinary mechanics, and "internal" coordinates describing where the atoms are relative to the center. Three of the $3n$ coordinates are necessary to specify where the center of mass is, leaving $3n - 3$ required to describe the internal motions of rotation and vibration about the center. If the molecule is linear, two coordinates are needed to describe rotation of the nuclei about the two rotational axes, and if not linear, three. The number of coordinates left to describe vibrations are then given by the rule that the number of vibrational coordinates equals $3n - 5$ for linear molecules and $3n - 6$ for nonlinear molecules.

For HCN and CO_2 the number is thus $3 \times 3 - 5 = 4$, as shown in Fig. 6.22, and for H_2O, H_2S the number is $3 \times 3 - 6 = 3$, as in Fig. 6.23. The classification and nature of the allowed distinct modes per molecules with three or four atoms is usually obvious, and for many modes mathematical treatments of the coordinates have been developed for the purpose.

Not all of the allowed vibrations need give rise to absorption of radiation, and a mode which does not is called *inactive*. An example is the "breathing" mode V_1 of C_6H_6, in which the molecule swells and contracts uniformly, and the similar mode for CO_2 ($O \longrightarrow C \longleftarrow O$). The reason radiation is not emitted or absorbed is because there is no *net* displacement of the charges, both electrons and nuclear, of the molecule, and hence there is no way for these vibrations directly to produce or absorb the electric and magnetic fields we call radiation.

These forbidden frequencies are another example of the *selection rules* encountered generally in the analysis of spectra. The frequencies of inactive modes must as a result be obtained from other types of evidence —for example the scattering of light in the Raman effect. Much of the success in relating observed frequencies for more complicated molecules to the molecular motions causing them is achieved by combination of results from different types of spectroscopic observation, together with a knowledge of the selection rules required by different possible structures.

Characteristic Vibration Frequencies

It has already been pointed out that vibration frequencies of diatomic molecules are markedly affected if one or both of the atoms is hydrogen. There are other characteristic properties of the various kinds of vibrations in polyatomic molecules which aid in interpreting vibration spectra in molecular terms.

The first property is that bending vibrations have lower frequencies as a class than stretching vibrations, and torsional modes about a bond are of still lower frequency (if the bond is single, but not if it is double). These differences are readily understood by the simplified picture of the electronic charges acting as a spring. For stretching of a bond, distortion of the charge distribution is necessary. This requires considerable energy and so corresponds to a stiff spring and high frequency. In bending, the distortion is less, the spring weaker, and the frequency lower. The strength of a single σ bond is not greatly changed by twisting around the axis of the bond, but a double bond of π type is very rigid, thus accounting for the differences in frequencies.

The second property, which is important in using vibrational spectra for either structural studies or analytical chemistry, is the fact that frequencies of vibration of a particular kind of bond or group are often affected only slightly or characteristically by the other attached atoms or groups. For example, a C—C single bond vibration frequency for most molecules lies within 100 cm^{-1} of the wave number 1000 cm^{-1}. The C—H stretch frequency depends on the other bonds to the carbon atom, being near 2890 cm^{-1} for an aliphatic compound, 3080 cm^{-1} if aromatic, and 3020 cm^{-1} for an ethylenic bond.

The presence or absence of absorption near any characteristic frequency is evidently a valuable clue to the presence of a particular bond or group in a molecule and to the nearby structure. The identification process which is obviously thus possible is not always unambiguous and should, like any other analytical procedure, be used with proper respect for its advantages and limitations. Even so, absorption vibration spectra are proving increasingly valuable for analysis and have great advantages for many problems. Suitable procedures for quantitative analysis—based, for example, on comparing intensities rather than just presence or absence of absorption—are also finding increasing use. Most of the characteristic vibration frequencies of molecules lie in the infrared between 1000 and 4000 cm^{-1} (10 μ to 2.5 μ), and hence infrared spectrometers with suitable sources and detectors are necessary.

Problems

6.1. In the simple treatment of the H_2 molecule in the text, two H_2^+-like orbitals are used to form the molecular orbital for the molecule. What important factor is neglected in this treatment?

6.2. In the quantum-mechanical description of the H_2 molecule, the wave functions corresponding to the ionic structures H^+H^- and H^-H^+ must make equal contributions. What can you say about the relative contributions of H^+F^- and H^-F^+ in the HF molecule? about the contributions of I^+Cl^- and I^-Cl^+ in the ICl molecule?

6.3. The OH_3^+ ion (or H_3O^+ ion, as it is commonly written) is present in significant concentration in acidic aqueous solutions and in small concentrations even in pure water and in ice. What structure or structures might be expected for this ion? With what common substance is it isoelectronic? [Some experimental evidence for the structure of this ion in the monohydrates of hydrogen halides is given in Ferriso and Hornig, *J. Chem. Phys.*, **23**:1464, 1955, and Richards and Smith, *Trans. Faraday Soc.*, **48**:1216, 1951.]

6.4. What would you predict as the most probable structures for the CH_3 radical? What hybridization is involved in each of these structures? (See Herzberg and Shoosmith, *Can. J. Physics*, **34**:523, 1956, for work on this radical.)

6.5. In boron trimethyl, $B(CH_3)_3$, the boron and three carbon atoms are coplanar with C—B—C angles of 120° (Lévy and Brockway, *J. Am. Chem. Soc.*, **59**:2085, 1937). What orbital hybridization is involved in this bonding? This compound combines readily with NH_3 to form $(CH_3)_3B$—NH_3, in which the C—B—C bonds are no longer planar. Suggest an explanation for this.

6.6. The $PdCl_6^=$ and $PtCl_6^=$ ions have octahedral structures. Write down the electron configuration for the Pd and Pt atoms. Suggest how the neighboring (with regard to energy level) d, s, and p orbitals might be used to form these complexes.

6.7. Molecular spectra in the region 300 cm^{-1} to 4000 cm^{-1} (near infrared) are usually associated with vibrational transitions. Pure rotational spectra are found in the microwave region, typically from 20,000 Mc/sec to 1,000,000 Mc/sec. What are the energy ranges, in calories per mole, associated with these regions? How do these energies compare to the energy kT, the classical average energy associated with a one-dimensional oscillator?

6.8. The internuclear separation in HCl is 1.27 Å. Calculate the separation in wave numbers of the three lowest frequency spectral lines due to rotational transitions.

6.9. What is the absorption wavelength and corresponding ΔE in calories per mole corresponding to a vibration-rotation transition in HCl, in which v changes from 0 to 1 and J from 2 to 3?

6.10. Stitch, Horig, and Townes (*Phys. Rev.*, **86**:813, 1952) studied the microwave spectra of some alkali halide vapors at high temperatures. A line at 26051.1 Mc/sec in the $NaCl^{35}$ spectrum was identified as the $J = 1 \longrightarrow 2$ transition in the ground vibrational state ($v = 0$). What is the internuclear distance in this compound?

6.11. Using the bond distances given in Table 6.4, find the center of mass of the linear N_2O molecule. What is its moment of inertia? At what wavelength will the transition corresponding to $J = 5 \longrightarrow 6$ be found?

6.12. The CF_4 molecule has the structure of a regular tetrahedron, with the four F atoms at the vertices and the C atom at the center. Electron diffraction studies (Hoffman and Livingston, *J. Chem. Phys.*, **21**:565, 1953) give a C—F distance of 1.32 Å. Calculate the moment of inertia of this molecule about an axis through one of the F atoms and the C atom.

6.13. How many vibrational modes are there for the tetrahedral methane molecule? Make a sketch showing the "breathing" mode of this molecule, a mode in which the C atom is fixed and the bond angles are unchanged. Would you expect this mode to be active in the infrared?

6.14. How many degrees of freedom—i.e., independent coordinates necessary to specify the position of every atom in space—are there for the nonlinear hydrocarbon C_nH_{2n+2}? How many of these correspond to vibrational modes?

6.15. What are the energy values, in calories per mole, associated with electronic transitions in the ultraviolet and visible regions from 1000 Å to 7000 Å?

6.16. In the hydrogen atom, only the electron-nucleus potential energy, $-Ze^2/r$, appears in the potential energy term of the wave equation. What electrostatic potential energy terms must be included in the exact wave equation for the hydrogen molecule? In a schematic representation of the molecule, label the distances involved in each energy term.

6.17. Using the Heitler-London method and the $1s$ orbitals of atomic hydrogen, write down the symmetric and antisymmetric orbital wave functions for the ground state of the hydrogen molecule. If the two nuclei were to collapse onto one another, giving one nucleus of double the charge, what would these functions reduce to? To what atomic orbitals are the reduced functions similar?

6.18. Repeat Problem 6.17, using the molecular orbital method to obtain the orbital wave function for the hydrogen molecule ground state.

6.19. If you wished to compare the relative stabilities of the H_2^+ ion and the H_2 molecule, what experimental measurement would you make?

6.20. Show that the dipole moment of a system of charges $\mu = \sum_i q_i r_i$, where r_i is the vector from some arbitrary origin to charge i is independent of the choice of the origin when the system has no net charge—i.e., when $\sum_i q_i = 0$.

6.21. In the investigation cited in Problem 6.10 the line corresponding to the same transition in $NaCl^x$ (x = mass of chlorine isotope) was found at 25,493.9 Mc/sec. What was the mass of the chlorine isotope? (Isotope substitution does not change the potential function for the molecule and the internuclear equilibrium distance is therefore the same if stretching effects are neglected.)

6.22. Compare the moments of inertia and the separation of rotational energy levels in the hydrogen and chlorine molecules. Would you expect electromagnetic energy to be absorbed by rotational energy changes in these molecules?

6.23. The energy of the lowest vibrational state in which a molecule can exist is called the zero point energy. What is this energy for the hydrogen molecule? If the binding energy of the hydrogen molecule is 110 kcal/mole (potential energy difference between separated atoms and atoms at the equilibrium internuclear distance), calculate the amount of energy required to dissociate the hydrogen molecule in its ground vibrational state.

6.24. Classically, when magnetic lines of force cut a conducting circuit, a current is induced in the conductor, whose magnetic field then opposes the original field. Consider the benzene and cyclohexane molecules as analogous to conducting circuits. What would you predict as to the relative size of the magnetic effects in these two compounds?

6.25. Would you expect the molecule HD to be active in the infrared? Give a reason for your answer. Is the value of the vibrational frequency lower or higher than for H_2?

6.26. What values would you predict for the Cl—Si—Cl angles in $SiHCl_3$? Compare with the experimental values determined by electron diffraction [Brockway and Beach, *J. Am. Chem. Soc.*, **60**:1836, 1938).

Suggested Readings

A good elementary account of molecular spectroscopy is given by G. M. Barrow in *The Structure of Molecules*, issued as a paperback (Benjamin, New York, 1963). *Introduction to Molecular Spectroscopy* (McGraw-Hill, New York, 1962) is a more detailed discussion by the same author.

Elementary descriptions of atomic and molecular quantum theory with a minimum of mathematics are given in *The Structure of Matter* by F. O. Rice and E. Teller (Wiley, New York, 1949).

Two books on chemical bonding and molecular structure which can be recommended highly are relatively nonmathematical: *The Nature of the Chemical Bond* (3rd ed.) by L. Pauling (Cornell, Ithaca, 1960) and *Chemical Constitution* (2nd ed.) by J. A. A. Ketelaar (Elsevier, New York, 1958). A variety of topics are taken up in *Quantum Chemistry* by K. S. Pitzer (Prentice-Hall, Englewood Cliffs, N.J., 1953). A more mathematical treatment is found in *Valence* (2nd ed.) by C. A. Coulson (Oxford, 1961).

There are many textbooks of quantum mechanics for students with adequate background in differential equations and classical mechanics. References to these more advanced books will be found in the books already cited.

Chapter 7

The Solid State

THE STRUCTURAL REGULARITY of most solids in which chemists are interested makes it possible to understand many of their characteristic properties with relative ease in terms of atomic and molecular structure. We will, therefore, discuss solids prior to the discussion of other states in which matter may exist—a departure from the conventional order, which generally places gases first, followed by liquids and solids. (Of the three, the liquid state is certainly the most difficult to understand.) This chapter is concerned with the description of some of the properties of the solid state, and with the theoretical and kinetic interpretations which might account for these properties.

7.1. Solids, Amorphous and Crystalline

While the average interatomic or intermolecular distances in solids are often significantly larger than the atomic, ionic, or molecular radii, solids generally have high densities. The specific gravity of iron, for example, is almost 8. Some solids, such as balsa wood, have relatively low densities, but most solids are denser than liquids and very much more dense than gases at ordinary pressures.

Another distinguishing characteristic of solids is their ability to maintain a certain form, and the fact that they will flow appreciably only under large forces. In contrast, a liquid assumes the shape of its container up to its surface, while a gas fills entirely any volume made available to it. This rigidity is of course somewhat variable from one solid to another and, for a given solid, may vary with the temperature or mechanical stress. Solids are likewise possessed of a certain amount of mechanical strength which liquids and gases do not have—a bending force must be applied to a piece of chalk before it will break. They are distinguished by a certain degree of hardness, a quality which can be more easily recognized than it can be precisely defined. Some solids, such as diamond, are exceedingly hard; others, such as lead, are quite soft.

Crystalline Solids

Crystalline solids are characterized by a very orderly arrangement of the particles of which they are composed. For this reason, they are easily subject to investigations which lead to rather complete knowledge of their structure.

These substances possess a definite ordered arrangement of ions, atoms, or molecules, so repeated throughout the mass of a small grain, or even a large chunk, that a sample taken from any minute section containing only a few atoms or molecules serves as a representative in miniature of the entire solid. As a result of this submicroscopic order there is order on the visible scale which is often manifested, for example, by the repetition of crystal faces at definite angles. Thus particles of ordinary table salt have a cubic structure. Other crystals are of other shapes, depending upon the material of which they are composed. A few examples of typical crystal habits are shown in Fig. 7.1.

A crystal may thus be regarded as composed of regularly spaced layers or sheets of fundamental particles, whether atoms, molecules, or ions. Because of this order by repetition in a crystal, a penetrating beam of X-rays striking these internal crystal faces will be diffracted at definite angles to give sharply defined patterns on a photographic plate.

These patterns are the result of the wave reinforcement of the beam in certain directions for which the waves scattered from the reflecting crystal layers are in phase, and the destruction of the beam in all other directions for which the geometry is such that the scattered waves are out of phase. X-ray patterns are in no way shadows of atoms or shadow-graph pictures of atoms, any more than the visible spectrum produced by the diffraction of ordinary light from a grating of ruled lines is a picture of the rulings. It is only by devising a model of the crystal struc-ture which can be shown by calculation to give the same X-ray pattern obtained from an actual crystal that knowledge of the arrangement of the atoms in a crystal is obtained.

Sharp melting points are a property of crystalline solids—the transition from the solid to the liquid state for pure substances is accomplished at the definite temperature called the melting point. This is in contrast to the melting of amorphous solids, to be discussed below.

Isotropic crystals are those whose properties are identical in all directions relative to the crystal axes. Electrical conductivity and the velocity of transmission of light, for example, are the same for any direction of transmission through a cubic crystal. Crystals belonging to systems other than cubic are anisotropic. Their properties are dependent upon direction, enabling them to exhibit optical rotatory power and the piezoelectric effect for crystals having sufficiently low symmetry. (The piezoelectric effect is the creation of electric charge by application of a mechanical stress upon two of the faces of a crystal—the principle on which a crystal microphone or phonograph pickup works.)

(a)

(b)

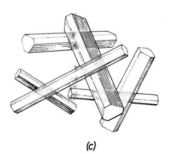

(c)

(d)

Fig. 7.1. *Typical crystal habits.*

Two crystals may possess nearly identical physical form and yet have different chemical composition, in which case they are said to be isomorphous. It has been previously shown (Section 2.8) how atomic weights may be determined by utilizing the fact that compounds forming isomorphous crystals have similar molecular formulas for the different elements entering into them.

Amorphous Solids

Many amorphous solids are somewhat like extremely viscous liquids, but in which the force of attraction between molecules is so great that the material is rigid. Glass is an example of an amorphous solid. Glassy substances have resemblances to both the solid and the liquid states. Upon heating they show no sharp melting point, but rather a gradual transition from solid to liquid; it is impossible to determine or define an exact temperature at which the substance ceases to exist as a solid and becomes a liquid. The softening point of a piece of glass tubing may be approximated, but not the melting point of glass.

While crystalline solids have a high degree of order, both with respect to other portions of the solid at close distance (short-range order) and to more remote regions (long-range order), amorphous substances possess no long-range order, but have a considerable degree of short-range order. This is the principal structural characteristic of amorphous solids, and in this they resemble the structure of liquids to a certain extent. This type of structure is not sufficiently understood to be further considered here; rather, the simpler but important and useful subject of crystal structure will be discussed in greater detail.

7.2. Crystallography and Crystal Systems

Crystallography is an old and, in many respects, fascinating science. Crystals assume very definite forms, which are independent both of size and of source. The science of crystallography is based on a few laws that express this geometrical regularity.

The "law of constancy of interfacial angles" states that the angles M between analogous faces of all crystals of a given substance are constant. Interfacial angles can be measured by finding one-half the angle through which a crystal must be rotated to obtain reflections from the two adjacent faces of a beam of ordinary light. Special instruments, such as goniometers, are made for the purpose of determining interfacial angles.

Second, there is the principle of symmetry. Nearly all crystals possess at least a small degree of symmetry, as revealed by the presence of a center of symmetry, of one or more axes of symmetry, or of planes of symmetry. A cubic crystal, for example, has a center of symmetry: any straight line that may be drawn through this point in the center will intersect opposite crystal faces at two equidistant points. It also possesses a number of axes of symmetry: 3 fourfold axes, 4 threefold axes, 6 two-fold axes. In each of these cases, the crystal when rotated about the axis reaches two or more positions in which it appears identical with its original orientation. For a fourfold axis, there are four such positions which are identical, for a threefold axis there are three, and so on. In addition to these axes of symmetry, the cube has nine planes of sym-metry, which divide the cube in half, each half the mirror image of the other. Most crystals have a lower degree of symmetry than a cube; there are then fewer planes or axes of symmetry, and there may be no center of symmetry. The various symmetry operations are shown schematically in Fig. 7.2.

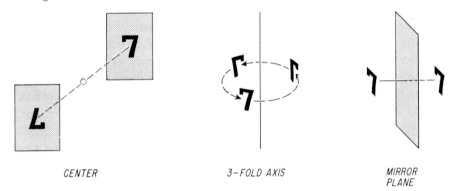

    CENTER   3-FOLD AXIS   MIRROR
                                                             PLANE

Fig. 7.2. *Three types of crystal symmetry.*

Crystal faces and planes parallel to them may be described by their points of intersection with a suitably chosen group of reference axes. According to the "law of rational indices," the distances of the intercept of any particular plane, along one of these axes, is a rational multiple of the intercept distance on the same axis of some other plane in the crystal. The simplest set of axes consists of three lines mutually perpen-dicular intersecting at the origin, but the set actually chosen and most convenient for a given crystal is dependent upon the geometry of that crystal. Figure 7.3 shows various planes intersecting a set of three mutu-ally perpendicular axes. Unit distances along the axes are determined by choosing some one plane as a reference plane and taking the distances of its three intercepts from the origin as the unit measure. A unit length a, along the axis x, may or may not equal a unit length, b, along the axis y, and both may differ from a unit length, c, along z.

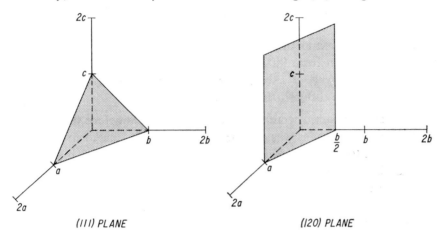

(*III*) PLANE   (*120*) PLANE

Fig. 7.3. *Miller indices for two crystal planes.*

In Fig. 7.3, A, the crystal face cuts the three axes at the unit distance on each. The ratio, $a:b:c$, of the three intercepts for this plane is $1:1:1$. This is the so-called "Weiss notation." The "Miller notation," which is the one in general use, is obtained by taking the reciprocal of each intercept, multiplying by a factor to reduce any fractions, and eliminating the punctuating colons. Thus the face in the above example is a (111) plane. In Fig. 7.3, B, the Weiss representation is $1:2:\infty$; the corresponding Miller notation is (210). The numbers so obtained are called Miller indices. (Note that the axis not intercepting the crystal face has a Miller index zero, the reciprocal of infinity, as intercept.)

Crystal Systems

The large number and variety of crystalline forms can be divided into seven fundamental systems, shown in Fig. 7.4, classified on the basis of the length of the axes and the axial angles.

1. Cubic (or regular)—3 equal axes, mutually perpendicular.
2. Tetragonal—3 mutually perpendicular axes, 2 of which are of the same length and the third longer or shorter.
3. Orthorhombic (or rhombic)—3 mutually perpendicular axes of 3 different lengths.

4. Hexagonal—3 coplanar axes of equal length meeting at angles of 120° to one another and 1 axis perpendicular to the plane of the first 3 and of a different length.

5. Monoclinic—3 unequal axes, 2 of them perpendicular and the third intersecting one of the first two at 90° and the other at some different angle.

6. Triclinic (or anorthic)—3 axes of unequal length intersecting at angles all different from 90°.

7. Rhombohedral—3 axes of equal length, intersecting with equal angles, which are different from 90°.

These seven systems were recognized many years before the existence of atoms and molecules was established, and the regular form of crystals was thought to result from their being constructed of many microscopic building blocks having one of the seven shapes shown in Fig. 7.4. With the discovery of X-rays, a powerful tool became available to study arrangements of atoms and molecules in crystals, and it was soon found that the elementary blocks, or unit cells, contained a small number of

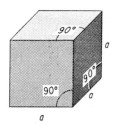
CUBIC

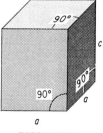
TETRAGONAL

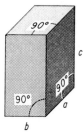
ORTHORHOMBIC

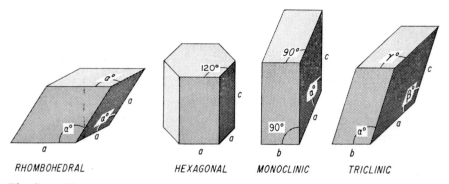
RHOMBOHEDRAL   HEXAGONAL   MONOCLINIC   TRICLINIC

Fig. 7.4. *The seven crystal systems.*

atoms, molecules, or ions at different places in the cell. The structure of a large perfect crystal is then simply a repetition of these cells extended indefinitely in three dimensions, the cells having identical shape and orientation and differing only in the number of displacements by simple translation from any starting point.

When the discrete arrangement of atoms in a unit cell is taken into account, it is necessary to make further distinctions among the various kinds in order to describe all possible symmetries of these arrangements. By studying the possibilities, Bravais showed in 1848 that a total of 14 classes is required. The extra number results because several of the crystal systems may have different atom arrangements which can be repeated indefinitely, these systems being cubic, tetragonal, orthorhombic, and monoclinic. Taking the cubic system, for example, atoms can be placed at each vertex of the unit cube (simple cubic), but two elaborations are also possible. One is to place an atom at the cube center (body-centered cubic); the other is to place an atom on each face (face-centered cubic). These structures are shown in Fig. 7.5. (Notice that

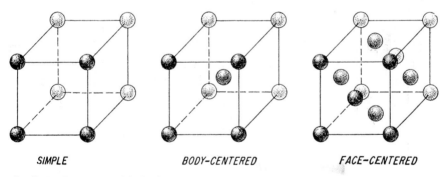

SIMPLE   BODY-CENTERED   FACE-CENTERED

Fig. 7.5. *The three cubic lattices.*

placing atoms at both the body center and the face centers produces a simple cubic arrangement and so is not another kind of structure.) Additions of body- or face-centered atoms are also possible in the other systems mentioned, the number of different structures resulting giving a total of 14 space lattices.

7.3. X-ray Methods in the Study of Solids

X-rays have proved a valuable aid in the investigation of crystal structure. A number of methods of utilizing these short wavelength radiations have been developed, among the earliest and most successful being that of the Braggs, father and son.

The Bragg treatment depends upon the existence of atoms in the crystal units lying in parallel planes. A monochromatic beam of X-rays

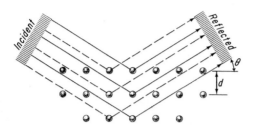

incident from a given plane will be scattered in phase with a parallel ray reflected from some other plane, if the distances traversed by the two rays differ by an integral number of wavelengths. This condition is satisfied only for certain definite angles of incidence, all other angles resulting in practically complete destruc-

Fig. 7.6. *Diffraction of X-rays by regularly spaced layers of atoms.*

tive interference, because a very large number of planes contribute in even a microscopic crystal. The angles at which reinforcement occurs must satisfy the Bragg equation

$$n\lambda = 2d \sin \theta,$$

where d and θ are as indicated in Fig. 7.6, and n is an integer. When this condition is met, one has what can be conveniently described as reflection, although the process is really one of diffraction. Once the

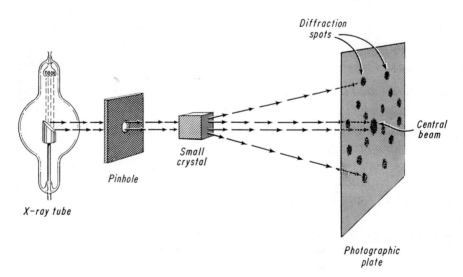

Fig. 7.7. *Arrangement for observing Laue diffraction pattern.*

wavelength λ of the radiation is known, the interplanar distance *d* involved can be calculated. The experiment requires a source of monochromatic X-rays, a crystal large enough for its faces to be identified, a means of varying the angle between crystal face and X-ray source, and a detector for the reflected rays. X-ray studies by means of Laue patterns antedate the Bragg type of analysis, but are more difficult to interpret. This method makes use of a beam of "white" X-rays (containing a continuous range of wavelengths) which is directed at a crystal, behind which is placed a photographic plate, as shown in Fig. 7.7. By the use of white X-rays, interference patterns can be obtained without the necessity of rotating or orienting the specimen sample.

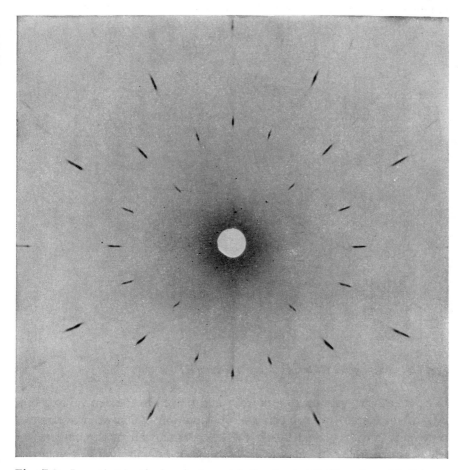

Fig. 7.8. *Laue photograph of a single crystal of rock salt (NaCl), taken with film at a distance of 45 mm from the crystal. [Courtesy Mr. Ward Robinson, Brown University.]*

When the wavelength and angle of the reflecting atomic layers is proper for reinforcement, a spot in the corresponding position will be produced in the photographic plate. Thus all principal planes will reflect, and the crystal acts toward the incident radiation as a three-dimensional diffraction grating. The resulting diffraction pattern contains small spots arranged symmetrically about a large central spot that represents the undeviated portion of the beam, as shown in Fig. 7.8. Laue patterns are most useful in determining the symmetry of the crystal, but interpreting them to yield information about the interplanar spacing is usually so difficult as to be impractical.

A third means for X-ray crystal study is the powder diagram. The apparatus is arranged as shown in Fig. 7.9. The crystalline substance

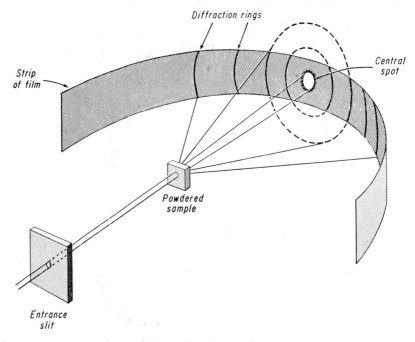

Fig. 7.9. *Arrangement for taking powder photographs.*

to be examined, ground to a powder and placed in the central axis of a cylindrical camera, is subjected to X-radiation of known wavelength. A strip of film is placed inside the cylindrical wall of the camera, in which the sample is centered. The sample is then rotated in the beam, which is perpendicular to the axis. Only those small crystals properly oriented at a particular instant will give rise to reflections. The rays are therefore diffracted as surfaces of solid angles, resulting in arcs of slight curvature where they are intercepted by the cylindrical film. The lines on the film are symmetrically displaced on either side of a central

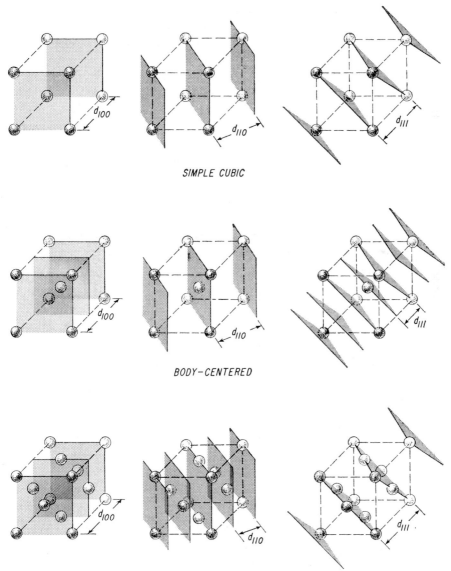

SIMPLE CUBIC

BODY-CENTERED

FACE-CENTERED

Fig. 7.10. *Diagrams illustrating differences in spacings of reflection planes in cubic structures.*

spot representing the undeviated beam. By measuring the distance between the images of the lines, and knowing the radius of the camera, it is possible to find the angle of reflection.

Since the wavelength is known, the distance between planes in the crystal may be calculated from Bragg's law. Often powder diagrams are used to identify substances by comparison with indexed and classified diagrams of known solids. The intensities of the scattered X-rays are dependent upon the location of the atoms, and hence are used in assigning locations from X-ray data.

Electron diffraction has been mentioned. Electrons have wavelengths close to those of X-rays, provided their velocity is properly adjusted. Because of the high degree of absorption of electrons by solids, however, this type of diffraction study finds greater usefulness in studying structures of molecules in gases, where the absorption is much smaller.

7.4. Unit Cells—Cubic Lattices

Some of the methods of X-ray analysis can be illustrated by considering the three members of the cubic system—the simple cubic, the face-centered cubic, and the body-centered cubic lattices. Many crystals are found in one or another of these three forms, which are capable of relatively simple treatment.

The planes of crystal units and the distances between planes in the three types of cubic lattices are indicated in Fig. 7.10. The ratios of the three important interplanar distances d_{100}, d_{110}, d_{111} for each lattice are easily found by simple geometry and trigonometry, with the following results.

$$\text{Simple cubic} \quad 1 : \frac{1}{\sqrt{2}} : \frac{1}{\sqrt{3}} \qquad = 1 : 0.707 : 0.577$$

$$\text{Face-centered cubic} \quad \tfrac{1}{2} : \frac{1}{2\sqrt{2}} : \frac{1}{\sqrt{3}} = 1 : 0.707 : 1.154$$

$$\text{Body-centered cubic} \quad \tfrac{1}{2} : \frac{1}{\sqrt{2}} : \frac{1}{2\sqrt{3}} = 1 : 1.414 : 0.577$$

These ratios are seen to depend on the structure and so may be used with the Bragg equation,

$$d = \frac{n\lambda}{2 \sin \theta}$$

in distinguishing between types of cubic lattices. If X-radiation of the same wavelength is used throughout the analysis, and only the first-order reflections are considered, so that n is constant,

$$d_{100} : d_{110} : d_{111} = \frac{1}{\sin \theta_1} : \frac{1}{\sin \theta_2} : \frac{1}{\sin \theta_3}$$

where θ_1 is the angle the X-ray beam makes with the (100) plane at the position of maximum reflection, and θ_2 and θ_3 the angles for maximum reflection from the (110) and (111) planes, respectively. Therefore the ratios of interplanar distances, which, as shown above, are characteristic of each type of cubic lattice, may be obtained from X-ray measurements. An example is the NaCl crystal, which at one wavelength yields maximal reflections at $\theta_1 = 5.9°$, $\theta_2 = 8.4°$, and $\theta_3 = 5.2°$. The reciprocal sine ratio of these angles is 1:0.705:1.14, corresponding to a face-centered cubic structure.

Measurements of different orders of reflection for the various planes gives additional information. The NaCl lattice is composed of inter-penetrating face-centered arrangements of sodium and chloride ions, as shown in Fig. 7.11, A. The structure is such that the individual (100)

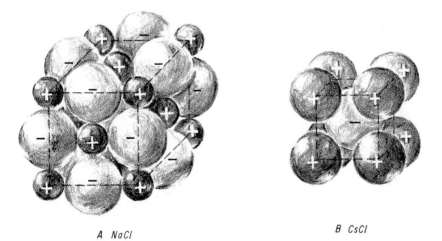

A *NaCl*   B *CsCl*

Fig. 7.11. *Structures of alkali halide crystals.*

and (110) planes contain both sodium and chloride ions, while the (111) planes are made up of either one or the other, a plane of sodium ions alternating with a plane of chloride ions in the crystal. For the different orders of reflection obtained in sodium chloride with either the (100) or the (110) plane, it is found that the reflected intensity drops off regularly with increasing values of n, as expected. The first-order reflection for the (111) plane, however, is weak, and the second-order reflection is considerably stronger. In succeeding reflections, those of odd-numbered orders are similarly weak.

The explanation of the intensity differences lies in the fact that the chloride ion, with 18 electrons, has greater scattering power than the sodium ion, with 10 electrons. An X-ray beam directed at the (111) plane at the correct angle for first-order reflection from the chloride ion planes will also be reflected from the (111) sodium ion planes, spaced halfway between chloride planes, so as to cause destructive interference. That there is any first-order reflection at all is due to the greater intensity of reflection from the chloride ion planes. In the case of KCl, where both ions have approximately the same scattering power, the interference is almost complete, and analysis of the (111) plane reflections in KCl shows practically no odd-order reflections at all. For even-order reflections, the rays reflected from the chloride (111) planes are retarded just one wavelength relative to those from the sodium plane and thus are in phase; hence reinforcement takes place.

The other important ionic crystal structure, exemplified by CsCl, is shown in Fig. 7.11, B. The reasons for this structure in preference to the NaCl structure are discussed in Section 7.8.

7.5. Covalent and Metallic Bonding in Crystals

The fundamental units of a crystal may be atoms, ions, or molecules, and the forces that bind these particles may be any of several different kinds. These different kinds of forces are very closely related to the structures of the constituent particles, and types of crystalline solids are classified logically in terms of the kinds of bonding possible. The reader can recognize, and should look for, such points of similarity with what has been said in Chapters 5 and 6 about atomic and molecular structure.

Covalent Bonding

One of the simplest crystals of the atomic type is diamond, which is composed of carbon atoms arranged tetrahedrally so as to form essentially one great molecule, as shown in Fig. 7.12, A. The tetrahedral bonds between the carbon atoms are covalent and identical in length (1.54 Å) with the sp^3 carbon-carbon bonds of saturated aliphatic hydrocarbons (for example, the C—C bond length in ethane). It is because of the strength of these bonds that diamond is the hardest of all crystals.

The other form of solid carbon, graphite, is interesting in comparison. As shown in Fig. 7.12, *B*, graphite has a layer structure, with a planar

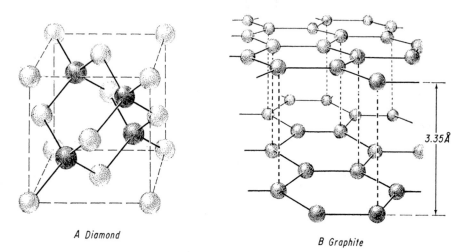

A *Diamond*

B *Graphite*

3.35Å

Fig. 7.12. *Structures of* (A) *diamond, and* (B) *graphite. Note in* (A) *the four bond lines from (for example) the black spheres to neighbors, and in* (B) *the hexagonal rings.*

hexagonal arrangement of carbon atoms in each layer. Within a plane, each carbon atom thus forms three equivalent bonds at 120° as obtained by sp^2 hybridization, with C—C distance of 1.42 Å; each layer is really an enormous covalently bonded flat molecule, with electron charge distribution like that in the benzene ring of an aromatic compound. The binding between successive layers, however, is very much weaker, so much so that description in terms of a chemical bond is not appropriate. This has the molecular consequence that the shortest distance between carbon atoms in adjacent layers is considerably larger than any carbon bond lengths in molecules, being 3.40 Å. The good lubricating properties and the flakiness of graphite are evidently nicely explained by the ease of displacing layers held together by relatively weak forces (for further discussion, see van der Waals forces).

Covalent bonding is not confined to crystals of elements with suitable numbers of outer shell electrons (for example, silicon, germanium, tin). Tetrahedral covalent bonds also provide stable bonding in compounds such as zinc sulfide (ZnS), silver iodide (AgI), and silicon carbide (SiC). In each of these, the two atoms together have eight bonding electrons, and have the proper number for supplying two electrons to each of four

bonds between unlike atoms. The resulting structures have the tetrahedral arrangement of neighbors as a possible result. Boron nitride (BN),
on the other hand, has a hexagonal layer structure resembling graphite.

The examples given suggest that covalent bonding in the solid is most
often important for elements and compounds of atoms near the center
of the periodic table. These solids, sometimes described as valence
crystals, are hard and are good electrical insulators, in contrast to crystal
types involving atoms nearer the beginning or end of rows in the periodic
table.

Metallic Bonding

A second type of binding in atomic crystals is exemplified by copper.
This metal crystal is made up of atoms packed as closely together as
spheres can be packed. In copper, the resulting structure is face-
centered cubic, as shown in Fig. 7.13, *A*.

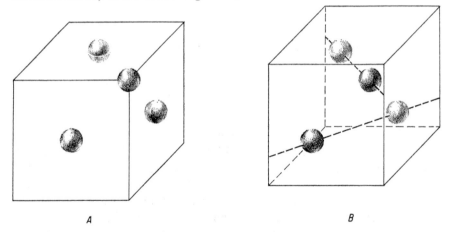

A   B

Fig. 7.13. *Illustration of how four atoms at a corner and three face centers of a unit cell
can be wholly contained in a unit cell of the same dimensions with displaced faces.*

The cubic unit cell, as shown, has one atom on each of its eight corners
and one on each of its six faces. Since each corner is shared by eight other
cells, and each face by one other, the number of atoms per unit cell is
$8 \times \frac{1}{8} + 6 \times \frac{1}{2} = 1 + 3 = 4$. If this argument does not appeal to the
reader, he may prefer a unit cell with boundaries displaced to avoid
sharing, as shown in Fig. 7.13, *B*. This cell has the same size as the one
in Fig. 7.13, *A*, and when repeated produces the same crystal. None of
its four atoms is shared, so the number per unit cell must be four.

Both of the types of representation illustrated in Fig. 7.13 are frequently found. Which one is more helpful in visualizing the complete structure depends on the features of most interest.

Copper, atomic number 29, has the following electron configuration: $1s^2\ 2s^2\ 2p^6\ 3s^2\ 3p^6\ 4s^1\ 3d^{10}$. The $4s$ (valence) electron can interact with valence electrons of other copper atoms. At the same time, there is available an unused $4s$ level, and the $4p$ level, close in energy to the $4s$, is unoccupied. Since there are these several available levels of similar energy in the free atom, a variety of electron configurations may result in bond formation and stable solid structures.

The strong directive forces occurring in diamond, which are responsible for its hardness, strength, and also brittleness, are absent in the case of the metallic bond, and this difference is reflected in the malleability of metals. Since there are many unoccupied orbitals available, electrons can move readily from atom to atom through the crystal; hence the good electrical conductivity. The catalytic properties of many metals can be explained by the fact that approximately the same energy is involved in making or breaking organic double bonds. Because of this, bonds can often be dissociated from organic molecules when they come in contact with the metal surface.

The elements forming solids, with such characteristically metallic properties as good conduction of electricity and heat, evidently are electropositive—that is, they give up one or more valence electrons readily. A subdivision of great importance into different metallic types is based on whether the d shells of the atoms are partially occupied. The type often called *simple metals* includes alkali metals (Li, Na, K) and lighter elements of the second and third groups. The second type contains notably the transition metals of the fourth row elements with unfilled $3d$ orbitals. The distinction between the two types occurs because the incomplete d shells result in characteristic differences in a variety of physical properties of the metals; these become most pronounced in the ferromagnetic elements iron, nickel, and cobalt, and in alloy combinations including one or more of them.

As a first approximation, the simple metals may be thought of as having their valence electrons completely free or nearly free to move about within them in what might be called "super molecular orbitals." Many of the properties of metals are simply understood by this concept— notably the ease with which electricity and heat are conducted by these highly mobile electrons. More sophisticated models are required, however, if metal properties are to be accounted for quantitatively. Except for lithium and sodium, the simple model fails, for example, to predict values in agreement with those measured for energy necessary to evaporate a metal into its atoms, even allowing for the electrical forces of nuclei and closed shell electrons. In some cases, consideration of bonding orbitals between neighbors is a more useful approximate approach.

7.6. The Band Model of Metals

A useful approximate description of the role played by valence electrons in determining properties of metals has been developed, which is called the band model. This is based on consideration of the changes in electron behavior when the atoms of the metallic element are brought together into the regular arrangement of the crystalline metal.

Copper atoms, as an example, have when isolated three filled orbitals and a simple $4s$ valence electron. The K ($n = 1$) orbital lies lowest in energy with its two electrons most closely bound to the nucleus; the L and M orbitals are progressively less tightly held and have charge distributions at larger distances, as discussed in Section 5.13; and the $4s$ valence electron is farthest of all from the nucleus, with appreciable probability of occupying a much larger region around it than do the inner shell electrons.

When copper atoms are brought together into the face-centered cubic

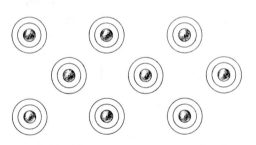

Fig. 7.14. *Plane of copper atoms in face-centered structure.*

structure of the metal, of which one layer is shown in Fig. 7.14, there is little overlapping of the closed shell charge distributions of the free atoms, but very considerable overlap of the $4s$ electrons. The overlapping modifies the behavior of these electrons very greatly and occurs in a large part of the volume. In its crudest form the band model consists of assuming that the result is a complete delocalization of the valence electrons, so that each valence electron has the volume of the metal available to it, rather than being confined to and identified with a particular atom. For N isolated atoms, there are originally N levels for $4s$ electrons, all of the same energy. When these electrons are divorced from their atoms (and assumed to occupy the entire crystal), they are no longer distinguishable, but no more than two can have exactly the same wave functions and energy, by the Pauli principle. The result is necessarily a range, or band, of energy levels—*N* in all—which if lower in energy than the atomic levels will correspond to a more stable structure when electrons are placed within it. A similar situation can occur for higher energies; the empty atomic levels, such as the 4*p* level in copper, become a higher energy band. Such a band is shown in Fig. 7.15, *A*, lying entirely above the lowest one; in Fig. 7.15, *B*, the possibility that the bands may overlap is illustrated.

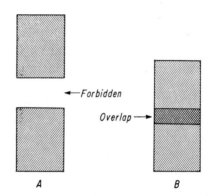

Fig. 7.15. *Electron energy bands:* (A) *with gap between bands;* (B) *with overlap of bands.*

We may now consider what happens when the *N* valence electrons of copper are put into the levels for copper, which are of the form shown in Fig. 7.15, *A*. Two electrons of opposite spin can occupy each level, and for lowest energy the *N*/2 lowest lying levels will be filled, leaving the upper half empty, as shown in Fig. 7.16. The electrons occupying

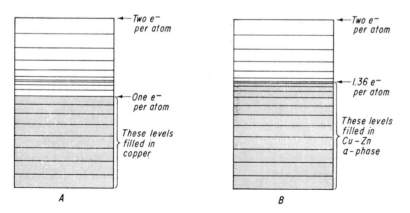

Fig. 7.16. *Schematic electron energy levels in lowest band for copper structure. Filling for copper is shown in* (A); *for* 36% *zinc, in* (B).

these levels move in different directions, depending on the state occupied, but in the absence of external forces as many move in any one direction as in the opposite one, and there is no net current flow from the motions. This exact compensation occurs by a pairing of levels of the same energy but opposite directions of electron motions and can be destroyed if some electrons are raised to higher levels, corresponding to an excess of electrons moving in a particular direction. An applied electrical potential difference can accomplish this and give rise to electrical conductivity, but only if empty levels are available into which electrons can be lifted by the small amounts of energy which ordinary potential differences can supply.

The band theory, by this argument, predicts that substances having partially filled energy bands will be conductors, while those substances which have a filled band with no empty levels at slightly higher energies will be insulators. In copper, the empty levels shown in Fig. 7.16, A are available, making conduction possible; alkali metals also have a band half filled with the single valence electrons per atom, and are also good conductors.

A very different condition can result if the element considered is divalent, as there are then $2N$ electrons for N atoms, which must fill N levels and hence a complete band. If the nearest empty levels are much higher, as in Fig. 7.15, A, electrons cannot easily be "unpaired" to contribute to electrical and thermal conductivity. Substances for which this is true are poor conductors or insulators; examples are sulfur, tellurium, and selenium (these solids actually consist of long chains of atoms). But the higher band may overlap the lower one, as in Fig. 7.15, B; then conduction is possible by exciting electrons into these readily available levels, even though the lower band is filled. This is known to be the case for beryllium and magnesium, which have a hexagonal close-packed structure and different band energies than cubic structures.

The separation of energy levels into bands with regions of forbidden energy corresponds very directly with the fact that particular wavelengths and directions of electron waves do not exist in the crystal. In Section 5.7 we discussed electron diffraction, in which it is observed that electron beams satisfying the Bragg conditions between atom spacings and electron wavelength are reflected from crystals, rather than being absorbed. Forbidden energy ranges for electrons in metals are found from the band theory for just these electron directions and wavelengths inside the crystal, the origin of the effects being the periodic distribution of nuclei and closed shell electrons in the structure. Classification of energy bands according to the effects of atom arrangement was first accomplished by L. Brillouin; the bands so obtained are often called *Brillouin zones*.

The band method is most useful for discussion of metallic elements and their mixtures, because the procedure of first delocalizing valence electrons and then considering effects of the ion cores on these electrons turns out to give a fairly good approximation to the important features of the solid properties. This treatment is evidently more similar to the molecular orbital method of forming molecules from atoms than to the valence bond method. Pauling has discussed metallic bonding by the valence bond method, involving the resonance concept to derive more stable structures from combinations of bonds between atoms and their nearest neighbors.

For nonmetallic elements, valence bond arguments often give a simpler interpretation of the solid structures than the band model. The so-called 8-n rule, which holds for many elements, is an example. In this rule, n refers to the column of the element in the periodic table, and it is true for many elements that they have 8-n nearest neighbors in the solid structure. Thus for group 7, atoms such as the halogens have one nearest neighbor—its partner in the stable molecule which is the structural unit of the solid. Group 6 elements will satisfy the rule for two nearest neighbors, such as are found in the infinite chains of atoms in solid selenium and tellurium, and in closed eight-membered rings in solid sulfur. Bismuth and antimony satisfy the rule to the extent that three of the six adjacent atoms in the solid are closer than the other three; carbon as diamond with four tetrahedrally arranged neighbors is the example par excellence of covalent bonding in a solid structure. For elements with fewer outer shell electrons, the rule sometimes works but a simple explanation in terms of shared electrons to form octets is no longer possible, as there are insufficient electrons.

7.7. Electron Alloys; Semiconductors

The band theory of metals can be extended to mixtures of elements, and in a number of cases provides simple explanations of otherwise puzzling properties. Here we shall consider briefly a few examples of interest and importance which occur when two elements are mixed together in a solid structure.

If a mixture of two metallic atoms of nearly the same size and valence is cooled from the melt, it is often found that a homogeneous crystalline solid is formed for wide ranges in the relative numbers of atoms of the two kinds. In such a case, the structure is one in which lattice sites are occupied randomly by one or the other kind of atom, as could be expected if the atoms are sufficiently similar. Alloys of copper with nickel are examples of this behavior.

"Electron Compounds" in Binary Alloys

A very different situation is found if the two kinds of atoms have different valences. Different structures are then found for different relative compositions. Brass, which is a copper-zinc alloy, forms several different solid crystal structures in different ranges of composition. Up to about 38% zinc, zinc atoms merely replace copper atoms in the same face-centered cubic structure as for pure copper. (Ordinary yellow brass with about 35% zinc falls in this range.) This is called the α phase.

For compositions close to 50% zinc (in terms of gram atomic weights, or in terms of the number of atoms of zinc and copper), a different structure is found, called the β phase, in which copper and zinc atoms are arranged in a body-centered cubic structure. At compositions centered about 62% zinc, a complex cubic structure of copper and zinc atoms, called the γ phase, is the stable form, while for 75% zinc another distinct ϵ phase with hexagonal structure occurs (pure zinc crystallizes in a distorted hexagonal lattice). The optimum compositions for these different solid phases can be represented by the formulas $CuZn$, Cu_5Zn_8, $CuZn_3$, but there is certainly no basis in conventional valence bond ideas for predicting any such combinations.

TABLE 7.1. *Compositions and Structures of Binary Metal Alloys.*

β phase (body-centered cubic)				
Composition	$CuZn$	$AgCd$	Cu_3Al	Cu_5Sn
Electrons/Atoms	3/2	3/2	6/4	9/6
γ phase (complex body-centered cubic)				
Composition	Cu_5Zn_8	Ag_5Hg_8	Cu_9Al_4	$Cu_{31}Sn_8$
Electrons/Atoms	21/13	21/13	21/13	63/39
ϵ phase (hexagonal)				
Composition	$CuZn_3$	$AgCd_3$	Ag_5Al_3	Cu_3Sn
Electrons/Atoms	7/4	7/4	14/8	7/4

A considerable number of other metal pairs form structures in a similar sequence, and with compositions quite as incomprehensible from simple valence theories. A few examples are $AgCd$, $AgCd_3$; Cu_3Al, Cu_9Al_4; Cu_5Sn, $Cu_{31}Sn_8$, Cu_3Sn. These and other alloys are listed in Table 7.1 according to the type of structure (β, γ, ϵ phases).

Hume-Rothery pointed out a remarkable feature of the compositions for all the alloys of any one structure; namely, that the ratio of *total* number of valence electrons from *both* atoms to the total number of atoms was the same for the different alloys. Thus the α phase alloys $CuZn$ and Cu_3Al have electron/atom ratios $3/2$ and $6/4 = 3/2$. The β phase alloys all have a value $21/13$ (for example, Cu_5Zn_8 has $(5 + 16)/(5 + 8) = 21/13$), and the ratio for γ phase alloys is $7/4$.

This remarkable consistency indicates that the various structures found are the ones which can accommodate the valence electrons most readily, regardless of the atom from which they come. The energy band model of delocalized electrons has precisely this indifference to the source of electrons for filling energy levels in the band, and in this model, the stable structure is the one which has the lowest total energy when all the electrons have been put in the lowest available energy levels for that structure. Approximate calculations of the positions of the bands and levels in the bands have been made; the results lead to predictions which agree quite well with the observed structures and compositions.

As an example of the approach, we may consider the explanation of the fact that copper dissolves up to about 40% zinc before another structure becomes more stable. The calculated spacing of energy levels in the lowest band for the face-centered copper structure is indicated schematically in Fig. 7.16. The levels are closely spaced in the band up to a point where there are 0.68 levels per atom, capable of holding 1.36 electrons per atom. The N electrons per N copper atoms thus fill the states to the level of one electron per atom. When zinc is present, the number of electrons per atom increases by one electron per zinc atom replacing a copper atom, and the composition 36% zinc fills all the closely spaced levels. (Number of electrons per atom = $1 \times 0.64 + 2 \times 0.36 = 1.36$.) Higher electron concentrations, however, must fill levels of rapidly increasing energy. (The sharp reduction in number of available levels occurs because many states are excluded by the interference effect discussed in the preceding section.) A structure of this kind is no longer one of low energy, and the stable form becomes the β phase structure, which calculations show to be capable of holding a larger number of electrons with lower total energy. Similar arguments have been successfully developed to explain the range of compositions for which the γ phase is most stable.

Effects of Impurities—Semiconductors

When a band is nearly filled with electrons, the properties of the substance become very sensitive to impurities or slight changes in composition. Tellurium is an example of the former: this element when very pure has a nearly filled band and is a poor conductor, but $\frac{1}{2}\%$ antimony causes the conductivity to increase by a factor 50. The reason, according to the band theory, is that antimony atoms contribute fewer electrons than tellurium; hence when they replace tellurium there are more vacant levels in the nearly filled band which can be utilized for conduction.

Similar effects can be produced by slight changes in composition. Cuprous oxide, with the precise formula composition Cu_2O, has no electrons available for conduction, the structure consisting of cuprous Cu^+ and oxygen O^{2-} ions. Usually, however, there is a slight deficiency of copper, which would for example be represented as $Cu_{1.98}O_{1.00}$. In this case, only 99 of every 100 oxygen ions can be formed by oxidation of Cu to Cu^+, the remaining two coming from further oxidation of two Cu^+ ions to Cu^{2+}.

For a structure filled with oxygen in regular lattice sites, two copper sites are missing per hundred oxygens, and two are occupied by Cu^{2+} ions. The conduction observed is explained by transfer of electrons from Cu^+ ions to adjacent Cu^{2+} ions which have a level of low enough energy to accept electrons readily. Substances in which such processes occur are variously called oxidation, defect, or p type semiconductors.

Electrons can also be provided in excess of numbers for filled states, an example being the case of zinc oxide, which normally has an excess of zinc over the stoichiometric composition ZnO. The excess zinc atoms can fit into spaces between zinc and oxygen ions of the regular structure, and can be oxidized to Zn^{2+} ions if levels of low enough energy are available for the electrons. An otherwise unoccupied energy band of conduction states can serve this purpose, and electrons in this band make conduction possible. Compounds with this state of affairs are called reduction, excess, or n type semiconductors.

These examples suggest the important effects which even minute composition differences can make in electrical properties. A spectacular development in recent years has been utilization of these effects for production of transistors. Not the least important work to make this possible was the development of methods to measure and control impurities within parts per million.

7.8. Ionic Crystals—Coulomb Forces

The simplest ionic crystals are those composed of atomic ions, and are characteristically formed from strongly electropositive and electronegative elements. The alkali halides are notable examples. They can be represented by the ionic formula M^+X^-, where M^+ is the metal cation, and X^- the halogen anion. As discussed in Section 7.5, these ions have spherical symmetry because of the complete valence shells, and the cations are smaller because of electron charge contraction by the net positive charge.

The important factors in determining the structures of alkali halide crystals are simply the Coulomb forces between the ionic electrical charges (which are attractive for ions of unlike sign and repulsive for ions of the same sign of charge), the spherical shape of the electron charge distributions for both kinds of ions, and the relative sizes of the ions. The resulting structures correspond to efficient packing of spheres, in which each ion has ions of opposite sign for nearest neighbors.

The two arrangements which best meet these conditions are the sodium and cesium chloride structures shown in Fig. 7.11. From these drawings, several characteristic features are evident.

1. Each ion has ions of opposite sign closest to it: six Cl^- ions about each Na^+ ion, and vice versa, in NaCl; eight Cl^- ions about each Cs^+ ion, and vice versa, in CsCl.
2. The structures are cubic: if there were no distinction between anions and cations the NaCl structure would be called simple cubic and the CsCl structure body-centered cubic.
3. The ion sizes are nearly the same in CsCl, and much different in NaCl—an important factor in the choice between the two structures.

The separation of ions determining the size of the unit cell is governed by the balancing of the net attractive Coulomb forces by the strong forces of repulsion which result if the closed shell electron charge distributions of adjacent ions overlap appreciably. These forces represent the exclusion principle requirement, which does not permit more electrons of low energy in the space of the closed shells. They change abruptly with distance, varying for different ions and atoms as some power varying from the inverse fifth to the inverse twelfth power of their distance of separation. This sudden onset of repulsive forces as two ions approach one another is not greatly different from having rigid spheres in contact, and the binding energy of the ions in the crystal is primarily the electrostatic effect of the Coulomb forces at the equilibrium distances. Calculations of this energy are in excellent agreement with experimentally determinable quantities, when small corrections are made for effects of repulsive forces and for other forces of attraction arising from mutual distortions of the electron charge distributions of the ions. (The thermochemical calculations necessary for comparison with experiment are described in Chapter 13, p. 371; the distortion forces in the next subsection, p. 171.)

The important role of relative ion sizes in determining structures of ionic crystals comes about to a large extent because Coulomb forces between spherical ions depend only on distance between the ions, regardless of direction. The preferred structures are thus ones with efficient packing and the *radius ratio* of ions is significant in understanding structures of many simple inorganic crystals. This is true, for example, in crystals with the formula MX_2, such as CaF_2, TiO_2, and SiO_2; the structures in these cases are ones which permit close packing without overlap of the larger ions. Many inorganic crystals contain oxygen ions which are enough larger than the positive ions that their size is a primary consideration.

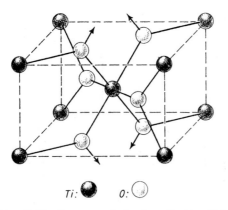

Ti: ●   O: ◉

Fig. 7.17. *Structure of titanium dioxide. Note that each titanium has six oxygen neighbors; each oxygen, three titanium neighbors.*

In crystals containing complex ions and polyvalent ions of both signs, electrostatic forces are just as important, but there are many different structures because the best balance of forces depends specifically on the charges and shapes of the ions. Discussion of the considerations which are important would go further into the subject of structural inorganic chemistry than is appropriate here, but one concept which is useful should be mentioned. This is Pauling's rule: in the stable structure, each ion is immediately

surrounded by just the number of ions of opposite signs for the sum
of valences of these ions shared with it to be just equal to its own valence.
This rule is easily seen to be satisfied by alkali halides: each Na^+
is surrounded by six Cl^- ions, but each Cl^- ion shares its valence equally
with the one Na^+ ion considered and five others, thus giving six valences of one-sixth from the neighbors of any Na^+ ion.

In the rutile structure of TiO_2, shown in Fig. 7.17, each Ti^{4+} ion has
six tetrahedral O^{2-} ion neighbors, and each O^{2-} ion has three Ti^{4+}
neighbors in a cubic arrangement. Thus each titanium shares its valence
of four as two-thirds per oxygen neighbor, which is equal to the two-
thirds share for each oxygen sharing its own valence of two with three
silicon ions.

The principles effective in the binding of ionic crystals which we have
discussed can be summarized as follows.

1. The dominant forces are the nondirectional electrostatic ones between charged ions.
2. Repulsive forces set limits on closest distance of approach and are
important in determining which packing permits ions to be close without
overlapping.
3. The numbers of closest neighbors of opposite sign (coordination
numbers) are such that each type
of ion "sees" a total charge equal
to its own valence.

7.9. Molecular Crystals

The solid types so far considered
have been ones in which atoms or
atomic ions are the unit of structure. Many of the most familiar
solid substances, however, are ones
in which the strong bonds of stable
molecules make these molecules the
structural units. The much weaker
attractive forces between molecules

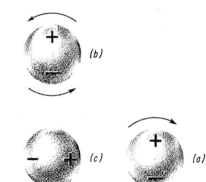

Fig. 7.18. *Directional nature of dipole forces. Molecule* a *is rotated clockwise by the forces of* c; *molecule* b *is rotated counterclockwise by* c.

in such cases are often called *van der Waals forces*, and arise from several
forms of interaction between the charges of neighboring molecules.

Dipole Forces

If the molecules composing a solid are electrically asymmetrical with a resultant dipole moment, the forces between positive and negative charges of neighboring molecules are not equal and depend on the relative orientations of the molecules, as illustrated in Fig. 7.18.

Induced Dipole Forces

Sufficiently symmetrical molecules have no permanent dipole moment, but all molecules are polarized in electric fields created by other charges —that is, the electron charges are displaced with respect to the nuclei. This polarization can result from electric fields set up by charges on metal plates of a condenser or electrolytic cell, or from fields of other molecules with permanent dipole moments, or from ionic fields.

London Dispersion Forces

Although the interactions of permanent dipoles with each other and with nonpolar molecules are important factors in understanding structures of molecular crystals, the classical electrical theory of these forces offered no explanation of the forces between atoms and molecules lacking in dipole moment. Thus, Coulomb's law applied to symmetrical atoms and neutral molecules would predict no force at all, whereas at sufficiently low temperatures all substances ultimately condense, and all except helium will become solid at atmospheric pressure.

Although such substances as argon, oxygen, and the many organic compounds lacking dipole moments melt at low temperatures, the existence of the solid form at all shows that there are real, although comparatively weak, attractive forces.

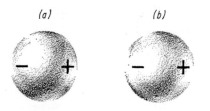

(a)   *(b)*

Fig. 7.19. *London forces. Atom* b *is polarized, as shown, when atom* a *is polarized.*

The origin of these forces, and the binding in solid structures of such molecules, remained a mystery until F. London in 1930 showed how they were to be explained as the average effect of instantaneous displacements of charge in the atoms or molecules.

The nature of the London forces can be appreciated if it is remembered that the charge distributions of such molecules as H_2, CH_4, and C_6H_6, are described as symmetrical without a dipole moment only as a statistical average (see the discussion of wave functions in Section 5.13). For this model, at any instant, the electron configuration may be quite unsymmetrical and act as a momentary dipole, but this dipole is continually shifting in amount and direction and produces no net affect over any ordinary period of time. However, the field at any instant polarizes any molecules nearby to cause an attraction, much as in Fig. 7.19.

The energy of the London attractive forces is not large compared to energies of metallic and ionic binding, and falls off rapidly with increasing distance (inversely as the sixth power of distance). The London forces are important, however, because they occur for *all* atoms, molecules, and ions, and because in many crystals they are the *only* attractive forces.

Repulsive Forces

As in other crystals, the minimum distances in molecular crystals must be large enough to avoid appreciable overlap of the electronic charges. The shapes of the constituent molecules thus play an important role in determining the molecular arrangements.

7.10. X-ray Structures of Some Molecular Crystals

Because molecules in crystals preserve to a large extent the shape and dimensions they have when isolated, studies of the atomic arrangements and relative positions in the solid form can give much valuable information about the nature, properties, and structure of molecules. Perhaps the most important single experimental method is the use of X-ray diffraction for structure determination, although, like any tool, it has definite limitations. The techniques and difficulties are described in detail in several books, and we shall present here only a few examples of structures established by X-ray methods.

Hexamethyl Benzene

This was the first benzene derivative to have its structure determined. It is found to have a layer structure with the molecules lying nearly in

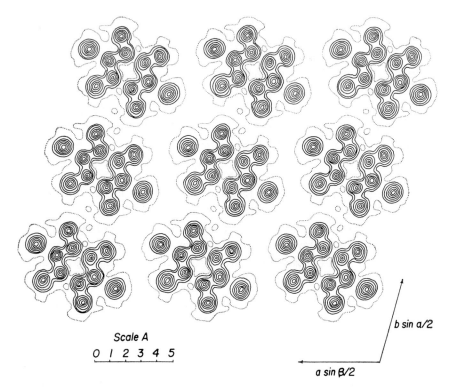

Scale A

0 1 2 3 4 5

b sin a/2

a sin β/2

Fig. 7.20. *Electron densities of hexamethylbenzene.*

parallel planes. The projection of the electron charge density on a plane perpendicular to one of the triclinic axes, shown in Fig. 7.20, brings out the hexagonal benzene ring and the methyl groups very clearly, as well as the fitting together of molecules governed by the size of the methyl groups.

Structures Involving Hydrogen Bonding

Hydrogen bonds frequently play an important part in determining structures of compounds which contain fluorine, oxygen, or nitrogen to which hydrogens are attached. An example of this is the structure formed by

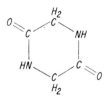

molecules of diketopiperazine in which NH—O bonds lead to infinite chains, as shown in Fig. 7.21.

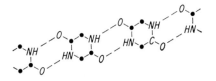

Fig. 7.21. *Linear chains of diketopipera-zine molecules held together by NH—O bonds.*

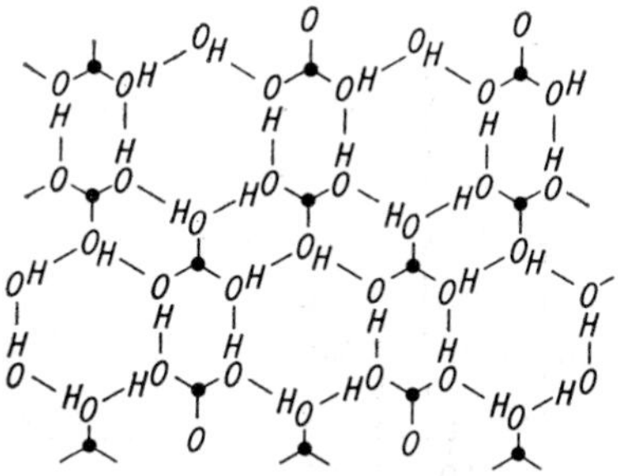

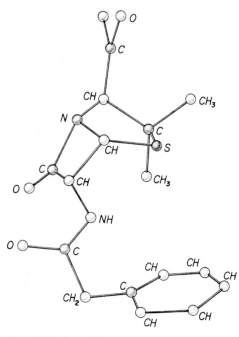

Fig. 7.22. *Layer structure of boric acid; boron atoms are indicated by solid circles.*

The structures of many hydroxy-acids are also very probably largely determined by hydrogen bonds. A complete analysis has been made of the layer structure of boric acid, H_3BO_3, the beautiful pattern of a layer being shown in Fig. 7.22.

Many other examples could be cited. Among organic molecules, it is probable that hydrogen bonds play an important part in determining properties of proteins, sugars, and hemoglobin, and many others.

Penicillin

One of the classic feats in X-ray structure analysis was determination of the structure of penicillin by Hodgkin and her coworkers during World War II. The complexity of the molecule makes successful anal-ysis of the observed diffraction

Fig. 7.23. *Penicillin structure.*

pattern a prodigious accomplishment, but the structure shown in Fig. 7.23 was completely confirmed by independent determination, using meth-ods of organic chemistry.

Problems

7.1. Show in a diagram of a cubic crystal all the appropriate symmetry elements described in the text. If necessary, use several drawings for clarity.

7.2. Compare the number of lattice points (atoms) per unit area in the 111, 110, and 100 planes of a simple cubic crystal. How do you think this factor might affect the intensity of X-radiation reflected from the various planes?

7.3. What are the intercepts, in terms of unit axial length, of the planes 221, 220, 110, 121? Sketch these planes in a diagram (or diagrams) representing a cubic crystal.

7.4. What is the interplanar distance in a NaCl crystal which shows a first-order $(n = 1)$ Bragg reflection at 5.9° with X-radiation of 0.581 Å?

7.5. According to the Bragg equation, for any given wavelength λ of X-radiation there is a lower limit to the interplanar spacing d which can give an observable diffraction spectra. What is this limit?

7.6. The standard method of measuring wavelength of X-radiation is by reflection from calcite ($CaCO_3$) crystals in which the utilized interplanar distance is 3.029 Å. What is the value of λ for characteristic X-radiation (K_α) from copper, for which the minimum angle at which reflection takes place is 14.70°.

7.7. X-radiation of 1.537 Å wavelength was used to obtain the powder diffraction pattern of a certain material. The radius of the cyclindrical camera was 5.20 cm; the distance on the film from a given reflected line to the undeviated portion of the beam was 2.65 cm. To what interplanar distance does this line correspond?

7.8. (a) What are the interplanar distances d_{100}, d_{200}, d_{220}, and d_{111} in the face-centered cubic crystal of NaCl if the edge of the unit cell is 5.64 Å? (b) What are the interplanar distances d_{100}, d_{200}, d_{110}, d_{222} in the body-centered cubic tungsten crystal if the unit cell edge is 3.16 Å? (c) Use the data of (b) to determine the density of tungsten, assuming the given value for the atomic weight.

7.9. How many atoms per unit cell are there in a NaCl crystal? How many per unit cell in the body-centered cubic CsCl structure (central ion "A" surrounded by 8 "B" ions)?

7.10. Aluminum crystallizes in a face-centered cubic structure with the edge of the unit cell equal to 4.04 Å. Its density is 2.70 g/cm³. Calculate Avogadro's number (N).

7.11. The potential energy (E_{12}) of a system of two ions can be described essentially as the sum of two terms—the first involving Coulombic forces and the second an empirical term accounting for repulsion as the charges overlap. The first term is

$$E_{12} = -\frac{Z_1 Z_2 e^2}{r}$$

(a) Show how this term is obtained, starting from Coulomb's law. (b) What is the Coulombic force between two univalent ions 2.82 Å apart? (c) What is the Coulombic potential energy corresponding to the system in (b)?

7.12. In a face-centered cubic crystal of identical atoms how many "nearest neighbors" does any given atom have? ("Nearest neighbors" are atoms with the same interatomic distance from the given atom, this distance being the smallest interatomic distance in the crystal.) What is the distance to these nearest neighbors in terms of a, the unit cell length? How many "next nearest neighbors" does the given atom have and at what distance are they?

7.13. (a) List five solids in which you might expect dipole-dipole energy to be an important part of the total potential energy. Give your reasons for choosing these solids. (b) List five examples each of molecular crystals, ionic crystals, metallic crystals, and valence bond crystals (e.g., diamond), along with their melting points and any other physical properties which you think reflect the different types of bonding in these crystals.

7.14. In the cuprous oxide crystal, the oxygen atoms are arranged on a body-centered cubic lattice. If one of these cubes is divided into 8 smaller cubes, it is seen that the copper atoms are arranged on a lattice which penetrates the oxygen lattice, with copper atoms at the centers of alternate small cubes. Show that with this arrangement the number of atoms of each component in a unit cell corresponds to the formula Cu_2O.

7.15. What are the symmetry elements associated with a tetrahedron? (Hint: Inscribe the tetrahedron in a cube.)

7.16. In a face-centered cube connect all of the face-centered points by lines between adjacent faces. What is the figure so constructed? How many groups of equivalent planes (planes having the same Miller index) are there in the figure?

7.17. A crystal has an n-fold symmetry axis with a group of faces parallel to this axis. What is the interfacial angle, in terms of n, associated with these faces? If $n = 6$, as in some quartz crystals, what is the angle?

7.18. Draw a crystal model of 8 ions ("A") as the corners of a cube surrounding a central ion ("C") and show that if each of the outside ions is in contact with its neighbors (including "C"), the radii of the ions must be in the ratio $R_C/R_A = 0.73$.

7.19. Draw a face-centered ionic crystal model and show that if each of the vertex ions ("A") is in contact with its neighbors, including the face-centered ion ("C"), the ratio of ionic radii must be $R_C/R_A = 0.41$.

7.20. Compare the cation-anion radius ratios obtained in Problems 7.18 and 7.19 with the ratios obtained empirically from alkali halide crystal measurements for CsCl and NaCl, respectively. (See discussion in Moore, *Physical Chemistry*, 1962, Prentice-Hall, New York.)

7.21. Show that the spacing between successive planes (Miller indices $h\,k\,l$) in a cubic lattice is $a/\sqrt{h^2 + k^2 + l^2}$, where a is the unit cell length. (Hint: $\cos^2 \alpha + \cos^2 \beta + \cos^2 \gamma = 1$, where $\cos \alpha$, $\cos \beta$, $\cos \gamma$ are the direction cosines of respective axes x, y, and z.)

7.22. Use a suitable diagram to show that the contribution E', to the Coulomb energy of a Na^+ ion in a NaCl crystal due to ions in the first 2 spheres of successive nearest neighbors is given by

$$E' = -\frac{e^2}{r}\left(6 - \frac{12}{\sqrt{2}} + \frac{8}{\sqrt{3}}\right)$$

where e = charge and r = distance between Na ion and its nearest neighbors.

7.23. The lattice energy for one mole of NaCl crystal is given by

$$U = -\frac{NAe^2}{r} + \frac{Be^2}{r^n}$$

where $A = 1.74756$ (Madelung constant—the value of the sum of the series of terms started in Problem 7.22), B = molar repulsion coefficient for NaCl (due to electron cloud overlap), and $n = 8$ for NaCl. (a) At the equilibrium ion separation, r_0, the energy is a minimum; show that this energy ($-U_0$) is equal to

$$\frac{NAe^2}{r_0}\left(1 - \frac{1}{n}\right)$$

(b) Calculate the crystal energy ($-U_0$) for NaCl and compare with the value obtained from thermochemical quantities, 181 kcal/mole. (See the Born-Haber cycle in Chapter 13.)

7.24. Use an appropriate diagram to show that induced dipole forces—either ion-induced dipole or dipole-induced dipole—are always attractive.

7.25. If the repulsion term in the crystal lattice energy of NaCl varies inversely as r^8, where r is the smallest interionic distance, and if the coefficient b is independent of the type of ion, what is the contribution to this repulsion term for a given ion due to second nearest neighbors as compared to that due to nearest neighbors?

Suggested Readings

An introduction to properties of solids from the physicists' point of view is *Elementary Solid State Physics. A Short Course* by C. Kittel (Wiley, New York, 1962). Relations of solid structure and properties to molecular constitution are discussed in the books by Pauling and Ketelaar, cited at the end of Chapter 6.

A compendium with a wealth of information is *Structural Inorganic Chemistry* (3rd ed.) by A. F. Wells (Oxford, 1962). For somewhat lighter reading, *Crystals and X-Rays* by K. Lonsdale (Bell, London, 1948) can be recommended.

Chapter 8

Equations of
State of Gases

THE STUDY of the properties of gases is important in chemistry for a number of reasons. A gas at low pressure and concentration is in many ways the simplest form of aggregation of atoms and molecules, and hence may be expected to have relatively simple properties, characteristic of the molecules composing it. These properties are of two types: the colligative properties depending only on the number, concentration, and energy of the molecules, and the chemical properties dependent on the particular kinds of molecules (chemical species) present. Chemical reactions in the gaseous state are of increasing importance in their own right; it is equally important that much useful information about properties of solutions and reactions in solution can be gained indirectly by study of their vapors.

In this first chapter on gases we consider the properties of gases described by the *equation of state*, which is the relation between pressure, volume, and temperature.

8.1. Some Basic Properties

The characteristic property of gases distinguishing them from liquids and solids is that a gas will, if given the opportunity, expand to fill any volume available to it. This can only be prevented by completely con-

178

fining the gas in a closed container and the force of the gas on the walls of the container depends markedly on the temperature. This is in contrast to liquids and solids, which determine for themselves definite volumes only slightly affected by external pressure and temperature.

As we have already seen, solids lose atoms or molecules by sublimation to form gases at any temperature if the pressure is sufficiently low, although the quantities of gas formed may be too small for detection. This is also true of liquids, as in the evaporation of water in an open dish. It is also a matter of general experience that formation of a gas from either condensed state of matter takes place more readily at higher temperature; at sufficiently high temperatures all matter assumes a state properly described as gaseous.

The study of the pressure necessary to confine a gas to a particular volume, the relation of this pressure to the quantity of gas and its chemical constitution, and the effect of temperature on the equilibrium conditions have all been important subjects for many years. Before examining the experimental evidence involving these relations, a brief review of the definition and meaning of the physical quantities measured is in order.

Volume

The significance of the term volume is unambiguous, nor does the problem of volume measurement involve any great subtlety or unfamiliarity in principle.

UNITS OF VOLUME   We shall use two units of volume measure: the cubic centimeter, abbreviated cm³ or cc; and the liter, abbreviated l; 1 l = 1000 cm³. (This equality is not exact, but it is good within the significance of most physical measurements. By definition, the equality 1 liter = 1000 milliliters is exact, and milliliters (ml) are often used rather than cc.)

Pressure

We have already referred to pressure in describing the effect of changing conditions on the state of substances. It is important to keep in mind the precise significance of this quantity as defined for scientific purposes. Pressure is measured as the ratio of the force applied normally (perpendicularly) against a surface to the area of that surface. When we refer to the pressure on a substance, or exerted by it, we are describing the result deduced directly or indirectly from such a measurement of the force applied to a definite area. The reason for the use of pressure rather than force as the fundamental quantity is simply that the necessary force for equilibrium of a bounding surface varies in proportion to the area of surface. The ratio of force to area, the pressure, is independent of the area, and remains the same unless the state of the substance also changes.

UNITS OF PRESSURE   The units in which pressure can be expressed are many and varied. This profusion has resulted from a variety of circumstances: the convenience of a unit of such size that the pressures it will specify are neither too small a fraction nor too large a number of such units, the nature of the indication of pressure given by the measuring device, the system of physical units preferred, and occasionally little more than the prejudice of the observer or group interested in the particular experiments.

The atmosphere, being everywhere on the earth's surface, exerts a pressure which is natural to assume as a unit for pressure measurement. But as this pressure is unfortunately variable, some "standard" atmosphere must be defined. The pressure necessary to support a column of mercury 760 mm in height at temperature of 0°C is therefore defined as the pressure of the normal atmosphere.

The height of a mercury column supported by the gas under measurement is frequently used, corresponding to a pressure difference at the upper and lower mercury surfaces expressed as X mm Hg (or other unit of length, as cm, or inches).

For very small pressures, a smaller unit is desirable; one often used is the micron, defined as 10^{-6} meters of mercury. Units of pressure more directly related to the force-area ratio are dynes/cm², lb/in.², or kg/cm².

Temperature

The third physical variable of fundamental importance is of course the temperature. Temperature is most directly defined and measured in terms of the change in properties of some substance, and in the past a number of scales have been established, using some arbitrary substance and property conveniently at hand without much scientific regard for its fundamental significance.

FIXED POINTS ON A TEMPERATURE SCALE   The accepted basis
for thermometry has for many years been to assign arbitrary values of
temperature to two fixed points at which some convenient substance has
definite properties. Changes in a suitable property (such as the volume
of a liquid) are then used as a means for subdividing the scale between
the defining fixed points and extending it beyond them. The two points
now used by agreement are the "ice point," the temperature of a mixture
of pure ice and water saturated with air in equilibrium under a pressure
of one atmosphere, and the "steam point," the temperature of pure
water boiling under a pressure of one atmosphere. In the Centigrade
or Celsius scale used in scientific work the values 0°C and 100°C are
assigned to these points; in the Fahrenheit scale, common in English-
speaking countries, the values 32°F and 212°F are assigned.

IDEAL GAS SCALE   The best choice of a suitable working property
and a suitable substance with which to measure other temperatures is
not obvious, as no two substances have precisely the same fractional
change in any property corresponding to a given change in temperature.
This is true, whether it be length, density, volume, electrical resistance,
or any other measurable property that is chosen. Fortunately, experimental study and underlying theory both show that at sufficiently low
densities the properties of all gases approach a common behavior, described by the *ideal gas law*, or equation of state. For a given temperature
increase the increase in pressure of a fixed volume of gas is in the same
proportion for any given gas if its density is sufficiently small. This
property is readily used to define and determine temperatures other than
those of the fixed reference points (as will be discussed in Section 8.3)
and many years of research have established an accurate scale based on
this definition. Once established, more conveniently used thermometers
can be calibrated against this ideal gas scale, and a common basis for
reporting temperatures is hence made possible.

THERMODYNAMIC SCALE OF TEMPERATURE   The ideal gas scale
of temperatures has limitations other than its inconvenience for routine
measurements; these limitations are especially apparent at low temperatures. Any gas ultimately liquefies at any practical pressure if the
temperature is sufficiently low, and gases can therefore no longer serve
as ideal thermometric substances over a range of temperatures approaching absolute zero.

Fortunately, a mass of empirical experience generalized by the second law of thermodynamics provides a means for defining temperatures in a consistent and useful way in any temperature region. This law, discussed in Chapter 14, is the ultimate basis for establishing the best temperature scale of all—the thermodynamic scale. Since the ideal gas scale agrees with the thermodynamic scale in regions where the former is practical, the ideal gas scale is a suitable standard of reference. In the next section a scale more logical than the centigrade scale will be shown to result by taking the zero of temperature at $-273.16°C$. On this *absolute scale*, all temperatures are $273.16°$ greater than on the centigrade scale if (for convenience) the size of the degree is taken equal to the centigrade degree. The greater logic of the scale comes from the fact that no lower temperatures than an *absolute zero* can be reached. To the present accuracy with which its value can be determined, this lower limit of temperature is $-273.16° \pm 0.01°$.

ABSOLUTE SCALE OF TEMPERATURE   We shall frequently employ absolute temperatures because many laws of nature and results of experiment are most simply expressed with this scale. Examples of this have already appeared in previous discussions, as in that on black-body radiation. Such temperatures are written as degrees Kelvin, the name being in honor of Lord Kelvin, who suggested the thermodynamic or Kelvin scale, and are indicated by the symbol $°K$. The normal boiling point of water is $373.16°K$ $(100°C)$, the freezing point of mercury is $234.27°K$ $(-38.89°C)$, and absolute zero is $0°K$.

Quantity and Concentration

One final consideration is essential for any exact discussion of properties of gases, or of matter in any form: the quantity of the substance present must be somehow specified. This may seem so obvious as to be trite, and there is certainly nothing very sophisticated about the statement, but it is important. It is probably true that some of the commonest errors students make in thinking about gases and solving problems concerning them are failure to specify the amount properly, or failure to recognize that changing quantities are involved.

The quantity of a gas may be expressed in terms of either the mass of the gas or the number of molecules. This may be in grams or milligrams, or in the number of gram atomic or gram molecular weights. The latter units have the advantage that the numbers of molecules concerned are proportional to them. Gram molecular weights are often for brevity called moles. By comparing numbers of moles of different gases one is then talking about relative numbers of molecules, and most properties of gases are more simply expressed when referred to the equal numbers of molecules rather than to equal masses but different numbers of molecules.

Although the total amount of a gas, however expressed, is important, the significant feature in determining many properties is its *concentration*, the amount of gas in a unit of volume. The best unit of concentration for gases is usually moles/liter, although g/liter and g/cm^3 are, among others, perfectly proper and often used. The latter units specify the value of a quantity more strictly defined as *density*.

8.2. Boyle's Law and the Effect of Quantity

The study of the dependence of pressure of a gas on its volume or concentration and on its chemical constitution is a very old subject. The familiar result which we call Boyle's Law has often been discussed as one of the earliest examples of a quantitative investigation of relations between observable properties.

Boyle's Law

The significant contribution of Boyle's study of gases was not the qualitative observation that decrease in volume of a sample of gas required application of larger pressure, but the fact that to a moderately good approximation the inverse relation could be quantitatively expressed by a simple equation:

$$PV = K \qquad (8.1)$$

Here K is a number depending only on the quantity of gas in the sample, and on the particular temperature at which corresponding values of P and V were determined.

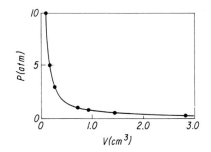

Fig. 8.1. *P-V diagram for 1 g of O_2 at 0°C.*

The familiar plot of P against V, as in Fig. 8.1 for one gram of oxygen at 0°C, is not a very good way to verify whether Eq. 8.1 accurately represents the data listed in Table 8.1.

TABLE 8.1. *Pressures and Volumes of 1 g of O_2 at 0°C.*

P (atm)	V (cm³)	PV
0.2500	2.8012	0.7003
0.5000	1.4003	0.7002
0.7500	0.9333	0.6999
1.0000	0.6998	0.6998
3.000	0.2328	0.6984
5.000	0.1394	0.6971
10.000	0.06937	0.6937

The plot does suggest that a hyperbola, as required by Eq. 8.1, could be made to fit by a good choice of K, but actual test by trial-and-error fitting would be a tedious process. A better way of plotting the data for testing Boyle's Law is suggested by the simple rearrangement of Eq. 8.1 to read

$$P = K\frac{1}{V} \qquad (8.2)$$

This is the equation of a straight line if we think of $1/V$ rather than V as the variable. The graph of P against $1/V$ in Fig. 8.2 shows that the points do fall within the accuracy of plotting them on a straight line through the origin, as stated by Eq. 8.2.

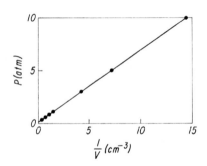

Fig. 8.2. *P versus* $1/V$ *for* 1 *g of* O_2 *at 0°C.*

ACCURACY OF BOYLE'S LAW
The advantage of the second way of plotting over the first is obvious —a straight line is the easiest of all curves to recognize and draw—but even this better representation of the precise data in Table 8.1 does not fully exploit their possibilities in testing Boyle's Law. A numerical way of doing better may well have occurred to the reader: of simply calculating the products PV and observing if they are constant within the precision of the measurements. Such values are listed in the third column of Table 8.1. They evidently change little for the different pairs of P and V values, but they definitely do change.

The nature of the change is readily evident if we return to a graphical representation, this time of the product PV plotted against $1/V$ as in Fig. 8.3. This plot shows that within the precision of the data the product

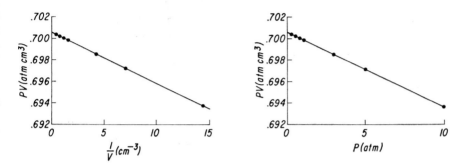

Fig. 8.3. *Plots of PV for 1 g af O_2 against $1/V$ (left) and against P (right).*

PV changes linearly with $1/V$. An equally suitable plot, and a more convenient one for many purposes, is of PV against P rather than $1/V$, and this plot is also shown in Fig. 8.3, at the right.

The straight line plots in Fig. 8.3 are pleasingly simple, but by no means should it be concluded that this behavior will hold good for all pressures or concentrations (of which $1/V$ is easily seen to be a measure for a particular sample). Studies extending to much higher pressures show definite curvatures which are, moreover, different for different gases, as shown in the data for O_2 and H_2 up to 1000 atmospheres, plotted in Fig. 8.4.

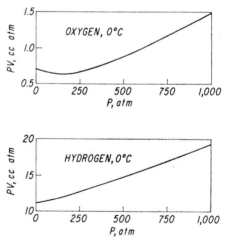

Fig. 8.4. *Variation of PV product for 1 g of O_2 and 1 g of H_2 at pressures to 1000 atmospheres.*

THE EFFECT OF QUANTITY   In examining the accuracy of Boyle's Law we have so far confined our attention to data for specific quantities of gas, namely one gram, and have not considered the effect of changes in the mass of gas used. The effect is very simple: increasing the mass of gas at constant temperature results in an exactly proportional increase in volume occupied at a given pressure. The pressure, which is a specific quantity measured as the force per unit area, thus depends only on the *concentration* of the gas—that is, the quantity of gas per unit volume. This statement is true whether or not Boyle's Law is accurate enough for our purposes: for example, two grams of nitrogen at 100,000 atmospheres occupies exactly twice the volume of one gram. The only stipulation we need make is that the temperature be the same—a most important restriction.

If Boyle's Law is sufficiently accurate, as it often is, its usefulness is extended by representing the dependence of PV on the mass, m, of gas explicitly, by writing $K = am$, where a is a constant independent of the mass. That this represents the effect of mass correctly is easily seen from the revised equation

$$PV = am \qquad (8.3)$$

since increasing m must increase V proportionately if P is to remain constant. The alternative form of this equation,

$$P = a\frac{m}{V} \qquad (8.4)$$

represents concisely our previous statement that the pressure varies directly as the density, m/V.

While the revision of Boyle's Law makes the new constant a independent of the mass of gas, as well as P and V, this constant does depend on the kind of gas. For example, the values of a for oxygen at 0°C and at low pressures is 0.700, but for hydrogen the value is 11.14. The difference has little to do with the much smaller inaccuracy of Boyle's Law, but instead results, as Avogadro realized, primarily from the fact that one gram of hydrogen contains a different number of molecules than one gram of oxygen.

To compare equal numbers of molecules of different gases, we introduce the number of moles (n), obtained by dividing the mass (m) by the molecular weight (M), or $n = m/M$. Since the Boyle constant K must be proportional to m for any particular gas, Boyle's Law in terms of n must be of the form

$$PV = A\frac{m}{M} = An \qquad \text{or} \qquad P = A\frac{n}{V} \qquad (8.5)$$

where A is independent of the quantity of gas. If now we calculate values of $A = PV/n$ at a given temperature for different gases, using measured values of P and V and the molecular weight, these values are nearly equal, irrespective of the gas. The agreement improves for lower pressures, as shown in Fig. 8.5, and in the limit of zero pressure the best smooth curves through the data meet at a common point. Thus at a constant temperature the quantity A is independent of the species of gas, and moles rather than grams express the quantity of gas. At 0°C A has the value 22.414 1-atm/mole for all gases.

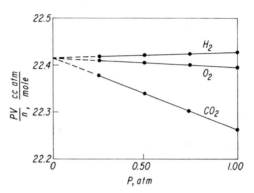

Fig. 8.5. *Values of PV/n for H_2, O_2, and CO_2 at pressures below 1 atmosphere.*

The calculations described can be inverted to determine an unknown molecular weight: if the value of PV for a sample of known mass, m grams, is determined at 0°C, then from Eq. 8.5, $M = Am/PV = 22.414$ m/PV. The value $A = 22.414$ will be the more nearly correct, and hence also the calculated value of M, the lower the pressure (or density) of the gas. Notice that in terms of density $d = m/V$, $M = 22.414\ d/P$. The accurate use of this means of finding M is called the method of limiting densities.

As an example, the data of Table 8.1 for oxygen at 0°C may be used to calculate densities d and ratios d/P, with the following results for pressures of 1 atm or less:

P	0.2500	0.5000	0.7500	1.0000
d	0.35700	0.7141	1.0715	1.4290
d/P	1.4280	1.4283	1.4286	1.4290

Examination of the data, or a simple graph, shows that the limiting value of d/P at zero pressure is $d/P = 1.4277 \pm 0.0001$. The weight of one mole of oxygen from the data is therefore

$$M = 1.4277 \left(\frac{g}{\text{liter atm}}\right) \times 22.414 \left(\frac{\text{liter atm}}{\text{mole}}\right)$$

$$= 32.000 \text{ g/mole} \pm 0.002$$

We have said nothing about the effect of temperature on the PV relation in gases, having confined our discussion to comparisons of different pressure, volumes, and quantities of gas, all measured at the same temperature. The influence of temperature is of fundamental importance at any pressure, and has a significant effect on the *way* in which gases deviate from Boyle's Law at high pressures. Hence the following section discusses the influence of temperature, before we examine the nature of further deviations from Boyle's Law in Section 8.6.

8.3. Temperature Scale and Thermometry

With knowledge of the implications associated with Boyle's Law, it is now possible to complete the discussion of the temperature scale and thermometry begun in Section 8.1. The limiting constant values A of Eq. 8.5 at low pressure for different temperatures fall nearly on a straight line when plotted against the temperature recorded by a liquid in glass thermometer. The way in which such a plot deviates from linearity is actually, as will be shown later, owing to the properties of the particular liquid thermometer rather than to the gas. The straight line behavior is described by the equation

$$A = b + ct \qquad (8.6)$$

where b and c are constants and t is the centigrade temperature.

The value of A determined at the temperature of melting ice ($0°C$ is defined by this point) is 22.4140 liter-atmospheres mole^{-1}, and the value of A at the temperature of boiling water under normal atmospheric pressure (by definition $100°C$) is 30.6194 l atm mole^{-1}. Thus, from Eq. 8.6, at $0°C$

$$A = 22.4140 = b$$

and at $100°C$, $A = 30.6194 = b + 100c$. Hence $b = 22.4140$ and $c = 0.08205$. Using these numbers in Eq. 8.6 gives

$$A = 22.4140 + 0.082054t = 0.082054(273.16 + t) \qquad (8.7)$$

It will be noted that this determination of A as a function of t is independent of any thermometer which might be used, and depends only on the values and definition of the two fixed points adopted.

Equation 8.7 can be simplified by setting $273.16 + t$ equal to some other temperature T, which has its zero 273.16 centigrade degrees below zero degrees centigrade. (This is recognized immediately as absolute temperature, defined previously.) Making the substitution in Eq. 8.7, we have

$$A = 0.082054 T$$

and from Eq. 8.5,

$$PV = n(0.082054) T$$

where P is in atmospheres, V is in liters, and T is in degrees absolute on the Kelvin scale (°K). The numerical constant is independent of pressure, volume, or temperature changes, although its value will depend upon the units used. This question of units is discussed in Section 8.4.

By agreeing to make the absolute temperature proportional to the limiting value of PV/n for low pressures, a simple thermometer scale is

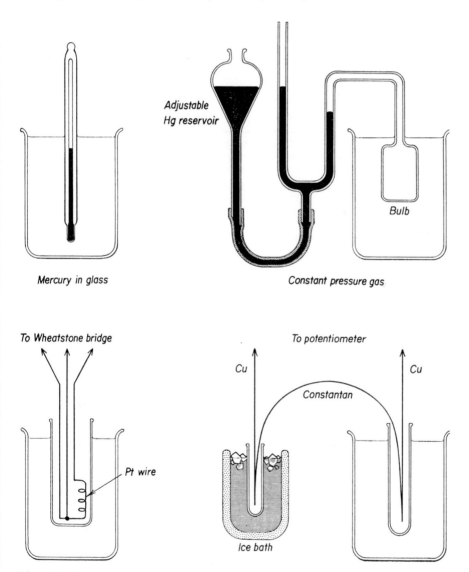

Fig. 8.6. *Ways of using various types of thermometers.*

obtained which is the same for all gases. This is the basis for the ideal gas temperature scale. To test the linearity of any thermometer, we need only to determine by it some temperature intermediate between the two fixed points defining the temperature scale and some temperature not intermediate to the two fixed points. Listed in Table 8.2 are several types of thermometers; the ways they could be used are indicated in Fig. 8.6. The apparent temperatures registered by them at temperatures of 50°C (t_1) and 200°C (t_2) on the ideal gas temperature scale are listed in Table 8.2.

The apparent temperatures are determined relative to the ice point,

TABLE 8.2.   *Apparent Temperatures as Registered by Various Types of Thermometers**

Type of Thermometer	t_1 (°C)	t_2 (°C)
Linear expansion of a copper bar	49.21	206.9
Linear expansion of a silver bar	49.50	203.96
Mercury in Jena 16^{III} glass	50.11	200.29
Platinum resistance	50.36	197.03
Platinum-rhodium thermocouple	46.9	223.4
Copper-constantan thermocouple	48.4	215.6
Constant-volume hydrogen gas	50.003	199.976
Constant-volume helium gas	50.001	199.994
Constant-volume neon gas	50.001	199.997
Constant-volume nitrogen gas	50.010	199.978
Constant-volume air gas	50.013	199.976
Constant-volume argon gas	50.014	199.971
Constant-volume oxygen gas	50.016	199.929
Constant-pressure hydrogen gas	50.004	199.976
Constant-pressure helium gas	50.000	199.999
Constant-pressure neon gas	50.002	199.990
Constant-pressure nitrogen gas	50.032	199.877
Constant-pressure air gas	50.033	199.874
Constant-pressure argon gas	50.034	199.863
Constant-pressure oxygen gas	50.035	199.839

* According to Equation (1-1) in M. A. Paul, *Principles of Chemical Thermodynamics.* (McGraw-Hill, New York, 1951).

t_0, according to the formula $t - t_0 = (100/\Delta)(r - r_0)$, where r and r_0 are the readings of the particular instrument used as a thermometer at temperatures t and t_0, and Δ is the difference between the instrument readings at the ice point and the steam point. It can be seen from the data in the table that the gas thermometers more consistently represent temperatures intermediate to, or beyond, the two fixed reference points than do other types of thermometer. This is one of the reasons for its use as a standard temperature scale against which other forms of thermometers, more convenient for day-to-day use or particular experimental arrangements, may be calibrated.

8.4. The Ideal Gas Law

The results of the two preceding sections make it possible to write a single equation which expresses concisely the ideal limiting behavior of gases at low densities. This equation may be written in various equivalent forms; of these many possible ones, the ones most often used are the following:

$$PV = nRT, \quad \text{where } n \text{ is the number of moles}$$

$$PV = \frac{m}{M} RT, \text{ where } m = \text{mass of the gas and}$$
$$M = \text{molecular weight} \qquad (8.8)$$

$$P = RTC, \quad \text{where } C = \text{concentration, such as}$$
$$\text{moles per liter}$$

Which form of the equation is most useful depends on the problem at hand, as does the choice of units in which the various quantities are expressed. The numerical value of R will of course depend on these units. Before listing the value for R in the most often useful units, the dimensions of R in terms of mechanical quantities are worth noting.

Since pressure by definition is a force per unit area, the product PV has the dimensions of force times length, characteristic of work and energy in mechanics, because volume varies as length cubed and area as length squared. Thus R must dimensionally be of the form energy per mole divided by absolute temperature. This is no mere coincidence, as the kinetic theory explanation of the gas law in the next chapter shows, and the most useful expression of R is in terms of energy, either as calories or joules per mole per degree.

The values of R for systems of units most often used are

$$
\begin{array}{ll}
0.082054 & \text{liter atm mole}^{-1}\ \text{deg}^{-1} \\
8.3144 & 10^{7}\ \text{ergs mole}^{-1}\ \text{deg}^{-1} \\
8.3144 & \text{joules mole}^{-1}\ \text{deg}^{-1} \\
1.9872 & \text{calories mole}^{-1}\ \text{deg}^{-1}
\end{array}
$$

The ideal gas law is often written as $PV = RT$. From our discussion it is clear that $PV = RT$ is only valid for a *particular* quantity of gas, namely one mole. But the occasions when a scientist deals with precisely this quantity will obviously be few and far between. Rather than convert actual volumes of other quantities of gas to the volume one mole would occupy, it is generally better to know and use the ideal gas law in the form appropriate to *any* quantity of gas and the actual volume that particular quantity occupies.

In the discussion of Boyle's Law, we saw that it is an idealization which real gases obey only approximately. This is equally true of the more general ideal gas law and it is important in any problem to recognize its limitations. At ordinary temperatures and pressures below one atmosphere, the accuracy is within a percent or two for ordinarily gaseous substances, and may be much better. At higher pressures or corresponding concentrations, the errors are considerably greater, and may be so large as to make the law useless for quantitative predictions.

If a more accurate representation of real gases is required, it can be had at the expense of using much more complicated and special equations (discussed in Section 8.8). Frequently the correspondingly greater effort of calculation to obtain better answers is more than the problem at hand warrants. As in all scientific practice, some judgment is required; the student should not discard the ideal gas law for a particular problem if it is good enough, nor should he use it if it is not.

In chemistry it is common to find that a simple general law is only an approximation; we shall encounter such situations often in our further study. Much of our understanding of chemistry has, moreover, come both from the discovery of such idealizations and from their explanation in simple terms. To an even greater extent, it has come from the study of the nature of the deviations from the simple behavior predicted by the ideal law and from understanding of the reasons for such deviations. The observant student will find this pattern underlying much of chemistry, and his appreciation of the progress and problems of chemistry will be greater if he sometimes stops to consider them in these terms. Deviations from idealized laws, or unpredicted results, should be welcomed by the investigator as keys to further and more fundamental understanding.

8.5. Mixtures of Gases

The ideal gas law in molar terms contains nothing in its expression referring to a specific gas and applies within its accuracy to any gas, if the quantity is expressed as the number of moles n or molar concentration C. This being true, the law should apply as well to mixtures of two or more gases, provided that n is taken to be the total number of moles and C the combined total concentration. That is, if n_1, n_2, n_3 are the numbers of moles of the three gases 1, 2, 3, all present in a container of volume V, with C_1, C_2, C_3 the corresponding concentrations, the PVT relation of the mixture given by the ideal law would be

$$PV = nRT = (n_1 + n_2 + n_3)RT \qquad (8.9)$$

or

$$P = CRT = (C_1 + C_2 + C_3)RT \qquad (8.10)$$

where the total number of moles $n = n_1 + n_2 + n_3$ and the total concentration $C = C_1 + C_2 + C_3$.

It has been found that these equations hold closely if the total concentration or pressure is not too high. The nature of the deviations at higher concentrations depends on the particular gas. Obviously one cannot expect—or at least, will not find—that the law for mixtures gives valid results at any higher pressures than does the simple law for either gas separately. To the extent that these effects are not of large magnitude, however, the equation is as useful for mixtures as for molecules of one kind only.

The constitution of gas mixtures is often conveniently described by the *partial pressures* of the individual gases. These are defined quantities; they are the pressures which the individual gases would exert if present separately, each at the concentration which it has in the actual mixture. Thus if n_1 is the number of moles of gas 1, then the partial pressure P_1 of this gas is

$$P_1 = \frac{n_1 RT}{V} \qquad (8.11)$$

and similar expressions apply for the other gases present. If there are three in all, we notice that for ideal gas behavior

$$P = (n_1 + n_2 + n_3)\frac{RT}{V} = P_1 + P_2 + P_3$$

Thus the total pressure P, which is the measured quantity, is ideally equal to the sum $P_1 + P_2 + P_3$ of the partial pressures. Equation 8.11 obviously can be written in terms of concentration $C_1 = n_1/V$ of gas 1 in the form

$$P_1 = C_1 RT,$$

and similarly for the other gases that are present.

A description of the composition of a gas mixture other than by the partial pressures is often useful: the *mole fraction* N_1 of gas 1 is defined as the ratio of number of moles of gas 1 to the total number n. Thus

$$N_1 = \frac{n_1}{n} = \frac{n_1}{n_1 + n_2 + n_3}$$

by definition for three gases. Since $P_1 = n_1(RT/V)$ and $P = n(RT/V)$, it is obvious from the definition of N, that $P_1 = N_1 P$; that is, the partial pressure of any one gas in an ideal mixture is equal to its mole fraction times the total pressure. Thus partial pressures, mole fractions, and concentrations are all possible for expressing the compositions of gas mixtures. If the mixture is too dense to be described as ideal, partial pressures lose simple significance, although they may still be defined by the relation $P_1 = N_1 P$.

The use of the relations governing gaseous mixtures deriving from the ideal gas laws may be illustrated by an experiment often performed as a physical chemistry laboratory exercise: the determination of the degree of dissociation of N_2O_4 to NO_2 by the reaction

$$N_2O_4 \rightleftharpoons 2NO_2$$

In the usual procedure, N_2O_4 is introduced from a storage cylinder into a test bulb of known volume V until a suitable pressure P is reached, and the weight m of gas is determined by the difference in weights of the bulb when filled with gas and evacuated. If the equilibrium mixture were wholly N_2O_4 this weight would be $m = nM$, where M is the molecular weight of N_2O_4. Since for ideal gases $n = PV/RT$, m should then satisfy the equation

$$m = \frac{PV}{RT}M$$

Actually the measured mass is less than calculated from this equation. Assuming that the only reaction which could occur is $N_2O_4 \longrightarrow$

$2NO_2$, this result is expected and the extent of dissociation can be calculated from the measured weight. For an ideal mixture, the *total* number of moles of both N_2O_4 and NO_2 is still given by $n = PV/RT$, but the weight is *not* given by nM because the molecules of NO_2 have a molecular weight of $\frac{1}{2}M$. Assume that before reaction n_0 moles of N_2O_4 were present, of which the fraction x are dissociated at equilibrium. At equilibrium, the xn_0 moles of N_2O_4 which have dissociated have formed $2xn_0$ moles of NO_2 and $(1 - x)n_0$ moles of N_2O_4 remain.

Compositions in the Gas Reaction $N_2O_4 = 2NO_2$

	Moles N_2O_4	Moles NO_2	Total Moles
Original	n_0	0	n_0
Equilibrium	$(1 - x)n_0$	$2xn_0$	$(1 + x)n_0$

Thus the total number of moles,

$$n = (1 + x)n_0 = \frac{PV}{RT}$$

The measured weight m of the gas is given by

$$m = n_0 M$$

since no mass is lost by the dissociation. Hence

$$m = \frac{PV}{RT(1 + x)} M$$

In this equation, all quantities are known or measurable except x, the fraction dissociated, which can therefore be calculated.

It is important to notice that the expression of the problem in terms of molar quantities from which weights are derived by the specified conditions leads to a simple solution, because the ideal gas law is simplest in terms of moles.

8.6. Deviations of Real Gases from Ideal Behavior

The deviations from ideal behavior of a few common gases at or near room temperature were considered in Section 8.2. The important influence of temperature on many properties of chemical substances is hard to overestimate, and the dependence of pressure volume relations of real gases on temperature is a good example of this importance.

Compressibility Factors

In considering the accuracy of Boyle's Law, it was convenient to examine at constant temperature the variation of the product PV with pressure or concentration, because Boyle's Law predicts the constancy of this product. For measurements at

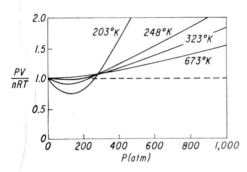

Fig. 8.7. *Compressibility factor for nitrogen plotted against pressure.*

different temperatures, it is correspondingly convenient to study the product PV/nRT as a function of pressure, for the ideal gas law predicts its constancy at the value unity regardless of variation in the quantities P, V, n, T individually.

The actual variation in the quantity PV/nRT, often called the *compressibility factor*, is easily visualized and compared by plots of this quantity against pressure for various temperatures.

The plots in Fig. 8.7, for nitrogen at pressures up to 1000 atmospheres, show that for pressures above about 400 atmospheres the factor is greater than unity and increases with pressure at temperatures between $-50°$C and 300°C, while at lower pressures the compressibility factor may have a value either greater or less than that

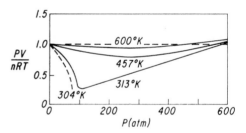

Fig. 8.8. *Compressibility factor for CO_2 plotted against pressure.*

for the ideal gas (unity). Similar plots for carbon dioxide in Fig. 8.8 show the same general type of behavior, but the temperature at which the deviations at low pressure change from negative to positive, and the magnitude of the deviations at the same temperatures, are quite different.

Similar examples could be given for many other gases showing the same broad general features, but with much individuality in detail. The substances chosen for illustration are gaseous at ordinary temperatures and pressures. Many others, not ordinarily thought of as gases, show the same general behavior at much higher temperatures. Ordinary water, for example, at temperatures below 100°C is a gas only when the pressure is less than atmospheric. For temperatures of several hundred degrees it exhibits pressure-volume relationships not unlike those in Figs. 8.7 and 8.8. Other substances exist as gases at appreciable pressures only when the temperature is still higher, and, if made up of large molecules, frequently decompose to form gases of smaller molecules.

Liquefaction of Gases

Even so-called permanent gases, such as hydrogen, helium, oxygen, nitrogen, and others are not at all permanent, but condense to a liquid at atmospheric pressure if the temperature is lowered sufficiently. The term "permanent" applied to such gases originally arose because no one had succeeded in reaching the low temperatures necessary for liquefaction. At present, all known substances have been liquefied, the most difficult task of all being finally achieved when Kamerlingh-Onnes succeeded at Leiden in 1908 in liquefying helium at a temperature less than 5°K (-268°C).

A characteristic feature of liquefaction is that on reducing the temperature sufficiently, at a fixed pressure, liquid begins to appear. Further withdrawal of heat has the familiar result that more of the gas turns to liquid, but the temperature will remain constant until no more gas remains. Subsequent cooling normally results in a gradual decrease in volume of the liquid, which however is much smaller than for gases. (An interesting exception is liquid water, which expands with decreasing temperature at temperatures lower than 4°C.)

The Critical Region

If the phenomenon of liquefaction is examined by increasing the pressure on a system containing the gas at constant temperature, the onset of liquefaction is marked by a point at which the pressure no longer increases as the volume decreases; instead, more and more of the gas is transformed into liquid. This characteristic pressure is called the *vapor pressure*, and is necessarily constant as long as both liquid and gas are present. When the volume is reduced until there is only liquid remaining, a second abrupt discontinuity occurs in the pressure-volume relationship, and large pressures are required to cause appreciable compression of the liquid.

At higher temperatures the range of volumes of a given quantity of substance over which the liquid and gaseous phases can coexist is smaller. Ultimately a temperature is reached above which there is no discontinuity in the variation of pressure with volume. This is called the *critical temperature* (T_c), and the corresponding values of P and V are called the *critical pressure* (P_c) and *critical volume* (V_c).

This whole pattern of behavior is best represented by isothermal curves on a pressure-volume diagram. The classic example for illustration is carbon dioxide, presumably because the phenomenon was first explored thoroughly for this compound (by Andrews in 1869), and because the critical pressure and temperature have convenient values.

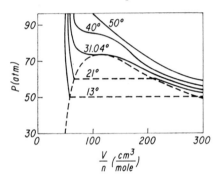

Fig. 8.9. *P-V isotherms for CO₂.*

From the PV curves for CO_2 shown in Fig. 8.9 the student should have no difficulty in associating the preceding description with the behavior described by the various curves. The critical temperature is 31.0°C and the corresponding critical pressure is 72.8 atm. The curve at 40°C shows inflections but nowhere is horizontal, and there is no visual evidence at this temperature of two phases of different properties. Instead, the gas density increases steadily, first rapidly and finally more slowly with pressure (a steeper curve in Fig. 8.9), the density and compressibility becoming more and more nearly of the magnitude characteristic of a liquid.

The PV diagram just discussed gives a more readily visualized representation of the changes in and near the critical region than do the plots of the compressibility factor (PV/nRT) against pressure, described previously. It is of interest, however, to refer to these plots for CO_2 and note that the onset of liquefaction corresponds to the dashed curve in Fig. 8.8. The isothermal curves have not been extended beyond this boundary delimiting the region where only gas is present. It is left to the student to consider how the curves should be extended to higher pressures.

The critical regions of other gases are similar (with appropriate modification of scale) to that for CO_2, and the ranges of pressure and temperature in which they are found will be suggested by the corresponding values of P_c and T_c listed in Table 8.3, together with their normal boiling points. It will be noted that the noble gases and gases composed of small, symmetrical molecules (such as N_2, CH_4, NO) have low critical temperatures. Thus they retain characteristically gaseous properties to low temperature and are not readily liquefied.

TABLE 8.3.   *Critical Constants and Boiling Points of Gases; van der Waals "Constants" (P_c in atm, V_c in cc/mole).*

Gas	T_c	BP	P_c	V_c	a [atm (liter/mole)^2]	b (cc/mole)
He	5.3	4.2	2.26	57.6	0.034	24
H_2	33.3	20.4	12.8	65.0	0.24	27
N_2	126.1	77.3	33.5	90.0	1.4	39
CO	134.4	81.1	34.6	90.0	1.5	40
O_2	154.3	90.1	49.7	74.4	1.4	32
NO	177.1	122.1	64	57.2	1.3	28
CH_4	190.2	111.7	45.6	98.8	2.3	43
CO_2	304.2	194.6	72.8	94.2	3.6	43
HCl	324.5	188.1	81.6	87		
H_2S	373.6	211.4	88.9	94.2	4.4	43
NH_3	405.5	239.7	112	72.0	4.2	37
SO_2	430.2	263.1	77.6	125	6.7	56
C_6H_6	561.6	352.7	47.9	256	19	121
C_2H_5OH	576.2	351.6	63.0	167	12	84
H_2O	647.3	373.2	278	56.7	5.5	31
Hg	1735	630	1042	40.1	8.1	17

Gases of polar molecules such as HCl and SO_2 condense more readily. One notes also that water has an exceptionally high boiling point and critical temperature, as compared with H_2S, for example. This behavior, characteristic of aliphatic alcohols also, to a lesser extent, is attributable to the ability of hydroxyl groups to form intermolecular *hydrogen bonds* which must be broken in evaporating the liquid. The influence of the quite distinct metallic bond in mercury is also evident. (All other metals but gallium have much higher melting and boiling points and much less is known of their critical properties.)

8.7. Molecular Origins of Deviations from Ideality for Gases

So far the discussion of the properties of gases has been primarily from an experimental point of view, with only incidental reference to the underlying reasons for similarities and differences in the behavior of gases. Such an empirical approach, however accurate, is obviously not satisfactory. The better understanding of the pressure-volume relations in gases has been the goal of investigators for many years. The basic principles of the kinetic-molecular theory developed as a result of their investigations, and will be considered in the next chapter. But some consequences of this theory can well be examined now in relation to the properties under discussion.

The first fact to be recognized is that the volume occupied by a gas at sufficiently low pressures to approach ideality is largely empty. At 0°C and atmospheric pressure, one mole of an ideal gas occupies the familiar volume of 22.4 liters, but the fact that one mole of liquid nitrogen, for example, requires only 34.7 cc indicates that only about one-thousandth of the actual space available at 0°C and one atmosphere would suffice for the volume of the molecules proper—that is, for the molecules to exist separately without overlapping electron charge distributions. Considering this circumstance, it is reasonable that the pressures of gases would be governed by the number, rather than by the kind, of molecules present.

The kinetic theory explains the pressure of a gas as a result of collisions of gas molecules with the confining walls and with each other. It is of fundamental importance to note that the pressure is the result of the kinetic energy of molecular translational motions, and that it is as a measure of this kinetic energy that the property of temperature is significant.

By ignoring the complications resulting from time spent by molecules under the influence of forces exerted by their neighbors, the ideal gas law can be deduced directly by applying the laws of mechanics to a system of many molecules in equilibrium free to move throughout the space of the confining vessel. If this is accepted, it is not surprising that the ideal result must be modified when the concentrations of molecules become so large that their size and the forces between them are no longer unimportant relative to the whole volume occupied and the forces resulting from their kinetic motion.

Intermolecular Repulsive Forces

As we know from much evidence of the sort discussed in preceding chapters, a molecule does occupy a statistically defined volume of space in which its electron charge concentration is significant. Other molecules can infringe appreciably on such a volume occupied by a molecule only if their energy as they approach is very high. At ordinary temperatures and pressures few molecules have the necessary energy, and it is therefore not unreasonable to think of each molecule in a container as excluding a definite fraction of the total volume from occupation by the other molecules.

If the total volume so excluded is nb' for n moles of gas, then the net volume available for motion in the container would be $V - nb'$. Van der Waals suggested that the V in the equation of state for the ideal gas be replaced by $V - nb'$ to take account of this effect. Hence one obtains the relation $P(V - nb') = nRT$, and

$$P = \frac{nRT}{V - nb'} \tag{8.12}$$

This replacement of V by $V - nb'$ in the ideal gas law is done in an arbitrary way which properly needs more fundamental justification, but it is easily shown that the result does fit *some* of the deviations of real gases from ideality moderately well with values of b' which are in reasonable agreement with their molecular sizes. Solving Eq. 8.12 for the compressibility factor, PV/nRT, gives the expression

$$\frac{PV}{nRT} = 1 + \frac{b'P}{RT}$$

Recalling our previous considerations, the plots of the compressibility factor against P should accordingly be straight lines of positive slope b'/RT.

This is the sort of behavior found at high pressures and, what is more, the decreasing slope with larger T is also observed. However, the experimentally obtained curves exhibit deviations at lower pressures which the formula above does not describe. Ignoring these for the moment, we can calculate values of b' required to fit the linear parts of the nitrogen curves at various temperatures as plotted in Fig. 8.7. The results tabulated below show that b' is fairly constant, as it should be if van der Waals' assumptions are reasonable.

TABLE 8.4. *Pressure Coefficients of Nitrogen.*

Temperature (°C)	Slope $= b'/RT$ (atm^{-1})	b' (cm^3/mole)
-50	0.00170	31.0
100	0.000935	28.6
300	0.000630	29.6

If the b' values really have even the rough molecular significance supposed, they should correspond to the volume excluded by one mole of nitrogen molecules. Regarded as spheres, nitrogen can be estimated to have a molecular volume of less than 10×10^{-24} cm^3, and we might suppose that the desired excluded volume is just the volume of N molecules, which is thus about 5 cm^3 (estimated from spectroscopic data). This is so much smaller than $b' \cong 30$ cm^3, estimated above, that we can hardly account for the discrepancy by supposing that it is because the nitrogen molecules are not actually spherical.

The difficulty is actually that the excluded volume is incorrectly computed. Two molecules can approach no closer than a distance $2a$ between centers if each is a sphere of radius a. The volume excluded by a pair of molecules is thus $(4\pi/3)(2a)^3$, or eight times the volume $4\pi a^3/3$ of one. Making the somewhat rash assumption that the total number of molecules in the gas excludes the same volume as half as many pairs of molecules leads to the conclusion that b' would correspond to *four* times the volume of the molecules in the quantity of gas. The value $b'/4 \cong 7.5$ cm^3 is thus to be compared with the value 5 cm^3 estimated for the molecular volume, and the agreement is fairly good.

Attractive Forces

The deviations from ideality at high pressures are approximately explained by a simple model of repulsive forces, but the model gives no help in understanding the negative deviations setting in at lower pressures and which become of greater importance at low temperatures. These deviations are particularly large near or below the critical temperature, when there is a possibility that higher pressures might cause liquefaction. (Compare Figs. 8.7 and 8.8.) Whether or not the liquid state will exist is governed by the presence of *attractive* forces strong enough that together with repulsive forces they will prescribe a volume only secondarily influenced by the external pressure. At higher temperatures the energies of the molecules are sufficient for them to overcome these forces and occupy volumes limited only by the container, but the attractive forces are not eliminated—their effect is rather a smaller part of the whole.

8.8. Van der Waals Forces

Van der Waals recognized the probable existence of attractive forces, now called van der Waals forces in his honor, although our understanding of them in terms of mutual polarization of molecular electron charge distributions came much later. These forces are significant for molecular separations of at least several molecular diameters, in contrast to repulsive forces, which are of importance only for "contacts" when molecular charge distributions begin to overlap significantly. It is thus not surprising that the attractive forces have more noticeable effects at lower densities.

Van der Waals argued that the effects might be represented as an internal pressure (P') acting to confine the gas, and so lowering the pressure (P) exerted by the gas on the confining walls. Instead of attempting a proper calculation of P' from molecular forces, which is a problem in advanced statistical mechanics, we can argue that the total attractive force acting upon a given molecule will be proportional to the number of neighbors in a region around it, and hence to the concentration n/V. The pressure on a surface is the force exerted by molecules striking a unit area of surface and it will be reduced by the total attractive force of all molecules on one another. The number is proportional to the concentration, and so the pressure P' should be of the form

$$P' = a \frac{n}{V} \frac{n}{V} = a \frac{n^2}{V^2}$$

The van der Waals constant a is a proportionality constant depending on the gas, but the derivation makes no attempt to calculate a from the forces between the molecules.

Van der Waals Equation

On the basis of such considerations, van der Waals proposed the equation known by his name:

$$P = \frac{nRT}{V - nb} - P'$$

or, on substituting for P' to express the effect of concentration,

$$P = \frac{nRT}{V - nb} - a \frac{n^2}{V^2} \tag{8.13}$$

It is not hard to see that the extra term an^2/V^2 does qualitatively account for the negative deviations. The compressibility factor Z predicted by Eq. 8.13 is

$$Z = \frac{PV}{nRT} = \frac{V}{V - nb} - \frac{a}{RT} \frac{n}{V} \tag{8.14}$$

The second term acts to decrease Z in proportion to the concentration, n/V, and is more important at low temperatures than at high because of the factor $1/T$. Since compressibility factors are usually plotted against P, as in Fig. 8.7, rather than (n/V), Eq. 8.14 should be expressed in terms of P to be directly comparable with such plots. The direct solution of Eq. 8.14 for n/V involves unpleasant algebra, since the equation is cubic in n/V, and so we resort to approximations to see the general nature of the exact result.

The subterfuge we adopt is of using approximate expressions for V and n/v in the correction terms involving a and b. The relation $P \cong nRT/(V - nb)$ is good enough for the purpose, and gives

$$\frac{n}{v} \cong \frac{P/RT}{1 + bP/RT}$$

and

$$V = \frac{nRT}{P} + nb$$

Using this in Eq. 8.14, with some rearrangement, we get

$$Z \cong 1 + P\frac{b}{RT} - \frac{a}{(RT)^2}\frac{P}{1 + (b/RT)P} \tag{8.15}$$

The first term in P is just the repulsion effect already discussed. The second is a negative term linear in P for small values of P, decreasing in value at high pressures. The combined effect is that Z initially increases or decreases, depending on whether b is greater or less than a/RT, but in either case ultimately increasing at high enough pressures; these effects are just of the form found. Whether or not the actual values of a to give a fairly good fit to the experimentally obtained curves for gases are reasonable is less simply decided than in the case of the constant b, but more complicated arguments do show them to be reasonable.

Critical Region

The curves predicted by van der Waals equation have a less obvious resemblance to the actual PV curves in the critical region. Because the equation is cubic in V/n, there exists the possibility of three real solutions for V/n for a single P. Calculations of P for various values of V/n and T give results which have the form shown in Fig. 8.10.

It is a somewhat tedious but straightforward problem in algebra and calculus to show that there are three solutions for V/n for RT less than

$8a/27b$ and one solution for larger values, and that there is a horizontal inflection at the value $RT = 8a/27b$.

The statements about real solutions follow from rules of algebra applied to cubic equations. The inflection point is of special interest because the point of inflection in actual PV curves is the critical point already discussed. The conditions for which van der Waals equation has an inflection point are thus worth examination for comparison with the experimental behavior. The calculus requirement that the derivatives (dP/dV) and (d^2P/dV^2) both be zero gives

$$\left(\frac{V'}{n} - b\right)^2 = \frac{RT'}{2a}\left(\frac{V'}{n}\right)^3$$

and

$$\left(\frac{V'}{n} - b\right)^3 = \frac{RT'}{3a}\left(\frac{V'}{n}\right)^4$$

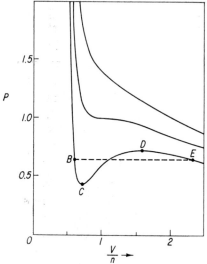

Fig. 8.10. *Plots of P-V relations predicted by the van der Waals equation. Pressures and volumes are in units of the critical values; the top curve is for a temperature 1.1 times critical, the center one for the critical temperature, and the bottom curve for 0.9 times critical.*

where the primes indicate values for the inflection point. Eliminating RT' gives $V'/n = 3b$, from which $RT' = 8a/27b$, and substitution in van der Waals' equation itself gives $P' = a/27b^2$. If the equation correctly represents the critical point, we should then have

$$P_c = a/27b^2 \qquad V_c/n = 3b \qquad RT_c = 8a/27b \qquad (8.16)$$

A simple test of the accuracy of these predictions can be made by comparing the compressibility factor calculated from them with observed values. Substituting the values from Eq. 8.16 in $Z = PV/nRT$ gives $Z_c = (a/27b^2)(3b)(27b/a) = 3/8 = 0.375$. The majority of actual values lie in the range 0.27–0.30. The considerable difference immediately shows the impossibility for most gases of choosing values of a and b which will give correctly all three of the quantities P_c, V_c, T_c.

The "saddle effect" and the maximum given by the equation at lower temperatures are, so to speak, the best that the equation can do to reproduce the actual flat section of the two phase liquid-gas region.

(This should not surprise us too much: simple equations do not naturally predict sudden breaks or discontinuities in the actual curves.) The dashed line in the drawing indicates an actual isotherm in this region (see Fig. 8.9 for CO_2) and we may inquire whether the **S**-shaped curve of the equation has any possible significance. The part of the van der Waals curve below B represents a continuation of liquidlike behavior rather than the equilibrium process of vaporization represented by the horizontal line. Such a *metastable* state can be realized—liquid water has been observed to withstand negative pressures of many atmospheres before vaporizing (cavitating) but only after very special precautions to remove any air or dust.

Proceeding toward the two-phase region from the gas side E, the continuation from E to D represents another metastable state of *supersaturated* gas (vapor) which can also be realized. But the part of the curve C–D cannot be made plausible, because it represents an unnatural situation in which increasing pressure would increase the volume!

The qualitative agreement of van der Waals equation with experiment and the way in which the assumptions underlying it can be made intelligible in terms of molecular forces justify its study, but it should by now be clear that it is not by any means exact. The true state of affairs in real gases requires much more detailed and complicated discussion. This is today a subject of active research, but it is not too difficult to show that the equation is no more than a first approximation to the effects of intermolecular forces. Experimental results, which are of course the ultimate test, also are not as simply explained. For example, different values of a and b can be deduced, depending on the range of P, V, or T values, to be fitted as well as possible by the best choice of constants. By the same token, no single pair of values for a and b can represent a wide range of actual P, V, and T values with great accuracy.

Even so, some values of van der Waals constants a and b are given in Table 8.4 because these values are of interest as indications of the relative magnitude of molecular forces and values. They may also be used for *rough corrections* of the ideal gas law at low pressures. The values listed were chosen to give the correct critical pressure and temperature, but this does not mean the equation is of high accuracy near the critical region, as critical volumes calculated from the equation may be too large by 50% or more.

Attempts to obtain better equations can proceed in either of two ways. The first might be called the engineering approach, of devising the simplest form of empirical equation capable of reproducing data of in-

terest as accurately as their precision justifies. The second is the theoretical molecular approach, of calculating the pressure under given
conditions from the properties of the molecules in the gas. We have so
far emphasized the ideas involved in the latter point of view. In the next
section we consider briefly some of the many possible equations which
are useful in describing the behavior of real gases more accurately than
is possible with the ideal gas law.

8.9. Equations of State and *PVT* Charts

Many possible forms of the *PVT* relation, the *equation of state*, have
been proposed with one or another objective in mind, the nature and
complexity of the equation being governed by the particular objective.
The fact that no single equation has become pre-eminent is sufficient to
show that the different objectives are to a certain extent conflicting, and
that specific differences between the properties of individual gases play
a significant part in determining these *PVT* relations. A thorough discussion of all these factors would be very lengthy and we can only hope
to suggest here some of the available possibilities.

Hougen-Watson Charts

The first representation of *PVT* data we consider is in the form of a
graph rather than an equation. It was developed by Hougen and Watson
to take advantage of the fact that plots of compressibility factors
$(Z = PV/nRT)$ against pressure have very similar appearance for different gases except for the scale. In other words, the individual curves
have very similar shapes for a range of values of temperature and
pressure.

If the curves are really similar, the differences of scale can be eliminated by using *reduced* temperatures and pressures—that is, by expressing
actual values as fractions, or multiples, of numbers characteristic of each
gas, these numbers being so chosen that plots using these reduced values
give the same, or nearly the same, curve for any gas. When such curves
have been devised, they can be then used to compute compressibility
factors (Z) from given values of pressure and temperature, if suitable
characteristic values are known. Once Z is known, the corresponding
volume can be computed from the definition $Z = PV/nRT$, since the
values of P and T are the starting point and hence known.

The characteristic numbers used by Hougen and Watson are the

values of temperature and pressure at the critical point of the gas, and
the reduced temperatures and pressures are then the ratios T/T_c and
P/P_c. The test of the usefulness of this choice is to see how nearly the
data for different gases fall on a common curve when Z is plotted against
P/P_c, for the same values of T/T_c. The necessary critical data for ten
gases from Table 8.3 have been used to obtain the plots in Fig. 8.11.

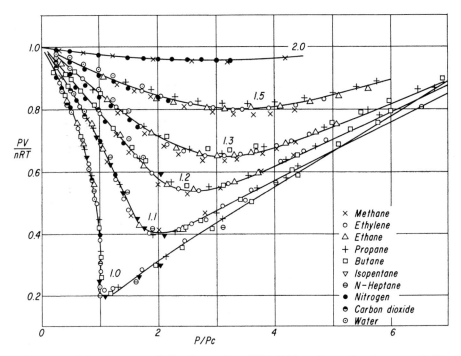

Fig. 8.11. *Plot of compressibility factor $Z = PV/nRT$ against reduced pressure P/P_c.
Curves are labeled with values of reduced temperature T/T_c. [After Gouq-Jen Su,
Ind. Eng. Chem., **38**:803 (1946).]*

Each curve in the drawing is for a particular reduced temperature,
but the points correspond to different actual temperatures of the individual gases because T_c is different. (For example, $T_c = 126°K$ for
N_2 and $647°K$ for H_2O.) The ranges of reduced pressures plotted similarly represent different actual pressures of a few hundred atmospheres
or less. Within these ranges of temperature and pressure, it is seen that
moderately accurate values for any of the various gases result from reading the values of Z corresponding to the average smooth curve, but the
possibility of errors of a few percent must be accepted. The approxima-

tion that gases with the same values of P/P_c and T/T_c have nearly the same value of V/V_c is called the *law of corresponding states*.

Average curves for wider ranges of T/T_c and P/P_c are plotted in Fig. 8.12, and larger charts which permit more accurate reading of values are available. In order to accommodate a wide range of pressures in a reasonable space, logarithmic scales of P/P_c and Z have been used in Fig. 8.12. It is to be noted that interpolation between curves is

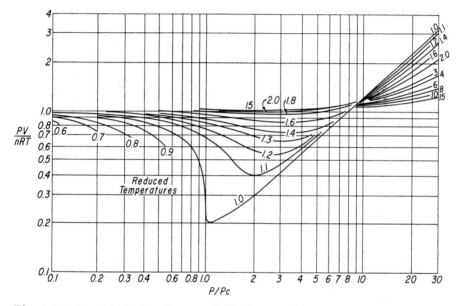

Fig. 8.12. *Logarithmic plot of compressibility factor against reduced pressure for reduced temperatures as indicated* [*After Hougen and Watson*, Chemical Process Principles, *Part II, Chapter 12 (Wiley, New York, 1947).*]

usually necessary in using Fig. 8.11 or Fig. 8.12, as only by coincidence will the temperature of interest correspond exactly to one of the reduced temperatures for which the curves are plotted.

Semiempirical Equations

Numerous equations of state can be found in the literature. We list two of the simpler ones.

Equation of Berthelot:

$$P = \frac{nRT}{V - nb} - \frac{A}{T}\frac{n^2}{V^2}$$

Equation of Dieterici:

$$P = \frac{nRT}{V - nb'} \exp\left(-\frac{a'}{RT}\frac{n}{V}\right)$$

The quantities A, b, a', b' are constants adjusted to fit the data for particular gases under conditions of interest, often by making the equation give good values of pressure near the critical point. It will be noticed that both involve an excluded volume nb or nb', just as in van der Waals' equation, but have different forms of the a term. Berthelot's equation is somewhat better than van der Waals equation for pressures of a few atmospheres and is most generally useful in this range; Dieterici's equation is capable of a better fit near the critical region.

It should not be concluded from the common appearance of terms of the form $(V - nb)$ that such terms are essential and inherently proper. That they are not can be appreciated from the fact that they permit volumes less than b per mole of gas, with b being several times actual values of the volume when molecules would begin to interpenetrate one another. Under extreme pressures, as exist in products from detonation of high explosives, for example, gases occupy volumes only a fraction of the b values describing lower pressure data.

At less extreme but high pressures the errors of the relatively simple equations are too great for such purposes as calculations of catalytic hydrogenation, and more accurate but more complicated equations are necessary in order to obtain sufficient accuracy. Perhaps the best known of these is the Beattie-Bridgman equation of the form

$$P = \frac{nRT}{V}\left[1 + B_0 \frac{n}{V}\left(1 - \frac{nb}{V}\right)\right]\left[1 - \frac{c}{T^3}\frac{n}{V}\right] - A_0\left(\frac{n}{V}\right)^2\left(1 - \frac{an}{V}\right)$$

The five constants A_0, a, B_0, b, c have been determined for a number of gases from experimental data, and by the use of this equation calculations of pressure may be made with an accuracy of 0.5% or better even near the critical point. The reader can appreciate the greater amount of calculation necessary by inspecting the equation. (It is not supposed that he will remember it.)

Virial Equations

Another form of equation is being increasingly used, in which the PV product is expressed as a series of terms in successively higher powers of pressure or concentration, the coefficients having values varying with the temperature. These virial equations may be written in the form

$$\frac{PV}{nRT} = 1 + B(T)\left(\frac{n}{V}\right) + C(T)\left(\frac{n}{V}\right)^2$$

$$+ \text{ terms in } \left(\frac{n}{V}\right)^3 \text{ etc., as necessary} \quad (8.17)$$

or, in terms of pressure, as

$$\frac{PV}{n} = RT + B'(T)P + C'(T)P^2 + \text{ terms in } P^3 \text{ etc., as necessary}$$

The notation $B(T)$ indicates that the coefficient B varies with temperature T. The quantities $B(T)$ and $C(T)$ are called the second and third virial coefficients.

There is no uniformity in the exact form of either virial equation. The first one, for instance, is sometimes written

$$\frac{PV}{n} = RT + B''\left(\frac{n}{V}\right) + C''\left(\frac{n}{V}\right)^2 + \cdots$$

and the virial coefficients B'', C'', and others so introduced are not the same as B, C, but are RT times as large. The forms we have used are as common as any, and have an advantage in that the so-called second virial coefficients $B(T)$ and $B'(T)$ are equal. This is not true of higher coefficients, however, and it can be shown that $C = B^2 + RTC'$.

The reader may wonder why, if the virial equations are two different ways of describing the same results, one or the other is not used exclusively. Experimentally it is often convenient to consider P the variable most directly measured and controlled, and the second form expressing PV in terms of P is then more useful. On the other hand, molecular theories, even the crude one represented by van der Waals equation, express deviations from ideality by calculating the pressure of a gas in a stated volume V and so lead to an equation expressing PV in terms of V or, better, the concentration n/V.

The virial coefficient B in either equation is approximately given by

$$B = b - \frac{a}{RT}$$

where b and a may be the van der Waals coefficients or different values to give better fit at lower pressures. (That van der Waals equation gives a result of this form is readily seen by comparing Eq. 8.14 and Eq. 8.17.)

There is no simple equation representing the dependence of B on T more accurately for different gases, and so tables or graphs of B for various temperatures are used. Similar tables for C or C' may be employed if accuracy at pressures above 10 atmospheres or so is needed.

Problems

8.1. (a) At 20°C, what is the force on a 100 cm² surface supporting a column of mercury 50 cm high? (b) At 20°C, calculate the pressure supporting each of the following: the column of mercury in (a); a column of water 3 m high; a column of glycerine 75 cm high. Express the answers in atmospheres, in dynes/cm², and in lbs/in².

8.2. The pressure at a certain altitude is 0.75 standard atmospheres. What will be the height of columns of the following liquids at 20°C: (a) mercury; (b) water; (c) sulfuric acid; (d) benzene?

8.3. A platinum resistance thermometer has a resistance of 9.81 ohms at 0°C, 13.65 ohms at 100°C, and 21.00 ohms at 300°C. (a) Is the thermometer accurately linear over this range? (b) If it is assumed linear between 0°C and 100°C, will a temperature of 50.0°C deduced from a resistance reading of 11.73 ohms be higher or lower than the actual temperature?

8.4. Using the temperatures for the ice point and for boiling water, derive the values of the constants in the equation which expresses the linear relation between the temperature in degrees Centigrade and the temperature in degrees Fahrenheit.

8.5. The density of hydrogen gas at 0°C and 1 atmosphere pressure is 0.0899 g/liter. (a) What is its molar volume? (b) What is its density at 2 atmospheres and 127°C?

8.6. The density of a certain gas at 0°C and 1 atmosphere is 1.9804 g/liter. (a) What is the gram molecular weight? (b) At what temperature would the gas have a density of 0.9902 g/liter ($P = 1$ atm)?

8.7. A gas is contained in a 10-liter flask under a pressure of 690 mm of mercury and at a temperature of 19°C. (a) How many moles are present? (b) How many molecules are present? (c) If the gas is helium, how much does it weigh?

8.8. The molar ratio of hydrogen to carbon in a certain hydrocarbon was found by analysis to be 2.5:1. One gram of the substance was volatilized in a 400-ml bulb at 47°C and the pressure brought to 1 atmosphere by allowing excess vapor to escape. The weight of the gas was found to be 0.884 g. What is the molecular formula for the compound?

8.9. A 6-liter flask contains CO_2 at a pressure of 0.96 atmospheres at 20°C. What volume of flask would be needed to hold (a) the same number of grams of nitrogen at the same temperature and pressure? (b) the same number of molecules of nitrogen at the same temperature and pressure?

8.10. One liter of oxygen was collected over water at a temperature of 21.5°C and a total pressure of 752.7 mm of mercury. What was the volume of the oxygen when dry under standard conditions?

8.11. If 6.3 g of carbon dioxide and 6.0 grams of carbon monoxide are present in an 18-liter flask at 20°C, (a) what is the mole fraction of each? (b) what is the total pressure and the partial pressure of each gas?

8.12. A gas mixture contains 14 g of nitrogen, 8 g of helium, and 8 g of oxygen at a total pressure of 1.8 atmospheres. If the temperature is 157°C, what is the total volume of the mixture?

8.13. At 250°C and 750 mm pressure, phosphorus pentachloride vapor is 81% dissociated ($PCl_5 \rightleftarrows PCl_3 + Cl_2$). What would be the volume of 2.08 g of the gas at these conditions of temperature and pressure?

8.14. (a) At 27°C and 1 atmosphere pressure the vapor formed from 3.12 g of N_2O_4 occupies 1 liter. Assuming it to be partially dissociated into NO_2 ($N_2O_4 \rightleftarrows 2NO_2$), calculate x, the extent of dissociation. (b) At 60°C and 1 atmosphere the apparent molecular weight of N_2O_4 is 60.2. What is the value of x?

8.15. The relative humidity in a room at 25°C was found to be 75%—i.e., the air contained 75% of the moisture it would contain if completely saturated. If the total pressure was 755 mm of mercury, how many moles of water vapor were present in one liter of wet air? If the wet air were cooled to 5°C and maintained at the same total pressure, how many moles of water vapor would be present in 1 liter of wet air?

8.16. A gas density bulb weighed 29.3215 g when evacuated. Filled with CO_2 at 40°C and 1 atmosphere, it weighed 30.0079 g. Filled with a mixture of CO and CO_2 under the same conditions, it weighed 29.9330 g. What was the percentage of CO in the gas mixture?

8.17. Moles and Batuecas (*Anales Soc. Españ. fís. quím.*, **28**:871, 1930) give the following pressure and density measurements on NH_3 at 0°C. (See also Dietrichson, Bircher, and O'Brien and Dietrichson, Orleman, and Rubin, *J. Am. Chem. Soc.*, **55**:1, 1933.)

p (atm)	d (g/liter)
1	0.77169
$\frac{2}{3}$	0.51182
$\frac{1}{2}$	0.38293
$\frac{1}{3}$	0.25461

Determine the atomic weight of nitrogen by using the method of limiting densities to determine the molecular weight of ammonia, assuming the known atomic weight of hydrogen.

8.18. The critical pressure, temperature, and density of ammonia are 132.4°C, 112.0 atm, and 0.234 gm cm^{-3}. (a) Calculate the van der Waals a and b coefficients from P_c and T_c. (b) Calculate a and b from V_c and T_c and compare with the results from part (a).

8.19. Use Eq. 8.15 to calculate values of the compressibility factor, Z, for nitrogen at $-50°C$. Make a plot of Z versus pressure.

8.20. Use the Hougen-Watson chart to find the volume of 880 g of CO_2 at 61.5°C and 51 atmospheres pressure.

8.21. When 30.6 liters of steam at 1 atmosphere is condensed at 100°C, the volume of the liquid is about 18 cm³. Had there been no intermolecular forces, what pressure would have had to be applied to bring about this change of volume?

8.22. Express the boiling points of a number of the substances listed in Table 8.3 as "reduced temperatures" and comment on the extent to which the results illustrate the "law of corresponding states."

8.23. A sealed glass bulb weighs 15.0123 g in air and 15.0706 g in pure nitrogen, both measurements being made at 20°C and 1 atmosphere pressure. What is the volume of the bulb? In a third gas under the same conditions the bulb weighs 14.8875 g. What is the density and molecular weight of the gas?

8.24. (a) Show that the van der Waals equation for n moles of gas is given by

$$\left(P + \frac{n^2a}{V^2}\right)(V - nb) = nRT$$

(b) What are the dimensions of the quantities a and b?

8.25. Arthur and Felsing (*J. Am. Chem. Soc.*, **68**:1883, 1946) reported the following data for CH_3NH_2 at 0°C:

p (atm)	d (g/liter)	P/d (cc atm/g)
0.2	0.2796	715.308
0.5	0.7080	706.215
0.8	1.1476	697.107

(a) Determine the 2nd virial coefficient, $B'(T)$, in the equation of state $P(V/n) = RT + B'(T)P + C'(T)P^2 + \cdots$, assuming that terms beyond $B'(T)P$ have negligible effect at these pressures. (b) Calculate the ideal molar volume ($= RT/P$) at standard conditions.

8.26. Use the data of Problem 8.25 to determine the coefficient $B(T)$ in the series

$$\frac{PV}{nRT} = 1 + B(T)\left(\frac{n}{V}\right) + C(T)\left(\frac{n}{V}\right)^2 + \cdots$$

8.27. Show that the two coefficients $B'(T)$ and $B(T)$ in Problems 8.25 and 8.26 are identical.

8.28. Use the data of Problem 8.25 to calculate the molecular weight of CH_3NH_2 by the method of limiting densities.

8.29. (a) At the critical point the three roots of the van der Waals equation (the equation is a cubic in V) are all equal; derive the formulas which give critical temperature (T_c), pressure (P_c), and volume (V_c) in terms of a, b, and R, the gas constant. Use these values to obtain the "reduced" van der Waal equation in terms of the reduced temperature, pressure and volume. (Hint: If $V = V_c$, then $(V - V_c)^3 = V^3 - 3V_c V^2 + 3V_c^2 V - V_c^3 = 0$. Equate powers of V in this equation with the terms of the same power in V from van der Waals equation written as a cubic equation in V.) (b) Derive the results of part (a) by calculus, using the conditions that at the critical point $(\partial P/\partial V) = 0$, $(\partial^2 P/\partial V^2)_T = 0$.

8.30. The "Boyle temperature" of a gas is defined as the temperature at which the second virial coefficient $B(T)$ is zero. (a) Show that at this temperature the plot of (PV/nRT) against pressure (P) or concentration (n/V) has zero slope in the limit of zero pressure, or zero concentration. (b) Experimentally, the ratio of the Boyle temperature T_{Boyle} to the critical temperature T_c is about $T_{Boyle}/T_c = 11/4 = 2.75$. Show that van der Waals equation predicts $T_{Boyle}/T_c = 27/8 = 3.375$, which is thus larger than the observed ratio. (Hint: Show that $B(T)$ for a "van der Waals" gas is $B(T) = b - a/RT$.)

8.31. What would be the calculated pressure of 3.7 g of nitrogen in a volume of 100 cm^3 at $-60°C$, (a) using the ideal gas law, (b) using van der Waals equation, (c) using the Hougen-Watson chart with a suitable method of successive approximations.

Suggested Readings

Most discussions of the properties of gases use results of thermodynamics and statistical mechanics which we have not yet examined; therefore readings in other books may well be deferred. A number of the references for Chapters 9 and 10 contain such discussions; another which can be recommended is *The Perfect Gas* by J. S. Rowlinson (Pergamon, New York, 1963).

Chapter 9

Kinetic Theory. Boltzmann's Equation

9.1. Evidence for Molecular Energy of Gases

There is abundant evidence that matter in any state, whether gas, liquid, or solid, has properties which are adequately explained only by assuming that the molecules of which it is constituted are in continuous motion. This state of internal motion is at all times present whether or not the substance has any motion as a whole. Some of the characteristics of this internal kinetic activity are most simply inferred from the behavior of gases, and in this section we review briefly some of the evidence for molecular motion and energy.

Adiabatic Changes

Any gas possesses the ability to do work against the external pressure which confines it to a definite volume. If this pressure is reduced, as by reducing the force on a piston or opening a valve, the gas expands to fill a larger volume made available by the outward motion of the piston or by the opening to surroundings at a lower pressure.

From elementary physics, such an outward displacement against an external force represents the performance of work by the gas, and can only happen as a result of some related change in energy of some form. That such changes can be provided by the gas is indicated by the fact that the work can be done in times too short for the gas to receive energy from outside sources, as by flow of heat. After expansion, the gas is cooler—dramatically so if CO_2 is released from a pressure cylinder, with resultant formation of "dry ice"—and the work of expansion is evidently done at the expense of internal changes in energy of the molecules. Adiabatic changes of this kind, in which no external effects other than work are involved, thus provide a direct way of observing the effects of changes in internal energy.

Isothermal Work

If expansion of a gas is to be at constant temperature, heat must be supplied to offset the cooling which takes place if the process of expansion is fast or if the container is insulated. The supply of heat is thus a means of increasing the total energy of the molecules of the gas, and it is reasonable from the molecular point of view to believe that this supply must come at the expense of the surroundings of the gas, such as a constant temperature bath. There are thus two kinds of exchange with the surroundings: by performance of work and by absorption of heat, and both must be considered in evaluating the results of measurements when temperature is fixed.

Heat Capacity

The increase of molecular energy with temperature is also indicated: to increase the temperature work must be done *on* a gas, or heat supplied, or a combination of both.

Doing work on a gas, with no heat supplied from outside, is simply the converse of adiabatic expansion. The temperature is raised by adiabatic compression. When no work is done on the gas, its temperature can be raised only when external heat is supplied, as by an electrical resistance coil, and greater pressure will be required to maintain the volume fixed. If there is no change in volume, no mechanical work can be done, and all the electrical energy dissipated by the heater must go into increased energy of the gas and its container. If, instead, the volume is allowed to increase by arranging that the pressure remain fixed, work *is* done and it is found that *more* electrical energy must be applied to produce the same temperature rise. It is thus essential to prescribe the conditions carefully before inferring anything quantitative about the internal changes, but the existence of such changes is plain from the necessity of supplying heat even if there is no work.

Other Effects

That molecules possess considerable kinetic energy of motion is suggested by the simple fact that in a gas which is mostly empty space the molecules do not come to rest in a closely packed region under the force of gravity.

At equilibrium of a gas with no mass flow the nature of the remaining individual motions is not immediately obvious. If motion without interference from other molecules is made possible—for example by releasing gas into an evacuated space—the rapidity with which pressure changes occur indicates that the speeds of the molecules must be very large. If, however, other molecules are present, the rate at which a gas spreads is much smaller: the presence of a noxious gas from an experiment makes itself known through a laboratory by diffusion, but the time required is seconds or minutes.

The difference in the two processes is reasonably explained only if the progress of gas molecules through the air is interrupted and deflected by frequent collisions with molecules of the air. We shall, therefore, have to recognize the existence of molecular collisions in any reasonable molecular theory of gases, and collisions are of essential importance in determining such properties of gases as diffusion, viscosity, and conduction of heat.

The effects we have described very briefly and qualitatively are ones of reasonably common experience. Less direct evidence of many sorts supports the conclusion that molecular energy is an essential characteristic underlying the behavior of matter in all its familiar forms, and that an adequate molecular theory must be a kinetic one, taking account of the motions of large numbers of molecules.

9.2. Kinetic Theory and the Ideal Gas Law

In accordance with the evidence just examined, the kinetic theory postulates that any gas consists of molecules moving at great speeds. The kinetic explanation of pressure is simply that it is the average result of the enormous number of collisions of molecules with the walls. In any one collision, a force must be exerted during the time of collision to turn the molecule back, and the product of force and the time it acts is from elementary physics equal to the change of momentum in the direction of the force. If we calculate the total change in momentum of all particles striking a fixed surface in *unit* time, this change must equal the *average* force which must be applied to the surface to prevent its motion. Otherwise stated, the average force must be just the amount to produce

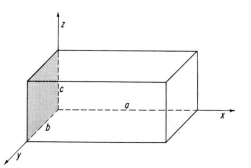

Fig. 9.1. *Rectangular box.*

the total momentum change of the molecules which struck and rebounded in the unit time (one second).

Calculation of Momentum Changes and Pressure

For simplicity, consider a container—a rectangular box as shown in Fig. 9.1—and choose the surface *bc*, at right angles to the *x*-direction along *a*, as the one for calculation of the force, and hence pressure exerted by the gas. A single molecule 1 approaching this surface with a velocity U_1, of which U_{x1} is the component in the *x*-direction, will rebound with the same speed but with its new velocity component U_{x1} in the opposite direction, as shown in Fig. 9.2. Calling its mass m, the change in momentum is from mU_{x1} to $-mU_{x1}$, and so by an amount $2mU_{x1}$. (The change is a decrease if velocity to the right is positive,

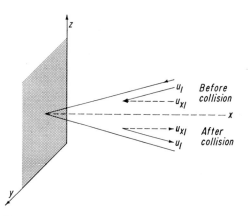

Fig. 9.2. *Reversal of perpendicular component upon collision with wall of box.*

and so the force to cause it must be to the left.) Similarly, the momentum change of a molecule 2 approaching with velocity component U_{x2} will be $2mU_{x2}$, and so on. To obtain the average force necessary to keep the wall from moving, we must next determine how many collisions of molecules with each speed U_{x1}, U_{x2}, $\cdots$ take place in one second, and from this the total momentum change. Although the molecules which strike the surface actually experience collisions with other molecules many times in a second unless the gas is at extremely low pressures, the numbers with average speeds U_{x1}, U_{x2}, $\cdots$ will not change in the course of time—simply because so many molecular collisions take place that at equilibrium as many molecules acquire a particular velocity as lose it. We therefore consider what happens if N_1 molecules travel with speed U_{x1} at all times, N_2 with speed U_{x2}, and so on.

Any one molecule with speed U_{x1} will travel from the right to left wall in a time $t = a/U_{x1}$ and will make a round trip in time $2a/U_{x1}$ seconds. It will in one second, therefore, strike the wall $U_{x1}/2a$ times. The total effect of N_1 such molecules striking the wall $U_{x1}/2a$ times with momentum change $2mU_{x1}$ each time is the momentum change

$$N_1 \left(\frac{U_{x1}}{2a} \right) 2mU_{x1} = \frac{N_1 m U_{x1}^2}{a}$$

The change for N_2 molecules of speed U_{x2} is similarly $\dfrac{N_2 m U_{x2}^2}{a}$ and for all possible groups of molecules the total change is

$$F_{ave} = \text{change in momentum per second}$$

$$= \frac{m}{a} \left[N_1 U_{x1}^2 + N_2 U_{x2}^2 + N_3 U_{x3}^2 + \cdots + N_n U_{xn}^2 \right]$$

Since F_{ave} is the average force, pressure P on the surface of area bc will be

$$P = \frac{F_{ave}}{bc} = \frac{m}{abc} \left[N_1 U_{x1}^2 + N_2 U_{x2}^2 + \cdots \right] \tag{9.1}$$

Relation to Molecular Kinetic Energy

The equation for pressure can be put into a form involving familiar physical quantities by the following considerations.

1. The product abc is just the volume V of the box.
2. The groups N_1, N_2, N_3, $\cdots$ in all must add up to the total number N of molecules in the container.
3. By the definition of an average, the sum $N_1 U_{x1}^2 + N_2 U_{x2}^2 + \cdots + N_n U_{xn}^2$ for all groups of molecules is just N times the average value

$(U_x^2)_{ave}$ of the x components of velocity squared. Hence Eq. 9.1 can be written

$$P = \frac{m}{V} N(U_x^2)_{ave}$$

4. We next recall the relation between any velocity U and its components U_x, U_y, U_z, that $U_x^2 + U_y^2 + U_z^2 = U^2$. This must be true for average velocities in particular, and so

$$(U_x^2)_{ave} + (U_y^2)_{ave} + (U_z^2)_{ave} = (U^2)_{ave}$$

5. Because the molecules are moving at random, the average values of U_x^2, U_y^2, and U_z^2 are all equal: $(U_x^2)_{ave} = (U_y^2)_{ave} = (U_z^2)_{ave}$. Hence we have $(U_x^2)_{ave} = \frac{1}{3}(U^2)_{ave}$, which enables us to write Eq. 9.1 in terms of the average of squared velocities rather than components:

$$P = \frac{1}{3V} Nm(U^2)_{ave} \tag{9.2}$$

6. The usefulness of replacing $(U_x^2)_{ave}$ by $\frac{1}{3}(U^2)_{ave}$ is apparent if we recall that $\frac{1}{2}mU^2$ is the *kinetic energy* of a particle of mass m moving with a speed U. Hence $\frac{1}{2}m(U^2)_{ave}$ is the *average kinetic energy* $(KE)_{ave}$ of a molecule moving about in the box, and we can write

$$PV = \frac{2}{3}N(KE)_{ave} \tag{9.3}$$

Comparison with Ideal Gas Law

The result of considering the impacts of molecules not subject to any complicating intermolecular forces is the kinetic theory basis of Boyle's Law, if we suppose that the average kinetic energy of a molecule is constant at fixed temperature. If we further compare the equation with the ideal gas law $PV = nRT$, where n is the number of moles, we see that the two agree if

$$\frac{2}{3}N(KE)_{ave} = nRT$$

But N, the number of molecules, is just N_0 (Avogadro's number) times the number of moles, $N = nN_0$, which gives

$$(KE)_{ave} = \frac{3}{2}\frac{R}{N_0} T \tag{9.4}$$

Kinetic Energy and Temperature

Equation 9.4 is of fundamental importance, as it shows that the significance of temperature is as a measure of average molecular kinetic energy. This interpretation of temperature is not confined to ideal gases, although, as we shall see, the correspondence for all forms of energy molecules may possess is not always as direct. It is always helpful, however, in thinking about the influence of temperature on chemical systems to keep in mind that their increases in temperature come about by increase in molecular energies, and that the order of magnitude of molecular energies in systems of many molecules is $(R/N_0) T$ per molecule, or RT per mole.

The ratio R/N_0 of universal constants has the same importance in considering problems on a molecular basis that the gas constant R has for molar quantities, and is encountered frequently as *Boltzmann's constant* $k = R/N_0 = 1.38 \times 10^{-16}$ ergs/molecule/degree $= 13.8 \times 10^{-24}$ joules/molecules/degree $= 3.30 \times 10^{-24}$ cal/molecule/degree.

The magnitude of an amount of energy kT is obviously very small on a basis of laboratory measurements, being at 300°K the quantity 4.14×10^{-14} ergs/molecule $= 9.9 \times 10^{-22}$ cal/molecule. For the numbers of molecules in ordinary quantities of matter, the total amount corresponding to kT per molecule is of a more familiar magnitude. For one mole of gas, the total kinetic energy as derived above is $\frac{3}{2}RT \cong 900$ calories at 300°K (27°C), while at 600°K the figure is ~ 1800 calories, a change corresponding to readily measurable amounts of heat or work.

The result derived, which can be written

$$PV = \tfrac{3}{2} n N (KE)_{\text{ave}}$$

can be generalized to include different kinds of molecules and then gives the result that PV is equal to a sum of terms of the same form, with one term for each kind of molecule. This result agrees with the ideal gas law for mixtures if the average translational kinetic energy is the same for *all* kinds of molecules and equal to $\frac{3}{2}kT$ per molecule, regardless of its number and kinds of atoms. This general consequence further indicates the fundamental character of the correspondence between average molecular energy and temperature.

The fact that the pressure of an ideal gas depends only on the number of molecules and temperature, the average translational energies being the same regardless of kind, should not lead us to the false conclusion that there are no differences. Other properties of ideal gases than pressure do depend on kind of molecules as well as number, the difference being that other kinds of motion than translation (displacement of the molecules as a whole) have an effect on the observed property.

Speeds of Molecules

Finally, the kinds of speeds molecules in gases possess under typical conditions can be deduced from the fact that their average kinetic energy is $\frac{3}{2}kT$. The average of velocity squared for a molecule of mass m is therefore

$$(U^2)_{\text{ave}} = \frac{2(KE)_{\text{ave}}}{m} = \frac{3kT}{m}$$

In terms of $R = Nk$ and molecular weight $M = Nm$, this is

$$(U^2)_{\text{ave}} = \frac{3RT}{M}.$$

The theory leads naturally to an average of U^2 rather than U, but we can obtain a measure of typical speeds from the root mean square speed (*RMS* speed), which is simply defined as the square root of $(U^2)_{\text{ave}}$. We see that

$$RMS \text{ speed} = \sqrt{\frac{3RT}{M}} \qquad (9.5)$$

This speed thus varies inversely as the square root of molecular mass, as expressed by molecular weight, and lighter molecules therefore move at higher speeds on the average—as obviously they must if all molecules are to have the same average kinetic energy at the same temperature.

As an example of the kinds of speeds of gas molecules under typical conditions, consider the *RMS* speed for oxygen at 300°K. As in all numerical calculations, and particularly those involving the gas constant, R, care must be taken with units. If we take R to be 1.99 cal/mole degree, with M in grams/mole, we get an answer in units of $(\text{cal/gram})^{1/2}$, which is not easily recognized as a unit of speed. With $R = 8.3 \times 10^7$ ergs/mole/deg, we get $(\text{erg/gram})^{1/2}$, which seems equally unreasonable until we remember that an erg, being the cgs unit of energy, is obtained as the product of mass in grams and velocity squared $(\text{cm/sec})^2$. The result for R expressed in ergs is, therefore, expressed in units of cm/sec. With $T = 300$°K and $M = 32$, we get

$$RMS \text{ speed} = \sqrt{\frac{3 \times 8.3 \times 10^7 \times 300}{32}} = 4.83 \times 10^4 \text{ cm/sec}$$

or a speed of about 1100 miles/hour.

Speeds of this order, of course, are average values only. There is no reason to suppose that within the gas all molecules travel with precisely this speed or that any one continues very long with this or any other speed. Individual motions and the frequency of molecular collisions are further subjects which need discussion before our picture of the molecular activity in gases is satisfactory; these questions are our next topic.

9.3. Molecular Collisions

From the knowledge of molecular size, number, and root mean square speeds, we can easily deduce that under any ordinary conditions, the molecules of a gas can not travel very far on the average between encounters and will experience many collisions each second.

Mean Free Path

If we imagine ourselves at the site of a molecule in a gas, we should expect, from kinetic theory, to see many molecules approaching and receding in all directions, with now and then a near miss and occasionally a direct encounter. At the same time, our point of observation will be moving on a series of straight paths, each terminated by another collision. We may make a simple but rough estimate of the distances traveled between impacts by assuming only one molecule is free to move and calculating what distance it would travel on the average before striking another somewhere in the vicinity.

Suppose that the one molecule A is traveling in one of the directions indicated in Fig. 9.3. If, for simplicity, we assume all molecules are

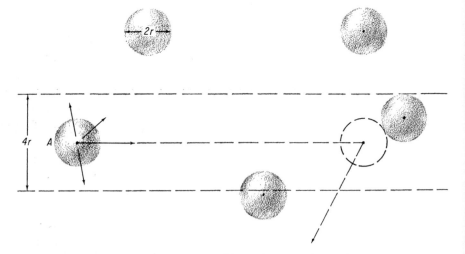

Fig. 9.3. *Collision between hard spheres, illustrating mean free path.*

spheres of radius r, a collision will first occur when the distance between the center of A and the center of B, for example, is less than $2r$. The distance traveled before collision occurs will clearly depend on the direction, and any single number can only represent some sort of average figure. The average distance is called the *mean free path* or λ.

To estimate the length of the mean free path (λ), consider the volume from which the centers of all other molecules must be excluded if no collision occurs. This space is the volume of a cylinder of radius $2r$ and hence is $\pi(2r)^2\lambda$. If each molecule on the average reserves to itself this volume between collisions, then—since N molecules collectively occupy the volume V—the volume per individual should be V/N, which gives

$$\pi(2r)^2\lambda = \frac{V}{N} \quad \text{or} \quad \lambda = \frac{1}{4\pi r^2}\left(\frac{V}{N}\right)$$

Since $V/N = m/d$, where m is the mass of the molecule and d the density of the gas, it is seen that the mean free path varies *inversely* as the density and depends on the effective radius r and mass of the kind of molecule. To obtain representative values of λ from this formula it is convenient to write it in terms of pressure and temperature.

Since $PV = nRT = NkT$, we have

$$\lambda \simeq \frac{1}{4\pi r^2}\left(\frac{kT}{P}\right) \tag{9.6}$$

For molecules of radius 2 Å, the mean free path at 300°K and 1 atmosphere is about 8×10^{-6} cm (800 Å). At a pressure of 10^{-5} mm of mercury reached by a good vacuum system, however, λ at 300°K has the very large value of some 6000 cm, or about 200 feet. From this figure, it is evident that a molecular beam at such pressures will suffer very little spreading by collisions with other gas molecules in apparatus of reasonable dimension, and low enough pressures permit the study of such beams without errors from scattering.

The argument used to obtain Eq. 9.6 should be recognized as a very rough one, oversimplified and intended only to obtain an answer of the correct order of magnitude. By taking into account the relative motion of other molecules and the distribution of their velocities, Maxwell obtained the more accurate result

$$\lambda = \frac{1}{\sqrt{2}\, 4\pi r^2}\left(\frac{V}{N}\right) \tag{9.6a}$$

from which the result above differs only by a factor $1/\sqrt{2} = 0.71$. It should be noted that Maxwell's result depends on the same kind of assumption made in obtaining the van der Waals b, that molecules can be considered not only as spheres but as rigid bodies. The true value of λ is more accurately obtained by much more complicated arguments, taking account of the true repulsive forces. It is also recognized that λ loses useful meaning in condensed phases where molecules are, so to speak, in a continuous state of collision.

Collision Frequencies

A rough estimate of the average frequency (f) of collisions of a given molecule is obtained if we divide the root mean square speed by the mean free path. This gives

$$f = \frac{\sqrt{(U^2)_{\text{ave}}}}{\lambda} = 4\pi r^2 \left(\frac{3RT}{M}\right)^{1/2}\left(\frac{N}{V}\right)$$

This expression is correct only as to order of magnitude; a better calculation gives

$$f = 4\sqrt{\pi}\, r^2 \left(\frac{RT}{M}\right)^{1/2} \frac{N}{V}$$

The quantity f from either expression is a very large number for gases at ordinary pressures and temperatures. For a molecule with $M = 50$ at 300°K and 1 atmosphere using $r \sim 4 \times 10^{-8}$ cm, one obtains $f \cong 10^{11}$ collisions per second.

The significance of f as calculated here should be remembered: it is the number of collisions experienced in one second by a *single* molecule of a gas. That it is so large under ordinary conditions leads to a number of important conclusions about rates of reaction in gases which are taken up later. It should be clear, however, that a realistic discussion of molecular energies in gases must from the beginning recognize the very high frequencies of molecular collisions which can exchange and redistribute energies.

9.4. Transport Properties of Gases

The high frequencies of collision and small distances traveled between collisions of molecules in gases ensure that molecules of a gas rapidly reach equilibrium average values of velocity and energy by continual transfer during their many collisions. The precise nature of the processes plays no role, however, in determining *equilibrium properties* of a gas outwardly at rest and unchanging with respect to its surroundings, and the mean free path or frequency of collisions do not appear in the gas law or equations for energy of a gas.

Collisions have a very direct bearing, on the other hand, in determining how a gas reacts to conditions in which the gas is not completely in equilibrium with itself internally. Three important situations of this kind are frequently studied, because of information they can give about the internal forces acting during collisions and because of practical problems in gas flow. These situations are indicated schematically in the drawings of Fig. 9.4, and may be described as follows.

1. *Viscosity.* To maintain different velocities of two adjacent surfaces requires forces applied to the surfaces, when the space between is occupied by a gas (or other fluid). These forces are larger if the separation is small and the area of the plates large, and they increase with the difference in velocities.

2. *Thermal Conduction.* If the temperatures in a tube of gas are different along the tube, energy as heat must be supplied the gas at the hot end and taken from the gas at the cold end. The amounts are larger if the tube is short and increase with the difference in temperature between the ends.

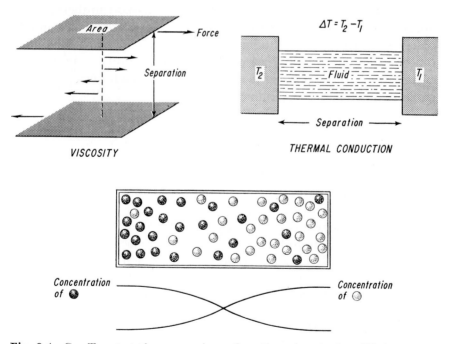

Fig. 9.4. *Gas Transport phenomena: viscous flow; thermal conduction; diffusion.*

3. *Diffusion.* If the concentrations of a gas are different at different points in a tube, motions of the molecules will act to equalize the concentrations. The rate of this "molecular flow," called diffusion, will be higher for large concentration differences, and if the distance between regions of a given difference is smaller.

In the phenomenon of viscosity, forces must be applied to cause shearing flow because the molecules of the gas striking the moving surface are not moving as rapidly in the direction of the surface and hence act to slow it down. The necessary force then supplies the increased momentum which the molecules acquire on rebounding. The result is a *transport of momentum* by the molecules from one surface to the interior of the gas and ultimately by collisions to the other surface. In thermal conduction, molecules entering a warmer region have less than the equilibrium amount for the region and are "cooler." The energy supplied them goes to increase their average energy, and "hotter" molecules returning to cooler regions result in a *transport of energy* from the source of heat to the point where it is removed. In diffusion there is *transport of mass* by net migration of molecules from regions of higher concentration, and the process is thus the mass counterpart of the momentum transport in viscosity and energy transport in thermal conduction. There is a difference in the way the processes are usually observed, as changes in diffusion flow during the approach to uniform concentration are usually measured, while for the others the force or energy supply corresponding to establishment of steady velocity or temperature differences is determined.

Viscosity

The way in which molecular motions in gas act to impede relative motion of bounding surfaces and produce the effect of viscosity can be illustrated simply.

Consider two surfaces, as in Fig. 9.5, *A*. If a force F is applied to the lower and a force $-F$ to the upper one, steady velocities $\frac{1}{2}U$ and $-\frac{1}{2}U$ will finally result. The reason for force being necessary can be seen from Fig. 9.5, *B*, showing molecules near the lower surface. Those which strike it must come from points above, where they last collided with other molecules before traveling without further interruption. They thus reach the surface with average speeds to the left, which are those of the more slowly moving gas at a distance of approximately a mean free path λ above the surface. On colliding, they will act to slow the surface down, much as a weight dropped on a moving belt would decrease its speed; if its speed is not to decrease, a force must be applied momentarily to the surface.

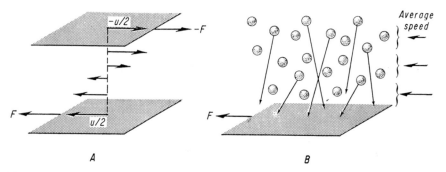

Fig. 9.5. *Viscosity effects between moving surfaces.*

There are, of course, many molecules reaching the lower surface in a second, all of which must be speeded up by the average force F to maintain a velocity difference in layers of the gas. It might be guessed that this force would increase with density, because the number of molecules involved is larger. This is not so, however, because with more molecules, the ones reaching the surface come from shorter distances above it and so need not be given as much extra momentum. This prediction by Maxwell was at first regarded with suspicion, and its proof by experiment was a triumph of the kinetic theory.

The necessary force F for a given velocity difference can be derived by equating it to the momentum change it must produce (Newton's second law).

This momentum change is the product of the increase in speed along x of molecules coming on the average from a distance a little less than λ above the surface times the mass of each molecule and number of molecules striking per second. For unit area, the number is $\frac{1}{2}(N/V)(U_y)$, since N/V is the number per unit volume and $(U_y)_{ave}$ their average speed of approach perpendicular to y (one-half, because only those approaching count). Each moves on the average with the speed of the gas flow a distance $\frac{2}{3}λ$ above the surface; the factor $\frac{2}{3}$ accounts for the different possible directions from which molecules can travel a distance λ to reach the surface. They therefore are moving more slowly by an amount $U(\frac{2}{3}λ/D)$ if D is the separation of the surfaces and U the total change in velocity. On collision with the surface, the momentum to be supplied is then $mu(\frac{2}{3}\lambda/D)$ per molecule, on the average. The force F/A per unit area necessary therefore is

$$\frac{F}{A} = mu\left(\frac{2}{3}\frac{\lambda}{D}\right)\frac{1}{2}\frac{N}{V}(U_y)_{\mathrm{ave}}$$

$$= \frac{1}{3}\left(\frac{Nm}{V}\right)(U_y)_{\mathrm{ave}}\lambda\frac{U}{d}$$

The ratio F/A to U/D can be measured and is defined as the coefficient of viscosity η. The theory thus predicts that

$$\eta = \frac{F/A}{u/D} = \tfrac{1}{3}d(U_y)_{\mathrm{ave}}\lambda, \tag{9.7}$$

since $(Nm/V) = d$, the density of the gas.

Thermal Conduction

The explanation of thermal conduction by kinetic theory employs similar arguments. As sketched in Fig. 9.6, molecules striking the hotter of two surfaces come from a cooler region of gas. They therefore reach the surface with less than their equilibrium amount of energy, and gain energy from the surface on collision. If the surface is not to cool down, energy must be supplied as heat. Two opposing effects, just as in viscosity, make the amount needed independent of the density: more molecules strike but each singly needs less energy.

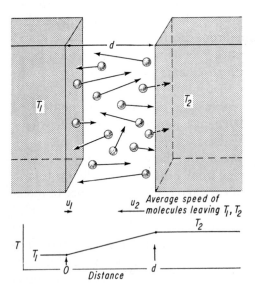

Fig. 9.6. *Thermal conductivity model for a gas.*

A derivation of the ratio of energy needed to the temperature gradient is much like the calculation for viscosity. However, the fact that molecules may possess both translational and internal energies, as discussed in the next chapter, must be considered. The treatment of this subject must go into more detail than is appropriate here, and will be found in a number of books on kinetic theory and heat. For present purposes it is important to recognize the significance of energy transport and the part played by molecular collisions and the mean free path in determining it.

Diffusion

As already mentioned, processes of diffusion are ordinarily studied differently in the laboratory than are viscosity and thermal conduction. The reason is one of experimental convenience, as it is not easy to devise arrangements for continuously supplying molecules to a region of high concentration (and removing them from others) without causing upsetting disturbances.

Internal transport of momentum and energy by the molecules themselves operate in viscosity and thermal conduction to neutralize gradients of velocity and temperature in gases (and in other states of matter, but by different means). These gradients correspond to work of forces acting to produce them, whether mechanical, electrical, or otherwise. Similar considerations apply to diffusion: the transport is of mass—molecules—to regions of lower concentration to neutralize concentration gradients,

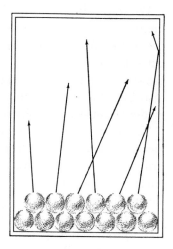

Slow diffusion into gas—
lower mean free path

Fast diffusion into
empty space—longer
mean free path

Fig. 9.7. *Effect of mean free path in gaseous diffusion.*

but the origin of the corresponding forces and work or potential of these forces is more subtle.

Establishing a situation in which one kind of molecule is more concentrated in one place than another requires work from outside, and by analogy with potential and potential energy of mechanics this change is described by an increase in *chemical potential*. The direction of natural processes is to decrease this potential, just as falling bodies go to regions of lower gravitational potential and electrical charge to regions of lower electrical potential.

Returning to the subject of diffusion, the mean free path between collisions plays a governing role, because it is a measure of the distance traveled before molecular motions are averaged by further collisions, as suggested by Fig. 9.7. The difference between rates of diffusion of one gas into another and rates of effusion into an empty space is readily understood on this basis. In the latter case, escaping molecules have no means of return, but in the former, diffusing molecules are frequently deflected by collisions after traveling short distances, and the net change is governed by smaller differences in numbers of molecules in different regions.

9.5. Possible Kinetic Energies of Translation

We found in Section 9.2 that the ideal gas law resulted from simple momentum considerations if the total kinetic energy of the molecules is proportional to the absolute temperature, regardless of the actual numbers of molecules having particular values of kinetic energy. The ideal gas law gives no information about the way in which the total energy is distributed among the molecules' temperature and concentration; other evidence must be considered to deduce anything further.

The first question to be considered is what translational kinetic energies are possible for molecules free to move about in a container of some prescribed volume V. Before quantum theory, it was supposed that *any* energy was possible, but, as we have seen in Chapters 5 and 6, quantum theory shows and experiment confirms that only discrete quantum states can exist. The energy differences between possible states of a particle free to move in a specified volume are largest when the particle is confined to a small space; the differences become smaller when greater freedom is allowed the particle. This is a general conclusion from quantum calculations of energies, and is important for the present subject because we should expect that with the volumes of laboratory dimensions available for motions of molecules as a whole, the possible states of energy would be very numerous and closely spaced.

The amount by which successive energy states must differ in momentum can be obtained from de Broglie's relation between wavelength and momentum. If a particle moves in the x-direction between walls of distance a apart, only those wavelengths in de Broglie's relation $\lambda = h/p$ are possible which are contained an integral number of times in the distance a. (This boundary condition is similar to those for other standing waves, such as sound waves in a closed tube and vibrations of a wire.) This will be true for $\lambda = a/n_x$ where n_x is an integer ($n_x = 1, 2, 3, \cdots$). The possible values of momentum are therefore given by $p_x = \pm n_x h/a$ ($\pm$ since p_x can be negative or positive) and successive values of p_x thus differ by an amount h/a. Similarly, motion in the y and z directions in a box with distances b and c between the walls will have only those momenta given by $p_y = \pm n_y h/b$ and $p_z = \pm n_z h/c$.

The molecular speeds U_{x1}, U_{x2}, $\cdots$, U_{xr} considered in deriving the ideal gas law thus may have only quantized values given by

$$U_x = \frac{p_x}{m} = \frac{n_x h}{ma},$$

where $n_x = 0, 1, 2, 3, \cdots$. These possible speeds are evenly spaced, since n_x is an integer, and the spacing h/ma is a very small change for molecules in containers of ordinary dimensions. If a is 10 cm, for example, and m is $32/(0.6 \times 10^{+24})$—the oxygen molecule—then the spacing of speeds is

$$\frac{h}{ma} = \frac{6.6 \times 10^{-27} \times 0.6 \times 10^{24}}{32 \times 10} \cong 1.2 \times 10^{-5} \text{ cm/sec}$$

In Section 9.2 it was deduced that molecules of oxygen at 300°K must have speeds of 10^4 cm/sec on the average and so there are some 10^9 different possible smaller speeds, U_x, all of which are evenly spaced. Similarly, large numbers of evenly spaced speeds U_y and U_z are also allowed if the other dimensions b and c of the container are of U order of centimeters or more, and the total number of speeds U for all the possibilities combined is evidently enormous.

The number of speeds between U_x and $U_x + dU_x$ depends on the size of the interval dU_x, and will be the same for a given size of this interval regardless of the value of U_x at which the interval begins (because the possible values are evenly spaced). However, the number of speeds *regardless of direction* is usually of more interest, as this determines the number of possible values of kinetic energy. Figure 9.8 shows the difference in the two cases geometrically. Since $U^2 = U_x^2 + U_y^2 + U_z^2$, the value of U is represented by a line from the origin to *any* point on a sphere of radius U. The number of speeds between U and $U + dU$, regardless of the direction of U, corresponds to the number of states for which the end of this line from the origin lies in the spherical shell between U and $U + dU$.

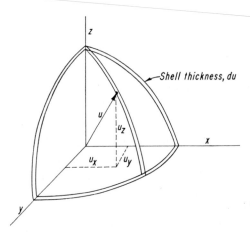

Since the number of states between U_x and $U_x + dU_x$ depends only on dU_x and similarly for y and z, the number in a little element of volume $dU_x dU_y dU_z$ anywhere in the shell is proportional to the size of this element. The total number of possibilities for U to be *somewhere* in the shell is then evidently proportional to its total volume. If the shell is thin (dU much less than U), its volume is the area $4\pi U^2$ of the sphere times the thickness dU; therefore

$$\text{number of states between } U \text{ and } U + dU = \text{constant} \times 4\pi U^2 \, dU \quad (9.8)$$

The constant will depend on the size of the container, because the spacings of possible speeds do, but not on U, because the spacings are even.

Fig. 9.8. *Components of the velocity vector.*

9.6. Distribution of Molecules in Energy States

In the preceding section we have seen that many speeds, and hence kinetic energies, are possible for molecules in an ideal gas, and in Section 9.3 we found that at a temperature T the *total translational* kinetic energy of N molecules is $\frac{3}{2}RT = \frac{3}{2}NkT$. In deducing the ideal gas law we assumed that different molecules could have different energies but reached no conclusion about what this distribution of energies was.

We can imagine many possible ways which might exist without violating our conditions, a few of which are as follows.

1. All the molecules have nearly the same energy $\frac{3}{2}kT$.
2. One molecule has virtually all the energy $\frac{3}{2}NkT$.

3. Half the molecules have essentially no kinetic energy and the others have twice the average value, or $3kT$ apiece.

4. A few molecules have high energies compared to kT, whence the rest have energies much less than kT.

The fundamental problem is to determine which of these or other possibilities is actually realized. It is important first to recognize that because of collisions or other interactions molecules are continually exchanging energy in complicated ways, depending on details of the many encounters. If all the molecules of a given *kind* are indistinguishable one from another, then we can specify only how many have a particular energy, or range of energy, or speed, without saying which ones.

The problem of predicting the average statistical behavior of a system of many molecules is the subject of *statistical mechanics*. A basic postulate of this subject is that all quantum energy states have the same a priori probability; that is, in the absence of further restrictions any one energy state is as likely to be occupied as any other. In our problem, however, there is a further restriction: the total energy of N molecules must be $\frac{3}{2}RT$. Because of this limitation on energy to be shared, all states cannot have the same probability of occupation, as an infinite amount of energy would be required for all possible states to be equally occupied.

At the same time, we should suspect that a condition of states too unequally occupied would be an unlikely result of processes leading to an equilibrium situation. Of necessity, the average numbers of molecules having a particular range of energy must stay constant at equilibrium, as a result of a balance between loss and gain of energy. The extreme case of only a few molecules sharing all the available energy is an unlikely result of continual exchanges. Having all molecules share quite equally the total amount of energy may seem at first sight a reasonable alternative, but this situation also can be shown to be too improbable a result.

It is possible to formulate statistically the probability of different distributions of the same total energy, and then as a problem in calculus to find which distribution of molecules among various energies is the most probable. The result of this calculation, which belongs in a course in statistical mechanics, is that the population of energy states is greater for states of low energy and is weighted by the *Boltzmann factor* $e^{-E/kT}$ if the temperature is not too low.

The result is expressed by an equation of the form

number of molecules in states of energy E

$$= \text{constant} \times e^{-E/kT} \times (\text{number of states in } E \text{ to } E + dE) \quad (9.9)$$

In this equation we have included a constant, which does not depend on the energy E, to allow for any desired total number of molecules, and have also included the multiplying factor of the number of states in the range dE to allow for differences in spacing of states according to the requirement of equal a priori probability. That is, other things being equal, twice as many molecules will have energy in a range dE if there are twice as many possible energy states in this range. The lesser number of molecules for larger values of E is represented by the smaller value of $e^{-E/kT}$.

The way in which the numbers decrease with larger E is conveniently represented by a sort of population chart for various values of E as shown in Fig. 9.9 for two cases: the first is for successive values of E differing by kT; the second corresponds to a temperature three times as great and hence has successive values of E differing by $\frac{1}{3}kT$. Comparison of the two cases shows that having kT larger increases the relative population of higher energies because more energy is available. This must be at the ex-

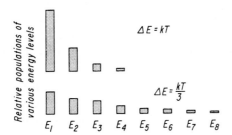

Fig. 9.9. *Boltzmann distribution factor populations for evenly spaced levels.*

pense of populations of lower energy states if the total number of molecules is the same. For this reason, the vertical line for the lowest state is drawn shorter in the second case to represent the smaller number.

An exponential function of energy represents the effect of energy on population because in a sense it is the smoothest function to balance the limitation on total energy against the greater number of possibilities for allotting molecules among a larger number of states.

We should note finally that the Boltzmann distribution factor has a much wider usefulness than for just the immediate problem of molecular speeds in gases; we shall encounter it in other problems where the statistical equilibrium of systems of many molecules is involved. At the same time, it should be remembered that it is not an exact expression for some extreme cases—notably gases of light molecules at low temperatures and free electrons in metals. These cases are very special ones, and we need not worry about inaccuracy in using the Boltzmann factor for most problems in chemistry.

9.7. The Maxwell Distribution of Velocities in Gases

With the results of the last two sections, we are in a position to write down and examine the form of the distribution of translational energies, or, equally well, the speeds of molecules in an ideal gas. The number of molecules with speeds between U and $U + dU$, which we write as $N(U)\,dU$, is given by

$$N(U)\,dU = \text{constant} \times e^{-E/kT} \times [\text{number of energy states} \atop \text{with } U \text{ in the range } dU]$$

where E is the translational kinetic energy $\frac{1}{2}mU^2$.

As shown in Section 9.4, the number of states is proportional to $4\pi U^2\,dU$. If we include the factor multiplying $U^2\,dU$ in a new constant C, we therefore have

$$N(U)\,dU = 4\pi C e^{-\frac{1}{2}mU^2/kT} U^2\,dU. \qquad (9.10)$$

Evaluation of C

The value of the constant C obviously depends on the total number of molecules N in the gas sample, as the number with any particular range of speeds must increase in pro-portion to the total number. As a corollary of this same propo-sition, we can deduce what the value of the constant C must be by requiring that the sum of values of $N(U)\,dU$ for *all* val-ues of U equal N.

Since the states with different values of U are very closely spaced and even a minute change in U includes many

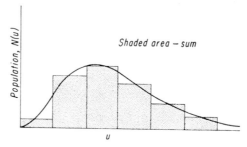

Fig. 9.10. *Difference between areas by summing and by integrating under a smooth curve.*

states, we can sum the values of $N(U)\,dU$ with completely negligible error by integrating $N(U)\,dU$ over all values of U from zero to in-finity. This can be seen from the drawing in Fig. 9.10, comparing the results of a sum and integration when the number of states is small. The difference between the two areas is not great for this fairly small number of states and becomes insignificant for the enormous number of our actual problem:

$$\int_0^\infty N(U)\, dU = N = 4\pi C \int_0^\infty e^{-\frac{1}{2}mU^2/kT} U^2\, dU \qquad (9.11)$$

Since the integral on the right is over all values of U, its magnitude is a function only of the values of m and kT. If the integration is possible, we shall therefore have a value for C in terms of N, m, and kT. Fortunately, the integral $\int_0^\infty x^2 e^{-x^2\,dx}$, to which our integral can be reduced by setting $x = U\sqrt{m/2kT}$, is known to have the value $\sqrt{\pi}/4$. We thus have

$$n = 4\pi C \left(\frac{2kT}{m}\right)^{3/2} \int_0^\infty x^2 e^{-x^2}\, dx = C\left(\frac{2\pi kT}{m}\right)^{3/2}$$

and so

$$C = N\left(\frac{m}{2\pi kT}\right)^{3/2}$$

Maxwell's Distribution

Using the result for C gives the most common form of *Maxwell's distribution of velocities:*

$$N(U)\, dU = 4\pi N \left(\frac{m}{2\pi kT}\right)^{3/2} e^{-\frac{1}{2}mU^2/kT} U^2\, dU \qquad (9.12)$$

The nature of this distribution function for one mole of nitrogen ($m = 28/0.6 \times 10^{+24} = 40 \times 10^{-24}$ g) at several temperatures is shown in Fig. 9.11.

We can see that this result embodies the characteristic features to be expected from our discussion of possible energy states and distribution among these states. At any one temperature, the number with a given speed at first increases with the speed because there are increasing numbers of states available. The opposing effect of the Boltzmann factor, which prevents too many molecules from having large energies, dominates for still higher speeds and the number decreases. At higher temperatures, there is more total kinetic energy, which is shared by more of the molecules having higher speeds

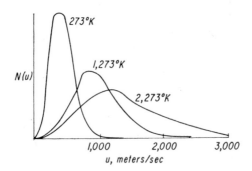

Fig. 9.11. *Distribution of molecular speeds in nitrogen.*

and the distribution is broader. (Its peak is lower because the area under the curve must be the same, since this area represents the total number, which we assumed to be one mole for all three temperatures.)

Distribution of Velocity Components

The form of distribution we have derived is for the speed U, regardless of direction. It is often useful to know the distribution of components of velocities in a particular direction, say along x. This distribution can be shown by methods similar to the ones we have used to be

$$N(U_x)\, dU_x \;=\; N\left(\frac{m}{2\pi k T}\right)^{1/2} e^{-\frac{1}{2}mU^2/kT}\, dU_x$$

This function is plotted in Fig. 9.12 for both positive and negative values of U_x, because negative values are as likely as positive ones for a particle free to move in either direction of x.

It will be noted that the most probable value of U_x when direction is considered is zero, and because of the sym-metry the average *velocity* U_x is zero. The average *speed* along x—without regard to whether x is in creasing or decreasing—is not zero, just as the average speed U in any direction is

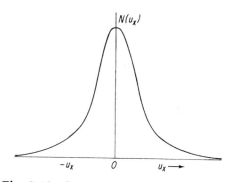

Fig. 9.12. *One-dimensional velocity distribu-tion.*

greater than zero. It is this value $(U_x)_{\text{ave}}$ which is appropriate for calcula-ting viscosity and similar transport properties of gases, discussed in Section 9.4.

The Average Kinetic Energy

The statistical theory which leads to the Boltzmann factor provides in its development for the total energy being fixed. This results in the quantity kT appearing in the exponent when the unit of energy kT is chosen to agree with the definition of the absolute temperature scale. Since this was done, the theory must necessarily give $\frac{3}{2}NkT$ for the total translational kinetic energy or $\frac{3}{2}kT$ for the average value per molecule if we compute the total energy by adding up the energies of different molecules in accordance with their distribution of speeds. Because this addition process to obtain the total energy is one frequently encountered, we shall carry it out here for the Maxwell distribution, to illustrate the process and verify that the system does have the total kinetic energy $\frac{3}{2}RT$ per mole, as it should.

The amount of kinetic energy possessed by $N(U)\,dU$ molecules with speeds U to $U + dU$ must be this number times the kinetic energy of each. This latter is very nearly $\frac{1}{2}mU^2$ for all if dU is very small, and so we have

$$\text{kinetic energy for speeds between } U \text{ and } U + dU$$

$$= \tfrac{1}{2}mU^2 N(U)\,dU$$

$$= 2\pi Nm \left(\frac{m}{2kT}\right)^{3/2} e^{-\frac{1}{2}mU^2/kT} U^4\,dU$$

The total kinetic energy for all possible speeds between zero and infinity is then

$$KE = 2\pi Nm \left(\frac{m}{2\pi kT}\right)^{3/2} \int_0^\infty e^{-\frac{1}{2}mU^2/kT} U^4\,dU$$

The substitution $x = U\sqrt{m/2kT}$, as before, gives the integral

$$\int_0^\infty e^{-x^2} x^4\,dx,$$

which is known to have the value $3\sqrt{\pi}/8$. We therefore have

$$KE = 2\pi Nm \left(\frac{m}{2\pi kT}\right)^{3/2} \left(\frac{2kT}{m}\right)^{5/2} \frac{3\sqrt{\pi}}{8} = \tfrac{3}{2}NkT$$

and the average value KE/N per molecule is $\frac{3}{2}kT$, in agreement with the result of the ideal gas law derivation.

The agreement of the result of adding up energies weighted by the numbers with these energies is not, as we have already indicated, a proof of its validity, but is rather a verification of the consistency of the methods employed.

Verifications of the Maxwell Distribution

Direct measurements to confirm that the molecules of an ideal gas do have speeds in the proportions stated by the Maxwell expression are not easily made. Some experiments have, however, given convincing direct evidence of the distribution and, within their rather large errors, agreement with the theoretical expressions.

An experiment by Zartman in 1931 employed a simple scheme, illustrated in Fig. 9.13. Bismuth was heated in the oven at the left to give

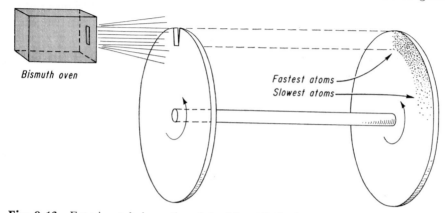

Fig. 9.13. *Experimental observation of the Maxwell distribution of molecular speeds.*

atomic vapor. Atoms escaping from the fixed slit in the oven could pass through the slit on the rotating disk and continue to a glass plate mounted on the other rotating disk. Where they hit depended on their speed, being further clockwise for the slower atoms because the plate rotated counterclockwise during the time of transit. The variation in density of bismuth deposit with position on the plate could thus be used to determine the relative numbers of molecules with different speeds. Within the fairly large errors of the experiment, the variation agreed well with the theory.

The most important and conclusive evidence in support of the Maxwell distribution is, however, the agreement of results deduced from it with properties of gases, whose dependence upon the existence and nature of the velocity distribution is less obvious than those described in the preceding paragraph, but which nevertheless can be measured more accurately.

Limitations of the Statistical Approach

It is important to recognize that the Boltzmann factor and the velocity distribution are expressions of average equilibrium properties. The Boltzmann factor can be used to predict the *fraction* of molecules having certain values of energy or speed. It does not tell us what each molecule is doing at a particular instant, nor would this more detailed information be of any use, as no one would seriously consider tabulating the positions and speeds of the 10^{20} or more molecules in a gas for comparison with such results.

The theory also makes no attempt to say *which* molecules of a gas have particular ranges of energy. Again, however, this is not a real deficiency because we have no way of knowing which are which, and no molecules retain particular speeds or energy for long. One oxygen molecule is indistinguishable from any other, if all contain only the oxygen 16 isotope. If some have mass 18 oxygen atoms, they are distinguishably different—being heavier they can be separated, by a mass spectrograph, for example—but these different molecules can be treated as a different group of indistinguishable molecules.

The real limitations of the statistical approach outlined are encountered when studying gases at low enough temperatures and in problems where molecules cannot be treated as independent. In such cases, it is not proper to discuss the energy of a single molecule as if there were such a quantity independent of the other molecules. Instead, one must consider the possible energies of the entire system of molecules. Appropriate but more difficult statistical methods of great generality have been developed for dealing with these more complicated problems, notably by Willard Gibbs.

Problems

9.1. What is the average translational kinetic energy of a monatomic gas at 150°C? Express your answer in ergs per molecule and in calories per mole.

9.2. One mole of an ideal gas in a closed container is heated from 30°C to 100°C. (a) What is the total translational kinetic energy before and after the change? (b) How much heat must be supplied to the gas to produce the increase in energy?

9.3. Avogadro's hypothesis states that equal volumes of all gases at the same temperature and pressure contain equal numbers of molecules. Show that this hypothesis follows directly from the kinetic theory of gases. Show also that Dalton's law of partial pressure is predicted by the theory.

9.4. The total momentum of a gas in a stationary container must be zero. How do you reconcile this with the kinetic theory picture that the molecules are moving with many speeds?

9.5. A molecule with components U_x, U_y, U_z of velocity strikes a wall perpendicular to the x-axis. (a) What are the components after the collision (assumed elastic)? (b) What are the components after collision with a wall which makes an angle of $45°$ with the x- and y-axes but does not intersect the z-axis?

9.6. State the two conservation laws which are obeyed by two molecules in collision. If the masses of the molecules and their velocities before collision are known, are the conditions imposed by these laws sufficient to determine the velocities after collision?

9.7. (a) What is the RMS speed of hydrogen molecules at $300°K$? (b) What is this speed at $1000°K$? Express both answers in cm/sec and in miles/hour.

9.8. Compare the root mean square speeds of O_2, N_2, and H_2 at $1000°K$. Suggest a reason why the earth's atmosphere contains a negligible amount of H_2 whereas the atmospheres of the massive planets such as Jupiter and Saturn contain appreciable amounts of this gas.

9.9. The rate of effusion of a gas through a very small hole from a container to an evacuated space is proportional to the average speeds of the molecules of the gas. (a) Explain why this is so. (b) Show that for the same pressure, temperature, and other conditions hydrogen will effuse four times faster than oxygen. (c) Show that increasing the temperature from $300°K$ to $400°K$ will increase the rate of effusion by 15% if the concentration is the same. What will the percentage increase be if the pressure is the same?

9.10. A gas has a density of 1.256 g/liter and a molecular weight of 32. What is its mean free path if $r = 2$ Å? What is the change in mean free path when the gas is heated at constant volume from its initial temperature of $200°K$ to $300°K$? What is the change in root-mean-square speed for this change?

9.11. Compare the mean free paths of H_2 molecules at $0°C$ and (a) 760 mm pressure, (b) 1×10^{-3} mm pressure, (c) 1×10^{-7} mm pressure.

9.12. At an altitude of 200 miles, the mean free path of hydrogen has been estimated to be as large as 1000 miles. If the temperature is $250°K$, to what pressure would this correspond?

9.13. If the molecular diameter of HI is taken to be 3.5×10^{-8} cm, how many collisions between HI molecules will take place per second per milliliter in the gas at $556°K$ at a concentration of 1 mole/liter? (Calculations of this type are important in a consideration of the speeds of chemical reactions.)

9.14. What are the units of η, the coefficient of viscosity, in terms of mass, length, and time?

9.15. Combine Eqs. 9.5, 9.6, 9.7 to show that the coefficient of viscosity (η) is independent of the density of the gas under the assumptions made in the derivation of these equations. What is the predicted form of temperature dependence of η if the collision radius r of the molecules is assumed independent of temperature?

9.16. Calculate the viscosity of a gas of molecules 2 Å in radius at 25°C. How does this compare with the viscosity of liquid water at the same temperature?

9.17. When a solution is centrifuged, what are the two opposing forces which determine the eventual steady-state concentration gradient?

9.18. If the possible values of the momentum of a particle moving in the x direction in a box are given by $p_x = \pm n_x h/2a$, where a is the x dimension of the box, what are the possible kinetic energy levels? For a box of dimensions, a, b, and c, what are the possible energy levels for a particle which can move in any direction with possible momentum components p_x, p_y, p_z?

9.19. (a) If the number of molecules with speeds between U and $U + dU$ is given by constant $\times 4\pi U^2 \, dU$, how many molecules have kinetic energies between E and $E + dE$? (b) Using the preceding result show that the distribution of kinetic energies has the form

$$dN(E, E + dE) = \text{constant } e^{-E/kT} E^{1/2} \, dE$$

(c) With the equation $\int_0^{\infty} e^{-ax} x^{1/2} \, dx = \pi^{1/2}/2a^{3/2}$, show that the constant has the value $2N/\pi^{1/2}(kT)^{3/2}$, where N is the total number of molecules.

9.20. Make plots similar to those in Fig. 9.11 for helium at temperature of 100°K and 300°K; that is, calculate $N(U)/N$ for suitable values of U and plot as a function of U. Explain the shifts in height and spread of the curve for 300°K as compared with the curve for nitrogen in Fig. 9.11.

9.21. What is the spacing between translational kinetic energy levels for helium molecules in a cubic box of volume a^3? For reasonable values of the quantum numbers how does this spacing compare with the average translational kinetic energy per molecule at 0°C for a box whose linear dimension is 1 cm?

9.22. Use the Maxwell distribution (Eq. 9.11) to determine the most probable value of the speed of a gas molecule as a function of temperature. (The most probable value is the maximum value of $N(U)$ when plotted as a function of U.) How does this value compare with the root-mean-square speed given by Eq. 9.5?

9.23. (a) The average value X_{av} of a physical quantity X is given by $X_{av} = \int x N(x) \, dx / \int N(x) \, dx$, where $N(x)$ is the number of states in which the value of the quantity is between X and $X + dX$ and the integration extends over all states. Write down the expression which gives the average speed, X_{av}, of a molecule of a gas according to the Maxwell distribution law. (b) What is $U_{average}$ for the molecules of a gas at a temperature T? (Use table of integrals if necessary.) Compare this value with the RMS and most probable speed.

9.24. (a) Set up the integral which gives the fraction of molecules having speeds between $\frac{1}{2}$ and twice the most probable speed at a given temperature. (b) Set up the integral which gives the fraction of molecules having a speed greater than some fixed value, *S*. (Evaluation of these integrals unfortunately requires special methods.)

Suggested Readings

A good introductory account of the kinetic theory of gases is given in *Molecules in Motion* by T. G. Cowling, which is available as a paperback (Harper, New York, 1960). A standard reference at a more advanced level is *Kinetic Theory of Gases* by E. H. Kennard (McGraw-Hill, New York, 1938).

The reader interested in the historical development of the subject will find original papers by Maxwell well worth reading, and they are conveniently available in reprint form as *Collected Papers of James Clerk Maxwell* (Dover, New York, 1952). He should be warned that some of the work is outdated, as not even the "greatest theoretical physicist of the 19th century" could anticipate the twentieth.

Chapter 10

Heat Capacities and Molecular Energies of Gases

FROM THE DISCUSSION of the kinetic molecular nature of gases the significance of temperature as a measure of translational kinetic energy has become apparent, but it remains to consider the ways in which the amount of this and other forms of molecular energy can be changed. The most familiar process of raising the temperature of any body, gaseous or otherwise, is of course by heating or "flow of heat." In this chapter we review first the experimental description of heat as a means of energy transfer and then consider the significance of the quantities of heat found necessary to raise the temperature of gases and solids. (Heat capacities of liquids are discussed in Chapter 11.)

10.1. Units of Heat and Work

That definite changes in temperature of a body can be accomplished without the action of any large-scale forces has long been recognized and described by the statement that heat was given off or absorbed by the body. The unit of quantity for such processes was originally described independently of mechanical effects by defining a standard amount,

246

taken to be the calorie—the amount gained or lost by one gram of water when the temperature was raised or lowered by one degree centigrade. Early in the nineteenth century, however, Joule and others found that equal quantities of heat defined in these units could invariably be produced by equal amounts of mechanical work, no matter how performed, provided the only result of doing work was to cause a change in temperature.

The whole effect of doing work on a system—by rubbing surfaces together, by passing an electrical current through a coil of wire, or otherwise—is thus to change the state of the system in a way equally well described by the amount of work or by the number of calories of heat absorbed, as standardized by the old definition in terms of water. Joule found that approximately 4.2×10^7 ergs of work raised the temperature of water 1°C. Later investigators found values of 4.18–4.19×10^7 ergs for water at 25°C, but slightly different values at other temperatures. A better definition of the calorie was evidently necessary if it was to be used. The present definition is that

$$1 \text{ calorie} = 4.184 \times 10^7 \text{ ergs} = 4.184 \text{ joules}$$

which corresponds very closely to the work needed to raise 1 g of water from 14°C to 15°C.

The recognition that heat can be expressed in terms of mechanical units today leaves no real necessity for the calorie as a unit. From the point of view of experimental measurements, it is in fact something of a nuisance, because in laboratory practice heat is almost always supplied electrically. Electrical energy is calculated from the product of voltage (V), current (I), and time (t), and if the customary units of volts, amperes, seconds are employed, the heat is given in *joules* by the formula

$$\text{heat (joules)} = VIt$$

The joule (1 joule $= 10^7$ ergs) is thus a natural unit and is in addition a basic unit of work and energy in metric systems. However, the use of the calorie in expressing results of thermal measurements is so entrenched by tradition that its general replacement by the joule in the near future is unlikely, even though the logic of doing so has been indorsed by a number of scientific groups.

10.2. Heat Capacities

The amount of work spent wholly as heat which is necessary to raise the temperature of a substance a given amount depends on the quantity of substance and on the magnitude of the temperature rise, as well as on the kind of substance. In order to obtain a quantity characteristic only of the kind of substance and its temperature, *heat capacities* are defined by relations of the form

$$Q = XC\,dT \qquad (10.1)$$

where Q is the heat required to raise the temperature an amount dT, X is the quantity of material expressed in whatever units are desirable, and C is the heat capacity for the unit quantity. The defining relation implies that for sufficiently small changes, dT, the value of C changes only slightly, and that Q is thus proportional to the size of dT. The justification is that this is true experimentally unless changes of state occur with accompanying latent heats, in which case the definition is meaningless. We shall often take the mole as the unit of quantity and indicate this fact by a bar over the symbol ($\overline{C}$). (A more general definition of molal quantities, suitable also when several chemical species are involved as in chemical reactions, will be introduced in Chapters 11 and 12.)

By adopting the term "heat capacity," we follow the usage common among chemists. Physicists often employ the term "specific heat," particularly in connection with the gram as unit of quantity, and this term is often found in reference tables. Neither choice is without disadvantages: specific heat may carry the implication that a ratio is meant (as in the case of specific gravity); heat capacity may give the erroneous impression that heat is contained in matter.

Heat Capacities C_P and C_V

The definition of heat capacity just given seems definite enough to be complete, and adequate for proceeding to study values for different gases, but it is not, because *different* amounts of heat are required for one and the same substance at the same temperature if the conditions of heating are different in other respects.

Consideration of a simple example will show the truth of this and also the nature of the reasons for differences. Suppose we consider one mole of nitrogen initially at 25°C and atmospheric pressure and measure the heat required to raise its temperature to 26°C. If the nitrogen is in a closed bomb, about five calories will be needed for the gas alone, and the pressure will be a little above atmospheric at the end. If instead the nitrogen is allowed to expand enough to remain at one atmosphere, seven calories will be necessary. If neither pressure nor volume is kept fixed, some other value will be found. The differences occur because something else may or may not be happening as the gas is heated. If it is allowed to expand against the confining pressure, work is done on the surroundings at the same time that the gas becomes warmer, and this is reflected in the greater amount of heat required.

A numerical value of heat capacity evidently has meaning only if the conditions under which it is measured are specified. While it would be possible to give values corresponding to both pressure and volume change in any combination permitted by the equation of state, the much simpler conditions of keeping one or the other constant are by far the most convenient ones for most purposes. As we shall see later, the values obtained at constant pressure or volume also can be used together with the equation of state to calculate the heat necessary when both pressure and volume change.

Because of these considerations, heat capacities at constant pressure and constant volume are defined in terms of the corresponding amount of heat absorbed, the quantity held constant being indicated by attaching its symbol as a subscript:

$$\text{at constant pressure,}\quad Q_P = XC_P\,dT \qquad\qquad (10.2)$$

$$\text{at constant volume,}\quad Q_V = XC_V\,dT \qquad\qquad (10.3)$$

Difference between C_P and C_V for an Ideal Gas

As already intimated, the difference between C_P and C_V lies in the fact that heating at constant pressure must both increase the internal energy of the gas and supply the energy used by the gas in doing external work, whereas heat at constant volume goes entirely to increase the internal energy, since no work is done.

For an ideal gas, the increase in internal energy for a given temperature rise is the same whether or not the gas expands at the same time. The truth of this statement can be demonstrated experimentally by measurements discussed in Chapter 12. It is already evident that it is true of the translational kinetic energy, which has the value $\frac{3}{2}RT$ per mole, regardless of the value of PV. Hence for the temperature change dT in an ideal gas, we may write

$Q_P - Q_V = X(C_P - C_V)\,dT =$ work done by gas in expanding at constant pressure through a temperature range dT

The amount of this work for an ideal gas has a very simple value, which is readily deduced from the definition of mechanical work as the product of force and displacement in the direction of the applied force. This is shown in elementary physics to be equal to the product of the pressure confining the gas and the volume change. Denote this change by dV; then

$$\text{expansion work against a constant pressure } P = P\,dV$$

The volume change for a gas heated from temperature T_1 to T_2 is just

$$V_2 - V_1 = \frac{nRT_2}{P} - \frac{nRT_1}{P} \tag{10.4}$$

or

$$V_2 - V_1 = \frac{nR}{P}(T_2 - T_1) \tag{10.5}$$

But $V_2 - V_1$ is the volume change dV and $T_2 - T_1$ the temperature rise dT and so

$$dV = \frac{nR}{P}\,dT \tag{10.6}$$

The expansion work $P\,dV$ for n moles of gas is therefore

$$P\,dV = nR\,dT \tag{10.7}$$

With this value of expansion work, the expression 10.3 for $C_P - C_V$ can be put in a very simple form: if the quantity X is expressed in moles, C_P and C_V are molal specific heats, and so

$$Q_P - Q_V = n(\overline{C}_P - \overline{C}_V)\,dT = nR\,dT \tag{10.8}$$

This can only be true if the following relation holds for the difference $\overline{C}_P - \overline{C}_V$:

$$\overline{C}_P - \overline{C}_V = R \tag{10.9}$$

Thus for an ideal gas $\overline{C}_P$ is numerically larger than $\overline{C}_V$ by an amount $R = 1.98$ cal/mole/°C, if the calorie is used as the unit of heat and work. If the pressure is too high for the gas to behave ideally, the work $P\,dV$ will not be equal to $nR\,dT$, *nor* will the energy of the gas be independent of P. The value $\overline{C}_P - \overline{C}_V$ will then be different from R by an amount depending on the departures from ideality. (We shall see later in Chapter 14 how to calculate the difference for any substance from other thermodynamic properties.)

For many purposes the ideal gas approximation is sufficiently accurate, and if this is so, the relation $\overline{C}_P - \overline{C}_V = R$ enables us to calculate either $\bar{C}_P$ or $\bar{C}_V$ if the other is known. Which of these is more readily determined experimentally depends on the temperature range, and often neither is easy because at ordinary pressures the densities are so small. An indirect method based on sound velocity, which determines the ratio C_P/C_V, as discussed in Chapter 12, is sometimes used.

10.3. Some Heat Capacities of Gases

In Table 10.1 there are collected a series of values for the heat capacity ($\bar{C}_V$) of a number of gases near room temperature. The values in the first column are for one gram of gas, and show wide variations. A much more satisfactory basis, as we should expect, is to consider the molar heat capacities listed in the second column. From the listed values it is

TABLE 10.1.   *Heat Capacities of Gases at 15°C.*

	Gas	$\bar{C}_V$ (cal/gm/°C)	$\bar{C}_V$ (cal/mole/°C)
Monatomic	He	0.75	3.00
	Ar	0.075	3.01
Diatomic	H_2	2.41	4.86
	HCl	0.138	5.02
	O_2	0.155	4.97
	Cl_2	0.085	6.03
Polyatomic	H_2S	0.193	6.55
	CO_2	0.153	6.71
	NH_3	0.400	6.81
	CH_4	0.404	6.48
	C_2H_6	0.318	9.51
	C_2H_6O	0.298	13.7

readily apparent that the classification by complexity of the molecule has its counterpart in the molar heat capacities. The monatomic gases He and Ar have virtually the same value of 3 cal/mole/°C as do the other noble gases. With the exception of chlorine, the diatomic gases have values not far from 5, but individual variations are noticeable. The polyatomic gases have still more individuality, with increasingly large values for the more complex molecules.

The problem presented by the heat capacity values for gases, of which the few chosen are reasonably representative, is thus of explaining the similarities and differences in terms of molecular constitution. Since all the energy supplied an ideal gas as heat at constant volume must go to increase the energies of the molecules, it should be evident that ability to explain the $\overline{C}_V$ values is a test of the correctness of the kinetic and quantum theories of molecular energies.

10.4. Translational Kinetic Energy and Heat Capacity

A partial explanation of observed specific heats comes in a simple way from the kinetic theory underlying the ideal gas law. According to this theory, an ideal gas at temperature T possesses a total translational kinetic energy $\frac{3}{2}RT$ per mole. In order to increase the temperature by an amount dT from T to $T + dT$, this energy must therefore be increased by the corresponding amount

$$\tfrac{3}{2}R(T + dT) - \tfrac{3}{2}RT = \tfrac{3}{2}R\,dT \qquad (10.10)$$

If, however, this increase is by heating at constant volume without any other source of energy, this increase in kinetic energy can only be the result of heat supplied in the amount

$$Q_v = \tfrac{3}{2}R\,dT \qquad (10.11)$$

From the definition of heat capacity ($\overline{C}_V$), we thus see that supplying the needs of translational kinetic energy requires that $\overline{C}_V$ have a value $\frac{3}{2}R = 2.98$ cal/mole/°C. This is just the value found for monatomic gases, and is in fact the explanation of their heat capacity.

For diatomic and polyatomic gases, however, the measured values of $\overline{C}_V$ at room temperature are considerably greater than the translational value of 3. A semblance of agreement on a common value of about 5 is recognizable for the diatomic gases (exclusive of chlorine) and the polyatomic gases take up 6 or more. The success of the kinetic theory for the equation of state of *all* ideal gases, monatomic or otherwise, and its ability to explain C_V for monatomic gases make reasonable the proposition that polyatomic gases must also require heat of amount $\frac{3}{2}R$ cal/mole/°C for increased translational energy at higher temperatures.

If this is true, however, the excess of 2 or more cal/mole/°C must be accounted for in some other way. The possibility of relative internal nuclear motions in molecules, as contrasted with atoms, suggests that the explanation of the larger heat capacities is to be found in changes in energy of internal rotational and vibrational motions of the molecules.

The success of the statistical theory of these quantized energies in explaining the heat capacities of polyatomic cases is the subject of the next section. Before turning to it, one important conclusion from what has so far been done deserves emphasis. This is that the individuality of heat capacities of molecular gases is found even in the ideal state, whereas the equation of state on a molar basis is the same for all gases at low concentrations. This contrast of itself suggests the significance of *internal* molecular energies for heat capacities, because only the translational motion of molecules as a whole is involved in determining the pressure of an ideal gas.

10.5. Dependence of Heat Capacities on Temperature

In the preceding section it was shown that the kinetic theory of translational energy of molecules provides only a partial explanation of the observed heat capacities of molecular gases at ordinary temperatures. In this section we consider first further evidence from the dependence of heat capacity on temperature. The values of $\bar{C}_V$ for several simple gases are plotted against temperature in Fig. 10.1.

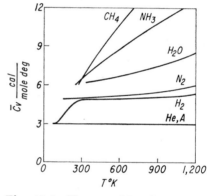

Fig. 10.1. *Heat capacities of gases as a function of temperature.*

From these curves, it is apparent that only the monatomic gases have $\bar{C}_V$ independent of temperature. For all the others, the values increase with temperature in one range or another. The behavior of the lightest, hydrogen, is particularly interesting because the value $\frac{3}{2}R$ characteristic of translational energy is reached at sufficiently low temperatures, thus suggesting that the internal contributions to C_V have, so to speak, been frozen out. For other heavier diatomic molecules there is little or no evidence of this effect, but values of approximately $\frac{5}{2}R = 5$ cal/mole/ centigrade degree are found at low temperatures, on which is superposed a gradual increase at higher temperatures. With a little good will, one can even read into the curves for NH_3 and CH_4 a beginning at $3R = 6$ cal/mole/centigrade degree and subsequent increase.

The values of heat capacities for various temperatures are frequently needed for thermochemical calculations of heats of reactions and reaction equilibria. For such purposes, equations fitting the data over temperature ranges of interest are often preferable to tables of values. This is particularly true if any manipulation of the values is involved, as in integration to find heat absorbed in a finite temperature change.

Empirical equations are usually given for $\bar{C}_P$ rather than $\bar{C}_V$, because most measurements are made at constant pressure. The most common form of equation is

$$\bar{C}_P = a + bT + cT^2,$$

where a, b, c are constants and T is in degrees Kelvin. Another form sometimes found to fit the data more accurately is

$$\bar{C}_P = a' + b'T + c'/T^2.$$

Either form of equation is a representation of measurements over some particular range of temperature, and should not be used outside that range.

EXAMPLE

The heat capacity of ethylene is represented over the range 300°K to 1500°K by the equation

$$\bar{C}_p = 2.706 + 29.160 \times 10^{-3}T - 9.050 \times 10^{-6}T^2$$

Calculate C_p at 300°K and 1000°K.

At 300°K, $\bar{C}_p = 2.706 + 29.160 \times 0.300 - 9.059 \times 0.0900$
$= 2.706 + 8.748 - 0.815 = 10.639$ cal/mole deg.

At 1000°K, $\bar{C}_p = 2.706 + 29.160 - 9.059 = 22.807$ cal/mole deg.

The equations can also be used to calculate total amounts of heat absorbed when the temperature is changed from an initial value T_1 to a new value T_2. Since the heat capacities vary with temperature, the total must be found by integration. Denoting the amount absorbed at constant pressure in an interval dT by dq_P, we have $dq_P = \bar{C}_P \, dT$ per mole of gas. Integration from T_1 to T_2, using the formula $\bar{C}_P = a + bT + cT^2$, gives

$$q = \int_{T_1}^{T_2} dq_P = a(T_2 - T_1) + \tfrac{1}{2}b(T_2^2 - T_1^2) + \tfrac{1}{3}c(T_2^3 - T_1^3)$$

EXAMPLE

The heat required to raise one mole of ethylene from 300°K to 1000°K at constant pressure is

$$q = 2.706(1000 - 300) + 14.580 \times 10^{-3}(1000^2 - 300^2)$$
$$- 3.020 \times 10^{-6}(1000^3 - 300^3)$$
$$= 18,942 + 11,809 - 2,938 = 27,813 \text{ cal} = 27.813 \text{ kcal}$$

Coefficients a, b, c for use in the first empirical equation are listed in Table 10.2; values for many other gases can be found in the literature. A number of uses of these equations will be made in later chapters.

TABLE 10.2.   *Heat Capacity Coefficients for Calculation of $\bar{C}_P$ of Gases. (The values listed permit calculations of $\bar{C}_P$ (cal/mole deg) with an accuracy of 1% or better in the range 300–1500°K.)*

Gas	a	$10^3 b$	$10^6 c$
H_2	6.947	−0.200	0.4808
HCl	6.732	0.4325	0.3697
HBr	6.578	0.955	0.1581
O_2	6.148	3.102	−0.923
N_2	6.524	1.250	−0.001
CO	6.420	1.665	−0.196
Cl_2	7.576	2.424	−0.965
Br_2	8.423	0.974	−0.356
H_2O	7.256	2.298	0.283
CO_2	6.214	10.396	−3.545
NH_3	6.189	7.887	−0.728
CH_4	3.381	18.044	−4.300
C_2H_6	1.375	41.852	−138.27
C_2H_5OH	3.578	49.847	−16.99
C_6H_6	−0.283	77.936	−26.30

Data from H. M. Spencer, *J. Am. Chem. Soc.* **67**: 1859 (1945), and earlier papers.

10.6. Forms of Internal Energy in Gases

The underlying molecular reasons for the greater heat capacities of polyatomic gases have long been attributed to the energies of rotation and vibration of the nuclei. The total energy of a system of many molecules is then the sum of many terms which, however, may be classified in the four groups.

1. *Translational kinetic energy:* terms of the form $\frac{1}{2}mU_x^2$, $\frac{1}{2}mU_y^2$, $\frac{1}{2}mU_z^2$; there are three for each molecule, corresponding to the three components U_x, U_y, U_z necessary to describe the speed (momentum) of the molecule as a whole.

2. *Rotational kinetic energy:* terms of the form $\frac{1}{2}I\omega^2$, where I is a moment

of inertia about an axis and ω the corresponding angular velocity. Three such terms are needed to describe the rotational energy of a molecule of three or more nuclei, but only two for diatomic molecules, because the moments of inertia about the nuclear axis (the bond axis) need not be considered.

3. *Vibrational energy:* as in the mechanical problem of a mass and spring, both kinetic and potential energy terms are required to describe a mode of vibration of two or more nuclei. For each possible mode two terms are thus required: one of the form $\frac{1}{2}mV^2$, where V is a vibrational velocity, and one of the form $\frac{1}{2}kx^2$ for the potential energy of a displacement x against a restoring force kx.

4. *Electronic energy:* most molecules are in their ground electronic states at ordinary temperatures, but an appreciable fraction may be in excited states at sufficiently high temperatures.

To a good approximation, for most gases it is possible to discuss the different forms of energy separately and to write

$$E_{\text{total}} = E_{\text{translation}} + E_{\text{rotation}} + E_{\text{vibration}} + E_{\text{electronic}}$$

From the experimental behavior of specific heats, as shown in Fig. 10.1, it is natural to suspect that the different terms have average values, and hence contributions to heat capacity, which depend on the temperature in some way characteristic of the molecule. The explanation of these effects must therefore be sought in the distribution of energies among the various possible energy states of the molecules.

Equipartition of Energy; Degrees of Freedom

As we have already seen, the distribution among the numerous, closely spaced energy states for translation resulted in an average contribution $\frac{3}{2}kT$ per molecule for the three component velocities U_x, U_y, U_z necessary to describe the translational kinetic energy as $\frac{1}{2}mU_x^2 + \frac{1}{2}mU_y^2 + \frac{1}{2}mU_z^2$. Maxwell was able to show that the contribution from other forms of motion should be $\frac{1}{2}kT$ for each independent term depending on the square of a coordinate and momentum which appears in the equation for the total energy. This result, known as the *theorem of equipartition of energy*, can be derived, assuming that the possible energy levels for the various forms of energy are so closely spaced that the differences in energy are much less than the value kT. Each distinct coordinate and momentum needed to describe the energy as a sum of squares is called a *degree of freedom*.

Maxwell proved his result before the advent of quantum theory with its prediction of discrete energy levels and had no reason to assume anything but the continuity of possible energies—in other words, that any value of energy associated with a particular form of motion was possible. His theorem is correct only as a limiting case because energy levels are in fact quantized. We have already discussed the translational energy for which the equipartition result of $\frac{3}{2}kT$ is valid even at very low temperatures because, as already shown, the spacing of energies is so very close. For the more restricted internal motions in molecules, this situation is not always realized and the actual energy states must be considered before reaching quantitative conclusions.

As a preliminary to more detailed discussion, we recall that rotational energy states of molecules give rise to emission and absorption of radiation at relatively low frequencies of the order 10^{10} cycles/sec, while vibrational frequencies in the infrared correspond to considerably larger energy differences and electronic frequencies in the visible and ultraviolet to still larger differences. On this basis, the states of rotation would first have energy differences small compared to kT with increasing temperature, then vibrational states, and finally electronic states. As we shall now discuss, their contributions to the average total energy become significant in just this order.

10.7. Rotational Heat Capacity

The simplest case of rotational energy is for a diatomic molecule. Since two velocities are needed to describe the rotational energy, the equipartition energy for rotation is $2 \times \frac{1}{2}kT = kT$ per molecule or RT per mole, and the corresponding heat capacity for translation plus rotation is predicted to be

$$\overline{C}_V = \tfrac{3}{2}R + R = \tfrac{5}{2}R = 4.95 \text{ cal/mole/C}°$$

For polyatomic molecules, three rotational velocities around independent axes of rotation are needed, and the equipartition heat capacity is

$$\overline{C}_V = \tfrac{3}{2}R + \tfrac{3}{2}R = 3R = 5.94 \text{ cal/mole/C}°$$

If we compare these results with experimental values, we see that there is an area of agreement near room temperature for the simpler gases, in that the specific heats of nitrogen and heavier diatomic molecules are about 5 cal/mole/C° and values of 6 or a little higher are found for the simpler polyatomic molecules. Hydrogen shows larger deviations at lower temperatures, and the more complex molecules have rapidly increasing values at room temperature; these contributions result from increasing vibrational energy, which we consider shortly.

The failure of equipartition of rotational energy for hydrogen comes about because the molecule is so light, and the rotational energy levels widely spaced as a result. The formula for allowed energies, which has been discussed before in Section 6.8, is

$$E_{rot} = \frac{h^2}{8\pi^2 I} J(J + 1) \qquad (10.12)$$

where h is Planck's constant, $J \, (= 0, 1, 2, 3, \cdots)$ is the rotational quantum number, and I is the molecular moment of inertia. Since the nuclear mass of protons is 1.68×10^{-24} g and the internuclear distance d is 0.75×10^{-8} cm, the moment of inertia for hydrogen is $I_{(H_2)} = 0.46 \times 10^{-40}$ g cm². For nitrogen, as an example of a heavier molecule, the mass $M_{(N)} = 2.32 \times 10^{-24}$ g and the nuclear distance $d = 1.09 \times 10^{-8}$ cm give $I_{(N_2)} = 14 \times 10^{-40}$ g cm², a figure 30 times

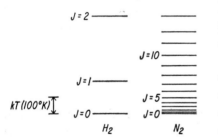

larger. The energy levels are compared with each other and with the energy difference kT in Fig. 10.2.

For nitrogen it is evident that even at 100°K some 20 levels have energy less than kT, while for hydrogen even the first excited state, $J = 1$, has energy greater than kT.

For nitrogen there are thus many states available to take up energy of the order kT available from collisions with other molecules, which

Fig. 10.2. *Spacing of rotational energy levels in hydrogen and nitrogen. At 100°K, $kT = 1.38 \times 10^{-14}$ ergs/molecule.*

have characteristically such amounts of translational energy. In hydrogen, however, very few molecules have enough translational energy at even 300°K to supply the rotational energy for more than the first or second excited states, and only at higher temperatures will many molecules have much rotational energy.

Since hydrogen is unique among molecules in the smallness of its moment of inertia (because the proton is the lightest of all nuclei), we should expect (as is actually the case) that failure of rotational equipartition is not important for other molecules. A partial exception is deuterium, which is heavier than hydrogen but not enormously so, and, as would be expected, appreciable anomalies in $\overline{C}_V$ are found below 100°K.

10.8. Vibrational and Electronic Specific Heat

The increases in specific heat of polyatomic gases above the value for translational plus rotational energies are mainly due to energies of vibration which become significant at high temperatures. As for rotation, the difference can be understood in terms of the vibrational energy levels deduced from molecular spectra.

Diatomic Molecules

Consider first the simplest case of a diatomic molecule which has one characteristic mode of vibration corresponding to change in bond length. The allowed energies of vibration are approximately given by the formula

$$E_{\text{vib}} = h\nu_0(v + \tfrac{1}{2}) \tag{10.13}$$

where $v = 0, 1, 2, \cdots$, is the vibrational quantum number. As discussed in Section 6.9, the values of the characteristic frequency ν_0 are determined by the nuclear masses and electronic change distributions but are not as simply related to fundamental quantities as the factor governing rotational energy levels.

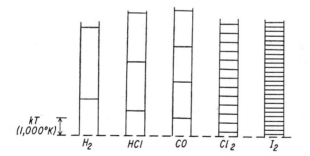

Fig. 10.3. *Vibrational energy levels of diatomic molecules. The lowest level in each case has the zero point energy $\tfrac{1}{2}h\nu_0$. The value of kT at 1000°K is 1.38×10^{-13} ergs/molecule and corresponds to $RT = 1990$ cal/mole.*

The vibrational energy levels for several molecules are shown in Fig. 10.3.

Although no simple statements of general validity can be made about the relative spacings, they are larger if one or both of the atoms is hydrogen, and are particularly large for molecular hydrogen, $h\nu_0$ being equal to the value of kT at 6000°K in this case.

At sufficiently low temperatures almost no molecules can acquire enough energy by collisions to reach an excited state and the molecules will have only the zero point energy $\frac{1}{2}h\nu_0$ independent of the temperature. When the spacing becomes comparable with kT, the equilibrium numbers in excited states will increase, and the amount of vibrational energy will increase with temperature. The heat which must be supplied to do this is represented by increasing values of $\overline{C}_v$.

Iodine and chlorine show changes in vibrational energy even at room temperature, and at temperatures above 1000°K the energy states are so closely spaced compared to kT that practically the equipartition heat capacity value of R for vibration is realized. For the lighter molecules CO and HCl, the effects only begin to become appreciable at 1000°K and for H_2 temperatures of several thousand degrees would be necessary.

Vibrations of Polyatomic Molecules

More possible internal modes of vibration exist for polyatomic molecules, the number increasing with the number of atoms. Some of these modes are associated with stretching of bonds and so are similar in kind to the single mode of diatomic molecules. There are also vibrations involving twisting or bending of bonds, and many of these deformations are much less "stiff." The energy quanta associated with such modes are correspondingly much smaller and can be supplied at much lower temperatures. The greater number of modes and the greater ease with which some acquire energy combine to give larger vibrational energies with greater temperature dependence.

The calculation of vibrational energies at various temperatures and the corresponding heat capacities can be carried out with great accuracy if the vibrational energy levels are known. It has been possible to assign these without serious ambiguity for simpler molecules (well more than 100 to date) from their spectra. Values so obtained from correct correlation of observed spectral lines with energy levels are more accurate than the results of heat capacity measurements, and an increasingly useful body of such results is accumulating. It should not be thought, however, that the thermal measurements have no value. For some gases and for most liquids and solids the theory and interpretation of the spectra are not adequately developed. In other cases comparison of the two sets of results can give other information about the constitution of the liquid or solid (see Section 15.8).

Electronic Heat Capacity

The energies required for excited electronic states of molecules are so high in most cases that the electronic energy does not change at ordinary temperatures, and so has no associated heat capacity. Two exceptions for which low-lying electronic levels make noticeable contributions at moderate temperatures are nitric oxide and molecular oxygen.

10.9. Results of the Quantum Theory of Vibrational Energy

In the preceding section, the underlying reasons for failure of vibrational energy to reach the equipartition values of RT for each mode of vibration have been discussed in terms of qualitative consideration of the spacing of energy levels in relation to thermal energy kT. The calculation of total vibrational energy of a system of N molecules or other vibrators which have energies $(v + \frac{1}{2})h\nu_0$ can be carried out in a way similar to that for translational energy and is outlined here.

As discussed in Section 9.5, the number of molecules with energy in the range E to $E + dE$ is proportional to the product of the Boltzmann factor $e^{-E/kT}$ and the number of states in the range of dE. For a vibrator there is only one state of any one energy E, and it is not necessary to consider the density of states, as it was in calculating the distribution of translational velocities. The number of molecules with any one energy $E = (v + \frac{1}{2})h\nu_0$ is therefore simply

$$N_v = Ae^{-(v+\frac{1}{2})h\nu_0/kT} \qquad (10.14)$$

where A is a constant depending on the total number of molecules.

The total energy E_{vib} is the sum of numbers of molecules in each state multiplied by the energy of each:

$$E_{\text{vib}} = \tfrac{1}{2}h\nu_0 N_0 + \tfrac{3}{2}h\nu_0 N_1 + \tfrac{5}{2}h\nu_0 N_2$$
$$+ \cdots + (v + \tfrac{1}{2})h\nu_0 N_v + \cdots \qquad (10.15)$$

The average energy per molecule is E_{vib} divided by the total number of molecules:

$$\left(E_{\text{vib}}\right)_{\text{ave}} = \frac{E_{\text{vib}}}{N} = \frac{\tfrac{1}{2}h\nu_0 N_0 + \tfrac{3}{2}h\nu_0 N_1 + \cdots}{N_0 + N_1 + N_2 + \cdots} \qquad (10.16)$$

since the total number N is the sum of the numbers in all possible states.

Using the Boltzmann expression (Eq. 10.14) for N_v gives

$(E_{\text{vib}})_{\text{ave}}$

$$= \frac{\frac{1}{2}h\nu_0 e^{-\frac{1}{2}h\nu_0/kT} + \frac{3}{2}h\nu_0 e^{-\frac{3}{2}h\nu_0/kT} + \cdots + (v + \frac{1}{2})h\nu_0 e^{-(v+\frac{1}{2})h\nu_0/kT} + \cdots}{-\frac{1}{2}h\nu_0/kT + e^{-\frac{3}{2}h\nu_0/kT} + \cdots + e^{-(v+\frac{1}{2})h\nu_0/kT} + \cdots}$$

(10.17)

It will be noticed that the factor A has disappeared because it is common to all terms and cancels. If the vibration frequency ν_0 is known, the series of terms in the numerator and denominator can be computed and summed to give $(E_{\text{vib}})_{\text{ave}}$ at any temperature T.

This would be a tedious process if the value of $h\nu_0/kT$ is large enough that the terms do not become rapidly smaller. Fortunately, it is possible to express Eq. 10.17 in a much better form for computation. This is done by first removing the common factor $\frac{1}{2}h\nu_0$ from terms in the numerator and canceling the common factor $e^{-\frac{1}{2}h\nu_0/kT}$ from numerator and denominator to give

$$(E_{\text{vib}})_{\text{ave}} = \frac{1}{2}h\nu_0 \frac{1 + 3e^{-h\nu_0/kT} + 5e^{-3h\nu_0/kT} + 7e^{-3h\nu_0/kT} + \cdots}{1 + e^{-h\nu_0/kT} + e^{-2h\nu_0/kT} + \cdots} \quad (10.18)$$

By writing $e^{-h\nu_0/kT} = x$ this has the form

$$(E_{\text{vib}})_{\text{ave}} = \frac{1}{2}h\nu_0 \frac{1 + 3x + 5x^2 + \cdots + (2n + 1)x^n + \cdots}{1 + x + x^2 + \cdots + x^n + \cdots} \quad (10.19)$$

If the indicated ratio of series in x is treated as a problem in long division, it can be seen to give

$$(E_{\text{vib}})_{\text{ave}} = \frac{1}{2}h\nu_0(1 + 2x + 2x^2 + \cdots + 2x^n + \cdots) \quad (10.20)$$

Finally, the series can be recognized as the result of dividing $1 - x$ into $1 + x$, and so we have

$$(E_{\text{vib}})_{\text{ave}} = \frac{1}{2}h\nu_0 \frac{1 + x}{1 - x} = \frac{1}{2}h\nu_0 \frac{1 + e^{-h\nu_0/kT}}{1 - e^{-h\nu_0 kT}} \quad (10.21)$$

(The reader may feel that this series of steps leading to Eq. 10.21 is hardly an obvious or logical one and may further wonder whether the divisions are legitimate. The steps are of course not demanded by the form of Eq. 10.17, but their possibility is realized when one has previously encountered some similar situation. The legitimacy of expressing the ratio of the series in the final closed form comes from the fact that $x = e^{-h\nu_0/kT}$ can by its definition never exceed a value of one when $h\nu_0/kT$ is positive, hence e^{-x} is always less than one.)

The vibrational heat capacity $\bar{C}_{\text{vib}}$ corresponding to the final result for $(E_{vib})_{ave}$ is obtained from the vibrational energy per mole $\overline{E}_{vib} = N_0(E_{vib})_{ave}$, since the increase in $\overline{E}_{vib}$ for an increase dT in temperature must be given by

$$d\overline{E}_{vib} = \overline{C}_{vib}\, dT \qquad (10.22)$$

if $\overline{C}_{vib}$ is the vibrational heat capacity. Hence $\overline{C}_{vib} = d\overline{E}_{vib}/dT$. Carrying out the differentiation gives

$$\overline{C}_{vib} = \tfrac{1}{2} N_0 h\nu_0 \left[-\frac{h\nu_0}{k}\left(\frac{1}{T^2}\right) \frac{e^{-h\nu_0/kT}}{1 - e^{-h\nu_0/kT}} \right.$$
$$\left. + \left(-\frac{h\nu_0}{k}\right)\left(-\frac{1}{T^2}\right) e^{-h\nu_0/kT}\, \frac{1 + e^{-h\nu_0/kT}}{(1 - e^{-h\nu_0/kT})^2} \right] \qquad (10.23)$$

Therefore

$$\overline{C}_{vib} = N_0 k \left(\frac{h\nu_0}{kT}\right)^2 \frac{e^{-h\nu_0/kT}}{(1 - e^{-h\nu_0/kT})^2} \qquad (10.24)$$

Since $N_0 k = R$, the universal gas constant, the vibrational heat capacity is thus R times a function of the quantity $h\nu_0/kT$, or equally well of the quantity $T/(h\nu_0/k)$. The variation of $\overline{C}_{vib}$ with temperature T can therefore be calculated once and for all at a sufficient number of different *reduced* temperatures $T/(h\nu_0/k) = T/\theta_v$, where the quantity $\theta_v \,(= h\nu_0/k)$ is a characteristic temperature for exciting vibrational energy. From the plot in Fig. 10.4, it is evident that most of the equipartition value R is realized for T larger than θ_v (when $T/\theta_v > 1$), and hence $kT > h\nu_0$.

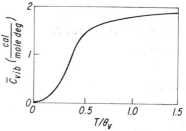

Fig. 10.4. *Vibrational heat capacity plotted against reduced temperature.* $(\theta_v = h\nu_0/k.)$

Comparison with Experiment

As an example of the accuracy with which Eq. 10.24, together with the values $\tfrac{3}{2}R + R$ for translation and rotation, represents the true heat capacity $\overline{C}_V$, a comparison is given in Table 10.3 of calculated values with the correct ones for carbon monoxide. The necessary value of vibrational frequency ν_0 is known from band spectra to be $\nu_0 = 6.50 \times 10^{13}$ sec^{-1} ($= 2168$ cm^{-1}), giving $\theta = h\nu_0/k = 3120°$K.

The agreement of $\tfrac{5}{2}R + \overline{C}_{vib}$, while a considerable improvement over

TABLE 10.3.   *Vibrational Heat Capacity of CO.*

$T°K$	$\overline{C}_{vib}$	$\frac{5}{2}R + \overline{C}_{vib}$	$\overline{C}_V$ (correct value)
500	0.18	5.15	5.13
1000	0.94	5.91	5.95
2000	1.63	6.60	6.68
3000	1.81	6.78	6.91
4000	1.89	6.86	7.03
5000	1.92	6.89	7.11

Data taken from J. C. Slater, *Introduction to Chemical Physics*, McGraw-Hill, New York, 1939.

the value $\overline{C}_V = \frac{5}{2}R = 4.95$ cal/mole/deg (without $\overline{C}_{vib}$), is not perfect. There are two reasons for the difference: first, the harmonic oscillator approximation for the vibrational energy levels is not exact, and second, there is a small effect from electronic contributions. Calculations of the additional effects give results which are in good agreement with experimental values. They are in fact more accurate than the directly measured quantities (heat capacities of gases are hard to measure with great accuracy).

10.10. Heat Capacities of Solids

Although discussion of the heat capacities of solids may seem out of place in a chapter otherwise devoted to properties of gases, the subject is appropriately considered at this point because the basic explanations are to be found in considering the vibrational energies of atoms and molecules of solids.

In the case of an *atomic* crystal, one mole contains N_0 atoms, and $3N$ coordinates are required to describe their positions; in addition, $3N$ components of velocity must be specified in order to define completely the motions of the atoms. There are thus $6N$ degrees of freedom. If equipartition of energy $\frac{1}{2}kT$ to each of these is justified, the total energy should be $6N_0(\frac{1}{2}kT) = 3RT$ for one mole, and the predicted heat capacity is $\overline{C}_V = 3R = 5.94$ cal/mole/deg.

The values of $\overline{C}_P$ for a number of atomic crystals at room temperature (Table 10.4) are seen to be in most cases not far from the classical equipartition value. The few values of $\overline{C}_V$ show the small but definite differences between $\overline{C}_P$ and $\overline{C}_V$ characteristic of solids ($\overline{C}_V$ is not readily measured but can be calculated from $\overline{C}_P$ and other data.)

TABLE 10.4.   *Heat Capacities of Elements at Room Temperature**

Substance	$\bar{C}_V$	$\bar{C}_P$
Lithium	—	5.5
Aluminum	5.50	5.81
Carbon		
diamond	1.4	1.44
graphite	—	2.07
Silicon	—	4.7
Iron	—	5.9
Nickel	—	6.2
Copper	5.6	5.85
Iodine	—	6.6
Lead	5.9	6.19

* Considerable differences exist between various values in the literature, and the values for $\bar{C}_V$ are especially uncertain.

Carbon (as diamond and as graphite) and silicon (to a lesser extent) are exceptions to the otherwise moderately good agreement. These two cases are not as exceptional as one might suppose, even though most other elements have $\bar{C}_V \cong 6$ cal/-mole/deg, because similar discrepancies are found for all solids *at sufficiently low temperatures.*

Values of $\bar{C}_P$ for some of the crystals in the table are plotted at different temperatures in Fig. 10.5. These curves show that the heat capacities all decrease at lower temperatures, approaching zero at sufficiently low temperatures, diamond and silicon being exceptional only in that the decreases are appreciable at room temperatures. The curves can also be seen to have very similar shapes if allowance is made for differences in scale of temperatures, and the reader may further have noticed that the curves are rather similar in shape to the gas vibrational heat capacity curve of Fig. 10.4.

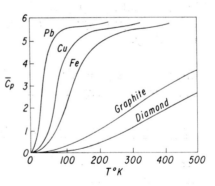

Fig. 10.5. *Heat capacities of solid elements versus temperature.*

Einstein Theory of Heat Capacities

Einstein in 1907 suggested that the temperature variation of solid heat capacities was the result of vibrations of the atoms about their average positions in the lattice. In his theory of solid specific heats he assumed that there were $3N_0$ such vibrations, one for each atom, and that all these vibrations were of the same frequency ν_0. In other words, each atom was supposed capable of three modes of vibration, which under these circumstances would have an average vibrational energy three times that deduced in Section 9.9 for $(E_{vib})_{ave}$ of a single mode. The Einstein result for heat capacity is correspondingly three times the value for $\overline{C}_{vib}$ of Eq. 10.24.

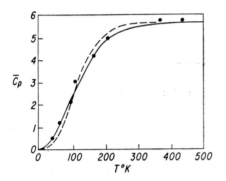

Fig. 10.6. *Heat capacity of aluminum: solid curve, Debye theory; dashed curve, Einstein theory.*

The Einstein result evidently gives the right high temperature value of $3R$ and, as comparison of Figs. 10.4 and 10.5 suggests, has the general form of the experimental curves. A more quantitative comparison shows definite disagreement no matter how the value of ν_0 in Eq. 10.24 is adjusted to improve the fit, as shown for the case of aluminum in Fig. 10.6. Similar careful studies of other substances have shown that such differences are general; Einstein's theory is thus an improvement but not an adequate explanation.

Debye Theory of Heat Capacities

The assumption of identical frequencies of atoms vibrating independently is not a realistic one for solids, in which the forces between the closely spaced atoms are strong. Under these conditions the motions of atoms must be greatly influenced by those of their neighbors, and are somewhat similar to motions of beads connected by springs to one another. As a model of this situation, Debye proposed in 1912 a theory in which the possible vibrations of the solid as a whole were treated in a fashion similar to that used for an elastic substance. By supposing that the $3N_0$ modes possible were those of standing waves of atom displacements, Debye was able to derive an expression for heat capacity which proves to be in much better agreement with experiment than Einstein's. The details of his derivation are too lengthy to be given here, and his final result unfortunately cannot be expressed as a simple function in the way that the simple vibrator expression could in Eq. 10.24. Some characteristic features of the result are, however, worth mentioning briefly.

Debye's equation, like that for vibrational heat capacity, is expressed in terms of a characteristic temperature called the Debye temperature, θ_D (or sometimes simply the Debye θ). Debye was able to relate this temperature to the sound velocity and the elastic properties of the solid, with the result that more compressible solids with low sound velocities have their elastic modes of vibration excited at lower temperatures. Just this order of acquisition of the equipartition of energy and classical heat capacity is shown by the substances in Fig. 10.5; lead, the softest and most compressible, behaves classically at temperatures above about 70°K, while diamond, which is very hard and incompressible, approaches classical behavior only for temperatures about 1500°K.

The kind of agreement with experiment of Debye's result, using compressibility data to evaluate the characteristic temperature, is shown for aluminum in Fig. 10.6, the solid curve being the result of the calculation and the circles the experimental points. A closer scrutiny shows that the agreement is by no means perfect and that Debye's model is only approximate, but the result is good enough to indicate that the basic nature of Debye's explanation is correct.

Although, as already stated, the Debye equation is not a simple algebraic expression, it reduces to a simple form at sufficiently low temperatures. The heat capacity for temperatures low enough that $\bar{C}_V$ is less than about $0.1\,R$ is given by

$$\bar{C}_V = B \times T^3$$

where the constant B can be calculated from θ_D or determined from the experimental data. This result, known as the T^3 law, is a very useful one for representing solid heat capacities at low enough temperatures.

Polyatomic Crystals

The theories described above are for atomic crystals and the relative motions of atoms in the crystal. In molecular crystals we might expect by analogy with heat capacities of molecular gases that contributions from internal molecular vibrations would be significant. Larger values are in fact found, as shown by the results listed in Table 10.5.

TABLE 10.5.   *Heat Capacities* ($\overline{C}_P$) *of Polyatomic Substances at* $300°K$.

Substance	C_P (cal/mole °C)
PbO	11.3
PbS	11.8
PbCl$_2$	18.4
AgCl	12.4
NaCl	12.0
BaSO$_4$	25.6
CaCO$_3$	23.4
Fe$_2$O$_3$	24.9
Fe$_3$O$_4$	36.0

The contributions from internal vibrations are to a fair approximation those of simple vibrational modes of atoms in the molecules, and some progress has been made on special theories for particular types of molecules. These are necessarily complicated, and an adequate discussion requires much longer and detailed development than is possible here.

Electronic Heat Capacity of Metals

The simplest picture of a metal bearing any resemblance to reality is one in which the valence electrons are free to occupy the entire volume of the solid. This "free electron" or "supermolecular orbital" model has been used with fair success in correlating a number of metallic properties (see Section 7.5). Prior to the quantum theory there was a fatal difficulty to the model, however; namely, that the $3N_0$ degrees of freedom of valence electrons of one mole of sodium, for example, ought if really free to contribute the classical amount $\frac{3}{2}R$ to the heat capacity, just as the $3N_0$ degrees of freedom of molecules of a monatomic gas give $\overline{C}_V = \frac{3}{2}R$. No such contributions are found, suggesting that the electrons cannot be free, yet such properties as electrical and thermal conductivity and optical reflectivity are fairly well explained by the free electron picture.

One of the earlier notable successes of quantum theory was the resolution of this classical paradox. The key to the explanation lies in two quantum effects: the spacings of energy levels for free electrons in a volume of laboratory dimensions, and the requirements of the Pauli principle.

In Section 9.4 we found that for atomic masses translational energy levels of a gas are very closely spaced compared to kT. For electrons with mass only 1/1800th that of the smallest atomic mass, the proton, this is no longer so at ordinary temperatures. The Boltzmann expression would therefore put considerable numbers of electrons in the lowest energy levels, a situation which violates the Pauli principle, which permits a maximum of only two electrons of opposite spin in any one energy state. Compliance with the principle therefore requires that the Boltzmann statistics and Boltzmann factor be suitably modified for electrons. When the corrected statistical results, known as the *Fermi-Dirac statistics*, are used, the calculated heat capacity of free electrons comes out to be a negligible part of the total heat capacity except at very low temperatures. The predicted unimportance at room temperatures is verified by experiment, and small contributions observed at temperatures of a few degrees absolute are in reasonable agreement with the quantum calculations.

Problems

10.1. The classical work of Count Rumford, relating heat produced to work done, showed that a horse, working the cannon-boring machinery for $2\frac{1}{2}$ hours, was able to raise the temperature of 12 kg of ice-cold water to its boiling point. These figures were used later (by Joule) to estimate the heat equivalent of work. What would the value be, using James Watt's suggestion that a working horse could supply 7.5×10^9 ergs/sec? How near is this to the accepted value?

10.2. In freezing weather ice forms in a tank at 1 kg/hour. What wattage of electric light bulb will just prevent freezing?

10.3. If 0.2 moles of an ideal gas are heated from 10°C to 25°C at constant volume, and at constant pressure, how much more heat is used at constant pressure than at constant volume?

10.4. Mayer observed that 1 g of air required 0.17 cal to raise its temperature 1° at constant volume, and 0.24 cal at a constant pressure of 1 atm. At constant pressure the volume increase was 2.83 cm^3/gm. Calculate the mechanical equivalent of heat from these data.

10.5. If 6 cal are used in raising the temperature of 40 g of mercury vapor 10°C at constant volume, what does this tell about the molecule of mercury vapor?

10.6. Estimate the temperature of a furnace if a 45.0-g block of platinum removed from it and dropped into 135 g of water at 9°C in a glass beaker (225 g) raised the temperature to 24°C. (Heat capacity of the glass equals 0.2 cal/g.)

10.7. The molar heat capacity (C_p) of CO is given by the relation $C_v = 6.60 + 0.0012\,T$. Calculate the heat needed to heat 3 moles of CO from 12°C to 38°C.

10.8. Compare the quantities of heat needed (a) to increase the pressure of one mole of an ideal gas, initially at 27°C, from 1 atm to 2 atm at constant volume followed by doubling its volume at a constant pressure of 2 atm, and (b) to double its volume, initially at 27°C and 1 atm pressure, at constant pressure, followed by increasing its pressure from 1 atm to 2 atm at constant volume.

10.9. (a) Calculate the amount of heat necessary to raise the temperature of one mole of steam from 100°C to 400°C at constant pressure, using heat capacity data from Table 10.2. (b) What error is made by neglecting the coefficient c? (c) What fraction of the total heat required is expended as work of expansion?

10.10. What are the equipartition rotational and vibrational heat capacities of the NNO molecule if it is assumed to be (a) linear, or (b) bent?

10.11. The wave numbers ($\bar{\nu}$) of electronic, vibrational, and rotational absorption spectra are of the order of 10^4 cm^{-1}, 10^3 cm^{-1}, and 10^1 to 10^2 cm^{-1} respectively. (a) What are the corresponding values of frequencies (ν) and wavelengths λ? (b) Compare the energy differences (spacings) associated with each.

10.12. Predict wave numbers ($\bar{\nu}$) you would expect to find in the infrared rotational spectra of chlorine (moment of inertia $= 114.8 \times 10^{-40}$ g cm^2). Explain why these are not observed in conventional spectroscopic absorption studies, but do contribute to the heat capacity. Estimate the temperature range in which the contribution differs appreciably from the equipartition value, and varies with temperature.

10.13. Compare the energy differences in the rotational levels of H_2 and N_2 for $J = 0$ and $J = 1$ with kT at 100°K and 300°K. From this comparison and the heat capacity curve for H_2 in Fig. 10.1, estimate the temperature range in which $\bar{C}_v$ for N_2 varies appreciably with temperature.

10.14. Below what temperature would deuterium be expected to behave as a monatomic gas with respect to heat capacity? The moment of inertia of the molecule is 0.918×10^{-40} g cm^2.

10.15. Predict temperatures at which the following gases could be expected to make appreciable use of thermal energy of molecules as vibrational energy. What is the effect on the heat capacity?

Gas	I_2	HBr	CO	HCl	H_2
Fundamental vibration frequency (cm^{-1}) = wave number	214.4	2650	2168	2989	4405

10.16. The average rotational energy of a system of diatomic molecules and the rotational heat capacity can be derived by methods similar to those used for vibrational heat capacities in Section 10.9. Using the formula $E(J) = (h^2/8\pi^2 I)J(J+1)$ and the fact that the number of states of this energy is $2J + 1$, show that the average rotational energy is

$(E_{rot})_{ave}$

$$= \frac{S(6e^{-2S/kT} + 30e^{-6S/kT} + \cdots + (2J+1)J(J+1)e^{-J(J+1)S/kT} + \cdots)}{1 + 3e^{-2S/kT} + 5e^{-6S/kT} + \cdots + (2J+1)e^{-J(J+1)S/kT} + \cdots}$$

where $S = h^2/8\pi^2 I$.

10.17. The series in Problem *10.16* must be summed numerically in the general case, but for temperatures high enough that $S \ll kT$, the series can be shown to give $(E_{rot})_{ave} = kT$ per molecule or RT per mole, thus agreeing with the equipartition result. Verify this statement by replacing the series by integrals, noting that $(d/dJ)[J(J+1)] = 2J + 1$, and evaluating the integrals. Explain why this procedure is valid if $S \ll kT$.

10.18. What difference would omission of the zero point energy $\frac{1}{2}h\nu_0$ in the formula for vibrational energy of a linear molecule make in Eqs. 10.21 and 10.24 for vibrational energy and heat capacity?

10.19. Infrared absorption is observed in CO at a frequency $\nu = 1.16 \times 10^{+1}$ sec^{-1}. Assuming that this arises from the $J = 0$ to $J = 1$ rotational energy transition, calculate the temperature at which the number of molecules in the $J = 1$ state is one-tenth the number with $J = 0$.

10.20. (a) From the plot of vibrational heat capacity as a function of T/θ_v, estimate the value of this reduced temperature at which one-half the equipartition value is reached. (b) From your result, obtain an expression for the frequency ν_0 in terms of the actual temperature. (c) From this expression and the plot in Fig. 10.6, what vibrational frequency ν_0 in Einstein's theory is required to account for the heat capacity of solid aluminum? Where is this frequency in the spectrum?

10.21. At low pressures, the heat capacity $\bar{C}_P$ of a gas is found to be independent of the pressure at which it is measured. Explain why this result would be expected for an ideal gas. Suggest reasons why $\bar{C}_P$ should depend on pressure at high pressures.

10.22. The following experiment was performed to find the mean heat capacity of N_2 up to high temperature. A gas mixture in the proportions 2 moles of H_2, 1 mole of O_2, and 2 moles of N_2 is placed in a bomb at 300°K and 1 atm. The mixture is exploded and the final pressure found to be 10.2 atm. The heat of formation of water vapor is $\Delta H_f = -57.8$ kcal and its mean heat capacity $\bar{C}_P = 11.3$ cal/mole °C. (a) What is the final temperature? (b) What is the average value of $\bar{C}_P$ for N_2 over the temperature range?

Suggested Readings

References on classical kinetic theory have been listed at the end of Chapter 9. Many good references on statistical mechanics, both classical and quantum mechanical, could be cited.

Two introductory accounts, both very readable, are *Elementary Statistical Physics* by C. Kittel (Wiley, New York, 1958) and *Equilibrium Statistical Mechanics* by F. C. Andrews (Wiley, New York, 1963). At a somewhat more advanced mathematical level is the excellent treatment in *Introduction to Statistical Mechanics* by G. Rushbrooke (Oxford, 1949).

Sources of heat capacity data are cited at the end of Chapter 13, p. 381.

Chapter 11

Some Properties
of Liquids
and Solutions

ON BEGINNING this chapter the reader may
wonder why it has not come sooner in the order of presentation, as
much more of chemistry is concerned with reactions in solution rather
than in the gaseous or solid states so far considered. The first reason for
deferring this discussion until now is that the behavior of liquids is more
complicated than that of solids and gases. The second is that the properties of liquids are better appreciated when one has some knowledge of
the nature of gases and solids, together with a conception of the underlying molecular origins responsible for their properties.

In comparing liquids with gases and solids, we are first concerned
with the characteristic properties which distinguish a liquid from a gas
or solid, and with the conditions under which a substance is in its liquid
state rather than either of the other states. With this background of
experimentally observed facts, we can then examine how they are to be
understood in terms of the kinetic molecular theory developed in the
earlier chapters.

In the second part of the chapter, some of the simpler properties of
solutions obtained by mixing liquids or dissolving a second substance in

a liquid will be considered. This discussion will be preliminary in nature, as it will be possible to analyze the behavior of solutions and reactions in solution in a much more searching way after the fundamental and very general laws of nature known as the first and second laws of thermodynamics have been discussed in later chapters. Even so, the molecular theories, necessarily approximate in order to be simple, are helpful in leading to a satisfactory qualitative picture of the observed behavior in general.

11.1. Comparison of Liquids with Gases and Solids

Liquids are usually considered to be intermediate between solids and gases, because most of the properties of liquids lie somewhere between those characteristic of gases and of solids. An obvious example of this is that the range of temperatures within which a substance is liquid lies above that in which it is solid and below that in which it is a gas. Similarly, considering relative pressures, gases exist at low pressures, become liquid only at higher pressures, and become solid at still higher pressures. Liquids are almost always less dense than solids and expand more with increasing temperature, but are denser, less easily compressed, and expand less than gases.

Many other examples could be given of the intermediate physical properties of liquids, but the value of any single property is not simply an average of the values for solid and gas, nor is a liquid in any general sense halfway between a solid and a gas. Rather, in most cases, any single property of a liquid is much more like that of either the solid or the gas, as examples of a few familiar properties will suggest. The densities of liquids are close to those of solids, being of the order 0.6 to 2 g/cm^3, whereas gas densities at ordinary pressures are but 1/100 to 1/1000 as much. Liquids and solids are likewise similar in their much greater resistance to compression. On the other hand, in terms of fluidity (which permits a substance to occupy volumes of different shapes), liquids much more nearly resemble gases. For liquids, however, the necessary force to make them flow from one vessel to another is orders of magnitude larger than for gases, and liquids characteristically increase in viscosity (resistance to flow) as their temperature is lowered, until they either freeze or become glassy.

It is interesting and instructive to study the temperatures and pressures at which different phases exist, and this is conveniently done by a form of *phase diagram* (see Chapter 20) in which the boundary values of temperature and pressure for different phases are plotted on a graph of pressure versus temperature. The phase diagram for carbon dioxide in Fig. 11.1 shows these boundary curves, and the regions of the different phases are labeled, as are the particular points with the terms which they define. (The significance of the critical point—the point of temperature and pressure beyond which the distinction between liquid and gas represented by the vapor pressure curve disappears —was discussed in Section 8.6.) At the highest pressure of about 80 atmospheres shown by the figure, there is still a difference between the solid and fluid phase. (Whether the latter should be called *liquid* or *gaseous* at that high temperature and great density is somewhat academic.)

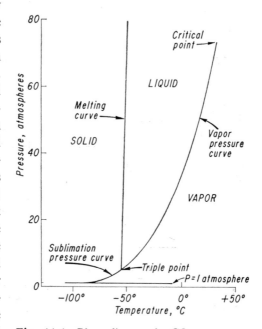

Fig. 11.1. *Phase diagram for CO₂.*

The possibility that there exists a solid-fluid critical point beyond which solid and fluid phases merge continuously has often been considered, with conflicting opinions resulting. To date no such point has been found for any substance, and the most extensive and reliable evidence indicates that the solid and fluid states in equilibrium along the melting curve become less rather than more similar at increasingly high pressures. For example, the pressure-temperature data for liquid helium presented in Fig. 11.2 show the melting curve (deduced from the measurements of volume changes with pressure) continued to 10,000 atmospheres and 60°K, values which are many times those of the critical point (2.26 atmospheres, 5.2°K). The densities of solid and liquid at 520 atmospheres and 8°K are 0.274 g/ml and 0.263 g/ml, while at 2260 atmospheres and 24°K they are 0.381 g/ml and 0.363 g/ml, and so are drawing farther apart rather than closer together.*

There is no reason to think that the behavior of other substances at

---

* **Data** from Dugdale and Simon, *Proc. Roy. Soc.*, Ser. *A*, **218**: 291 (1953), Figures 4 and 9.

correspondingly high pressures, compared to those of their critical regions for gas and liquid, would be different in kind from that of helium.

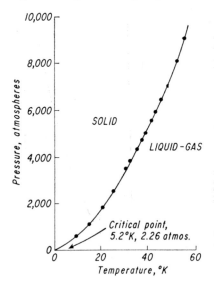

Fig. 11.2. *Melting point-pressure curve for helium.*

From this point of view, the distinction between solid and fluid is thus more clear cut than the one between liquid and gas, which is recognizable only over the restricted range between the triple point and critical point. There is then some justification, when one considers pressure ranges of many thousands of atmospheres, for regarding the liquid phase as something of an aberration of the fluid state and for considering the vapor pressure curve for the liquid-vapor equilibrium as a vestigial appendix. At the same time, however, this limited region is one of importance for a vast number of substances, and one in which molecular forces of the solid state remain important because of the close distances between molecules.

The partially solidlike nature of the arrangements of neighboring molecules in liquids has been studied in a variety of ways; one of the most important is the measurement of the scattering of a beam of X-rays by a liquid. The method is similar to that used in obtaining powder diagrams of solids (described in Section 7.3 and Fig. 7.9), with the sample of liquid replacing the powdered solid. When a photographic film is exposed, the scattered beam produces a blurred series of rings about the central spot produced by the direct beam, as shown in Fig. 11.3. Only the two or three rings closest to this central spot are easily distinguished, the rings merging into one another at larger angles. The result is thus a solidlike pattern but more diffuse. It is a consequence of the arrangement of the argon atoms relative to one another in the liquid, and if this liquid were perfectly amorphous without any structural regularity of atomic arrangement, the pattern would be completely diffuse.

While this X-ray scattering is itself evidence for some form of structure on the molecular scale, it is fortunately possible to make more specific and quantitative calculations about this structure from the observed variation of scattered X-ray intensity with angular distance from the central spot. The necessary theory requires the development of the algebraic prediction of the patterns resulting from different possible arrangements of neighboring atoms about any one atom, and then the mathematical deduction as to which average arrangement is most consistent with the actual pattern.

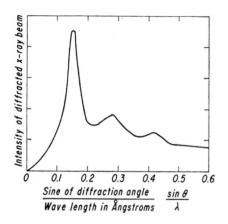

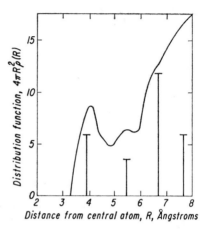

Fig. 11.3. *X-Ray diffraction intensity pattern for liquid argon. [From Einstein and Gingrich,* Phys. Rev., **58:** 307 (1940).]

Fig. 11.4. *The atomic distribution in liquid argon. (Vertical lines represent idealized distribution in crystalline argon.)* [*From Einstein and Gingrich,* Phys. Rev., **58:** 307 (1940).]

For argon, this process leads to a calculated distribution of atoms at different distances from any single one, as shown in Fig. 11.4. The sequence of solid vertical lines representing atoms at discrete fixed distances (as in the solid) is blurred into a series of peaks and valleys diminishing into a smooth parabola at large distances. (This parabola simply represents the fact that the *volume* of a shell of constant thickness increases as the square of its radius, which is the distance from the central atom.)

Thus, in the case of liquid argon, neighboring atoms are more likely on the average to be packed at distances close to those of the solid structure, but they do not occupy such positions rigidly or exclusively. This behavior is described as (partial) short-range order, the long-range regularity characteristic of a solid crystal structure being absent. Other liquids studied in this way show similar behavior, indicating that a liquid must possess some average local regularity of arrangement on the molecular scale (especially if strong directed forces exist between the molecules, as in "hydrogen bonding"). This molecular arrangement is, however, continually fluctuating, as evidenced by the observed processes of viscous flow and, notably, of diffusion of a liquid into itself or another liquid at rates enormously greater than those for solids.

11.2. Vapor Pressure of Liquids

Every liquid will evaporate and turn into a gas if the pressure is reduced sufficiently. The pressure necessary for the liquid to exist at a given temperature is equal to the pressure of the vapor (gas) of the molecular species constituting the liquid, and the existence of the liquid is not dependent upon the pressure of any other gas over the liquid (except in a very minor way). A liquid in an open vessel hence evaporates in the course of time despite the pressure of the external atmosphere, because the molecules escaping from the liquid to form the vapor are dispersed away from the liquid surface by circulation or diffusion.

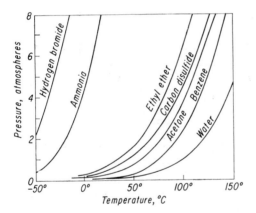

The reverse process of condensation will only build up to reach equilibrium between liquid and vapor if there is a sufficient concentration of molecules in the vapor. The pressure for equilibrium between rates of evaporation and condensation at a given temperature is called the *vapor pressure*. This equilibrium pressure must be determined experimentally by some arrangement which prevents indeterminate loss of vapor: for example, by employing a closed system from which other gases have been removed, or by collecting and determining the amount of vapor given off.

Fig. 11.5. *Vapor pressure curves for several liquids.*

Vapor pressures increase at an accelerated rate with increasing temperature, as shown for several liquids in Fig. 11.5 and Table 11.1.

From the graphs it is evident that a simple linear plot of pressure versus temperature cannot give much accuracy of interpolating values over any appreciable range of temperature. Neither is it immediately obvious what kind of algebraic relation, if any, exists between the two

TABLE 11.1.   *Vapor Pressures of Liquids.*

Temperature (°C)	Ammonia (atm)	Carbon Disulfide (atm)	Water (mm Hg)	Ethyl Ether (atm)	Benzene (atm)	Acetone (atm)
−60	0.2161	0.0046		0.0054		
−40	0.7083	0.0184		0.025		
−20	1.8774	0.0612				
0	4.238	0.168	4.579	0.244		
20	8.459	0.392	12.535	0.582		0.243
40	15.34	0.813	55.324	1.212		0.555
60	25.80	1.54	149.38	2.275		1.14
80	40.90	2.69	355.1	3.939	0.99	2.12
100	61.82	4.42	760.0	6.394	1.76	3.67
120	89.80	6.90	1489.1	9.861	2.94	6.01
140		10.3	2710.9	14.58	4.64	9.33

Values are from the *Handbook of Chemistry and Physics*.

quantities. A useful and instructive result is obtained if we plot the logarithm of pressure, rather than pressure, and the reciprocal of the *absolute* temperature, rather than a linear scale or one involving the temperature in degrees Centigrade. The same data used for Fig. 11.5 are plotted in this way in Fig. 11.6. For the seven examples the experimental values closely approximate straight lines; and this nearly linear behavior is found for all liquids. A straight line drawn for best average fit must satisfy an equation of the form

$$\log P = \frac{A}{T} + B \quad (11.1)$$

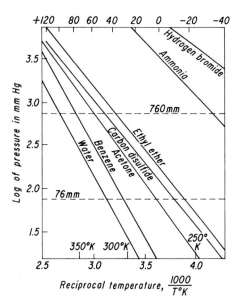

Fig. 11.6. *Logarithm of vapor pressure as a function of the reciprocal temperature for several liquids.*

where A and B are constants which can be evaluated from the slope of the line and the value of $\log P$ at some point on the line.

EXAMPLE

From the vapor pressures of ethyl ether at $0°$ and $50°$, 185 mm and 1277 mm, respectively, calculate the values of A and B for an equation of the form of Eq. 11.1.

At $0°C$, $P_1 = 185$ mm, $\log P_1 = 2.267$, and $1/T_1 = 0.003660$,

$50°C$, $P_2 = 1277$ mm, $\log P_2 = 3.106$, and $1/T_2 = 0.003093$.

To obtain the slope A, $\log P_2 - \log P_1 = 0.839$,

$$1/T_2 - 1/T_1 = 0.000567$$

hence $A = 0.839/-0.000567 = -1479$.

From this value and the pressure given for $0°C$,

$$B = 2.267 + 1479 \times .00366 = 7.680$$

The equation is then

$$\log P \text{ (mm)} = -(1479/T) + 7.680$$

While this simple form of equation is only an approximation, it is sufficiently accurate for many purposes, and the constants of this equation have been determined for many liquids. Values for the pressure of the vapor over the liquid or solid phases are listed for hundreds of substances in various reference tables.

Many important chemical properties are temperature-dependent in a form approximating that of Eq. 11.1; namely, that the logarithm of the quantity varies linearly with reciprocal absolute temperature. This is true of coefficients of viscosity, of equilibrium constants, and of rate constants of chemical reactions, to name but a few examples. (Note that vapor pressure is a measure of the position of equilibrium for a very simple reaction: liquid $\rightleftharpoons$ vapor.) In the later consideration of equilibrium laws (Sections 14.12 and 15.4) and the nature of rate processes (Chapter 22), the general underlying reasons for this behavior—and in particular a direct relation of the constant A to the energy change of the process which the equation describes—will be discussed. Because this form of equation occurs so frequently, it is important to be familiar with its use and to be able to make calculations from it readily.

11.3. Some Empirical Relations among Properties of Liquids

The physical properties of liquids have been extensively investigated for generations, and it is not surprising that a variety of similarities and regularities in the behavior of different liquids have been found on comparing the various measurements, which have made it possible to advance a number of simple relations expressing these experimental correlations. In a few cases these have proved to be a consequence of fundamental general laws, but for the most part they are only approximate rules of thumb which may work quite well in some instances and fail rather badly in others. Rules in this latter category can, despite their limitations, be very useful for estimating behavior under different conditions, and hence it is worthwhile to mention a few of the more important ones here.

Dühring's Rule

This rule concerns the relative changes of vapor pressure with temperature for different liquids. Referring to Fig. 11.6, it will be noticed that the different curves for log P versus $1/T$ converge at the higher pressures and smaller values of $1/T$. If these lines are extended smoothly, they intersect in a small region close to the point $1/T = 0$, as shown by the dashed lines in Fig. 11.7. (Values of $1000/T$ rather than of $1/T$ are plotted for greater convenience.)

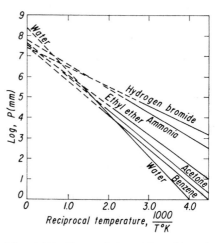

Dühring's rule is based on the approximation that the extrapolations of the different vapor pressure curves meet at a common value for $1/T = 0$. To the extent that this is true, an unknown vapor pressure at any temperature can be estimated from the value at any other temperature. For example, the normal boiling point is the temperature at which

Fig. 11.7. *Extrapolation of logarithm of vapor pressure versus reciprocal temperature to $1/T = 0$, for various liquids; an illustration of Dühring's rule.*

the vapor pressure is 760 mm (by definition). It is known that ethyl sulfide boils at 90.3°C, and the vapor pressure at 20°C is desired. If, as on the graph of Fig. 11.7, a line is drawn from log $P = 7.70$ for $1/T = 0$ through the point log $P = 2.88$ for $T = 363.5$°K ($1000/T = 2.76$), the value of log P for $T = 293$°K ($1000/T = 3.41$) can be read 1.74, giving $P = 55$ mm. (The correct value is 64 mm.)

Dühring's rule can be expressed in various forms, but all depend on the idea of a common intercept at $1/T = 0$ and the use of a graphical method or a geometrical method involving similar triangles. It is evident that it is not an exact rule, as the curve for water, for example, has an intercept at $\log P$ (mm) $= 8.5$, rather than the rough average value 7.7 appropriate for organic liquids which was used in the calculation for ethyl sulfide. Too much reliance, therefore, cannot be placed in the rule. Finally, the intercept, whether 7.5 or 8.5 or some other value, has no fundamental significance, as all liquids reach the critical point at some temperature considerably short of infinity.

Boiling Point Rule

Another rule relates the normal boiling point and critical temperature by the statement that the absolute temperatures of these two points are approximately in the ratio two to three:

$$\frac{T(bp)}{T(cp)} \simeq \frac{2}{3} \simeq 0.67 \qquad (11.2)$$

Reference to Table 8.3, where these temperatures are given for several substances, permits the demonstration that the rule works fairly well except in the cases of helium and mercury, which deviate considerably. There is no reason to expect any general underlying law which can account for the approximate validity of the rule in many cases.

Trouton's Rule

This rule relates the boiling point and the heat of vaporization of the liquid at the boiling point, which we shall call ΔH_{vap}. If the latter is expressed as the number of calories necessary to vaporize one mole of liquid, then for many liquids

$$\frac{\Delta H_{vap}}{T(bp)} \simeq 21 \qquad (11.3)$$

A few actual values of the ratio are ammonia 23.2, carbon tetrachloride 20.4, benzene 21.2, methane 19.8, nitrobenzene 20.1, hydrogen sulfide 21.1.

The conspicuous deviations from the value 21 for the ratio are for substances of low boiling point (hydrogen and helium) and those in which there are strong directed intermolecular forces in the liquid, or in both liquid and vapor. Water and ethyl alcohol are examples of the latter, because of the interaction between neighboring hydroxyl groups (hydrogen bonding); for them the ratio is about 26. For acetic acid, largely made up of double molecules $(CH_3COOH)_2$, the ratio is 15.

A similar but more accurate rule may be obtained by calculating the ratio $\Delta H_{vap}/T$ for temperatures which are in all cases the same fractional value of the critical temperature. This amounts to accepting the validity of a law of corresponding states for corresponding reduced temperatures, as was found to hold moderately well for gases (Section 8.9). Here again, however, abnormal liquids such as water and the alcohols are conspicuous exceptions.

The Rectilinear Diameter for Liquid and Vapor Densities

An interesting empirical relation for the equilibrium between liquid and vapor as the critical point is approached concerns the densities (or concentrations) of the two phases. The relation is illustrated in Fig. 11.8, in which the concentrations in moles/liter of liquid and gaseous acetone are plotted against temperatures up to the critical point at 235°C, the upper curve evidently being for the more dense liquid phase.

The approach to a common value is expected, since the critical point exists, with no distinction thereafter between properties of liquid and gas. The rule of the rectilinear diameter is simply that the averages of gas and liquid concentrations at different temperatures below the critical point lie on a straight line (the dashed line of Fig. 11.8). The average densities for acetone

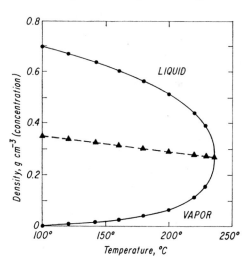

Fig. 11.8. *Rule of rectilinear diameters, for acetone.*

(indicated by triangles) fit quite well on a straight line drawn for best average fit of the points above 100°C.

The rule is useful in the determination of the critical density from densities measured at lower temperatures, rather than by the difficult direct measurement. It is also interesting because it can be understood qualitatively in terms of a very simple model for the liquid structure.

According to a simplified form of the so-called "hole theory" of liquids, a liquid has the structure of a solid, in which at any temperature a certain number of the spaces to be occupied by molecules are empty. The number of these holes increases as the liquid is heated, since molecules are evaporated to form more vapor. The liquid density thus decreases and the gas density increases until the two phases become indistinguishable. Without further discussion of changes in the packing and spacing of molecules at different temperatures in the liquid, the argument will not explain the change in the average liquid-vapor density with temperature, but it does support an interesting view of the nature of liquids.

11.4. Viscosity and Diffusion in Liquids

The ability of a liquid to flow in response to external forces is a characteristic property which implies that the molecules are able to rearrange themselves, rather than being fixed in definite unchanging order, as in a perfect crystal. The relation between flow rate and shearing force is expressed by the viscosity, already discussed for gases in Section 9.4.

A closely related property is diffusion, by which differences in concentration of any one kind of molecules or ions in the liquid are gradually equalized by net migration to the regions of lower concentration. The distinction from viscosity is in the fact that no external forces are applied to produce the flow, the driving force being thermal activity of the molecules themselves.

Measurement of Viscosity

Viscous flow of a liquid is established by applying a shearing force across a layer of the liquid, as indicated in Fig. 11.9. The coefficient of viscosity η is defined by the relation between the shearing stress (force per unit area) and velocity gradient (ratio of velocity change to thickness of the liquid layer):

$$\frac{F}{A} = \eta \frac{dU}{dy} \tag{11.4}$$

An arrangement of two parallel plates, as indicated in Fig. 11.9, A, could be set up to measure η, but other methods of producing shear and measuring flow give better results. A common one is Poiseuille's

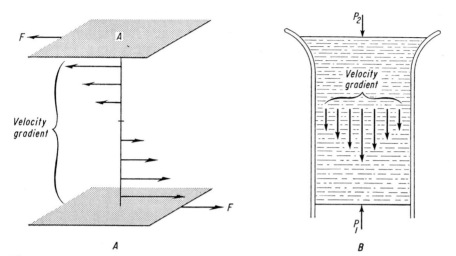

Fig. 11.9. *Shearing forces and velocity gradients in liquids:* (A) *shear flow;* (B) *Capillary tube method.*

method, Fig. 11.9, B, in which the rate of flow of liquid through a vertical capillary tube is measured, the applied force being the pressure difference between ends of the capillary, resulting from gravity or some externally applied pressure. Shear flow results because liquid at the walls of the tube is held stationary, while inner layers have increasing speeds of flow. The relation of viscosity to measured volume V and time t of flow, pressure difference, and capillary dimensions can be derived by integration of Eq. 11.4, with the result

$$\eta = \frac{\pi R^4}{8L} \frac{(P_1 - P_2)}{V/t} \qquad (11.5)$$

where R is the capillary radius, L its length, and $P_1 - P_2$ is the pressure difference across the liquid between the ends of the capillary.

Another method of producing shear flow is by applying a torque to rotate two coaxial cylinders at different rates; the liquid occupying the space between thus experiences slip in radial layers. Usually the outer cylinder is fixed, and the rate of rotation of the inner one for a known torque can be used to determine η.

Viscosity and Temperature

Values of viscosity determined by such methods as just described are listed for a number of liquids in Table 11.2. (The unit used, called the poise, is the cgs unit of viscosity for force in dynes, length in centimeters, time in seconds, and hence has dimensions gm cm sec⁻¹.) For comparison, values of viscosity are listed for air as a representative gas.

TABLE 11.2.   *Viscosities (Poise) of Liquids at Various Temperatures (°C).*

Liquid	0°	20°	40°	60°
Water	0.0179	0.0101	0.0065	0.0047
Glycerol	46.	8.5	—	—
Benzene	0.0090	0.0065	0.0049	0.0039
Chloroform	0.00706	0.00571	0.00474	0.00400
Diethyl ether	0.00295	0.00243	0.00200	0.00168
Air	0.000171	0.000181	0.000191	0.000200

These examples illustrate the general fact that liquid viscosities are higher than those of gases, a fact that is perhaps not surprising in view of the much greater density. A more striking difference is that viscosities of liquids increase rapidly at lower temperatures, while gases have the opposite change (that is, become more fluid when cooler).

Study of viscosity data for greater temperature ranges shows definitely that the variation is far from linear; instead the dependence is often fitted by an exponential formula. This is shown by the plots in Fig. 11.10 of log η versus $1/T$ for several liquids, which (water excepted) are nearly straight lines. Thus the data can be fitted quite closely by the formula

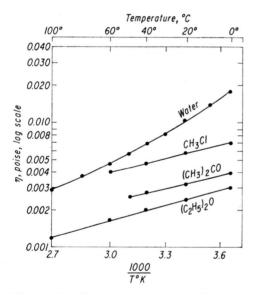

Fig. 11.10. *Viscosities of several liquids versus reciprocal absolute temperature.*

$$\log \eta = \frac{A}{T} + B \qquad \text{or} \qquad \eta = Ce^{B/T}$$

As mentioned in Section 11.2, this is the same type of equation as the one which describes vapor pressures fairly accurately.

Diffusion and Self-diffusion

The phenomenon of diffusion in liquids has most often been studied by following changes of concentration of a solute added in one part of the liquid, in which case the motion is of one kind of molecules (solute) in another (solvent). The rates of such processes are found to parallel differences in solvent viscosity quite closely, but they also depend on the nature of the solute molecule, as is to be expected.

In recent years, tracer techniques have made possible the study of self-diffusion; that is, the rate at which molecules of the liquid itself, which are initially in one part of the liquid, gradually move throughout its volume. For water this can be accomplished by using isotopic molecules, such as H_2O^{18} added to ordinary water, H_2O^{16}. The concentration of O^{18} isotope in samples from different parts of the liquid can then be determined from the greater density of the water containing O^{18}, which is proportional to the number of "tagged" H_2O^{18} molecules in the sample. In other cases, radioactive isotopes can be used and concentrations determined by measurements of radioactivity. Such studies show rates of diffusion at different temperatures, which change by very nearly the same relative amounts as the viscosity change. (The rates are naturally larger for smaller viscosity.)

Molecular Processes

The difference of viscosity and diffusion behavior in liquids from that for gases indicates that very different forms of molecular activity must take place. It will be recalled from Section 9.4 that the kinetic theory of gases explains the effects in terms of molecules moving freely between collisions with other molecules, which exchange momentum and energy. In liquids, however, the density is such that molecules must be considered as continuously in collision, or at least interacting strongly. From X-ray evidence (Section 11.1) each molecule of a liquid has on the average a quite definite arrangement of immediate neighbors; at the same time, these arrangements must change frequently to produce the observed flow and diffusion rates.

These considerations make reasonable a picture of molecules in a liquid spending most of their time in quite definite local arrangements, which frequently break up, however, and reform in new ones. The "hole theory" model already mentioned can provide an explanation of the flow by molecules occasionally squeezing past their neighbors into adjacent vacancies; other models do not invoke the presence of such holes as literally. They all, however, indicate the importance for molecular transfer of sufficient localized energy that the molecules can break away from one temporary position to reach others.

One can thus visualize a sort of "molecular square dance" with frequently shifting partners and groups. The energy necessary is evidently derived from that of the molecules themselves—their thermal energy. Since this is greater at higher temperatures, the rates of flow and diffusion increase. The nature of such "activation energy," which is an important concept for many problems of chemical kinetics, is discussed further in Chapter 22.

11.5. Equation of State Relation of Liquids

As explained in the discussion of gases, equation of state indicates the relation between pressure, volume, and temperature. For gases, this relation at low concentrations has the particularly simple form of the ideal gas law; the general nature of the deviations at higher concentrations can be understood in terms of attractive and repulsive forces between the molecules. At the very high concentrations of molecules found in liquids, however, these forces are exceedingly strong and involve many molecules simultaneously, with the result that the situation is much more complicated. Although much effort has been, and is being, put into developing adequate theories of liquids, existing theories have two serious faults: they are very complicated, and at the same time so approximate that they are not very accurate. It can be expected that great progress will be made, but the present situation is such that we must content ourselves with but a description of observed behavior, and only a suggestion of some of the important factors involved. No such simple equation of state as that for gases can be stated.

Thermal Expansion

The usual rule is that liquids expand with increasing temperature at a rate which is greater at high temperatures. At atmospheric pressure, this is usually expressed by an equation giving the specific volume of the liquid (reciprocal of density) at some standard reference temperature and the temperature, expressed in convenient units. If temperature (t) is in degrees centigrade and the standard value of volume is V_0 at $0°C$, a commonly used equation is of the form

$$V = V_0(1 + at + bt^2 + ct^3) \tag{11.6}$$

where a, b, c are empirical constants chosen to fit the observed values of V at temperature t and V_0 at $t = 0$. (The volume could be equally well expressed as the molar volume, but through custom, specific volume is used.)

The successive terms, at, bt^2, ct^3, in Eq. 11.6 are increasingly small in the range of t over which the equation fits the data, and often it is only necessary to use the first, or first and second terms. The coefficient a has typically the magnitude 10^{-3}, while b is of order 10^{-6}, and c of order 10^{-8}. Thus for a temperature change of $1°C$, the change in volume is about 0.1%, while over $50°C$ the change is 5% as an average figure, with actual values ranging from $2-10\%$ for the majority of liquids. The typical values given in Table 11.3 indicates their behavior is of this

TABLE 11.3. *Specific Volume, V (ml/gram) of Liquids at Different Temperatures.*

$V = V_0(1 + at + bt^2 + ct^3)$, where t is temperature in °C.

Liquid	Density at 0°C (g/ml)	V_0 (ml/g)	$a \times 10^3$	$b \times 10^6$	$c \times 10^8$	Equation Valid over Range (°C)
Acetic acid	1.0724*	0.93249	1.0630	0.1264	1.0876	16–107
Acetone	0.81248	1.23080	1.328	3.8090	−0.87983	0– 54
Benzene	0.90705*	1.10248	1.17626	1.27776	0.80648	11– 81
Bromine	3.1875	0.31373	1.06218	1.87714	−0.30854	0– 59
Carbon disulfide	1.2931	0.77334	1.13980	1.37065	1.91225	−34– 60
Carbon tetrachloride	1.63255	0.61254	1.18384	0.89881	1.35135	0– 76
Chloroform	1.52643	0.65512	1.10715	4.66473	−1.74328	0– 63
Ethanol	0.80625	1.24031	1.012	2.20	—	27– 46
Ether	0.73629	1.35816	1.51324	2.35918	4.00512	−15– 38
Mercury	13.5955	0.073554	0.4460	0.215	—	0–100
Pentane	0.64539	1.54945	1.4646	3.09319	1.6084	0– 33
Phenol	1.0920*	0.91575	0.8340	0.10732	0.4446	36–157
Water	0.99987	1.00013	−0.06427	8.5053	−6.7900	0– 33

Equation for V and constants a, b, and c from *Smithsonian Physical Tables* Ninth Revised Edition (1954). Values for density at 0°C from International Critical Tables. Those marked * are extrapolated.

nature, and gives an indication of the magnitude of liquid specific volumes.

A frequently used quantity, the coefficient of thermal expansion, is easily derived from Eq. 11.6. This coefficient, usually denoted by α, is defined by the derivative

$$\alpha = \frac{1}{V}\left(\frac{\partial V}{\partial t}\right)_P \tag{11.7}$$

(In this definition we have used the partial derivative symbol ∂, rather than total derivative symbol d, and the subscript P to indicate that only the change in volume at *constant pressure* is meant; the derivative given is only a part of the total derivative which might be taken. The constant pressure is here one atmosphere, but may be any other value of interest.)

By differentiating Eq. 11.6 with respect to temperature one obtains

$$\alpha = \frac{V_0}{V} (a + 2bt + 3ct^2) \qquad (11.8)$$

When t is small (not more than a few degrees) V_0 and V are nearly enough the same to be called equal as an adequate approximation, and the terms $2bt$, $3ct^2$ can be neglected in comparison with a; then $\alpha \cong a$. Hence a is very nearly the same as the coefficient of thermal expansion, which from its definition is the fractional change in volume per degree change in temperature.

Compressibility of Liquids

The decrease in the volume of a liquid as it is compressed is of interest, suggesting the usefulness of the concept of "holes" (or looseness of molecular arrangement) in the liquid, already mentioned in connection with the rule of the rectilinear diameter. Appreciable compression of a liquid requires pressures of many atmospheres, and therefore for many purposes it is adequate to call a liquid incompressible. At tremendous pressures, obtained by special techniques, however, considerable compression does occur, and for three simple liquids the decrease in the molar volume (specific volume × molecular weight, $cm^3/mole$) with increasing pressure up to 15,000 atmospheres is given in Fig. 11.11, taken from the work of P. W. Bridgman.

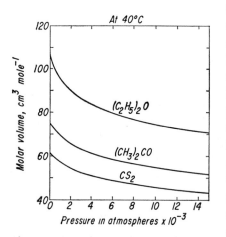

Fig. 11.11. *Molar volumes of three liquids at high pressures. [Data from P. W. Bridgman, Physics of High Pressures.]*

The evident general pattern is that the decrease in volume with increasing pressure is much less for pressures above the first few thousand atmospheres. The initial decrease finds a ready explanation as the result of the "slack volume" being squeezed out of the liquid so that it becomes more solidlike. There is no indication, however, that any limiting volume is approached at sufficiently high pressure; instead, there remains a further, although smaller, compressibility at even the highest pressure. This indicates that apparently the molecules themselves can be distorted by sufficient force. This proposition does not do violence to the Pauli principle or the quantum picture of electron charge distributions, because the effort expended supplies the energy necessary for more compact and higher energy charge distributions.

For pressures up to a few hundred atmospheres, the specific volume of the liquid is adequately described by a linear relation of the form

$$V = V_0(1 - AP) \qquad (11.9)$$

where V is the specific volume at pressure P, V_0 the specific volume at zero pressure (practically, V_0 *for liquids* can be taken as the volume at one atmosphere), and A is a constant.

The coefficient of compressibility of a substance, usually denoted by β, is—like the expansion coefficient α—defined as a partial derivative:

$$\beta = -\frac{1}{V}\left(\frac{\partial V}{\partial P}\right)_T \qquad (11.10)$$

(Again, partial derivatives and subscript T are used to indicate that the change is determined at constant temperature T.)

The negative sign is used in the definition to make β a positive quantity, $(\partial V/\partial P)_T$ being always negative. (It is easily deduced that if the volume V is fitted by a linear equation of the form Eq. 11.9, the value of β is approximately equal to A.)

11.6. Dielectric Constant and Polarization of Molecules

An important characteristic of a liquid is its polarity. The word polarity is used with a variety of meanings, but behind them all is the nature of the response to electrical forces of the constituent molecules. These forces always include the electric fields of other molecules, to which may be added fields produced externally. Both the forces and the response to them play important roles in determining properties of liquids, in particular their ability to act as electrolytic solvents.

Dielectric Constant

A measurable result of molecular charge displacements is the dielectric constant of a substance, which can therefore be useful as a means of studying molecular behavior. In elementary physics the concept of dielectric constant is usually introduced by noting the change in the force acting between two electrically charged particles (as given by Coulomb's Law) when they are immersed in the given substance. For fixed charges q_1 and q_2 at a separation R, the force F is changed from the value $F = q_1 q_2 / R^2$ for charges in vacuum to

$$F = \frac{q_1 q_2}{\epsilon R^2} \qquad (11.11)$$

where ϵ is defined as the dielectric constant of the substance.

Values for the dielectric constant ϵ of different substances are found to be larger than one, meaning that intervening molecules reduce the force between charged particles to a smaller value than when there is no intervening matter. For a substance like water, with $\epsilon = 80$ at room temperature, this reduction of force is very large; for benzene or cyclohexane, with ϵ about two, the effect is much smaller. These differences have an important bearing on the ability of charged ions to exist in solution, as discussed in Sections 17.14, 18.3, and 18.13. Measurements of force between charges could in principle be used to calculate dielectric constants, but more convenient and more accurate methods, based on other consequences of the Coulomb Law of force between charges, are always employed in actual practice.

A useful electrical effect of the dielectric constant of a substance is that concerning the capacitance of a condenser containing the substance. Such a condenser, consisting of two metal plates connected to a battery or generator, is shown in Fig. 11.12. The ratio of charge Q on one plate (with $-Q$ on the other) to the potential difference V is defined as the capacitance of the condenser. If the condenser is evacuated, this ratio depends only on the size and separation of the plates and is appropriately called the geometric capacitance:

$$C_g = \frac{Q}{V} \text{ (vacuum)} \qquad (11.12)$$

If the space between the plates is filled with a liquid or gas, the measured capacitance is larger (that is, Q is larger or V is smaller than before), and electrical theory shows from Coulomb's Law that the new capacitance C is larger by a factor ϵ:

$$C = \epsilon C_g \qquad\qquad (11.13)$$

Measurement of the increase $C - C_g = (\epsilon - 1)C_g$, by use of a capacitance bridge or other electrical circuits, then can be used to obtain the value of $\epsilon - 1$ or ϵ for the substance.

Electric Moments of Molecules

The reasons for the dielectric constant and the capacitance increase can be understood by considering how the electrons and nuclei of the molecules in the substance are affected by forces from other electric charges, such as the charges $+Q$ and $-Q$ on condenser plates, as in Fig. 11.12, A. Such charges produce an electric field E (force per unit

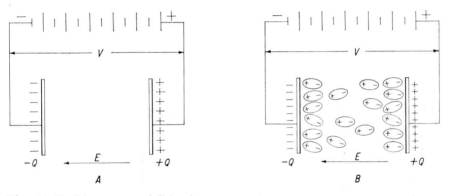

Fig. 11.12. *Measurement of dielectric constant.*

charge) at any point between the plates, as shown in Fig. 11.12, A. Electron charges, being negative, will be forced to the right, and positive nuclei to the left, until equilibrium with internal forces is reached. The result is distortion of the charge distribution, as indicated in Fig. 11.12, B.

This distortion effect occurs for all atoms and molecules. If the molecules are already polar, with a dipole moment μ, as discussed in Section 6.4, there will be an additional effect which can be much larger. A molecule such as HCl has unsymmetrical electron and nuclear charge distribution even in the absence of an applied electrostatic field. When a field is applied, the molecule is twisted by the torque acting on these charges in the direction to displace electrons to the right and nuclei to the left. In the average orientation, this displacement is far from complete, because collisions and other forces between molecules act to destroy it, but nevertheless an appreciable effect results.

The two effects of the induced polarization and of the dipole moments both change the electrical fields in the substance, as seen from Fig. 11.12, B. Positive charges now lying displaced to the left produce fields which on the average oppose the fields due to the charges $+Q$ and $-Q$ on the condenser plates. The same effect also obtains from the opposite displacement of electrons, and the result is a decreased resultant field E in the space between the condenser plates. This smaller field must mean either a smaller potential difference V for the same charges $+Q$ and $-Q$, or increased charge $+Q$ on the plates if V is to have the same value as before the introduction of gas or liquid. Either change makes the ratio Q/V larger, the increase depending on the magnitude of the molecular charge orientation and distortion.

Electrical theory shows that the change $\epsilon - 1$ due to charge displacements is proportional to the net charge displacement per unit field of the molecules in a unit volume. If m is the average displacement (or *electric moment*) per molecule resulting from distortion and net orientation of permanent moments by the field E, and N/V is the number of molecules in a unit volume, the equation yielded by theory is

$$\epsilon - 1 = 4\pi \frac{N}{V} \frac{m}{E} \qquad (11.14)$$

With this equation, dielectric constant measurements can be related to molecular properties which determine the value of m/E, as discussed below.

Nonpolar Gases

The simplest fluid of any interest is a gas of nonpolar molecules at low enough densities that the electric forces between molecules can be neglected. The nonpolar molecules acquire a moment m proportional to the field: $m = \alpha E$. The quantity α, called the polarizability, is the sum of charge displacements per unit field. Inserting this in Eq. 11.14 gives

$$\epsilon - 1 = 4\pi \frac{N}{V} \alpha \qquad (11.15)$$

In Table 11.4 are listed experimental values of ϵ for several gases, together with values of α calculated by Eq. 11.15. Since ϵ is a dimensionless ratio, α must have dimensions of volume to make $N\alpha/V$ dimensionless in Eq. 11.15; the units of the values listed are cm^3. It will be noticed that

TABLE 11.4.   *Dielectric Constants of Nonpolar Gases at 25°C and 1 atmosphere.*

Gas	ϵ	α (cm³) $\times 10^{24}$
He	1.000068	0.22
H_2	1.00027	0.88
O_2	1.00052	1.7
N_2	1.00058	1.9
CH_4	1.00084	2.7
CO_2	1.00098	3.2
CS_2	1.00290	9.4

all are of order 10^{-24} cm³, and hence of the same order as the volume occupied by the electrons of a single molecule. This is reasonable, since induced polarization results primarily from electron charge displacements. It will be noticed also that the polarizability increases roughly as the number of electrons in the molecule.

Polar Gases

If the gas is composed of polar molecules, a further contribution to $\epsilon - 1$ comes from the net moments produced by the slight alignment of the molecular moments when the external field is applied. This extra effect per molecule is proportional to the dipole moment μ of the molecule, and to the ratio of this moment to the average thermal energy kT, which energy is a measure of the effectiveness of collisions in nullifying the directing action of the field. The mean statistical result of these influences is expressed quantitatively by

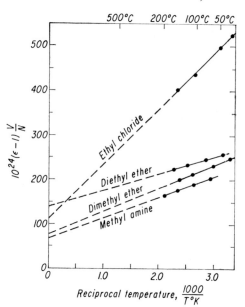

Fig. 11.13. *Polarization as a function of temperature for four gases. [Data from Table 26 of Böttcher,* Theory of Electric Polarisation, *American Elsevier, New York, 1952.]*

$$\epsilon - 1 = 4\pi \frac{N}{V} \alpha + 4\pi \frac{N}{V} \frac{\mu^2}{3kT} \qquad (11.16)$$

This equation has been very useful for determining dipole moments of molecules, as from a series of measurements of ϵ at different temperatures and known concentrations one can solve for both α and μ^2. The procedure is illustrated by the plots in Fig. 11.13 of values of $(\epsilon - 1)(V/N)$ for several gases against $1/T$. To be in agreement with Eq. 11.16, the points for a given gas should be on a straight line of intercept $4\pi\alpha$ at $1/T = 0$, and slope $4\pi\mu^2/3k$. The plots are linear, and the values of μ calculated from the slopes are listed in Table 11.5, together with the values of a number of other dipole moments similarly determined.

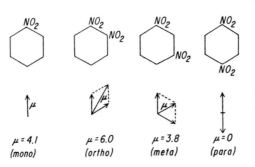

$\mu = 4.1$ (mono) $\mu = 6.0$ (ortho) $\mu = 3.8$ (meta) $\mu = 0$ (para)

Fig. 11.14. *Functional group contributions to the dipole moments of mono- and di-nitrobenzenes.*

Much information of chemical interest obtains from a knowledge of dipole moments, as already shown by the discussion of hydrogen halides in Section 6.4. Mere knowledge of the existence or absence of a dipole moment can be useful; for example, the existence of a dipole moment shows that the water molecule cannot be linear, whereas carbon dioxide is, possessing a zero moment. The numerical value of dipole moment can indicate relative orientations of polar functional groups in a molecule, a larger dipole moment resulting when the electric moments of these groups are so directed as to give a large resultant. This effect is illustrated in Fig. 11.14 for the three dinitrobenzenes. A variety of other

TABLE 11.5. *Dipole Moments of Molecules from Dielectric Constants of Gases.*

Molecule	μ (esu cm) $\times 10^{18}$	Molecule	μ (esu cm) $\times 10^{18}$
$(CH_3)_2O$	1.29	CH_3OH	1.72
$(C_2H_5)_2O$	1.11	CH_3Cl	1.90
CH_3NH_2	1.24	$CHCl_3$	0.95
C_2H_5Cl	2.00	C_6H_5Cl	1.57
H_2O	1.86	$C_6H_5NO_2$	3.95
H_2S	0.93		

examples are discussed in monographs on the subject. (See the references at the end of the chapter.)

11.7. Refractive Index and Dielectric Constant of Liquids

The preceding discussion of gases has been a necessary preliminary to the consideration of the dielectric behavior of liquids, because of the need to appreciate the relation of dielectric constants to molecular properties in the simple case where molecular interactions can be neglected. The electrical forces between molecules become more important when the molecules are closer together, and it is therefore not surprising that the simple expression of Eq. 11.16 obtained by neglecting these forces should fail for dense gases and to a greater extent for liquids. These forces in polar molecules are different in their nature and consequence than they are in nonpolar molecules, and to complicate the problem further are sensitive to the finer details of the charge distributions as well. There are, however, general trends of behavior and approximate relations which are chemically interesting and useful, and these are now considered.

Nonpolar Liquids

The first conclusion reached by examining liquid dielectric constant values is that they are uniformly larger than would be expected on the basis of Eq. 11.15. Thus, for *n*-pentane the dielectric constant calculated with $\alpha = 10.1 \times 10^{24}$ cm^3 is $\epsilon = 1.66$ at 20°C, but the measured value is $\epsilon = 1.84$. These differences are attributable to the fact that the strength of the electric field at any one molecule is larger than the average for the whole medium because a molecule is not randomly located and oriented with respect to its neighbors. A calculation of the average molecular field at a single molecule produced by regularly arranged molecules predicts that the polarization is increased by a factor $(\epsilon + 2)/3$. Including this approximate correction factor for *nonpolar molecules* in Eq. 11.15 gives the expression

$$\epsilon - 1 = 4\pi \frac{N}{V} \alpha \left(\frac{\epsilon + 2}{3} \right) \tag{11.17}$$

This equation is usually more conveniently expressed by first writing $N/V = N_0\rho/M$, where N_0 is Avogadro's number, M the molecular weight, and ρ the density, and then rearranging to give the result

$$\frac{\epsilon - 1}{\epsilon + 2} \frac{M}{\rho} = \frac{4\pi}{3} N_0 \alpha \qquad (11.18)$$

If we use $\alpha = 10.1 \times 10^{-24}$ cm^3 for pentane in the revised equation, then $\epsilon = 1.83$ at 20°C, in good agreement with the measured $\epsilon = 1.84$.

Refractive Indices

A useful application of Eq. 11.18 is based on the relation between the dielectric constant of a nonpolar liquid and its refractive index. The refractive index (n) of a substance, it will be recalled, is the ratio of the speed of light in vacuum to its speed in the given substance. A light wave considered as a moving electromagnetic field is reduced in speed as the result of its interaction with the electric charges in the atoms and molecules of the substance. Maxwell, in the nineteenth century, first recognized this electromagnetic nature of light, and was able to show that the dielectric constant ϵ and refractive index n should satisfy the relation $\epsilon = n^2$.

This relation was derived independently of molecular theory (indeed, Maxwell's work was done when little was known about the properties of atoms and molecules), and requires for its validity only that ϵ and n^2 result from the same molecular origins. This restriction is necessary because usually only electronic displacements have time to be effective in the rapid alternations of visible light (frequency of 10^{14} cycles per second), while dielectric constants measured at much lower frequencies are the result of both electronic and nuclear displacements.

Thus ϵ can be replaced by n^2 in Eq. 11.18 if electronic contributions alone are considered. Using the notation α_{el} to emphasize this, Eq. 11.18 can be written

$$\frac{n^2 - 1}{n^2 + 2} \frac{M}{\rho} = \frac{4\pi}{3} N_0 \alpha_{el} = M_r \qquad (11.19)$$

where M_r is the *molar refraction*. The refractive index n may be measured for light of various frequencies in the visible spectrum, the frequency most commonly used being that of the yellow D lines of sodium, often indicated by n_D. (A stipulation as to the frequency or wavelength is necessary because of dispersion; that is, n varies somewhat with frequency for most liquids, usually being larger toward the blue end of the spectrum.)

The dependence of the refractive index n upon the same electronic structure responsible for α_{el} expressed in Eq. 11.19 shows the refractive index to be a physical constant of the liquid, and is often useful as a test of identity or purity. This use is enhanced by the fact that values of α_{el}, and hence M_r for a molecule can be estimated from the sum of values characteristic of the constituent atoms, the functional groups in which they occur, and the bond types present in the molecule. This is best understood by the consideration of examples.

EXAMPLES OF ADDITIVE MOLAR REFRACTIONS   The values of M_r for a series of compounds differing only in the number of CH_2 groups are as follows:

Liquid	*n*-Pentane	*n*-Hexane	*n*-Heptane	*n*-Octane
M_r	25.27	29.91	34.55	39.19

From these data, it is evident that the increase in M_r is regular and about 4.618 per CH_2 group. The larger part of this is attributable to the electronic polarizability of the carbon atom, as the difference between 4.618 for CH_2 and 6.818 for CH_4 of 2.200 corresponds to an increase of 1.100 per H atom and hence a contribution of 2.418 per carbon.

The structural features of bonds in a molecule also affect the refraction, as can be seen by comparing values for ethane, CH_3—CH_3 and ethylene, CH_2=CH_2. For the first, $M_r = 11.38$, in good agreement with the sum $2 \times 2.418 + 6 \times 1.100 = 11.436$ from the atomic refractions. For ethylene, however, the observed value $M_r = 11.02$ is 1.78 larger than the sum $2 \times 2.418 + 4 \times 1.100 = 9.236$. The excess is plausibly attributed to the more loosely held electrons of the double bond, and

TABLE 11.6.   *Atomic and Group Refractions.*

Atom	M_r	Group or Bond	M_r
H	1.100	Double bond (C=C)	1.733
C (Single bond)	2.418	Triple bond (C≡C)	2.398
O (carbonyl, C—O)	2.211	—C≡N group	5.459
O (hydroxyl, O—H)	1.525		
O (ether, R—O—R)	1.643		
Cl	5.967		
Br	8.865		
I	13.900		

similar comparisons for other liquids show fairly constant values for which an average can be taken to be 1.733 per double bond.

By carrying out a series of suitable comparisons, a table of atomic refractions and structure contributions to molecular refractions can be built up to enable one to calculate molecular refractions by simple addition. Such a list is given in Table 11.6. Examples of its use are left to the reader for solution in the problems at the end of the chapter.

Polar Liquids

If the molecules of a liquid are polar, the dielectric constant is larger than the values in the range 1.7 to 2.5, characteristic of nonpolar liquids. Moreover, it varies considerably with temperature, as shown in Table 11.7. Although the trend to larger dielectric constants at low

TABLE 11.7.   *Dielectric Constants of Polar Liquids at Various Temperatures.*

$t°C$	H_2O	CH_3OH	$CHCl_3$	CH_3Cl	C_6H_5Cl	$C_6H_5NO_2$
−40			6.12	13.8		
−20		42.9	5.61	12.6		
0	88.1	38.0	5.18		6.04	
20	80.4	33.6	4.81		5.71	35.8
40	73.3	29.8	4.57		5.41	32.2
60	67.1				5.15	29.1
80	61.6				4.89	26.2

temperatures is like the dependence predicted by Eq. 11.16, the molecular interactions present in liquids again spoil any quantitative use of the equation. This is shown graphically in Fig. 11.15, where experimental values of ϵ for several liquids are plotted against the values of $(N/V)\mu^2/3kT$ calculated from the dipole moment μ, density, and temperature. If Eq. 11.16 were correct, the values of ϵ should fall a little above the dashed line of slope 4π. (Above the line because the small term $4\pi(N/V)\alpha$ also appears in Eq. 11.16.)

Beyond showing that Eq. 11.16 is inadequate for polar liquids, the graphs of Fig. 11.15 suggest further that there exists normal and anomalous behavior of liquids which is significantly related to their constitution. The dielectric constants of acetone, nitrobenzene, and alkyl halides fall near the solid line in Fig. 11.15, but values for water and alcohols, hydrogen peroxide, and hydrogen cyanide are less regularly behaved and are much larger.

The anomalous group is made up of liquids having hydrogen bonding and includes some important solvents, notably water. It is therefore worthwhile to consider briefly the underlying origin of their exceptional behavior. The term "hydrogen bonding" is something of a misnomer if it is construed to mean sharing of electron charge or of a proton by adjacent molecules. A hydrogen bond is rather a strong interaction of hydrogen bonded to oxygen, nitrogen, or fluorine in one molecule with the electron charge of one of these elements in a neighboring molecule; molecular identities, however, are not destroyed. According to present evidence the interaction is best described as an electrostatic attraction which causes the coordination of the positions of neighboring molecules to a considerable extent.

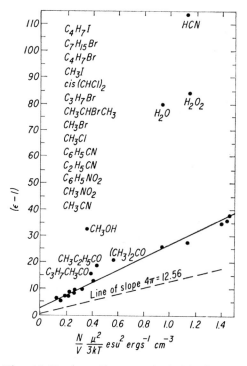

Fig. 11.15. $(\epsilon - 1)$ *versus* $(N/V)(\mu^2/3kT)$ *for several liquids. (Liquids listed represent un-labeled points from left to right.)*

These attractive forces are important only for hydrogen interactions with electronegative elements of the first row (O, N, F). For these, the hydrogen bond is a sufficiently stronger and more specific force, compared with the van der Waals attraction, that many physical properties of hydrogen bonding liquids and solids are very considerably different than they would be otherwise; at the same time these "bonds" are far weaker than true primary chemical bonds between atoms or groups in stable molecules.

The effects of hydrogen bonding on molecular arrangements are illustrated in Fig. 11.16, showing the form this bonding is believed to take in several cases. These are based largely on X-ray structure determinations, magnetic interactions of protons in nuclear resonance experiments, and infrared vibration-frequency analyses.

In the absence of specific forces such as hydrogen bonds, leading to preferred arrangements, the behavior of normal liquids (Fig. 11.15) indicates a fairly regular behavior of dielectric constant in relation to the permanent dipole moment μ and the temperature, which does not change greatly in kind for differing structural details of the molecules. By a more detailed statistical consideration of intermolecular forces, Onsager has been able to account moderately well for this general behavior, and Kirkwood further provided a theory taking into account such special effects as hydrogen bonding.

The principal conclusions from the properties of polar liquids are that the dipole moments of the free molecules have a characteristic part in determining their dielectric properties, and that there are large, special effects resulting from hydrogen bonding for most liquids of high dielectric constant. These conclusions are important in solution chemistry because, as developed in Chapters 18 and 19, the dielectric constants of liquids have an important bearing on their solvent behavior.

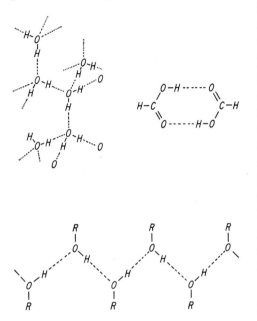

Fig. 11.16. *Effects of hydrogen bonding on molecular arrangements: water, a tetrahedral arrangement; formic acid, a dimerization; an alcohol—ROH—a chain arrangement.*

11.8. Solutions—Some Concepts

Solutions are comprised of a mixture of two or more distinct molecular species—whether atoms, molecules, or ions—rather than being composed of a single kind of molecules, or possibly of several kinds in equilibrium with a single species. Solutions are molecular mixtures which are homogeneous when observed on larger than a molecular scale, in contrast with other forms of mixtures which are heterogeneous, with two or more distinct phases present, such as droplets of oil in water. Solutions occur as solids, liquids, or gases. This discussion is primarily concerned with solutions in the liquid state.

Certain equilibrium mixtures are termed liquids rather than solutions because of the ready interconvertibility of the various species present. Water of sufficient purity surely ought to be called a liquid rather than a solution, although the evidence is convincing for the existence in liquid water of the ions H_3O^+ and OH^-, to the extent of about one part in 550 million at 25°C. To call this system a solution would be unreasonable, not because the number of ions is small, but because they are the result of the continual rapid conversion and reconversion represented by the equation

$$2H_2O \rightleftharpoons H_3O^+ + OH^-$$

Furthermore, the species H_3O^+ and OH^- cannot be removed from the mixture to produce water free of these ions; more neutral molecules would immediately dissociate to form more ions. Similarly, pure acetic acid is a liquid in which a large fraction of the molecules are paired by hydrogen bond to form double molecules, or dimers, but again there is an equilibrium between the two species and there is no way to realize a liquid which will exist as monomers or dimers alone.

In describing solutions the species present in largest quantity is commonly called the *solvent*, and the species present in smaller quantities *solute*. This distinction is natural and useful if only a limited quantity of one species can dissolve in a given amount of the other as, for example, sodium chloride, only 37 grams of which can dissolve in 100 grams of water at 25°C. For the case of two liquids which can be mixed in all proportions, such as benzene and toluene or methyl alcohol and water, the species are on an equivalent basis and neither acts uniquely as the solvent. The terms solvent and solute thus have no necessary or invariable significance in describing solutions.

Substances which may be mixed to form solutions are many in kind and variety, and there will be here mentioned only a few important classes. Water can be one component species of many solutions, as it will tolerate significant quantities of many other substances, whether these are liquid, gas, or solid separately, and frequently, as in the case of salts, the molecular species are ions derived from the solute molecules. In this last respect, the solvent power of water is a somewhat special property, deriving from its high dielectric constant. Large concentrations of ions are possible in only a few other solvents, ethanol, hydrocyanic acid, and liquid ammonia being notable examples. Despite the special character of ionic aqueous solutions, they are of great importance, as they include solutions of many acids, bases, and salts. They will be specially considered in later chapters.

Water is a good solvent for many other substances, including a great variety of organic materials, as for example in the fluids of living organisms. At the same time, water is by no means a universal solvent; many substances are dissolved only sparingly in water but are readily soluble in organic solvents such as ether, gasoline, benzene, carbon tetrachloride, and so on.

Although simple generalizations about solubilities of different substances are quickly found to have exceptions, certain distinctions in behavior are evident. With few exceptions, salts are practically insoluble except in water and other solvents of higher than average dielectric constant, in which they form ionic solutions, as already mentioned. A second useful observation is that a substance dissolves more readily in a solvent the more similar its molecules to the solvent. Great numbers of mixtures of hydrocarbons which form solutions in almost the complete range of proportions are commonplace in petroleum and its refined products, although they are not generally soluble in water. On the other hand, methyl and ethyl alcohols (CH_3OH and C_2H_5OH) are soluble in all proportions in one another and with water (HOH). There are many other examples of the compatibility of similar or related substances in solution, a few of which will be examples for later discussions of solution laws.

11.9. Units of Concentration in Solutions

To study quantitatively any properties of solutions, the relative amounts of the two species must necessarily be specified. There are a number of commonly used systems to express concentrations in solutions, each of which has its peculiar advantages and disadvantages. In the tabulation below, we list the more important and frequently used means of stating solution compositions, together with some indication of their origins or their special properties.

1. *Weight fraction* is determined as the weight of solute divided by the total weight of the solution. Other weight relationships are also used, such as the *weight ratio* (or *weight percent*), defined as the number of grams of solute per 100 g of *solvent*. These are perfectly definite as to the relative amounts of solute and solvent, but they are innocent of any intelligence

about the relative numbers of molecules present. But there are circumstances when this unit may be desirable or necessary, as in the case of
solutions of polymer molecules of unknown or variable sizes.

2. *Formality* expresses the solute concentration as the number of gram
formula weights (based upon an assumed empirical formula for the
substance) dissolved per liter of *solution*. A related quantity is *weight
formality*, defined as the number of gram formula weights per 1000 g of
solvent. Because formality is based on an arbitrary formula for the
solute it represents the number of molecules or ions in solution only to
the extent that the formula corresponds to some actual number of atoms
or ions. It is most useful in describing solutions of salts, which, completely ionized in the pure crystalline state, do not exist in the molecular
form as such. For example, while the gram formula weight of sodium
chloride is 58.4489, corresponding to the assigned formula, $NaCl$, it
contains Avogadro's number of sodium ions and an equal number of
chloride ions. The gram formula weight makes definite the amount of
solute, even if the formula is wrong or inadequate, so long as it is
commonly accepted.

3. *Molarity and molality (weight molarity)*. In these two systems, the
quantities of *solute* species are expressed as gram molecular weights, or
moles, of the species. *Molarity* refers to the number of gram molecular
weights of solute per *liter of solution; molality* is the number per 1000 g of
solvent. It will be noticed that molarity relates the number of moles of
solute to the volume of solution, which fits naturally into the volumetric
procedures of practical laboratory work; molality relates solute and
weight of solvent, as in gravimetric procedures. The latter units are
independent of temperature changes; for the former, the temperature
must be specified. Use of these units implies a knowledge or assumption
about the molecular formula for the solute, and the concentration
expressed will be proportional to the number of solute molecules in the
given amount of solvent.

4. *Normality* is used to express the concentration of solutions where
the solute is known to partake in a chemical reaction in a well-defined
manner—for example, the reaction of an acid with a base or of an
oxidant with a reductant. Most often the solute involved will be ionizable
if not already ionized, although in the case of oxidants and reductants,
the charge on the ions is not necessarily related to the normality of the
solution. Normality is defined as the number of gram equivalent weights
of solute per *liter of solution; weight normality*, sometimes used, the number
per *1000 g of solvent*. The equivalent weight is precisely defined as the

weight of a substance which will react with or displace 1.0080 g of hydrogen, 8.0000 g of oxygen, or 35.457 g of chlorine. Often it can be more readily expressed as the gram atomic weight divided by the valence, for an element; as gram molecular weight or gram formula weight divided by the sum of either the positive or negative valences; or, in case of oxidation-reduction reactions where a radical itself undergoes change, the gram formula weight divided by the valence change suffered by the constituents of the original radical. To avoid any possible ambiguity, it is well to express the normality of a solution with respect to a particular reaction.

5. *Mole fraction.* This is a more "symmetrical" concentration unit than those previously defined, as it describes *both* solute and solvent in terms of numbers of molecules (moles) rather than at most just the solute. The mole fraction of a particular species in solution is the number of moles of that species divided by the total number of moles of all species of the solution. The sum of all mole fractions is hence necessarily unity.

The complete equivalency accorded all chemical species making up the solution in stating its composition in mole fractions simplifies and illuminates the properties of many solutions, some of which are not obvious when other units are used. This is particularly true when different solvents are considered relative to a given solute, and when two substances are totally miscible over the entire range of composition, making the designation of solvent and solute completely arbitrary. At the same time more knowledge is required concerning the actual components of the solution, as mole fractions can only be calculated from measured weights by using known values of molecular weights of the chemical species involved.

11.10. Calculation and Conversion of Solution Composition

From the definitions of the preceding section, the following equations determine the composition of a component in solution in the units to be used hereafter:

1. The *weight fraction* (f_i) of a component denoted by i is

$$f_i = \frac{w_i}{w}$$

where w_i is the weight of i and w is the sum of weights of all constituents of the solution.

2. The molarity (C_i) is

$$C_i = \frac{n_i}{V}$$

where n_i is the number of moles of i, and V is the number of liters of solution. If V is expressed in milliliters, then $C_i = n_i(1000/V)$. The *formality* is similarly determined, using gram formula weights rather than moles.

3. The molality (m_i) is

$$m_i = n_i \frac{1000}{w_A}$$

where n_i is number of moles of i and w_A is *weight of solvent A in grams*. If w_A is expressed in kilograms, $m_i = n_i/w_A$.

4. The *mole fraction* (N_i) is

$$N_i = \frac{n_i}{n}$$

where n_i is the number of moles of i and n is the total number of moles in the solution—that is, the sum of numbers of moles of all constituents.

The problem of converting the composition of a given solution from one scale to another occurs frequently. Confusion in such calculations can be avoided by first calculating the weights of the different constituents from the composition as expressed, and then using these together with the density of the solution to calculate the composition in the desired units. The procedure for a binary solution is simple and straightforward, as demonstrated in the following calculations. If the weight of solvent A is w_A grams and that of solute B is w_B grams, then the weight fraction is

$$f_B = \frac{w_B}{w_A + w_B} = \frac{1}{1 + (w_A/w_B)} \qquad (11.20)$$

and the mole fraction is

$$N_B = \frac{w_B/M_B}{(w_A/M_A) + (w_B/M_B)} = \frac{1}{1 + (M_B/M_A)(w_A/w_B)} \qquad (11.21)$$

where M_A and M_B are the molecular weights of A and B. Similarly, the molarity is

$$C_B = \frac{w_B/M_B}{V} = \frac{w_B/M_B}{(w_A + w_B)/1000\rho} = \frac{1000\rho}{M_B} \frac{1}{1 + (w_A/w_B)} \qquad (11.22)$$

if ρ is the density of the solution in g/ml, the volume in liters being $V = w/1000\rho$. Finally, the molality can be written

$$m_B = \frac{w_b}{M_b} \frac{1000}{w_A} = \frac{1000}{M_B} \frac{1}{(w_A/w_B)} \qquad (11.23)$$

EXAMPLE

A five weight percent solution of ethyl alcohol in chloroform has a density of 1.419 g/ml at 25°C. Calculate N_B, C_B, m_B of chloroform for this solution.

Solving for w_A/w_B from $f_B = 0.050$ gives

$$1 + \frac{w_A}{w_B} = \frac{1}{0.050} = 20$$

whence $w_A/w_B = 19$.

Substituting in the other equations, with $M_B = 46$, $M_A = 119.4$,

$$N_B = \frac{1}{1 + (46/119)19} = 0.120$$

$$C_B = \frac{1419}{46} \times \frac{1}{20} = 1.54 \text{ moles/liter of solution}$$

$$m_B = \frac{1000}{46} \times \frac{1}{19} = 1.14 \text{ moles/kg of solvent}$$

11.11. Vapor Pressures of Solutions

Measured vapor pressures for different compositions and temperature of binary solutions alone constitute an immense quantity of data in the literature. A comprehensive survey of these data would make apparent certain distinctive types of behavior which aid in classifying solutions. The simplest type of behavior is most likely to occur in a solution of two liquids composed of molecules of similar size and related constitution.

An example of the so-called *ideal behavior* exhibited by solutions of sufficiently similar liquids is provided by the system ethyl bromide and ethyl iodide. Since both liquids are fairly volatile near room temperature (at 16.7°C their vapor pressures are respectively 452 mm and 163 mm), the total pressure of the vapor over a solution of the two is large and readily measured. Vapor pressures measured by Guthrie for various weight fractions of ethyl iodide are listed in Table 11.8 and plotted in Fig. 11.17 (at left). The smooth curve is seen to be definitely convex against the lower abscissa when the concentration is expressed as weight fraction of ethyl iodide. If the mole fraction of ethyl iodide is used to express the

TABLE 11.8.   *Vapor Pressures Above Ethyl Bromide-Ethyl Iodide Solutions at 16.7°C.*

Wgt % EtBr	Mole %	P (mm)
100	100	452
90	92.8	428
80	85.1	405
70	76.9	380
60	68.2	361
50	58.9	332
40	48.8	306
30	38.0	276
20	26.3	247
10	13.7	215
0	0	163

concentration, as in Fig. 11.17 (at right), the points may be closely approximated by a straight line.

Within the experimental error, the total vapor pressure of this binary solution varies linearly with the mole fraction of either component (the fraction of the *number* of molecules of one kind present). Similar results have been found for a number of other pairs of related liquids, such as

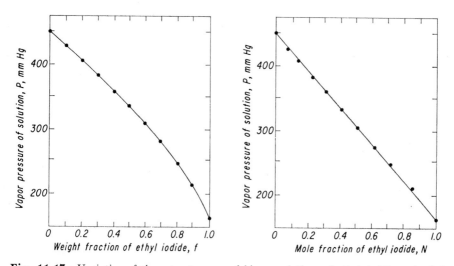

Fig. 11.17. *Variation of the vapor pressure of binary solutions of ethyl iodide and ethyl bromide with composition (expressed as weight fraction and mole fraction of EtI).*

benzene and toluene, ethylene dibromide and propylene dibromide, chlor- and bromo-benzene, and n-butyl-chloride and -bromide. For solutions of benzene and toluene, both the total pressure and the partial vapor pressures of the two components have been determined at 20°C, as given in Table 11.9 and plotted against mole fraction in Fig. 11.18.

TABLE 11.9.   *Partial Pressures (mm Hg) of Benzene-Toluene Solutions at 20°C.*

$N_{C_6H_6}$ (liquid)	$N_{C_6H_6}$ (vapor)	$P_{C_6H_6}$	$P_{C_6H_5CH_3}$	P
0.00	0	0	22	22
0.27	0.52	18	17	35
0.44	0.74	34	12	46
0.55	0.79	41	11	52
0.67	0.86	49	8	57
1.00	1.00	75	0	75

Since $N_{\text{toluene}} = 1 - N_{\text{benzene}}$, both partial pressures are conveniently plotted against the mole fraction of benzene. To a good approximation,

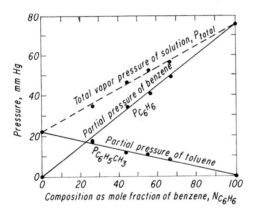

Fig. 11.18. *The vapor pressure and partial vapor pressure of benzene-toluene solutions as functions of the composition at 20°C.*

the partial pressure of each component is proportional to the mole fraction of that component in the liquid, being equal to the vapor pressure of pure liquid when its mole fraction is one.

The linear relation of partial pressures to liquid compositions indicated by Fig. 11.18 are expressed by

$$P_A = P_A^0 N_A$$
$$P_B = P_B^0 N_B$$

(11.24)

if A and B represent the two components and P_A^0, P_B^0 are the vapor pressures of the pure liquids. This proportionality of vapor pressure to both mole fraction and the vapor pressure of the pure component is known as *Raoult's Law*, and solutions for which this is true over the entire composition range are called *ideal solutions*.

The total pressure P of the vapor (assuming ideal gas behavior) is simply $P_a + P_B$, and so is given by

$$P = P_A^0 N_A + P_B^0 N_B$$
$$= P_A^0 N_A + P_B^0 (1 - N_A) = P_B^0 + N_A(P_A^0 - P_B^0) \qquad (11.25)$$

since the sum of mole fractions must be one. This is the equation of the dashed line in Fig. 11.18, and evidently the same form of equation describes the data for ethyl bromide-ethyl iodide solutions in Table 11.8 and Fig. 11.17. This simple behavior represented by Eqs. 11.24 and 11.25 is a reasonable one when the molecules of the two liquids are closely similar. In that case there will be little difference when the molecules of one kind are surrounded largely by molecules of the same kind or by varying proportions of the other species, and the ease with which a given molecule can escape from the liquid to the vapor will be practically the same regardless of the concentration. The number of molecules of the given species in the vapor, to which its partial pressure is proportional, hence depends only on the molecular concentration (mole fraction) of this species in the solution.

It is important to remember that the linear variation of vapor pressure over an ideal solution is with respect to mole fractions *of the liquid*, not of the vapor. When the vapor pressure of the ideal solution is plotted against the composition of the vapor rather than the composition of the solution, the linear relationship disappears. Such a plot is given in Fig. 11.19.

The difference can be described by the statement that *the vapor is richer in the more volatile component*—that is, the component which has the higher vapor pressure P^0. The

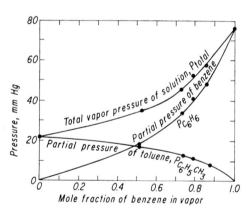

Fig. 11.19. *Vapor pressure and partial vapor pressure of benzene-toluene solutions as functions of the vapor compositions at 20°C.*

reason is that the more volatile component vaporizes more readily at a given concentration of solution than the less volatile, enhancing its concentration in the vapor.

The composition of the vapor in equilibrium with a liquid of given composition is easily calculated. Denoting the vapor mole fractions by

Y to avoid confusion with those of the solution, from definition of partial pressures (Section 8.5) $Y_A = P_A/P$ and $Y_B = P_B/P$. Then from Eqs. 11.24 and 11.25,

$$Y_A = \frac{P_A}{P} = \frac{P_A^0 N_A}{P_A^0 N_A + P_B^0 (1 - N_A)}$$

$$= \frac{P_A^0 N_A}{P_B^0 + (P_A^0 - P_B^0) N_A} \qquad (11.26)$$

from which Y_B is immediately obtained, since $Y_B = 1 - Y_A$. Inspection of Eq. 11.26 shows that if P_A^0 is greater than P_B^0, then Y_A is greater than N_A (the vapor is richer in A than the solution).

Although ideal behavior is more apt to be found for pairs of obviously closely related liquids, some examples of ideal or nearly ideal behavior are known for less obviously similar liquids. Two cases of this kind are benzene-ethylene dichloride at 50°C and cyclohexane-carbon tetrachloride at 40°C. The vapor pressures for the latter are plotted in Fig. 11.20 to illustrate what is meant by nearly ideal behavior. On the whole, however, relatively few solutions behave this simply—so few, indeed, that the justification for the attention given ideal solutions should be mentioned. The reasons are that ideal behavior is the simplest possible, that real solutions in some respects approximate such behavior over limited ranges of concentration, and that the nature of the *deviations* from ideal behavior gives valuable information about interactions of molecules in solution.

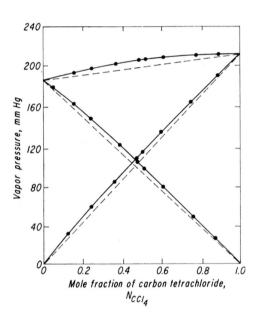

Fig. 11.20. *Vapor pressure curves for cyclohexane-carbon tetrachloride solutions at 40°C.* [*From Scatchard, Wood, and Mochals,* J. Am. Chem. Soc., **61:** 3208 (1939).]

The vapor pressures of real solutions may be either greater or less than those calculated assuming Raoult's Law (ideal behavior), as illustrated by the vapor pressure-composition plots in Fig. 11.21 for carbon disulfide-acetone and chloroform-acetone solutions. The departures of the actual partial pressures from linear proportionality with mole fraction are considerable in both cases, and it will be noticed that they are in the same sense for both components of each solution; that is, the deviations are either both positive (greater than ideal) or both negative. This is true for all solutions, as may be proved from the laws of thermodynamics.

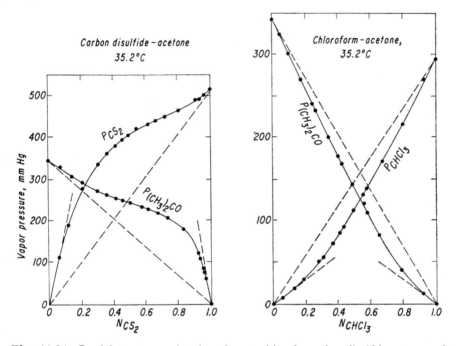

Fig. 11.21. *Partial pressure as function of composition for carbon disulfide-acetone and chloroform-acetone solutions.*

From a molecular standpoint, which of the two kinds of deviation is to be found depends on both the relative strength of interactions between like and unlike molecular species and on the possibilities available for arranging the different kinds of molecules. The more common deviation is positive, as in the carbon disulfide-acetone example, and is understandable if the forces of attraction between unlike molecules contribute less to stability of the solution than do those between like molecules. This can be the case if one or the other species is "associated"—that is, its molecules have strong specific interactions such as hydrogen bonding. Positive deviations can also be expected if the molecules are greatly dissimilar in size and shape, so that they fit together with more difficulty and escape more readily; ionic or dipolar forces will introduce further complications. This very qualitative exposition has its counterpart in detailed molecular theories, but a proper molecular interpretation of solution properties is still far from complete.

The less common negative deviations are easily explainable if the molecules composing the two liquids have for special reasons particularly great affinities for one another. It is noteworthy that the examples of such deviations are ones in which there are other reasons for inferring such strong attractions, some so great as to result in compound formation. This happens in aqueous solutions for solutes such as the halogen acids, nitric acid, and perchloric acid, which become hydrated when they are dissolved; hydrogen bonding between the two species can occur in such systems as carboxylic acids dissolved in water or pyridine in formic acid.

11.12. Dilute Solution Laws

Regardless of the specific type of possible deviations, there is one feature characteristic of all vapor pressure curves of binary solutions, however far they otherwise deviate from ideality. This concerns the behavior at either end of the concentration range, when one component is present in much smaller amount than the other. For a sufficiently dilute solution, both the solute and solvent vapor pressure curves approach a limiting linear variation with concentration.

This linear behavior is evident in all four dilute solution limits of the data plotted in Fig. 11.21, for example. Considering specifically dilute solutions of carbon disulfide in acetone (left side of Fig. 11.21 (a)), the vapor pressure of acetone initially decreases linearly and lies close to the ideal solution line until the concentration of carbon disulfide approaches the mole fraction 0.05; and the vapor pressure of carbon disulfide initially rises linearly from zero at zero concentration but along a *different* line than the ideal solution line. The same is true for dilute solutions of acetone in carbon disulfide (right side of Fig. 11.21 (a)), as is also the case for dilute chloroform-acetone solutions and indeed all dilute solutions.

The changes in concentration dependence and the approach to a linear dependence can be brought out by consideration of the ratios

$$P_{CS_2}/N_{CS_2} \qquad P_{(CH_3)_2CO}/N_{(CH_3)_2CO}$$

listed in Table 11.10. For solutions sufficiently dilute in carbon disulfide

TABLE 11.10.   *Vapor Pressures (mm Hg) of Carbon Disulfide-Acetone Solutions at 35.2°C.*

N_{CS_2}	P_{CS_2}	$P_{(CH_3)_2CO}$	P_{CS_2}/N_{CS_2}	$P_{(CH_3)_2CO}/N_{(CH_3)_2CO}$
0	0	343.8	—	(343.8)
.0624	110.7	331.0	1772	339
.0670	119.7	327.8	1785	352
.1212	191.7	313.5	1580	357
.1991	271.9	290.6	1360	363
.8280	464.9	180.2	561	1047
.9191	490.7	123.4	535	1530
.9359	491.9	109.4	526	1680
.9549	496.2	85.9	521	1900
.9692	502.0	62.0	519	2020
1.0000	512.3	—	(512)	—

From data of J. v. Zawidski, *Z. Physik. Chem.*, **35**: 129 (1900).

$(N_{CS_2} < 0.07)$, the ratio P/N for the solute CS_2 is 1780 and for the solvent acetone 340, within the precision of the data. At the other extreme, the ratio P/N, for CS_2 as solvent, approaches a limiting value 512 and the ratio for the solute acetone approximates 2000.

These results can be expressed by two equations, one for the solvent and one for the solute. The *solvent* relation is just *Raoult's Law*, already discussed for ideal solutions. In nonideal solutions, its validity is restricted to the solvent at low concentrations of solute. Using the subscript 1 to refer to solvent, Raoult's Law is

$$P_1 = P_1^0 N_1 \qquad\qquad (11.27)$$

for the solvent in dilute solutions. The significance of this limiting relation lies both in its linear form and in the fact that the constant P_1^0 is the vapor pressure of pure solvent. (Notice in the example of the CS_2-acetone solutions that P_1/N_1 for acetone as the solvent approaches the value $P_1^0 = 344$ for pure acetone, and P_1/N_1 for CS_2 as the solvent approaches $P_1^0 = 512$, the vapor pressure of pure CS_2.)

For the solute, the limiting relation is also linear, but the proportionality constant is *not* the vapor pressure of pure solute; in the example, the ratio P/N for CS_2 as solute is 1780, more than three times the value $P_{CS_2}^0 = 512$ for pure CS_2, and the difference for acetone as solute is even larger. This important distinction is emphasized because the limiting *solute* relation was first observed by itself (*Henry's Law*). With the subscript 2 to denote the solute, Henry's Law, giving the vapor pressure of the solute in sufficiently dilute solutions, can be written

$$P_2 = KN_2 \qquad (11.28)$$

Henry's law can equally well be expressed in terms of solute molality or molarity, because these units differ from mole fractions in dilute solutions by a nearly constant factor. Thus one can as well write $P_2 = K'm$ or $P_2 = K''C$, where K' and K'' are new constants differing from K by the ratio of units of concentration used.

The constant K is characteristic of the solution at the particular temperature, but cannot be identified with any properties of the pure solute. The difference between solute and solvent behavior is reasonable in considering that solvent molecules are escaping from and returning to a liquid which is still largely solvent, and so interact primarily with other molecules of their own kind. Solute molecules, on the other hand, are surrounded in dilute solutions almost exclusively by solvent molecules, and so their ease of escape depends on their affinity for the molecules of solvent. The common and controlling factor in both cases is the concentration of molecules available for transfer to the vapor phase.

Both Raoult's Law and Henry's Law are approximations, with accuracy sufficient to be useful only if the solution is sufficiently dilute. What the usable range of concentration is will depend on the particular components of the solution and the accuracy needed; no general statements are possible. Thus an ideal solution is one for which Raoult's Law is valid at all concentrations, and Henry's Law also, which is then identical with Raoult's Law. In carbon disulfide-acetone, the deviations are considerable when the solute mole fraction is 0.1. For solutions with larger deviations from ideality, the valid range is still smaller, as in the 1-propanol-water solutions shown in Fig. 11.22. Positive deviations

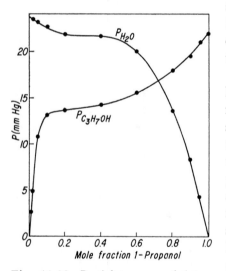

Fig. 11.22. *Partial pressures of 1-propanol-water solutions at 25°C.* [*Butler, Thomson, and Maclennan,* J. Chem. Soc., **674** (1933).]

of this kind become so great in many cases that the limit of solubility is reached, resulting in a second phase in equilibrium with the solution. Situations of this kind are discussed further in Chapter 20. A particularly important class of solutions showing large deviations are solutions of salts in water, for which the electrical forces between the solute ions have effects which are appreciable even at solute molalities no greater than 0.01, and which diminish slowly for lower concentrations. Such systems will receive their necessary special consideration in Chapters 17 and 18.

Despite their approximate and limited validity, dilute solution laws are important and useful in discussing many properties of solutions and reactions in solution, and good use of them will be made for such purposes. It is therefore important to have a clear appreciation of their significance and their limitations.

Problems

11.1. Make plots like Fig. 11.6 for the vapor pressure of bromobenzene from 30°C to 397°C (critical point) and for chloroform from -60°C to 160°C, using data from the *Handbook of Chemistry and Physics*. From the graphs obtain values of A and B for the straight-line approximation of Eq. 11.1 to the data.

11.2. The vapor pressure of *n*-butyl alcohol is approximately represented by the formula $\log P \text{ (mm)} = -2443/T + 9.136$ in the range 75–117°C. Calculate P at 80°C and at 110°C.

11.3. The vapor pressure of ethyl propionate is 27.8 mm at 20°C and the boiling point is 99.0°C. Calculate the value at 60°C, assuming an equation of the form of Eq. 11.1 is valid, and compare the result with the measured vapor pressure at 60°C.

11.4. Bromobenzene boils at 156.2°C. (a) Use this value to estimate the temperature at which the vapor pressure is 90 mm. (b) From tabulated values of vapor pressure at different temperatures, obtain a more accurate value by interpolation. How well does your answer to (a) agree with it?

11.5. Estimate the heats of vaporization of ethyl propionate and bromobenzene from their boiling points by Trouton's rule and compare with measured values in the literature.

11.6. The critical temperature of ethyl acetate is 250.1°C. The densities d_l of the liquid and d_v of the vapor, in gm/cm³, at lower temperatures are as follows:

t°C	180	200	220	240
d_l	0.6653	0.6210	0.5648	0.4778
d_v	0.0388	0.0580	0.0891	0.1499

Use these data to test the rule of the rectilinear diameter and to obtain a value for the critical molar volume.

11.7. The boiling point of argon is $-186°C$, the critical temperature is $-122°C$, and the heat of vaporization at the boiling point is 37.6 cal/g. (a) Use these values to test the boiling-point rule and Trouton's rule. (b) Look up data for liquid and vapor densities and use them to test the rule of the rectilinear diameter. (c) Look up vapor pressure data and plot $\log P$ versus $1/T$. Is Eq. 11.1 a good approximation? Is Dühring's rule?

11.8. Look up viscosity data for acetone and n-butyl alcohol and plot $\log \eta$ versus $1/T$. Are the curves more nearly straight lines than for plots of η versus T?

11.9. Measured viscosities (in centipoise) of heptane at several temperatures are as follows:

$t°C$	0	17	25	40	70
$\eta(cp)$	0.524	0.461	0.386	0.341	0.262

By a suitable graph and interpolation obtain a value for the viscosity at 55°C.

11.10. Pentane is sometimes used as a thermometer fluid (especially for low temperatures). A thermometer is made with a glass bulb of volume 2.0 cm³ to which a capillary stem of inside diameter 0.5 mm is attached. If the bulb is just filled to the bottom of the stem at $-50°C$, how far will pentane rise in the capillary when the temperature is 0°C? Assume an average volume expansion coefficient 0.00142 per degree for pentane and neglect expansion of the glass.

11.11. A strong steel bomb is filled with chloroform at 0°C, sealed off, and heated to 50°C. Calculate the pressure in the bomb if the compressibility of chloroform at 60° is 2.0×10^{-6} per atmosphere, assuming that the bomb does not expand appreciably. (This procedure is sometimes used to obtain high pressures without pumps.)

11.12. Cylinders of gases such as nitrogen, argon, and hydrogen are supplied with pressures of 2000 lb/in.² or more, but butane is supplied at a pressure of only about 30 lb/in² absolute, and warnings are issued about overfilling such cylinders. Explain.

11.13. The dielectric constant of gaseous carbon disulfide is 1.00290 at 25°C and 1 atm and is 1.00250 at 75°C and 1 atm. Show that within their accuracy these values indicate that CS_2 is a nonpolar molecule.

11.14. The dielectric constant of liquid oxygen is 1.507 at $-193°C$ and its density is 1.182 g/cm³, while the dielectric constant of the gas at 20°C and 1 atm is 1.000495. Which equation—Eq. 11.15 or Eq. 11.18—better represents these values?

11.15. Dielectric constants of gaseous ethyl chloride at a constant density of 0.00157 g/cm³ and several temperatures are as follows:

$t°C$	25	65	105	145
$\epsilon - 1$	.00773	.00703	.00643	.00599

Make a plot like that of Fig. 11.13 and determine the dipole moment from the slope of the best straight-line fit to the points.

11.16. The dipole moment of monochlorobenzene is 1.70 debye units, while the dipole moments of ortho-, meta-, and paradichlorobenzene are 2.53, 1.67, and 0 debye units. Discuss the relation of these values.

11.17. The dipole moment of toluene is 0.37 debye units, that of chlorobenzene is 1.70, and that of *p*-chlorotoluene is 2.03. The dipole moment of nitrobenzene is 4.10 debye units and that of *p*-chloronitrobenzene is 2.60. Discuss these values in terms of the polarity of the substituted groups.

11.18. Calculate the molar refraction of *n*-nonane from the refractive index 1.4056 and density 0.7177 gm/cm³ at 20°C. Compare with the value obtained from the additivity rule.

11.19. The refractive index of 1-pentyne (*n*-propyl acetylene) is 1.4079 at 18°C and the density is 0.6977 gm/cm³. Compare its molar refraction with the value calculated from Table 11.6.

11.20. Allyl alcohol, C_3H_6O, has a refractive index 1.4135 and density 0.855 at 20°C. Discuss the molar refraction in relation to structure of the molecule.

11.21. A 10% solution by weight of KCl in water has a density of 1.063 gm/cm³. Calculate the molality and molarity of KCl in the solution.

11.22. A 30 percent solution by weight of ethanol in water has a density of 0.9507 g/cm³ at 25°C. What are the molality and the mole fraction of alcohol in solution? What is the molarity of water (i.e., moles of water per liter of solution)?

11.23. The density of a 3.0% solution by weight of ethanol in chloroform is 1.442. (a) Calculate the molality, molarity, and mole fraction of ethanol. (b) Calculate the molality and mole fraction of a 3.0% solution of chloroform in ethanol.

11.24. A solution contains 70% water, 10% acetic acid, and 20% ethanol by weight. Calculate the mole fraction of each in solution.

11.25. The vapor pressures of ethyl bromide and ethyl iodide at 20°C are 386 mm and 109 mm, and they form nearly ideal solutions. (a) What is the composition (mole fraction) of the solution which boils at 300 mm pressure? (b) The solution continues to boil until the mole fraction of ethyl bromide is 0.30. What is the pressure at this time?

11.26. Calculate the vapor compositions above the two solutions of Problem 11.25.

11.27. Vapor pressures in mm Hg above solutions of ethyl acetate in carbon tetrachloride at 50°C are listed below.

N_{EtAc}	P_{EtAc}	P_{CCl_4}
0	0	306.0
.0965	34.4	276.8
.1197	42.6	272.0
.1978	67.0	249.5
.2149	72.3	245.5
.3265	103.0	214.1
.4250	126.5	189.6
.5984	175.0	136.5
.6838	196.5	110.4
.7481	213.3	90.1
.8064	228.4	70.7
.8488	239.7	56.2
1.0000	280.5	0

(a) Make a plot similar to those in the text of these vapor pressure composition data. Are the deviations from ideality positive or negative? (b) By suitable numerical analysis, find the composition ranges in which Raoult's Law and Henry's Law would operate.

11.28. The vapor pressures of *n*-butyl chloride and *n*-butyl iodide, which form very nearly ideal solutions, are 29 mm and 12.5 mm at 50°C. Calculate the composition for the first drop of distillate from a solution with 0.20 mole fraction of *n*-butyl iodide. Is it richer or poorer in the more volatile component than is the solution?

11.29. From Fig. 11.21, estimate the composition of the first drop of distillate from a solution with 0.20 mole fraction of carbon disulfide. Compare its composition with that of the solution, as done in Problem *11.28.* How do you explain the difference?

11.30. The vapor pressure of $CHCl_3$ at 50°C is 540 mm and that of CCl_4 is 320 mm; solutions of the two are nearly ideal. (a) A solution which is initially 25% chloroform is gradually evaporated by reducing the pressure gradually without removing any vapor from the space above the liquid (as by withdrawing a piston). What is the composition of the last drop of liquid? (b) What is the composition of the last drop if the vapor is continuously removed?

11.31. (a) Show for a liquid whose vapor pressure satisfies Dühring's rule— i.e., $\log P \text{ (mm)} = -(A/T) + 7.70$—that $A = 4.82 T_b$. (b) What does a comparison of this result with Trouton's rule (Eq. 11.3) suggest about the significance of A? (A more fundamental derivation of such a relation from the second law of thermodynamics will be given in Chapter 14.)

11.32. (a) Show that for a small vapor pressure change ΔP, the corresponding temperature change ΔT according to Eq. 11.1 is

$$\Delta T = \frac{T^2}{2.3A} \frac{\Delta P}{P}$$

(b) This result can be used to obtain an approximate formula for correcting observed boiling points T_0 to give T_b at 760 mm Hg. Show, using the result in (a) and the result $A \cong 4.82T_b$, that such a formula is

$$T_b = T_0 + \frac{T_0}{8450} (760 - P)$$

11.33. (a) Show that Eq. 11.1 can be expressed in the form $P = P_0 e^{-w/kT}$, where $P_0 = e^{2.3B} = 10^B$ and $w = 2.3kA$. (b) The result in (a) shows a similarity to the Boltzmann factor $e^{-E/kT}$ for numbers of molecules with energy E. If A has the value $1479°K$, as for ethyl ether, what is the value of w in cal/molecule and cal/mole? Compare the latter with the heat of vaporization of ethyl ether.

11.34. A variety of evidence indicates that both acetic and formic acid molecules associate in the vapor to hydrogen bonded dimers of the form

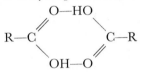

From the polarities and arrangement of the C=O and OH groups, what can you say about the dipole moments of single molecules and such dimers? Would the dielectric constant of partially dimerized vapor be larger or smaller than if there were no association?

11.35. Liquid formic acid has a very large dielectric constant, ~55 at room temperature, which decreases rapidly at higher temperatures; acetic and higher carboxylic acids have much lower values (less than 7), which increase at higher temperatures. What do these facts suggest about association in the liquids?

11.36. Dipole moments of molecules are in some cases roughly the vector sum of moments due to bonds or groups. The C—H bond has been estimated to have a moment of about 0.4 debye. (a) Methane is nonpolar and tetrahedral. What is the moment of a CH_3 group? of a CH_2 group with two normal bonds? (b) Use these results to show that normal paraffins C_nH_{2n+2} are all nonpolar if all the bonds are equivalent and tetrahedral.

11.37. (a) Show that the molarity C of a sufficiently dilute solution is approximately expressed in terms of the molality m by the relation $C = m\rho$, where ρ is the density. (b) At what molality will this relation be in error by 1% if the solute has a molecular weight of 50 and the solvent is water?

11.38. In the text, Henry's Law for the solute is written $P_2 = KN_2$; that is, the amount of solute is expressed by the mole fraction N_2. The law can also be expressed $P_2 = K_m m_2$ or $P_B = K_c C_2$ (i.e., in terms of molality or molarity) if the solutions are sufficiently dilute. Show that K_m and K_c are then related to K by the expressions $K_m = KM_1/1000$ and $K_c = KM_1/1000\rho$, where M_1 is the molecular weight of solvent and ρ is the solution density.

11.39. An equimolar solution of benzene and toluene at 20°C is half evaporated; the total numbers of molecules in solution and in the vapor are equal. Calculate the composition of each phase as mole fractions, and the total vapor pressure.

11.40. Solutions of carbon disulfide in methylal at 35°C had compositions and vapor pressures in mm Hg as follows:

N_{CS_2}	0	.0489	.1030	.1640	.2710
P_{CS_2}	0	54.5	108.3	159.5	234.8
$P_{C_3H_8O_2}$	587.7	558.3	529.1	500.4	451.2

(a) By numerical analysis, determine the range of concentration in which a Henry's Law constant can be chosen to reproduce the vapor pressure to ±2 mm, and the range in which Raoult's Law is obeyed to this precision. (b) Are the deviations positive or negative? Does the fact that the vapor pressure of pure CS_2 is 514.5 mm at 35°C lead to the same conclusion?

11.41. A 0.05 formal solution of KCl in water at 100°C has a vapor pressure 1.28 mm less than the vapor pressure of pure water at this temperature, and the vapor pressure of KCl is entirely negligible. (a) Calculate the mole fraction of solvent in the solution, assuming Raoult's Law. (b) From the answer to (a), calculate the apparent molality of KCl. What does the difference of this value from the weight formality of 0.05 suggest about the solution?

Suggested Readings

Few books are devoted to liquids and solutions as such except at an advanced level, but many contain discussions of topics in this chapter, including of course textbooks or treatises on physical chemistry. More specialized monographs on solution behavior are listed at the end of Chapters 17, 18, and 19.

The basic principles of dielectric behavior are described very clearly by the most important contributor to the original theories in the book *Topics in Chemical Physics, Based on the Harvard Lectures of Peter Debye* by A. Prock and G. McConley (Elsevier, New York, 1962). A comprehensive discussion of dipole moments and dielectric properties is given in *Dielectric Behavior and Structure* by C. P. Smyth (McGraw-Hill, New York, 1955). Tables of dipole moments for some 6000 compounds are given in *Tables of Experimental Dipole Moments* by A. L. McClellan (Freeman, San Francisco, 1963).

The chemical and physical effects associated with hydrogen bonding are considered at length in *The Hydrogen Bond* by G. C. Pimentel and A. L. McClellan (Freeman, San Francisco, 1960).

Chapter 12

The First Law of Thermodynamics

IN THE DISCUSSION of properties of gases in Chapter 10, the interactions of a gas with its surroundings were related to the changes in intensity of molecular motions in the body of the gas. The interactions considered were the absorption of heat work done by expansion, and it was possible to relate the quantity of heat or work quite simply to changes in energy of the system.

The state of any substance—gas, liquid, or solid—changes of course if it gives off or takes up heat and does mechanical, electrical, or other form of work on its environment. The details of the internal changes which take place if the molecules interact appreciably with each other, as they do in liquids and solids, and especially if chemical reaction occurs, may be very complex—so much so that adequate molecular theories have not been developed for much important and interesting chemical behavior.

Despite the incompleteness of present knowledge, however, a more limited statement can be made of the relation between the interactions of *any* substance with its surroundings and the overall change in state of the substance. This relation, the first law of thermodynamics, does not provide as many details of the change of state as would be provided by a molecular theory. But laboratory results have proved it so generally true that the first law is called a law of nature. Because this law is based directly on experiment and, properly stated, knows no exception, it can always be used with confidence for knowledge or predictions of value. This is the case even in situations where no accurate theory exists to describe molecular details of what is happening and how it happens.

12.1. Heat, Work, and Change of State

The study of the relation of heat and work in different processes has been of major importance for centuries. Early thinking about the subject was marked by a great variety of theories, and the confusion only began to be resolved in the eighteenth and nineteenth centuries. Then systematic investigation and controlled experiments gave a solid basis for testing conflicting ideas, and led to quantitative statements embodying and expressing measurable relations.

For a long time many people held to the calorific theory of heat as an intrinsic constituent of matter which could be set free under proper conditions. Count Rumford in 1798 was able to reduce this proposition to absurdity by experiments in which he could generate heat indefinitely and in unlimited amount, provided only that continued mechanical effort was exerted by such processes as scraping a metal surface with a blunt tool. Such effects imply a connection between heat and mechanical work, rather than the existence of heat in matter as a substance in itself, without regard to other influences.

Heat Equivalent of Work

Joule, by experiments over the early years of the nineteenth century, was able to find a direct equivalence between the amount of heat produced and the mechanical work necessary, *provided* no other changes occurred. This equivalence is embodied in the quantitative relation already mentioned, that the expenditure of 1 joule ($= 10^7$ dyne cm, or ergs) of work will evolve 0.23901 calories as heat if there is no change in the working substance, such as change of phase, bodily motion, or so on. If there are such changes, Joule's equivalence no longer holds good.

Any change in temperature of the machine doing the work or of other materials involved represents the absorption of a given quantity of the heat produced. This must, of course, be taken into account when determining the equivalence. A simple example, an electrical heating element which is placed in a well-insulated calorimeter, will demonstrate this. A given amount of electrical work will result in the equivalent amount of heat given to the calorimeter, allowing for the temperature rise and heat capacities of all components involved: the material within the calorimeter, the calorimeter container, the thermometer, the heating element, and so forth.

Relation to Change of State

A second important characteristic of heat and work is that different given amounts of heat or amounts of work separately supplied to or taken from a substance can produce the same change in its condition; the sums of the amounts of heat and work for a given change must, however, be the same.

For example, one mole of nitrogen gas initially of volume 24.5 liters at 25°C and 1 atmosphere, compressed by application of external work to 20 atmospheres in a perfectly insulated cylinder, reaches a temperature of nearly 430°C with no heat supplied as such, the final volume being 2.88 liters. The necessary work amounts to 2000 calories (8367 joules). If, instead, the gas is compressed from 1 to 20 atmospheres, keeping the temperature at its initial value of 25°C, and then heated to 430°C, keeping the pressure constant at 20 atmospheres, the same final volume of 2.88 liters will be realized. However, the work done on the gas would be but 970 calories, and the net amount of heat supplied to the gas by its surroundings during the two steps would be 1030 calories.

Still a third possible process, the compression of the nitrogen to the final volume of 2.88 liters while the temperature is kept at 25°C, followed by heating this fixed volume to the same final temperature of 430°C, would require that 1265 calories of work be done on the gas and the net heat supplied be 735 calories. The work done and net heat supplied are all measurable quantities and for the different steps are obviously substantially different, despite the fact that the gas undergoes exactly the same change in state for the whole process: from 24.5 liters volume at 25°C and 1 atmosphere to 2.88 liters at 430°C and 20 atmospheres. Thus the total amounts of either the heat absorbed or of the work done will each depend on the particular steps in the process used to produce the change. This situation is generally true.

Internal Energy

One important consistency is shown by the numbers just listed, which illustrates the first law by example: in all three cases, the *sum* of the heat absorbed by and the work done on the gas is the same, namely 2000 calories. Countless other measurements of heat and work, whether electrical, mechanical, or otherwise, show exactly this same constancy, regardless of whether the substance is liquid, solid, or gas, *provided* the same total change in state of the substance for the whole process is considered. Further, the constancy is not restricted to changes of a single substance, but is observed equally when chemical reaction occurs between different molecular species.

The change occurring when given amounts of materials under specified initial conditions react to give products in certain final conditions, may take place in a variety of ways. These may involve different amounts of heat and work separately, but the combined total involving both heats of reaction and all forms of work done on or by the reaction system is always the same. The quantity represented by this sum is then evidently a measure of the difference between the initial and final states, and can properly be used to specify the change in the system itself, rather than only its interaction with its surroundings.

This property of substances which changes during a process as the net effect of heat and work through interactions with the surroundings is called the *internal energy*. For ideal gases it is precisely the quantity discussed in Chapter 10, and its value is designated by the symbol E, the notation ΔE representing the difference of the values for two states of a system.

As pointed out in Chapter 10, the value of the internal energy (E) for an ideal gas is simply the sum, for all molecules in the gas, of the translational, rotational, and vibrational energies of the individual molecules. For more complex systems, the molecular interpretation of the internal energy is more complicated, as forces between molecules and the consequent energies of interaction make important contributions to the total internal energy. The prediction of the internal energy from molecular properties is then necessarily more difficult, but this in no way makes the internal energy less valid as a property of the more complicated system.

Changes in internal energy will result from other forms of interaction than heat transfer and work of expansion or compression. This is because the system can be subjected to a variety of forces by its surroundings. Electrical forces of the sort discussed in Section 11.10 are an example, as are forces resulting from magnetic fields. The force of gravity may also make a difference, although for most chemical processes its effect on the internal energy is negligible in comparison with those resulting from changes in molecular energies. If any or all of these forces act on a system, the work done by or against them must be considered correspondingly. Important examples of this in chemistry occur when the system does electrical work during a chemical reaction, as in a galvanic cell; this subject will receive detailed attention in Chapter 17.

12.2. Statement of the First Law

In the preceding section the concept of the first law of thermodynamics has been expressed in words, and in Chapter 10 the first law was used implicitly in discussing heat capacities of ideal gases. In this section a working equation as an expression of the law, adequate for most chemical calculations, will be stated and discussed. To do this, certain symbols and conventions regarding the signs of the various quantities involved must be adopted. We shall use those commonly employed by American chemists.

1. *Heat.* The symbol q represents heat *absorbed* by a system *from* its surroundings. Therefore q is positive if heat flows to the system, negative if the flow is from the system to the surroundings.

2. *Work.* The symbol w represents work *done by* the system *on* its surroundings. Thus w is positive if the direction of displacement is against opposing external forces, as for an expanding gas. (This is the opposite of the convention used by many English and European writers, that work done *on* the system by the surroundings is positive.)

3. *Internal energy.* The symbol E is used to represent the internal energy and ΔE represents a positive change (increase) in E. An infinitesimal change, dE in the notation of the calculus, is likewise positive if E increases by the change.

With these conventions, the content of the first law may be expressed by

$$\Delta E = q - w \qquad (12.1)$$

That is, the increase in the internal energy of a system will be equal to the heat absorbed by the system *from* its surroundings minus the work by the system *on* its surroundings. The *difference*, $q - w$, occurs because w has been defined as positive for work done *by* the system; it is readily seen to give the sensible result that work done (w positive) acts to decrease the internal energy (E), while heat absorbed (q positive) acts to increase E.

A further stipulation of the first law is that *the value of E depends only on the state of a system* and is independent of the system's previous history. The change ΔE for a process then depends only upon the change of state of a system resulting from the process—that is, the difference between its final and initial states. It is independent of the particular route or steps comprising the process itself.

The very simple expression of Eq. 12.1 achieves full meaning and usefulness only if the further stipulation is fully appreciated. Thus, for the example previously cited involving the heating and compression of nitrogen, $\Delta E = 2000$ calories whenever one mole of nitrogen is changed from the state 25°C and 1 atmosphere to 430°C and 20 atmospheres by any of the processes described in Section 12.1 or by any other routes. If E_2 is the final value of E after absorbing heat q and doing work w, and E_1 the initial value, then $\Delta E = E_2 - E_1$, where states 2 and 1 are defined by the pressure, volume, and temperature of the system, and are in no way dependent on the combinations of q and w used to produce the change.

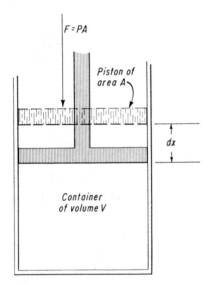

F = PA

Piston of area A

dx

Container of volume V

Fig. 12.1. *Expansion work.*

12.3. Expansion Work

In order to apply Eq. 12.1 quantitatively, the amount of work done must be definitely expressed in terms of measured quantities. The simplest form of work, and one which must often be considered, is that done by a substance in expanding against an external pressure, P. The work required for a given expansion can be calculated from the definition of work as the product of a force and the displacement in the direction of the force. In Fig. 12.1, the substance is considered confined in a container of volume V by a piston of area A. Since by definition the pressure is force per unit area, the force F on the piston is given by $F = PA$. If the piston is displaced outward a distance dx so small that P changes insignificantly, the work is $PA\,dx$. But the product $A\,dx$ is equal to the change in volume of the substance, dV, from which the work of expansion is seen to be

$$w_{\exp} = P\,dV \tag{12.2}$$

This expression is valid only for uniform, hydrostatic pressure. It holds regardless of the shape of the substance, or whether it is contained by a simple cylinder and piston arrangement or in some other manner. Equation 12.2 can be derived with equal validity from consideration of the expansion of a gas in a rubber balloon, or that of a lump of coal with no container at all. It applies to any simple volume increase dV against an external pressure P.

It is important to recognize that the work (w) of Eq. 12.2 is against the pressure (P) exerted by its surroundings, and against which the substance can expand. This will not be the same as the pressure within the substance itself or the pressure necessary to keep the substance from expanding, and if it were not at least slightly different, no expansion could occur. This is demonstrated by reference to Fig.12.2: a gas at pressure, P_1, in a bomb is allowed to escape, through a capillary to the atmosphere at a lower pressure P_0, or alternatively to push a piston supported by the pressure P_0. The work done by the gas when it expands to occupy a volume dV outside the capillary, or when it displaces the piston so that it sweeps out the volume dV, is against P_0, not against the internal equilibrium pressure P_1, and so is given by $w_{exp} = P_0 \, dV$.

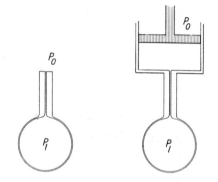

Fig. 12.2. *Free versus equilibrium expansion.*

While it is obvious that the expansion could not take place unless $P_1 > P_0$, it is also true that the particular expansion process of Fig. 12.2 results in *less work* done than had the outside pressure P_0 been equal to P_1. The maximum work possible clearly is done when P_0 is but infinitesimally less than the equilibrium value. (If P_0 were precisely equal to P_1 there would be no flow of gas outward, while for P_0 greater than P_1, gas outside would flow inward.)

The work obtained when $P_1 = P_0$ is called the *maximum reversible work:* maximum because any other external pressure P would result in less work done by the system, reversible because if P_0 barely exceeds P_1, the process would be reversed, resulting in contraction rather than expansion of the confined gas. The amount of work done *on* the gas if P_0 barely exceeded P_1 and drove the piston inward to *decrease* the volume by an identical amount dV would be equal to that done by the gas in the expansion described. From this discussion, it is seen that the equilibrium pressure can be used for P in Eq. 12.2, only if this is the actual external pressure. In this case the work (w) will have the maximum reversible value for the particular volume change dV.

A simple expression can be obtained for the reversible work when an ideal gas undergoes expansion. In this case the equilibrium pressure is given by $P = nRT/V$, and the work for an infinitesimal expansion, dV, is

$$w_{exp} = P\,dV = nRT\frac{dV}{V} \tag{12.3}$$

If a continued expansion is maintained under reversible conditions by keeping the value of P equal to nRT/V for all values of V, the work can be calculated by integrating successive increments:

$$w_{exp} = \int nRT\frac{dV}{V}$$
$$= \int_{V_1}^{V_2} nRT\frac{dV}{V} \tag{12.4}$$

where the initial and final volumes are V_1 and V_2. For an isothermal expansion, with T kept constant by supplying heat as necessary from a thermostat, this can be integrated:*

$$w_{exp} = nRT\int_{V_1}^{V_2}\frac{dV}{V} = nRT\ln\frac{V_2}{V_1} \tag{12.5}$$

Suppose, on the other hand, that the external pressure is maintained at a fixed value P_0, while the volume increases from V_1 to V_2. Then the work is

$$w_{exp} = \int_{V_1}^{V_2} P_0\,dV = P_0\int_{V_1}^{V_2} dV = P_0(V_2 - V_1) \tag{12.6}$$

In either case, no work is done if the volume does not change, for if $V_2 = V_1$, $\ln V_2/V_1 = \ln 1 = 0$ in the first case, and $V_2 - V_1 = 0$ in the second.

For ordinary quantities of gas at moderate pressure and temperature, the work in isothermal expansion varies from a few calories to a few thousand calories. For example, one mole of any ideal gas expanding

---

* The symbol ln stands for natural logarithms to base e, reserving the symbol log for common logarithms to base 10. For any number x, $\ln x = 2.3026 \log x$.

reversibly to ten times its original volume V_1 at $T = 300°K$ does the work

$$w_{exp} = 1.99 \times 300 \ln \frac{10V_1}{V_1} = 1.99 \times 300 \times 2.303 \log 10$$

$$= 1380 \text{ calories}$$

The work of expansion of liquids and solids is usually much smaller because volume changes at ordinary pressures are much less.

It should be emphasized that Eq. 12.5 is valid *only* for an ideal gas. For gases of nonideal behavior, the work for a given volume change will differ from that given by Eq. 12.5 because the pressures during the change will not be equal to nRT/V. The amount of work must then be calculated from Eq. 12.2, using the true values of P rather than those calculated from the ideal gas law. Using the van der Waals approximation for the pressure,

$$P = \frac{nRT}{V - nb} - a \frac{n^2}{V^2}$$

and the expression for isothermal w_{exp} becomes the more complicated integral

$$w_{exp} = nRT \int_{V_1}^{V_2} \frac{dV}{V - nb} - an^2 \int_{V_1}^{V_2} \frac{dV}{V^2} \qquad (12.7)$$

The evaluation of these integrals, and calculations in special cases of the difference between Eqs. 12.5 and 12.7, are left as problems for the student to solve. For pressures of a few atmospheres, the differences between ideal behavior and real gases are not large enough to be serious in any but very accurate calculations, and Eq. 12.5 is usually an adequate approximation.

12.4. Free and Reversible Adiabatic Expansion

In Chapter 10 it was noted that the internal energy (per mole) of a hypothetical ideal gas depends only on the temperature of the gas, and not on the volume occupied as long as the temperature remains fixed. It was shown further that this was to be expected if the molecules move essentially independently of one another. In this section an experiment devised by Joule in 1845 will be considered, which with the first law verifies the earlier statement from Chapter 10.

A thoroughly insulated system consisting of two chambers immersed in water has one chamber evacuated and the second containing gas at a given pressure (Fig. 12.3). The gas is allowed to flow from the second chamber into the first until the pressures in the two are equal. At the end of the process, the gas occupies the combined volume of the two chambers (although there has been no expansion of the system against its surroundings), and it is at a lower pressure. No change in temperature of the water can be detected; thus the process involves no gain or loss of heat by the gas, and $q = 0$. Since the gas expansion displaces nothing in the external surroundings, no external work is done and $w_{\exp} = 0$. The first law, Eq. 12.1, then becomes simply

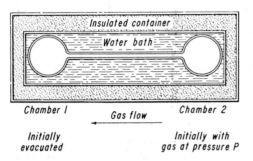

Chamber 1   Chamber 2
            Gas flow

Initially   Initially with
evacuated   gas at pressure P

Fig. 12.3. *Joule's experiment on gas expansion.*

$$\Delta E = 0 \qquad (12.8)$$

for free expansion. Actually Joule's measurement of temperature was rather insensitive. More refined experiments on this free expansion show that for $\Delta E = 0$, the temperature change is very small; conversely, if the temperature is kept fixed, the change in E for gases at ordinary temperatures is only a few calories per mole for a change in pressure of one atmosphere.

The internal energy of an ideal gas does change with temperature at both low and high pressures, the underlying molecular explanation attributing this to more intense molecular motions. The first law provides a means of calculating the increase of E with temperature from experimental measurements. Inspection of Eq. 12.1 suggests the means, for if no work is done by a gas when it is heated, then $\Delta E = q$, the heat absorbed during the process. To permit no work to be done ($w = 0$), the gas may be heated at constant volume, and the heat (q_V) absorbed to produce a temperature change from T_1 to T_2 may be measured. Then $\Delta E_V = q_V$. For the infinitesimal change $T_2 - T_1 = dT$, and just as in Section 10.2, q_V may be expressed as $nC_V\,dT$, where C_V is the heat capacity per mole at constant volume, and n the number of moles. The corresponding change dE_V is

$$dE_V = nC_V\,dT \qquad (12.9)$$

and since

$$dE_V = \left(\frac{\partial E}{\partial T}\right)_V dT$$

$$\left(\frac{\partial E}{\partial T}\right)_V = nC_V \qquad (12.10)$$

Over moderate intervals of temperature for many gases, C_V depends only slightly with temperature, and Eq. 12.9 can then be integrated very simply to give

$$\int_{T_1}^{T_2} dE_V = E_{T_2} - E_{T_1} = \int_{T_1}^{T_2} nC_V\, dT = nC_V \int_{T_1}^{T_2} dT = nC_V(T_2 - T_1)$$

or

$$E_{T_2} - E_{T_1} = nC_V(T_2 - T_1) \qquad (12.11)$$

For example, for diatomic gases, C_V is approximately 5 cal mole^{-1} deg^{-1} near room temperature, and heating 1 mole from 25°C to 75°C increases E by $E_{75°} - E_{25°} = 5(348 - 298) = 250$ calories.

Returning to the Joule experiment for a moment, the temperature drop one might naively expect does not materialize because the gas in its expansion had no way to do work on the surroundings and thus lose internal energy. Cooling by expansion is possible if work can be done, especially if the gas cannot gain energy by absorption of heat.

An expansion of a system without transfer of heat to or from its surroundings, where $q = 0$, is called an *adiabatic* expansion. A particular kind of adiabatic change is one in which expansion work is done reversibly by an ideal gas. To realize this, suppose that a piston and cylinder arrangement as in Fig. 12.1 is perfectly insulated, and the gas allowed to expand by reducing P reversibly. Since no heat can be absorbed from the surroundings, the gas loses internal energy by doing work on the piston and becomes cooler. The amount of work at any particular temperature T for volume change dV is given by Eq. 12.3, and since $q = 0$ for an adiabatic change, the first law requires that

$$dE = -w = -nRT \frac{dV}{V} \qquad (12.12)$$

This equation gives a condition on the relation between energy change and volume change, both of which depend on the temperature. To determine volume as a function of temperature, Eq. 12.10 can be used to express dE in terms of dT with the result

$$nC_V\, dT = -nRT \frac{dV}{V} \qquad (12.13)$$

or, on rearrangement to separate the variables,

$$\frac{C_V}{R}\frac{dT}{T} = -\frac{dV}{V} \tag{12.14}$$

For temperature ranges over which C_V is constant, both sides can be integrated from an initial temperature T_1 and volume V_1 to any final values T_2 and V_2, with the result

$$\frac{C_V}{R}\ln\frac{T_2}{T_1} = -\ln\frac{V_2}{V_1} \tag{12.15}$$

or

$$\frac{C_V}{R}\log\frac{T_1}{T_2} = \log\frac{V_2}{V_1}$$

This equation shows that an increase in volume (V_2 greater than V_1) is accompanied by a decrease in temperature (T_2 less than T_1), and conversely, compression is accompanied by an increase in temperature. Both results are as expected, and the changes can be calculated by Eq. 12.15.

As an example, consider the compression of one mole of helium at 300°K to half its original volume. The ratio of final to initial temperatures is from 12.15:

$$\log\frac{T_2}{T_1} = \frac{R}{C_V}\log\frac{V_1}{V_2} = -\frac{2}{3}\log\frac{1}{2}$$

or

$$\log\frac{T_2}{T_1} = \frac{2}{3}\log 2 = 0.201$$

and so

$$T_2 = 1.59\,T_1 = 478°\text{K}$$

Thus the temperature rises by $478° - 300°$ or $178°$. (Note that only *ratios* of volume and temperature appear in Eq. 12.15; also that the quantity of gas does not appear in the equation.)

Other forms of Eq. 12.15 are sometimes convenient. If antilogs of both sides are taken, one obtains

$$\left(\frac{T_2}{T_1}\right)^{C_V/R} = \left(\frac{V_2}{V_1}\right)^{-1}$$

or

$$V_2(T_2^{C_V/R}) = V_1(T_1^{C_V/R}) \tag{12.16}$$

The relation between pressures and volume in an adiabatic expansion, rather than that between temperature and volume, is also useful. Since an ideal gas has been assumed, $T_2/T_1 = P_2V_2/P_1V_1$, which on substitution in Eq. 12.15 gives

$$\frac{C_V}{R} \ln \frac{P_2}{P_1} = -\left(1 + \frac{C_V}{R}\right) \ln \frac{V_2}{V_1}$$

or

$$\ln \frac{P_2}{P_1} = -\left(\frac{C_V + R}{C_V}\right) \ln \frac{V_2}{V_1} \qquad (12.17)$$

For an ideal gas, $C_V + R = C_P$ (Section 10.2), and the ratio of heat capacities $\gamma = C_P/C_V$ may be introduced to give, after rearrangement,

$$P_2V_2^\gamma = P_1V_1^\gamma$$

or

$$PV^\gamma = \text{constant} \qquad (12.18)$$

The nature of the difference between the relation $PV^\gamma =$ constant (for the adiabatic process with its accompanying temperature change) and the relation $PV =$ constant (for an isothermal process) is shown in Fig. 12.4.

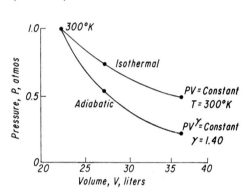

Fig. 12.4. *Adiabatic and isothermal expansion of an ideal gas.*

12.5. Adiabatic Compression and the Speed of Sound

The reversible adiabatic process described in the preceding section may have appeared rather impractical to the reader, because of the requirements that there be no heat exchange with the surroundings and that the pressure never depart very far from equilibrium as the gas expands or is compressed. These conditions are not easy to fulfill simultaneously with conventional laboratory apparatus, but there is an important natural process in which both are satisfied quite accurately—in the propagation of an ordinary sound wave.

A sound wave is no more than a succession of ordinary pressure waves progressing through a medium of gas, liquid, or solid. If the medium is a gas, the changes in pressure of which the waves are composed are initiated by a reed, loudspeaker cone, human larynx, and so on, and propagated by molecular collisions within the gas. The changes of pres-

sure from slightly above to slightly below the equilibrium pressure of
the gas occur so rapidly, at the sound frequency, that there is no chance
for exchange of heat with the surroundings. A sound thus constitutes a
good approximation to a reversible adiabatic process, and its speed will
be governed by the relations governing adiabatic expansion.

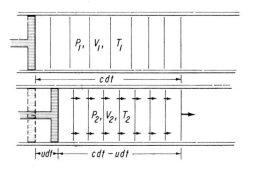

Fig. 12.5. *Kundt's tube.*

Consider a sound wave
started by a forward motion
of a piston in a tube, as in the
familiar Kundt's tube laboratory apparatus (Fig. 12.5). The
initial forward component of
velocity given molecules at the
piston face is transmitted to
neighboring molecules at a
rate approaching that of the
molecular speeds in the gas.
(Compare the measured speed
of sound in oxygen at 25°C, of 3.3×10^4 cm/sec, with the RMS speed
of oxygen molecules at 27°C of 4.8×10^4 cm/sec from Section 9.2.)

Assume that at the end of a time interval dt, the sound wave compression, set up by the piston moving forward a distance $u\,dt$, has traveled a
distance $c\,dt$, where u is the average speed of the piston during the interval, and c is the speed of the compression wave in the gas. The gas
ordinarily occupying a length $c\,dt$ of the tube has thus been compressed
into the length $c\,dt - u\,dt$, and it consequently has both higher pressure
and higher temperature and, in addition, is all moving forward with
speed u. The speeds c and u are, from Fig. 12.6, obviously related to the
decrease in volume of the gas compressed by the piston, and if dV is the
volume change, then

$$\frac{u}{c} = -\frac{dV}{V} \qquad (12.19)$$

In order to deduce how c or u depends on the gas temperature and
pressure, some further relations are needed. One is given by Newton's
second law, as the forward momentum of the gas set in motion must by
this law equal the product of the net force acting on it and the time
during which it acted. Per unit area, this force is equal to the pressure
difference $P_2 - P_1 = dP$. The mass of the column of gas 1 cm² in area
and $c\,dt$ centimeters long is $\rho c\,dt$, where the density $\rho = MP/RT$. The
column is moving with the speed u. Hence its momentum is
$[(MP/RT)c\,dt]u$, and

$$\frac{MP}{RT} c\, dt\, u = dP\, dt$$

or

$$cu = \left(\frac{RT}{M}\right)\frac{dP}{P} \qquad\qquad (12.20)$$

Solving Eqs. 12.19 and 12.20 for c gives

$$c^2 = \frac{RT}{M}\frac{V}{P}\left(\frac{dP}{dV}\right) \qquad\qquad (12.21)$$

The ratio dP/dV can be found from Eq. 12.18 for reversible adiabatic compression, since the pressure differences and flow velocities are small enough for the process to be reversible and in the short time interval no heat is lost to the surroundings. (With the rapid alternation of pressure associated with a train of sound waves, the temperature rise upon compression is equaled by the fall during rarefaction.) Differentiating Eq. 12.18, $(PV^{\gamma} = \text{constant})$ gives

$$V^{\gamma}\, dP + P\gamma V^{\gamma-1}\, dV = 0$$

or

$$\frac{dP}{dV} = \frac{\gamma P}{V} \qquad\qquad (12.22)$$

Substituting into Eq. 12.21, the sound velocity is given by

$$c^2 = \frac{\gamma RT}{M}$$

or

$$c = \sqrt{\frac{\gamma RT}{M}} \qquad\qquad (12.23)$$

This result is interesting because speeds calculated by this equation for gases with known values of $\gamma = C_P/C_V$ are in very close agreement with measured values, if the sound pressures are not large. Typical values are given in Table 12.1. This agreement confirms the assumption that compressions in such sound propagation are essentially reversible adiabatic processes. With confidence in the validity of Eq. 12.23, it can be used conversely to measure the value of γ with considerable accuracy, and hence, knowing the gas constant R, the values of C_P and C_V. For an ideal gas, $C_P - C_V = R$. From the value of $\gamma = C_P/C_V$ one may obtain $C_V = R/(\gamma - 1)$ and $C_P = \gamma R/(\gamma - 1)$.

TABLE 12.1.   *Heat Capacity and γ in Gases.*

Gas	t (°C)	C_p (per g)	C_p (per mole)	γ
NH_3	15	0.5232	8.910	1.310
CO	15	0.2478	6.941	1.404
CO_2	15	0.1989	8.754	1.304
H_2	15	3.389	6.832	1.410
He	-180	1.25	5.004	1.660
Ar	15	0.1253	5.005	1.668
CH_4	15	0.5284	8.476	1.310
O_2	15	0.2178	6.970	1.401

12.6. Relations Based on the Property of the Internal Energy as a Function of State

The fact that changes in the internal energy (E) of a substance depend only on the difference in initial and final states (that is, only on differences in P, V, T, and any other variables needed to define the state) means that this change can be expressed as the sum of changes for any desired sequence of steps. If a substance is raised in temperature by an amount dT, holding its volume constant, and then volume is increased by dV, holding the temperature constant, the total change dE is the sum of the separate ones:

$$dE = dE_V + dE_T \qquad (12.24)$$

where dE_V is the change in E for the increase dT, when V is fixed, and analogously for dE_T. The changes dE_V and dE_T are conveniently expressed in terms of partial derivatives and the increments dT and dV:

$$dE_V = \left(\frac{\partial E}{\partial T}\right)_V dT, \qquad dE_T = \left(\frac{\partial E}{\partial V}\right)_T dV$$

With this language of calculus, Eq. 12.24 becomes

$$dE = \left(\frac{\partial E}{\partial T}\right)_V dT + \left(\frac{\partial E}{\partial V}\right)_T dV \qquad (12.25)$$

Previous considerations have shown that $(\partial E/\partial T)_V = C_V$, where E and C_V are molar values. The nature of the dependence of E on volume expressed by the derivative $(\partial E/\partial V)_T$ varies with the particular substance and its physical state. In the case of an ideal gas, the conclusion from Joule's experiment described in Section 12.4 gives this simply: since

$dE = 0$ by the conditions of the experiment, and the observed constancy of temperature requires that $dT = 0$ for low pressures, Eq. 12.25 becomes

$$\left(\frac{\partial E}{\partial V}\right)_T dV = 0$$

for an ideal gas, and since the volume V changed, dV is not zero, leaving as the only alternative that

$$\left(\frac{\partial E}{\partial V}\right)_T = 0 \qquad\qquad (12.26)$$

for an ideal gas.

A corollary of Eq. 12.25 is often useful. In writing this expression, the independent variables were considered to be V and T, the corresponding values of P being determined according to the equation of state of the substance. The pressure and temperature could equally well have been selected as the independent variables, and this is often more convenient. In such case, the derivative $(\partial E/\partial T)_P$ is required, especially in considering changes at constant pressure. For P constant and increase in temperature dT,

$$dE_P = \left(\frac{\partial E}{\partial T}\right)_P dT$$

The volume change dV_P corresponding to this increase in temperature is

$$dV_P = \left(\frac{\partial V}{\partial T}\right)_P dT$$

By limiting Eq. 12.25 so that pressure is constant, dE_P will replace dE, and substituting in it the two equivalences immediately above, we obtain

$$\left(\frac{\partial E}{\partial T}\right)_P dT = \left(\frac{\partial E}{\partial T}\right)_V dT + \left(\frac{\partial E}{\partial V}\right)_T \left(\frac{\partial V}{\partial T}\right)_P dT$$

Since dT is a common factor, this equation can be satisfied only if

$$\left(\frac{\partial E}{\partial T}\right)_P = \left(\frac{\partial E}{\partial T}\right)_V + \left(\frac{\partial E}{\partial V}\right)_T \left(\frac{\partial V}{\partial T}\right)_P \qquad (12.27)$$

(The student of partial differential calculus will recognize this as a familiar result. There will be occasion to use other change of variable formulas like Eq. 12.27 in later sections. It is important for the reader to realize that Eq. 12.27 is a purely mathematical result, valid in this case because E is a function of state, and dE an exact differential with value independent of the processes used to produce the change of state.)

A simple and important use of Eq. 12.27 is in obtaining an expression for the difference $C_P - C_V$ of specific heats at constant pressure and constant volume. For a substance heated at constant pressure, the heat q_P absorbed is $C_P\, dT$, which by the first law is

$$q_P = C_P\, dT = dE_P + w$$

But $dE_P = (\partial E/\partial T)_P\, dT$, for which the expression in Eq. 12.27 can be substituted. Using the resulting expression and the value for $w = PdV_P = P(\partial V/\partial T)_P\, dT$ gives

$$C_P = \left(\frac{\partial E}{\partial T}\right)_V + \left(\frac{\partial E}{\partial V}\right)_T\left(\frac{\partial V}{\partial T}\right)_P + P\left(\frac{\partial V}{\partial T}\right)_P$$

But $(\partial E/\partial T)_V = C_V$, and so the difference $C_P - C_V$ is given by

$$C_P - C_V = \left[\left(\frac{\partial E}{\partial V}\right)_T + P\right]\left(\frac{\partial V}{\partial T}\right)_P \qquad (12.28)$$

For an ideal gas, however, $(\partial E/\partial V)_T = 0$ (Eq. 12.26), and since $V = RT/P$, then $(\partial V/\partial T)_P = R/P$. This gives immediately the result of Section 10.2:

$$C_P - C_V = R \qquad (12.29)$$

If the substance is not an ideal gas, $(\partial E/\partial V)_T$ is not zero, nor is $(\partial V/\partial T)_P = R/P$, and Eq. 12.28 rather than Eq. 12.29 must be used. This requires both a knowledge of the actual equation of state and a way of evaluating $(\partial E/\partial V)_T$. The first can be obtained directly by experiment, but the value of the derivative is best found by use of the second law of thermodynamics, discussed in Chapter 14.

12.7. The Joule-Thomson Experiment

Joule's experiment on free expansion of gases is extraordinarily difficult to perform accurately. The difficulties led Lord Kelvin (then William Thomson) to suggest a more sensitive method of revealing any effects of internal molecular forces on internal energy of gases; this he developed with Joule over a period of several years following 1852.

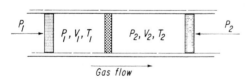

Fig. 12.6. *Joule-Thompson experiment.*

The basic idea of the experiment is indicated schematically in Fig. 12.6. Gas in the left reservoir, at pressure P_1 and temperature T_1, is allowed to leak slowly through a porous plug A to the right reservoir, in which the gas is at a lower pressure P_2 and reaches some new temperature T_2. (The purpose of the slow leak through the plug is to keep the kinetic energy resulting from the gas flow sufficiently small as to be negligible.) The pressures P_1 and P_2 in the two reservoirs are kept constant by suitable movement of the two pistons or by using very large reservoirs.

The whole apparatus is sufficiently well insulated to make any heat transfer to or from the surroundings negligibly small, so that $q = 0$. In the experiment, after steady flow conditions of the gas through the plug have been realized, the difference in the temperatures on each side of the plug is measured. One might offhand expect that the exit gas would always be cooler, but actually it is sometimes warmer, if the initial temperature of the gas is above a specific value dependent on the particular gas. The cause of this variable behavior can be appreciated by using the first law to analyze the change in conditions of the transferred gas.

The important distinction between the Joule-Thomson experiment and the Joule experiment is that in the transfer of gas from the first to the second reservoir, work is done on it in the left reservoir by the pressure P_1 of the left reservoir, and in the right reservoir the gas does work against the exit pressure P_2 in making room for itself. If the volume per mole of this gas at the left is V_1 and at the right V_2, the net work done by the gas for each mole flowing through the porous plug is $P_2V_2 - P_1V_1$, since the pressures P_2 and P_1 are kept constant by the external pressures on the pistons during the gas flow. If the final value per mole of the internal energy is E_2 and the initial value E_1, then $\Delta E = E_2 - E_1$. Since no heat is absorbed, the first law requires that

$$E_2 - E_1 = -w = -(P_2V_2 - P_1V_1)$$

or

$$E_2 + P_2V_2 = E_1 + P_1V_1 \tag{12.30}$$

The gas must therefore change its state in such a way as to keep the quantity $E + PV$ constant. If the product PV decreases on expansion to the lower pressure P_2, then the internal energy must increase by the same amount, and vice versa. An increase in E would for an ideal gas mean a rise in temperature—that is, T_2 greater than T_1; this is not necessarily the case if the gas is not ideal, but suggests how either a *rise or fall* of temperature is possible under the conditions of the experiment.

The temperature change for most gases undergoing a Joule-Thomson expansion at ordinary temperature and pressure is negative; that is, the gas is cooled. For air at $0°C$ and atmospheric pressure, the temperature falls approximately 0.275° per change in pressure of one atmosphere, while for CO_2, the decrease is about 1.37°C. Hydrogen behaves differently, for under these same conditions the temperature *rises* by about 0.013°C; the rise becomes greater at higher temperatures, being .039° at 100°C.

The effects for different gases under various conditions are best compared by defining the *Joule-Thomson coefficient*,

$$\mu = \left(\frac{dT}{dP}\right)_{E+PV} \qquad (12.31)$$

where the sum $E + PV$ is constant. Its value is dependent upon the particular gas, the pressure, and the temperature. When the value of μ is positive, the gas cools on expansion; when negative, expansion results in warming. The coefficient becomes positive for all gases under certain conditions of pressure and temperature. The pressure and temperature corresponding to this *inversion point* ($\mu = 0$) may be plotted for a gas as its *inversion curve*, and this curve may also be calculated. The form of the inversion curve is shown in Fig. 12.7, from which it is seen that if the

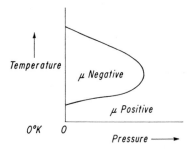

Fig. 12.7. *Inversion curve for the Joule-Thompson coefficient.*

pressure is sufficiently high, μ will always be positive, and at lower pressures there will exist lower and upper limits of temperature within which μ is negative. As typical values, for hydrogen μ becomes positive below -80.5°C at 113 atm pressure; for helium, below -228°C at ordinary pressures; for nitrogen, below approximately -160°C, or alternatively above approximately $+275$°C, at 100 atm.

[The significance of the constant sum $E + PV$ in the Joule-Thomson expansion will be better understood after the study of the enthalpy, $H\ (= E + PV)$, in Section 12.8.]

From the point of view of molecular theory, these differences are a reflection of the change in relative importance of attractive and repulsive intermolecular forces at different temperatures and from one gas to another. At temperatures sufficiently high relative to the critical temperature, repulsive forces predominate (see Section 8.7), and the expansion of the gas allows the potential energy of these forces to increase the translational energy of the molecules; hence there is a higher final temperature. But if attractive forces predominate, as they do at sufficiently low temperatures, translational energy is lost during expansion to overcome their effect, and the gas cools.

The Joule-Thomson effect is obviously of practical importance in artificial refrigeration. It is also of importance to chemists, for in addition to providing information about interactions of molecules in a gas, it indicates that under suitable conditions expansion cooling can be used to liquefy hydrogen and even helium. To achieve the low temperature of the inversion point below which the Joule-Thomson cooling can be used requires, however, that the gas be precooled sufficiently by other means. In a commercially available helium liquefier (the Collins cryostat), the necessary initial cooling can be achieved by making the helium do work in small engines, thereby reducing the energy and temperature sufficiently for Joule-Thomson expansion to produce further cooling. (Practically, the liquefaction is usually facilitated by precooling with liquid nitrogen.)

12.8. Another Thermodynamic Function: the Enthalpy

The discussion so far has centered on the internal energy as a function of the state of a substance, as given by the first law from measurements of heat and work. As has been shown, changes in the internal energy E are particularly easy to determine if measurements are made at constant volume, for with no volume change $w = 0$ and $dE = q_V$, which is the heat supplied to the system during the process. Often, however, measurements are more conveniently made under a different but equally definite condition in which the pressure is held constant. This is especially true for chemical reactions, which are commonly carried out in open vessels at atmospheric pressure.

Changes of state from solid to liquid and liquid to gas are examples of physical processes occurring naturally at a fixed pressure rather than at constant volume, and heats of solution or mixing are conveniently studied at constant pressure. Chemical reactions are readily followed and the heat absorption associated with them measured at constant pressure. It is therefore eminently worthwhile to determine what property of the system is dependent upon the heat supplied or removed at constant pressure.

From the first law, if only work of expansion is done at constant pressure P, then for a slight change

$$dE_P = q_P - P\,dV$$

If the pressure is constant, $P\,dV = d(PV)$ by considering the formula of the calculus, $d(PV) = P\,dV + V\,dP$, since $V\,dP$ is zero. Using this gives

$$dE_P + d(PV)_P = q_P$$

or

$$d(E + PV)_P = q_P$$

This equation is valid for any change so long as P remains constant. For a substantial change in conditions it may be written

$$\Delta(E + PV)_P = q_P$$

where the symbol Δ means an arbitrary increase, rather than the infinitesimal one indicated by the differential d.

From this reasoning, the heat q_P absorbed at constant P is a measure of the change, not in E, but in $(E + PV)$. Like E, this sum depends only on the state of the system, since P and V have this same property. (Notice that $P\,dV$ does not.) The quantity $E + PV$ so measured is at least as useful as E in characterizing chemical behavior and it is therefore useful to designate it by its own name and symbol. It is called *enthalpy*[*] and represented by the symbol H. Hence by definition

$$H = E + PV \qquad (12.32)$$

and

$$dH_P = q_P \text{ for an infinitesimal process}$$

$$\Delta H_P = q_P \text{ for a finite process}$$

Although changes in enthalpy are equal to heat absorbed only if pressure is fixed, the enthalpy function has meaning and is useful in comparing different states between which the pressure is different. That it has meaning is evident from the fact that both E and PV can be determined at different pressures; that it is also useful will be apparent from further study of chemical processes.

In review, the Joule-Thomson experiment was so devised that the expanding gas had the restriction that the value of H be unchanged: the conditions $E_2 + P_2V_2 = E_1 + P_1V_1$ can be written $H_2 = H_1$, where H_2 and H_1 are the final and initial values. This situation is sometimes expressed by the statement that the Joule-Thomson expansion takes place at constant enthalpy ($\Delta H = 0$), and this is indicated by writing the Joule-Thomson coefficient as

---

[*] Some writers use the name heat content. The less familiar sounding term enthalpy avoids any implication that substances contain heat. Heat is associated with a process and is not a property.

$$\mu = \left(\frac{\delta T}{\delta P}\right)_H$$

It is of interest to examine the magnitude of enthalpy changes in some representative processes at constant pressure, and, by comparison with PV changes, to see what portions correspond to differences in internal energy and what portions to PV work. In the vaporization of water at 100°C, 9700 calories of heat must be supplied per mole; $\Delta H = q_P = 9700$ cal/mole. The product PV changes from .001 to 30.2 liter-atmospheres, or $\Delta(PV) = 30.2 \times 1.987/0.082 = 930$ cal/mole. Thus of the 9700 calories supplied, 930 calories, or less than 10%, goes into PV work; the remaining 8970 calories must therefore be necessary to overcome the attractive forces of the molecules of the liquid and permit their separation so that the resulting gas occupies a volume of 30.2 liters.

At the melting point of water, the molar heat of fusion is 1430 cal/mole. The internal energy change is here slightly greater than the enthalpy change, however, because of the anomalous contraction of water on melting. The product $\Delta(PV)$ is accordingly negative, but amounts only to 0.05 cal/mole. The change in internal energy, ΔE, is very nearly equal to the change in enthalpy, $\Delta H = 1430$ cal/mole.

The difference between the change in enthalpy and the change in internal energy, $\Delta H - \Delta E$, is substantially greater relative to ΔH for processes involving the heating of gases at constant pressure. For example, increasing the temperature of one mole of nitrogen from 25°C to 75°C at one atmosphere pressure requires 350 calories (increase in enthalpy) of which 100 calories is required for the change in $PV (= \Delta H - \Delta E)$, and the rest corresponding to the increase in the internal energy, $\Delta E = 250$ calories.

The difference between ΔH and ΔE for changes in temperature is also evident in the difference between the values of specific heats at constant pressure and at constant volume. The equality $C_V = (\partial E/\partial T)_V$ was derived and used in Sections 12.4 and 12.8. Following the same reasoning for heat absorbed at constant pressure results in the expression

$$dH_P = q_P = C_P\, dT$$

which, since $dH_P = (\partial H/\partial T)_P\, dT$, requires that

$$\left(\frac{\partial H}{\partial T}\right)_P = C_P \qquad\qquad (12.33)$$

The heats absorbed or evolved by chemical reaction per mole are frequently very much larger than those for physical processes of the sort just considered. For example, the combustion of hydrogen by the reaction $H_2(g) + \frac{1}{2}O_2(g) = H_2O(g)$ gives off 57,800 calories at 18°C, and so $\Delta H = -57,800$ calories. Very little of this total is accounted for by the decrease in the product PV, as at one atmosphere the volume decrease of 0.50 moles gives $\Delta PV = -290$ calories. Thus virtually all the heat liberated comes from the energy decrease of the chemical combination. Heats of chemical reaction are typically of the order of tens or even hundreds of kilocalories per mole; they result primarily from chemical, rather than physical, changes of state. The subject of thermochemistry, which is the study of such thermal changes, is of such practical importance and fundamental interest that major attention will be given it in Chapter 13.

12.9. The First Law and Fundamental Relations of General Principles of Energy

In the discussion of the first law, the effects of mechanical work and heat absorbed have been related to changes in internal energy of the substance (or substances) or systems involved. These may not seem to have much relation to the concepts of work and kinetic energy as first presented in elementary physics. In problems in mechanics, the amount of work done by an unbalanced force on a massive object is equated to the increase in kinetic energy (KE) of the mass:

$$\Delta(KE) = -w = \text{work done } by \text{ the force} \qquad (12.34)$$

In seeming contrast, the first law as used in this chapter has made no mention of kinetic energy as such, but rather equates work done *on* a substance to the difference between its increase of *internal* energy and the amount of heat absorbed, as is seen by rearranging Eq. 12.1 to read

$$\Delta E - q = -w = \text{work done } on \text{ system} \qquad (12.35)$$

Since internal energy and kinetic energy of mass motion are not the same thing, these two equations involving work appear to be either contradictory or confusingly unrelated. Neither of these unpleasant conclusions is correct, as different conditions exist for the two, which are both special cases of more general problems to which the first law may be applied.

In the elementary physics problem involving the kinetic energy of the mass, the work by an external force is considered done on a rigid mass which is implicitly assumed incapable of changing its internal state, or of doing anything but accelerate and acquire kinetic energy from the action of the externally applied force. In the problems for which the first law as stated can be used, the substance affected is tacitly assumed *not* to acquire kinetic energy of motion as a whole, but to possess an internal activity and energy of its constituent molecules which can be affected either by heat or by various other forms of energy or work.

The "static" form of the first law of thermodynamics is adequate for many chemical situations, because chemists for the most part keep their systems in one place, rather than causing them to accelerate in space; there is thus no change in kinetic energy to be reckoned with. Nevertheless, there are chemical processes of importance in which mass flow occurs in addition to internal changes in molecular activity and arrangements. Obvious ones are the burning of gases, as in combustion and in jet engines, and explosions involving violent energy release and mass motion; there are many other flow processes in which kinetic energy changes are substantial, though less spectacular.

To include all factors involving processes where changes in kinetic energy of the mass are relatively large compared with the total energy, a more general form of the first law must be employed, which includes kinetic as well as internal energy. This more general form is simply

$$\Delta E + \Delta(KE) = q - w \qquad (12.36)$$

For the mechanics problem of an inert mass with no internal changes or heat absorbed, $\Delta E = 0$ and $q = 0$, and one obtains $\Delta(KE) = -w$, which is Eq. 12.34. For a substance with internal changes, but no mass motion as a whole, and hence no "external" kinetic energy, $-\Delta(KE) = 0$, and the first law as previously stated results: $\Delta E = q - w$.

The more general expression of Eq. 12.36 is a necessary condition when both internal energy and kinetic energy changes occur, and it thus gives the total consequences for a system of the heat and work involved in changing its conditions. The first law alone is insufficient to determine the division of heat plus work into the different forms of energy, as many different combinations of possible values of ΔE and $\Delta(KE)$ can give the same total. There are, however, other restrictions which govern moving systems—the principles of conservation of mass and of momentum—and those must be considered in addition to the conservation of energy as expressed by the first law.

An example may be seen in the derivation of sound velocity, given in Section 12.5. This problem is also one in which the kinetic energy of mass flow must be considered when the pressure differences are large, as may be found in waves resulting from an explosion, or a shock front from an object moving at very high speed. Under such conditions of shock or explosion pressures, rather than sound pressures, a significant part of the work done results in kinetic energy of mass motion in addition to the increased internal energy. The adiabatic conditions must then be calculated using $\Delta E + \Delta(KE) = -w$ rather than $\Delta E = -w$, and the result is a different adiabatic law than $PV^\gamma = $ constant, even for an ideal gas.

Problems

12.1. Calculate the heat and work in each step of the second and third processes described in Section 12.1 for changing 1 mole of nitrogen from 24.5 liters at 25°C to 2.88 liters at 430°C by integrating the relations $w = P\,dV$ and $q = C\,dT$. Assume that nitrogen behaves ideally with $\bar{C}_P = 7$ cal/mole deg independent of temperature.

12.2. (a) Ten moles of nitrogen initially at a pressure of 100 atmospheres and 40°C is allowed to expand isothermally and reversibly to a final pressure of 20 atmospheres. Calculate the work done by the gas, assuming ideal behavior. (b) The same gas is allowed to expand into the open air through a throttling valve slowly enough that its temperature remains constant. Calculate the work done when the pressure of the gas has fallen to 20 atm.

12.3. Four liters of gas at 25°C and 3 atm expands without loss of heat until the volume is 5 liters and the pressure 2 atm. The heat capacity $\bar{C}_V = 3$ cal/mole deg, independent of temperature. (a) Calculate the final temperature. (b) Calculate ΔE and ΔH, assuming ideal behavior. (c) Was the adiabatic process reversible?

12.4. Two moles of nitrogen are compressed adiabatically and reversibly from 1 atm at 300°K to a pressure of 5 atm. Calculate the final temperature and volume, assuming an average $\bar{C}_P = 6.90$ cal/mole and ideal behavior.

12.5. (a) Show that for a gas satisfying van der Waals equation

$$\left(P + \frac{n^2a}{V^2}\right)\left(V - nb\right) = nRT$$

the reversible work done in compressing from volume V_1 to volume V_2 at constant temperature is given by

$$w_{\text{exp}} = nRT \ln\left(\frac{V_2 - nb}{V_1 - nb}\right) + n^2a\left(\frac{1}{V_2} - \frac{1}{V_1}\right)$$

(b) Also show that this differs from the value $w_{exp} = nRT \ln (V_2/V_1)$ for an ideal gas by an amount

$$\Delta w_{exp} = nRT \ln \left(\frac{1 - nb/V_2}{1 - nb/V_1}\right) + n^2a \left(\frac{1}{V_2} - \frac{1}{V_1}\right)$$

12.6. Look up the van der Waals constants for nitrogen, and calculate the work in compressing 5 moles at 0°C from 50 liters to 3 liters at 0°C. By how much does this differ from the amount of work if the gas were ideal?

12.7. Will the actual work of compressing a gas be greater or less than the value for an ideal gas when the temperature is very high? when it is very low (i.e., less than the critical temperature)? Explain your answers in terms of attractive and repulsive forces.

12.8. The latent heat of vaporization of SO_2 is 94.9 cal/g at the boiling point $(-10°C)$. Calculate the work done by 1 mole of SO_2 in vaporizing at 760 mm pressure, and the amount by which the internal energy increases. What fraction of the heat of vaporization goes into the increase of internal energy?

12.9. Repeat the calculations of Problem *12.8* for SO_2 at 60°C, obtaining the necessary data from a handbook or other source.

12.10. The latent heats of vaporization of liquids vary greatly, but are usually greater than 3 kcal per mole at the boiling point (1 atm). Which is the more important part of such heats, the part required for expansion work, or the part to increase the internal energy of the vapor relative to the liquid?

12.11. Ten grams of water at 0°C and 1 atm is changed to steam at 100°C and 1 atm by the following three different routes: Calculate the heat and work done for each route, and show that for each the change in internal energy is the same. (a) The water is heated to 100°C and vaporized at 760 mm to steam. (b) The pressure on the water is reduced to the vapor pressure of 4.58 mm at 0°C. The vapor produced is next heated to 100°C at this pressure, and then compressed to 760 mm pressure. (c) The vapor produced at 0°C as in (b) is heated at constant volume to 100°C and then compressed to 760 mm pressure.

(Data for the calculations: Latent heat of vaporization of water = 596 cal/g at 0°C, 540 cal/g at 100°C. Average heat capacity of water = 1.00 cal/g from 0° to 100°C, average C_P for water vapor from 0° to 100°C is $C_P = 0.44$ cal/g.)

12.12. For small isothermal changes in volume, the volumes of liquids and solids are related to pressure by an equation of the form

$$V = V_0 \left(1 - \frac{P}{B}\right)$$

where V_0 is the volume at zero pressure and B is a constant, although its value depends upon the temperature. For water at 10°C, B has the value

20,000 atm. (a) What is the volume change in compressing 50 g of water from 1 to 200 atm? (b) How much work must be done? (c) Compare this work with the amount of work to compress 50 cm³ of gas at 1 atm and 10°C to a pressure of 200 atm.

12.13. Show that the speed of sound from the formula $c = (\gamma RT/M)^{1/2}$ is in units cm/sec if R is expressed in units ergs/mole deg.

12.14. Calculate the speed of sound in water vapor, oxygen, and nitrogen at 25°C.

12.15. By what percentage will the speed of sound change in a gas if the temperature is decreased from 25°C to -50°C? (Assume γ is independent of temperature.)

12.16. (a) The speed of sound in methane at 0°C is 432 m/sec. What are $\bar{C}_P$ and $\bar{C}_V$, assuming M is known? (b) Use the value of $\bar{C}_P$ to calculate the speed of sound at 100°C.

12.17. (a) Show by integrating the equation $w = P\,dv$ that the work done by an ideal gas in a reversible adiabatic change from (P_1, V_1) to (P_2, V_2) is

$$w = \frac{P_1 V_1 \gamma}{1 - \gamma}\,[V_2^{1-\gamma} - V_1^{1-\gamma}]$$

if the gas satisfies $PV\gamma = $ constant, with γ independent of temperature. (b) Show that this result can be transformed to

$$w = -\frac{\bar{C}_V}{R}\,(P_2 V_2 - P_1 V_1) = -C_v(T_2 - T_1)$$

12.18. One kind of irreversible adiabatic expansion is one in which the confining pressure is reduced from an initial value P_1 to some lower constant value P_2 and the gas expands until equilibrium is reached. (a) Show that the initial and final temperatures T_1 and T_2 satisfy the equation

$$n\bar{C}_V(T_2 - T_1) = -P_2(V_2 - V_1)$$

where V_1 and V_2 are the initial and final volumes. (The equation is correct only if $\bar{C}_V$ is independent of temperature.) (b) Show that for an ideal gas with constant $\bar{C}_V$

$$T_2 = \frac{\bar{C}_V + (P_2/P_1)R}{\bar{C}_V + R}\,T_1$$

12.19. Calculate T_2 for one mole of hydrogen expanding from $P_1 = 10$ atm at 300°K to $P_2 = 1$ atm, as in Problem 12.18. Is the temperature T_2 higher or lower than for the reversible adiabatic expansion from P_1 to P_2?

12.20. Show for an ideal gas, with $(\partial E/\partial V)_T = 0$ by definition, that $(\partial H/\partial V)_T$ and $(\partial H/\partial P)_T$ are also zero.

12.21. (a) Show that $(\partial H/\partial T)_V = \bar{C}_V + V(\partial P/\partial T)_V$ for one mole of substance. (b) Starting from $dH = (\partial H/\partial T)_P\, dT + (\partial H/\partial P)_T\, dP$, show by a derivation similar to the one in Section 12.6 that

$$\bar{C}_P = \bar{C}_V + \left[V + \left(\frac{\partial H}{\partial P}\right)_T\right]\left(\frac{\partial P}{\partial T}\right)_V$$

12.22. For one mole of a gas satisfying van der Waals equation, the value of $(\partial E/\partial V)_T = a/V^2$. Show that

$$\left(\frac{\partial V}{\partial T}\right)_P = \frac{R}{P - (a/V^2) + (2ab/V^3)}$$

and hence that

$$\bar{C}_P - \bar{C}_V = R\,\frac{P + (a/V^2)}{P - \dfrac{a}{V^2} + \dfrac{2ab}{V^3}}$$

12.23. From the result of the preceding problem, with values of a and b for CO_2, calculate $\bar{C}_P - \bar{C}_V$ for CO_2 at 50°C and 20 atm. By how much does this differ from the ideal gas value?

12.24. The assumption that $\bar{C}_V$ is a constant, made in deriving the adiabatic equations of Section 12.4, is often not a very good one. Thus for methane, $\bar{C}_V = 6.80$ cal/mole deg at 300°K and 8.61 cal/mole deg at 400°K, $\bar{C}_V$ can often be written in the form $\bar{C}_V = A + BT$ with reasonable accuracy, a and b being constants. Show that for this form of $\bar{C}_V$ the reversible adiabatic equation becomes

$$\frac{A}{R}\ln\frac{T_2}{T_1} + \frac{B}{R}(T_2 - T_1) = -\ln\left(\frac{V_2}{V_1}\right).$$

(This equation is transcendental in temperature; that is, it cannot be solved explicitly for T_2. One way of finding the value of T_2 for known values of V_2/V_1 and T_1 is by trial and error—i.e., by trying different values of T_2 until one is found for which the two sides of the equation are equal. With a little practice, this can be done quite quickly.)

12.25. For methane $\bar{C}_V = 3.38 + 0.018T$. (a) Using the equation of Problem *12.24* and the trial-and-error method as described, calculate the final temperature of 1 mole of gas initially with volume 10 liters at 300°K after it is adiabatically compressed to 5 liters volume. (b) Compare the more accurate result with the value obtained by using $\bar{C}_V$ as a constant equal to 6.80, the value at 300°K.

12.26. (a) Calculate the rise in temperature of 1 g of nitrogen gas at 300°K and 1 atm when a sound wave with pressure difference of 0.01 atm passes through it. (Assume reversible adiabatic heating.) (b) Calculate the increase in internal energy per gram, using

$$dE = -nRT\,\frac{dV}{V} \quad \text{and} \quad \frac{dV}{V} = -\frac{1}{\gamma}\frac{dP}{P}$$

(c) For comparison, calculate the flow speed of the gas from Eq. 12.19, $u = -c(dV/V)$ (where dV is the amount by which the volume is decreased by the pressure $dP = 0.01$ atm), and from u, the increase in kinetic energy, $\Delta(KE) = \frac{1}{2}u^2$ (for 1 g). Is the change in kinetic energy a significant fraction of the change in internal energy for this pressure difference?

12.27. Show that for a mixture of two gases, one with mole fraction N_1 and heat capacity $\bar{C}_{V_1}$ per mole and the other with mole fraction N_2 and heat capacity $\bar{C}_{V_2}$ per mole, the value of γ for the mixture is

$$\gamma = \frac{N_1 \bar{C}_{P_1} + N_2 \bar{C}_{P_2}}{N_1 \bar{C}_{V_1} + N_2 \bar{C}_{V_2}}$$

Also show that if M is the mass of 1 mole of the mixture, then $M = N_1 M_1 + N_2 M_2$, where M_1 and M_2 are the molecular weights of the two gases. Hence show that the speed of sound in the mixture is

$$c = \left[\frac{N_1 \bar{C}_{p_1} + N_2 \bar{C}_{p_2}}{N_1 \bar{C}_{V_1} + N_2 \bar{C}_{V_2}} \frac{RT}{N_1 M_1 + N_2 M_2} \right]^{1/2}$$

12.28. Use the result of Problem 12.27 to calculate the speed of sound in air (as a mixture of N_2 and O_2 in 4/1 mole ratio) at 20°C.

12.29. Show that the slope of the adiabatic curve in a PV diagram is always steeper than the slope of the isotherm intersecting the adiabatic curve at any particular temperature, assuming the ideal adiabatic law.

Suggested Readings

An excellent introduction to thermodynamics is given in the paperback *Elementary Chemical Thermodynamics* by Bruce H. Mahan (Benjamin, New York, 1963). A somewhat more advanced treatment is given by M. W. Zemansky in *Heat and Thermodynamics* (4th ed., McGraw-Hill, New York, 1957); this book is written primarily for the physicist and is notable for the clarity with which thermodynamic principles are stated and illustrated.

Chapter 13

Thermochemistry

THE SPECIALIZED BRANCH of thermody-
namics which has proven extremely useful to chemists—thermochemistry
—has to do with the quantitative consideration of the energy changes
which accompany chemical processes, or perhaps "near-chemical" processes such as solution or hydration. Interestingly enough, thermochemistry served in itself as one point of departure for the development of the
science of thermodynamics.

Thermochemistry provides a basic tool for the chemist, both in the
description and understanding of simple chemical processes, and also
in supplying data for the solution of thermodynamic problems of chemistry.

13.1. Heat Content or Enthalpy

Thermochemistry is considered principally as an empirical science
and is important for its utilitarian applications. Practical consideration
of simple chemical processes shows that for the most part they take place
in open vessels with no restriction on changes in volume of the reacting
masses, although ordinarily under the constant pressure of the atmosphere. While changes in the internal energy E are convenient for
describing the change in properties when a reaction takes place at
constant volume, the enthalpy (or heat content) H, is more satisfactory
for describing processes at constant pressure. As defined in Section 12.8,

the latter quantity combines pressure and volume with the internal energy.

$$H = E + PV \qquad (13.1)$$

For the changes in energy accompanying any process,

$$\Delta H = \Delta E + \Delta(PV)$$

and if this process is occurring at constant pressure,

$$\Delta H = \Delta E + P\,\Delta V \qquad (13.2)$$

However, from the discussion in the preceding chapter, the heat absorbed for a process occurring at constant pressure is

$$q_P = \Delta E + w \qquad (13.3)$$

and where the work done is limited to pressure-volume work, $w = P\,\Delta V$ and

$$q_P = \Delta E + P\,\Delta V = \Delta H \qquad (13.4)$$

The change in enthalpy, ΔH, is thus seen to be equal to the heat absorbed in a reaction occurring at constant pressure.

13.2. The Laws of Thermochemistry

In the early development of thermochemistry, two laws were promulgated on empirical grounds, which are, however, derivable from the more general treatment of thermodynamics. The first of these resulted from some observations of Lavoisier and Laplace, and bears their names: the quantity of heat required for the decomposition of a compound into its constituent elements is equal to the quantity of heat evolved in the formation of an equal quantity of the compound from its elements. Our present knowledge of the first law of thermodynamics makes it clear that just such a result is a necessary consequence. It also makes it clear that thermochemical equations can be reversed by writing them in the opposite direction and simultaneously reversing the sign of the enthalpy change. From the extension of this by a subsequent law, this reversibility applies to any thermochemical equation:

$$C(s) + \tfrac{1}{2}O_2(g) = 2CO(g), \qquad -\Delta H = \quad 26.4 \text{ kcal} \qquad (13.5)$$
$$CO(g) = C(s) + \tfrac{1}{2}O_2(g), \qquad -\Delta H = -26.4 \text{ kcal} \qquad (13.6)$$

or further,

$$CH_2Cl_2(g) + Cl_2(g) \rightleftharpoons CHCl_3 + HCl(g)$$
$$-\Delta H = \quad 38.6 \text{ kcal} \qquad (13.7)$$

$$CHCl_3(l) + HCl(g) \rightleftharpoons CH_2Cl_2(g) + Cl_2(g)$$
$$-\Delta H = -38.6 \text{ kcal} \quad (13.8)$$

Here $-\Delta H$ is the heat evolved at constant pressure for the equations as they are written. (The change in enthalpy for the reaction as written would be ΔH.)

The second law of thermochemistry is known as Hess's Law of constant heat summation. It states that the heat evolved or absorbed during a given chemical reaction is the same whether the reaction takes place in one or in several steps. (It depends only on the initial and final states.) For example, the reaction

$$C(s) + O_2(g) \rightleftharpoons CO_2(g) \qquad -\Delta H = 94.4 \text{ kcal} \qquad (13.9)$$

can be written in two steps:

$$C(s) + \tfrac{1}{2}O_2(g) \rightleftharpoons CO(g) \qquad -\Delta H = 26.4 \text{ kcal} \quad (13.10)$$
$$CO(g) + \tfrac{1}{2}O_2(g) \rightleftharpoons CO_2(g) \qquad -\Delta H = 68.0 \text{ kcal} \quad (13.11)$$

showing that the stepwise oxidation of carbon to carbon dioxide is equal to the heat of the direct reaction. (This is the expected result, since the enthalpy change is recognized as a thermodynamic quantity, dependent only on the initial and final states.)

13.3. Thermochemical Equations

In writing thermochemical equations, certain conventions, in addition to those for ordinary chemical equations, are here adopted for the sake of consistency. The energy change accompanying the process is recorded as the change in enthalpy. Thus, for an exothermic reaction (in which heat is given off) the enthalpy change carries a negative sign, as in Eq. 13.9. For an endothermic reaction (in which heat is absorbed), the change in enthalpy is positive; for example,

$$C_6H_6(g) + H_2(g) = C_6H_8(g), \qquad \Delta H_{355°} = 5.565 \text{ kcal}$$

(In strictly thermochemical notation, the heat of reaction Q is taken as heat evolved, and given a positive sign. Thus $Q = -\Delta H$. However, it is less confusing if the conventions of thermodynamics regarding sign are used consistently, as is done in this text.)

In order properly to account for the energy changes accompanying changes in phase, it is necessary to note the state in which each reactant or product appears in the reaction. This notation (g, l, s, or aq) is enclosed in parentheses immediately following the formula for the product or reactant, indicating it to be in the gaseous, liquid, solid state, or in aqueous solution.

The heats of reaction being dependent upon the temperature, it is important to indicate the temperature for which the value given was obtained. The subscript following the enthalpy symbol, H, refers to the absolute temperature at which the reaction takes place. In the hydrogenation of benzene given above, the value $\Delta H_{355°} = 5.565$ kcal was obtained for the reaction at the temperature 355° absolute. When no temperature is indicated, it may be assumed that the value given is that for room temperature (20°–25°C).

13.4. Heats of Reaction

As a chemical reaction takes place, energy changes in part result in the evolution or absorption of heat. Equations 13.5 to 13.8 are illustrative of the manner in which these reactions may be represented. In many cases they can be measured directly, in some type of calorimeter. (Techniques for measurement are described in numerous standard references, texts, or laboratory manuals.)

A typical reaction is the combustion of methanol:

$$CH_3OH(l) + \tfrac{3}{2}O_2(g) = 2H_2O(l) + CO_2(g),$$
$$\Delta H_{298°} = -173.64 \text{ kcal} \quad (13.12)$$

Because heats of combustion are measured experimentally with relative ease, they are often used in determining other heats of reaction, particularly of organic reactions, by means of Hess's Law of constant heat summation. It is, for example, difficult if not impossible to measure directly the heat of reaction for the polymerization of acetylene to benzene, $3C_2H_2(g) = C_6H_6(g)$, which takes place at high temperatures (500°C). However, the heats of combustion of acetylene and benzene are easily measured:

$$C_2H_2(g) + \tfrac{5}{2}O_2(g) = 2CO_2(g) + H_2O(l),$$
$$\Delta H = -310.62 \text{ kcal} \quad (13.13)$$

$$C_6H_6(g) + \tfrac{15}{2}O_2(g) = 6CO_2(g) + 3H_2O(l),$$
$$\Delta H = -789.08 \text{ kcal} \quad (13.14)$$

By subtracting Eq. 13.14 from three times Eq. 13.13, one obtains

$$3C_2H_2(g) = C_6H_6(g), \quad \Delta H = -142.78 \text{ kcal} \quad (13.15)$$

While a fairly precise value of the heat of reaction is obtained in this case, it is determined as a difference between two relatively large numbers. For many reactions where the heat of reaction is small, this difference method requires the determination of the heats of combustion with great accuracy in order to avoid large errors in the calculated heat of reaction. Thus, in determining the heats of hydrogenation of unsaturated hydrocarbons, which are in the range 20–60 kcal/mole, precise values are better obtained by their direct measurement in spite of the experimental difficulty, than from differences in heats of combustion, which are separately of the order of 700–1000 kcal.

13.5. Heats of Formation. Standard States

The heat of reaction for the formation of a compound from its elements is called the heat of formation. By the adoption of conventions defining certain *standard states* of the elements, standard tables of the heats of formation for various compounds from elements in these standard states (and also for elements in states other than their standard states) are obtained. These tables are extremely useful for the calculation of heats of reactions at constant pressure, these calculations being possible because these heats are equal to changes in thermodynamic properties, dependent only on the initial and final states. Since heats of reaction always involve only differences in enthalpy, the absolute enthalpy content of the reactants and products is of no consequence, and it is important only that the conventions adopted in defining the standard states be rigorously followed.

For the standard state, the temperature is 298.16°K (25°C) and the pressure is one atmosphere, and the element in its pure form is in the state (gas, liquid, or solid, or aqueous solution) which is stable under those conditions. The molal enthalpy of the element in this standard state is often arbitrarily defined to be zero. For the element in any other possible allotropic forms, its enthalpy will have a value equal to the enthalpy difference between the standard state and the particular state. (This applies equally to conditions of temperature and pressure other than those of the standard state.)

For compounds, values of the standard heats of formation, ΔH^0, can be obtained by determination of the enthalpy change accompanying the formation of the compounds from the elements in their standard state, either by direct measurement or by indirect determination. Examples follow showing the determination of heats of formation.

At 25°C and 1 atmosphere pressure, the heat of combustion of hydrogen gives directly the heat of formation of water:

$$H_2(g) + \tfrac{1}{2}O_2(g) \rightleftharpoons H_2O(l), \qquad \Delta H^0_{298°} = -68.313 \text{ kcal} \qquad (13.16)$$

To determine the heat of formation of carbon monoxide, the following heats of combustion are measured:

$$C(\text{graphite})(s) + O_2(g) \rightleftharpoons CO_2(g), \ \Delta H^0_{298°} = -94.052 \text{ kcal} \quad (13.17)$$

$$CO(g) + \tfrac{1}{2}O_2(g) \rightleftharpoons CO_2(g), \qquad \Delta H^0_{298°} = -67.636 \text{ kcal} \quad (13.18)$$

Subtracting Eq. 13.18 from Eq. 13.17,

$$C(\text{graphite})(s) + \tfrac{1}{2}O_2(g) \rightleftharpoons CO(g), \qquad \Delta H^0_{298°} = 26.416 \text{ kcal} \quad (13.19)$$

(It may be noted that this heat would be very difficult to measure directly, because some CO_2 would also be formed, giving a measurement involving ΔH^0 for both CO and CO_2.) For heat of formation of an allotropic form (hypothetical, in this case)

$$\tfrac{1}{2}H_2(g) \rightleftharpoons H(g), \qquad \Delta H^0_{298°} = 52.089 \text{ kcal} \qquad (13.20)$$

From tables in which the standard heats of formation for various chemical substances are collected, heats of reaction can be calculated. For example, for the reaction

$$C_2H_4(g) + H_2(g) \rightleftharpoons C_2H_6(g)$$

the enthalpy change (heat of reaction) will be equal to the standard heat of formation of ethane (-20.236 kcal) minus the sum of the heats of formation of ethylene (12.496 kcal) and hydrogen (zero kcal), or $-20.236 - 12.496 = -32.732$ kcal.

In Table 13.1 will be found values of standard enthalpies of formation for a limited number of inorganic and organic compounds. Extensive tables in the literature give values for many more substances.

The advantage of tables giving the standard heats of formation for all known compounds is obvious even by the above brief demonstration, since from such data the heat of reaction may be calculated for any reaction. The only significantly different alternative would be the gargantuan task of tabulating all known chemical reactions and their respective heats of reaction.

13.6. Heats of Solution

Heats of combustions and of formation are but two of the many classes into which possible enthalpy changes of physical and chemical processes can be grouped. Some of the more important types for changes in solution are discussed in this and the next section.

Considerable amounts of heat may be absorbed or evolved when two

TABLE 13.1. *Enthalpies of Formation of Various Compounds from the Elements at 25°C.*

Formula	ΔH^0 (kcals)	Formula	ΔH^0 (kcals)
$HBr(g)$	−8.66	$C_6H_6(g)$	19.820
$HCl(g)$	−22.06	$CO(g)$	−26.42
$HI(g)$	6.20	$CO_2(g)$	94.05
$H_2O(g)$	−57.80	$CuSO_4(s)$	−184.00
$H_2O(l)$	−68.32	$CaO(s)$	−151.9
$H_2S(g)$	−4.815	$CaCO_3(s)$	−288.45
$H_2Se(g)$	20.5	$NH_3(g)$	−11.04
$H_2Te(g)$	36.9	$NaCl(s)$	−98.23
$CCl_4(g)$	−25.5	$NaBr(s)$	−86.03
$C_2H_2(g)$	54.194	$K_2SO_4(s)$	−342.66
$C_2H_4(g)$	12.496	$NO(g)$	21.60
$C_2H_6(g)$	−20.236	$SO_2(g)$	−70.96
$CHCl_3(g)$	−24	$SO_3(g)$	−94.45
$CH_2Cl_2(g)$	−21.0	$ZnSO_4(s)$	
$C_2H_5OH(g)$	−56.24		

Values taken from *Handbook of Chemistry and Physics* (38th ed.).

liquids are mixed, or a solid dissolved in a liquid. The amount absorbed is evidently the value of ΔH for the process: (solvent) + (solute) = (solution), and so can be written

$$\Delta H = H(\text{solution}) - [H(\text{solvent}) + H(\text{solute})]$$

The value of ΔH obtained by calorimetric measurement depends on the total quantities of the species mixed and their relative amounts, which determine the concentration of the resulting solution. In order to have comparable figures for different concentrations, it is necessary to refer the measurements to some fixed quantity of solute or solvent. This can be done in a number of ways which are useful for different purposes.

Integral Heats of Solution and Dilution

One definite quantity is the heat per mole of solute added. If n_1 moles of solvent and n_2 moles of solute are mixed, this quantity is $\Delta H/n_2$ and is called the *integral heat of solution*. Values of $\Delta H/n_2$ for the system ethanol-water at 0°C and several mole ratios n_1/n_2 are listed in Table 13.2.

TABLE 13.2.   *Enthalpy Change on Mixing n_2 moles of Ethanol with 55.5 moles of Water (1000 gm).*

n_2	ΔH (cal)	n_1/n_2	$\Delta H/n_2$ (cal/mole)
0.329	−1130	169	−3430
0.443	−1520	125	−3420
0.555	−1890	100	−3410
0.890	−3020	62.4	−3390
1.109	−3740	50.1	−3370
1.328	−4490	41.9	−3350
1.67	−5540	33.2	−3320
2.22	−7200	25.0	−3240
6.18	−14,600	9.00	−2360
(∞)	—	0	0

These values correspond to such processes as

$$C_2H_5OH + 25H_2O = C_2H_5OH \text{ (3.84 mole \%)},$$
$$\Delta H/n_2 = -3240 \text{ cal/mole}$$

$$C_2H_5OH + 9H_2O = C_2H_5OH \text{ (10 mole \%)},$$
$$\Delta H/n_2 = -2360 \text{ cal/mole}$$

The differing values reflect the change in heat of solution with changing concentration, and the difference of the values is the quantity called the integral heat of dilution. Thus diluting from 10 mole % to 3.84 mole % solution has a heat of dilution $\Delta H = -880$ cal/mole:

$$C_2H_5OH \text{ (10 mole \%)} + 16H_2O = C_2H_5OH \text{ (3.84 mole \%)},$$
$$\Delta H = -880 \text{ cal/mole}$$

For dilute solutions (n_1/n_2 large), the values $\Delta H/n_2$ approach a limiting value, as shown by the plot in Fig. 13.1, *A*, of $\Delta H/n_2$ against the solvent-solute mole ratio n_1/n_2, which approaches infinity for pure solvent. Extrapolation of the plot of $\Delta H/n_2$ versus molality, Fig. 13.1, *B*, gives −3460 cal/mole for this limiting value, called the heat of solution at infinite dilution. It corresponds to the heat absorbed when one mole of solute is added to an enormously larger quantity of solvent, and represents therefore the heat supplied when solute molecules are transferred from surroundings of other solute molecules to an environment wholly of solvent molecules.

The integral heats of solution for final solution concentration other than infinitely dilute have a less simple significance, as progressive additions are first to pure solvent, then to increasingly less dilute solutions, and the integral heat is an average ΔH over the total change in solution concentration. Values of ΔH representative of addition to a solution of particular concentration are called differential heats, and are partial molar values.

The partial molar, or *differential heat of dilution*, $(\partial \Delta H/\partial n_1)_{n_2}$, represents the heat absorbed per mole on adding solvent (1), the amount n_1 being already so large that it is but infinitesimally changed. Similarly for the solute, the partial molar or *differential heat of solution*, $(\partial \Delta H/\partial n_2)_{n_1}$, is the heat per mole of solute added, the amounts again being such that their changes have negligible effect.

Various methods exist for evaluating differential heats. A direct one for obtaining the differential heat of dilution is from the slope of the curve in Fig. 13.1, *A*. This slope is $d(\Delta H/n_2)/d(n_1/n_2)$, which, if n_2 is

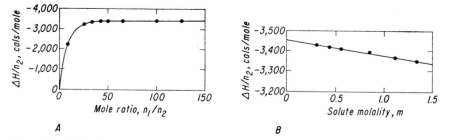

A   *B*

Fig. 13.1. *Enthalpy change per mole of ethanol upon mixing with water in the relative quantities indicated:* (A) *as function of mole ratio,* n_1/n_2; (B) *as function of solute molality,* m.

fixed, is equivalent to $[\partial(\Delta H)/\partial n_1]n_2$. For the differential heat of solution, one could correspondingly find the slope of the plot of $\Delta H/n_1$ against n_2/n_1.

Obtaining accurate slopes from tangents to such curves is often difficult and other better or more convenient processes have been devised. One often used, the method of intercepts, involves plotting values of $\Delta H/(n_1 + n_2)$ against mole fraction of solvent N_1, and deducing the desired quantities from the slope of this curve. Details of this and other procedures will be found in texts on thermodynamics (see references at end of chapter).

A solution process accompanied by considerable heats of mixing usually means nonideal behavior of vapor pressures, as ideal solutions can be shown by purely thermodynamic reasoning to have no heat absorbed or evolved when the species are mixed.

The evolution of considerable amounts of heat on adding alcohol to water implies stronger binding of alcohol to water molecules than to other alcohol molecules, with the result that potential energy released on mixing must be removed from the system if the temperature is not to rise. As this suggests, heat changes on mixing give useful evidence about molecular interactions, and quantitative analysis of such measurements is valuable in developing theories of solutions.

In the case of other special processes, the meaning of the thermal changes associated with the process is obvious. The heat of hydration for calcium chloride, for example, is the value of ΔH for the reaction

$$CaCl_2(s) + 6H_2O(l) \rightleftharpoons CaCl_2 \cdot 6H_2O(s), \quad \Delta H = -22.55 \text{ cal} \quad (13.21)$$

13.7. Heats of Neutralization and Ionization

The heat of neutralization accompanying the neutralization of one equivalent of a strong acid by a strong base is, as would be expected, practically independent of the strong acid or base involved. For example, from the consideration of the equation $H^+ + Cl^- + Na^+ + OH^- \rightleftharpoons Na^+ + Cl^- + H_2O$, it is seen that the essential reaction in aqueous solution is

$$H^+ + OH^- \rightleftharpoons H_2O \qquad (13.22)$$

The value $\Delta H_{298°} = -13.8$ kcal for this "deionization" of water is a reasonable good average value for all heats of neutralization. (Because the equilibrium state of water is affected by the kinds and number of ions present, small variations are found.)

Heats of ionization corresponding to the enthalpy changes occurring with the formation or removal of positive and negative ions in solution are important quantities for the chemistry of solutions. One often has need for heats of ionic reactions such as the following:

(a) $\frac{1}{2}H_2(g) + \frac{1}{2}Cl_2(g) + H_2O(l) = H^+(aq) + Cl^-(aq)$,
$$\Delta H^0 = -40.0 \text{ kcal}$$

(b) $\frac{1}{2}H_2(g) + \frac{1}{2}Br_2(l) + H_2O(l) = H^+(aq) + Br^-(aq)$,
$$\Delta H^0 = -28.9 \text{ kcal}$$

(c) $Na(s) + \frac{1}{2}Cl_2(g) + H_2O(l) = Na^+(aq) + Cl^-(aq)$,
$$\Delta H^0 = -97.3 \text{ kcal}$$

(d) $Na(s) + \frac{1}{2}Br_2(l) + H_2O(l) = Na^+(aq) + Br^-(aq)$,
$$\Delta H^0 = -86.2 \text{ kcal}$$

(e) $K(s) + \frac{1}{2}Cl_2(g) + H_2O(l) = K^+(aq) + Cl^-(aq)$,
$$\Delta H^0 = -100.0 \text{ kcal}$$

$$(13.23)$$

Many more heats of ionization are known and a table of them could be compiled. Such a table would be very bulky and tedious to use, and fortunately can be replaced by a much more compact one giving the same information, made possible through a property of ionic reactions illustrated in the examples just cited. Comparison of (a) and (c), and (b) and (d), shows that the heats of ionization of compounds with hydrogen ion as the cation is larger than those of compounds with the sodium ion by 57.3 kcal/mole, whether the anion is Cl^- or Br^-. (Compare with differences in ionic conductivities discussed in Section 18.7.) The heats for reactions with the chloride ion are likewise smaller than for bromide ion by 11.1 kcal/mole, regardless of the particular cation (as illustrated by comparing reactions (a) and (b), and (c) and (d) above).

The consistency of these differences carries the strong implication that a definite amount of heat, absorbed or evolved, is characteristic of every ion formed in solution, and that this value is independent of the particular ion of opposite sign. Thus any single ionization reaction, such as formation of $HCl(aq)$ by the reaction $\frac{1}{2}H_2(g) + \frac{1}{2}Cl_2(g) + H_2O(l) = H^+(aq) + Cl^-(aq)$, may be regarded as the sum of single ion reactions with single ion heats of formation:

$$\frac{1}{2}H_2(g) + H_2O = H^+(aq) + e^-, \qquad \Delta H^0 = \Delta H^0[H^+(aq)] \qquad (13.24)$$

$$\frac{1}{2}Cl_2(g) + e^- + H_2O = Cl^-(aq), \qquad \Delta H^0 = \Delta H^0[Cl^-(aq)] \qquad (13.25)$$

added together, give

$$\frac{1}{2}H_2(g) + \frac{1}{2}Cl_2(g) = H^+(aq) + Cl^-(aq),$$
$$\Delta H^0 = \Delta H^0[H^+(aq)] + \Delta H^0[Cl^-(aq)] \qquad (13.26)$$

(It will be noted that electrical charge has been balanced in the single ion equations by including e^- as reactant or product, even though it cancels in the complete reaction.)

The data necessary for the calculation of heats of ionization are thus reducible to a tabulation of heats of formation of single ions, if these can be determined. Here, however, the situation actually faced is that measurable heats of reaction always involve both positive and negative ions in equivalent amounts, and from them there is no way of determining values for either ion alone. The value $\Delta H^0 = -40.0$ kcal for the formation of $HCl(aq)$ could be, for example, equally well the result of $\Delta H^0[H^+(aq)] = +20$ kcal and $\Delta H^0[Cl^-(aq)] = -60$ kcal, of values -70 and $+30$ kcal, or of any other pair resulting in the net value of -40 kcal for the formation $H^+(aq) + Cl^-(aq)$.

The absolute values for single ions are thus not available, but the fact that when added together they must give the correct value for the compound involved does make the values for all ions definite, and known relative to any one particular value. Whatever its value, the heat $\Delta H^0[Cl^-(aq)]$ for formation of the $Cl^-(aq)$ ion must be the difference between -40 kcal and $\Delta H^0[H^+(aq)]$ for the hydrogen ion. It likewise must be true that $\Delta H^0[Na^+(aq)]$ is less than $\Delta H^0[H^+(aq)]$ by 57.3 kcal/mole. These necessary relations can be expressed by the equations

$$\Delta H^0[Cl^-(aq)] = -40.0 \text{ kcal} - \Delta H^0[H^+(aq)] \qquad (13.27)$$

$$\Delta H^0[Na^+(aq)] = \Delta H^0[H^+(aq)] - 57.3 \text{ kcal} \qquad (13.28)$$

and similarly

$$\Delta H^0[Br^-(aq)] = -28.9 \text{ kcal} - \Delta H^0[H^+(aq)] \qquad (13.29)$$

$$\Delta H^0[K^+(aq)] = \Delta H^0[H^+(aq)] - 60.0 \text{ kcal} \qquad (13.30)$$

Chemists generally have agreed to make all such comparisons with the hydrogen ion as in the two examples above, and to tabulate heats of ionization for single ions in terms of their difference from that for the hydrogen ion. Hence the value -40.0 kcal/mole is found for $\Delta H^0[Cl^-(aq)]$ in Table 13.3, the value -57.3 for $\Delta H^0[Na^+(aq)]$, and so on. The heat of any complete reaction with both ions can then be obtained simply as the sum of the positive and negative ion values because $\Delta H^0[H^+(aq)]$ cancels out in any balanced reaction. For reaction of sodium and chlorine in water, for example, we have

$$\Delta H^0[Na^+(aq)] + \Delta H^0[Cl^-(aq)]$$
$$= \{\Delta H^0[H^+(aq)] - 57.3\} + \{-40 - \Delta H^0[H^+(aq)]\}$$
$$= -97.3 \text{ kcal} \qquad (13.31)$$

which is exactly the result obtained by omitting $\Delta H^0[H^+(aq)]$ and writing

$$\Delta H^0[Na^+(aq)] + \Delta H^0[Cl^-(aq)] = -57.3 + (-40)$$
$$= -97.3 \text{ kcal} \qquad (13.32)$$

since $\Delta H^0[H^+(aq)]$ cancels out. This cancellation always occurs for any complete reaction; thus using the values relative to the $H^+(aq)$ ion always gives the correct answer, whatever the actual value for $\Delta H^0[H^+(aq)]$ may be.

The comparison of all single ionization values to that for the $H^+(aq)$ ion is often described by saying that $\Delta H^0[H^+(aq)]$ is zero, by convention. This statement causes no harm if one understands that the actual value for $\Delta H[H^+(aq)]$ whatever it is, makes no difference in calculating measurable heats of *complete* ionic reactions, and can therefore be called zero or *any other number* for such purposes. Various attempts have been made to do on paper by calculation what cannot be done by measuring heats of reactions (namely, the determination of actual ΔH of the process $\frac{1}{2}H_2(g) \rightleftharpoons H^+(aq) + e^-$), but no unchallenged or certain values have been obtained.

The heats of formation of ions have so far been discussed without considering possible effects of ion concentration. That is, the question as to whether the quantity of solution in which one mole of HCl is formed affects the value of ΔH, has been ignored. Actually real differences do exist and the measured heats depend somewhat on concentration, but only in a small manner. The ΔH^0 values discussed and the ones on which Table 13.3 is based refer to ionization in very dilute

TABLE 13.3.   *Heats of Formation of Ions in 1 Molal Aqueous Solution at 25°C.*

Ion	$-\Delta H^0$ (kcal)	Ion	$-\Delta H^0$ (kcal)	Ion	$-\Delta H^0$ (kcal)
H^+	0	Sn^{2+}	-2.40	NO_3^-	49.79
Li^+	66.6	Pb^{2+}	0.50	HCO_3^-	164.6
Na^+	57.33	Fe^{2+}	20.80	CO_3^{2-}	161.1
K^+	60.31	Fe^{3+}	9.60	$C_2H_3O_2^-$	117.6
NH_4^+	31.46	Co^{2+}	16.5	PO_4^{3-}	254.5
Ag^+	-24.90	Ni^{2+}	15.2		
Hg^+	-20.1	OH^-	54.53		
Hg^{2+}	110.2	Cl^-	39.55		
Cu^{2+}	-16.50	Br^-	28.95		
Zn^{2+}	36.60	I^-	13.32		
Cd^{2+}	17.40	HS^-	3.40		
Hg^{2+}	-40.20	S^{2-}	-10.00		
Ca^{2+}	129.5	HSO_3^-	147.5		
Sr^{2+}	130.0	SO_3^{2-}	146.9		
Ba^{2+}	128.4	SO_4^{2-}	215.8		
Mn^{2+}	49.2	NO_2^-	25.60		

From Partington: *Advanced Treatise on Physical Chemistry*, Vol. I, and Prutton and Maron: *Fundamental Principles of Physical Chemistry*.

solution. As an indication of the difference with varying concentration, ΔH^0 for HCl at great dilution has the value -40.02 kcal, while for a

0.056 molal solution $\Delta H = -39.91$ kcal. The difference of 0.11 kcal (0.25%) is clearly the change in enthalpy with dilution, which is small if the solution is dilute.

The usefulness of data for heats of formation of ions can be illustrated by many examples; two are given below and the reader will find a number of others in the problems at the end of the chapter.

1. The heat of formation for ions of different valences can be calculated as for univalent ions if due account is taken of the numbers of ions formed. Thus for formation of K_2SO_4 in solution from the elements by the reaction

$$2K(s) + S(g) + 2O_2(g) \rightleftharpoons 2K^+(aq) + SO_4^{2-}(aq)$$

the heat of formation of the aqueous ionic solution is

$$\Delta H^0 = 2\Delta H^0[K^+(aq)] + \Delta H^0[SO_4^{2-}(aq)]$$
$$= 2(-60.0) + (-216.9)$$

or $\Delta H^0 = -336.9$ kcal. The factor 2 is required because 2 moles of $K^+(aq)$ ion are formed by the reaction as written.

2. Ionic heats can be used also to determine heats of reaction when one ion in solution is replaced by another, as when zinc deposits copper from a copper sulfate solution:

$$Zn + Cu^{2+}(aq) \rightleftharpoons Cu + Zn^{2+}(aq) \qquad \Delta H = ?$$

The value of H for this reaction is just the difference of ionic heats of formation:

$$Zn = Zn^{2+}(aq) + 2e^-, \qquad \Delta H^0(Zn^{2+})(aq) = -36.43 \text{ cal},$$
$$Cu = Cu^{2+}(aq) + 2e^-, \qquad \Delta H^0(Cu^{2+})(aq) = 15.39 \text{ cal}$$

Subtraction of the second from the first gives $Zn + Cu^{2+}(aq) \rightleftharpoons Cu + Zn^{2+}(aq)$ and hence $\Delta H = -36.43 - (15.39) = -51.82$ kcal/mole. The displacement is thus strongly exothermic (corresponding to the observation that dissolving a zinc salt evolves much more heat than dissolving the corresponding copper salt).

13.8. Variation of Heats of Reaction with Temperature

Often heats of reaction are desired at temperatures other than the standard $T = 298°K$, for which heats of formation are usually listed in tables. Direct measurement is one possibility, but often equally useful information can be obtained by calculations based on the first law and on the enthalpy being a property only of the state of the system. These calculations require knowledge of heat capacities of the reactants and products and the value of ΔH at any one temperature.

Consider a known heat of reaction at a particular temperature, corresponding to the difference in enthalpy between the products and the reactants. For a given change in temperature, the change in the enthalpy of the reactants may be calculated from the heat capacity at constant pressure, as shown in Section 12.8. $\left(\int_{H_1}^{H_2} dH = \int_{T_1}^{T_2} C_P \, dT. \right)$ The change in the enthalpy of the products corresponding to the given change in temperature may be similarly determined, and thus, from the calculated values of the enthalpy of the reactants and products at the second temperature, the enthalpy difference corresponding to the heat of reaction at the second temperature is obtained.

Expressed as an equation, the change in heat of reaction with temperature is

$$\Delta H_{T_2} - \Delta H_{T_1} = \int_{T_1}^{T_2} [C_P(\text{products}) - C_P(\text{reactants})] \, dT \qquad (13.33)$$

As an example, consider the hydrogenation of ethylene:

$$C_2H_4(g) + H_2(g) \rightleftharpoons C_2H_6(g), \qquad \Delta H_{355°} = -32.824 \text{ kcal} \quad (13.34)$$

The heat capacities at constant pressure for the products and reactants are given with sufficient accuracy in the range $300°K$ to $500°K$ by the following relations:

$$\overline{C}_P(H_2) = 6.62 + 0.8 \times 10^{-3}T \qquad (13.35)$$
$$\overline{C}_P(C_2H_4) = 4.10 + 21.9 \times 10^{-3}T \qquad (13.36)$$
$$\overline{C}_P(C_2H_6) = 3.82 + 29.5 \times 10^{-3}T \qquad (13.37)$$

To calculate the change in the heat of reaction if carried out at $455°K$ rather than at $355°K$, one integrates between the two temperatures:

$$\Delta H_{455°} - \Delta H_{355°} = \int_{355°}^{455°} [C_P(C_2H_6) - C_P(H_2) - C_P(C_2H_4)] \, dT \quad (13.38)$$

$$= \int_{355°}^{455°} [3.82 + 29.5 \times 10^{-3}T - 6.62 - 0.8 \times 10^{-3}T$$
$$- 4.10 - 21.9 \times 10^{-3}T] \, dT$$

$$= \int_{355°}^{455°} [-6.90 + 6.80 \times 10^{-3}T] \, dT$$

$$= -6.90(455 - 355) + 3.40 \times 10^{-3}(455^2 - 355^2)$$

$$= -6.90 + 3.40 \times 10^{-3} \times 81,000$$

$$= -415 \text{ cal}$$

Hence

$$\Delta H_{455°} = -32,824 - 415 = -32.41 \text{ kcal}$$

13.9. Adiabatic Flame Temperatures

Reasoning similar to that used to determine change in heat of reaction with temperature can also be applied to estimating the temperature of flames produced by burning gases in air or in oxygen. In such flame reactions, the temperature changes and changes in reaction products as the flowing gases are mixed and ignited become quite complex, but some simplifying assumptions and idealizations make it possible to calculate approximate maximum temperatures without considering all the details of the actual processes.

If a gas such as methane is burned in air, the reactions to form CO, CO_2, $H_2O(g)$, and dissociated products evolve considerable heat. For complete combustion to CO_2 and water, the reaction is

$$CH_4(g) + 2O_2(g) \rightleftharpoons CO_2(g) + 2H_2O(g),$$
$$\Delta H^0_{298°} = -191.8 \text{ kcal} \quad (13.39)$$

If the reaction is carried out in a bomb calorimeter, this heat is transferred to the bomb and surroundings to produce a small temperature rise. Independent determination of the quantity of heat supplied through an electric heating coil to produce the same rise in temperature of the bomb then gives the value of ΔH^0. In an open flame, however, only a small part of the heat of reaction is given to the surroundings during the short time the burning gases are in the flame zone. Instead, most of the energy released by the reaction goes into the increased energy of the remaining gases; the products at high temperature later cool down by conduction, convection, and radiation.

An upper limit on the highest temperature reached can be calculated by neglecting heat transfer to the surroundings entirely. For this approximation to the initial state of the products, the process is adiabatic and at constant pressure, as at one atmosphere. Hence for this idealized process, $\Delta H = q_P = 0$. The final temperature must then be the one for which the total heat evolved at various stages is exactly taken up by the heating of product gases, and the actual sequence, as already suggested, is complicated. The end result, however, can be calculated by *any* sequence of changes for which the sum of changes ΔH is zero.

The simplest such sequence is to assume complete burning at 298°K, for which $\Delta H^0_{298°} = -191.8$ kcal, followed by the rise in temperature for which $\Delta H_T = +191.8$ kcal. From Eq. 13.39, the product gases heated are 1 mole of $CO_2(g)$ and 2 of $H_2O(g)$, and if oxygen is supplied from the air nearly 8 moles of $N_2(g)$ will also be present and will be heated to the final temperature T. Expressing the change of ΔH in terms of the heat capacities gives

$$\Delta H_T = 191,800 = \int_{298°}^{T} [C_P(CO_2) + 2C_P(H_2O) + 8C_P(N_2)]\, dT \quad (13.40)$$

and the final temperature T is the one for which this equation is true. Because flame temperatures are high, values for C_P which are valid between 298° and high temperatures should be used. For a very rough estimate of T, the values at room temperature may be used: $C_P(CO_2) = 9.33$, $C_P(H_2O) = 8.95$, $C_P(N_2) = 6.90$ cal/mole deg, which when substituted in Eq. 13.40 give

$$\Delta H_T = 191,800 \cong \int_{298°}^{T} [9.33 + 17.90 + 55.20]\, dT$$

$$82.4(T - 298) \cong 191,800 \qquad\qquad (13.41)$$

$$T \cong 2640°K$$

This figure is certainly too high, because the room temperature values of C_P used are too small for the temperature involved. The high value shows the need to use equations for C_P that are good to temperatures of something like 2000°K. Such equations (when available) are usually written in the form $C_P = a + bT + cT^2$. When such expressions are substituted in Eq. 13.40 and the equation integrated, an equation cubic in T evidently results. We shall not carry through details of this process or of evaluating T; the result yields a value $T \cong 2330°K$. Even this figure is too high, because at temperatures above 1000°K, both CO_2 and H_2O dissociate appreciably with absorption of heat, thus lowering the final temperature further. Allowance for this gives a value of about 2100°K.

Although accurate calculations of maximum temperatures become complicated because the temperatures are so high, the thermodynamic estimate of them can be made by a much simpler route than one corresponding to the actual sequence of processes. It is also easy to see from the thermodynamic argument why flames in pure oxygen are so much hotter than flames in air, the reason evidently being that there is then no atmospheric nitrogen present with the products to absorb much of the heat of reaction (note Eq. 13.41). As a result, flame temperatures of order 4000–5000°K can be reached in pure oxygen.

13.10. Dissociation and Bond Energies

In the discussion of heats of reaction, little has been said about their relation to the changes of molecular energies. Since chemical reaction involves breaking and forming chemical bonds, the energies required or released in the molecular processes involving bonds must be reflected in the measured heats of reaction; thermochemical data can therefore give useful information about molecular energies.

The simplest kind of evidence comes from the measured heats of dissociation for the breakdown of simple molecules into atoms. Such reactions as $H_2 \rightleftharpoons 2H$, $O_2 \rightleftharpoons 2O$, and $Br_2(g) \rightleftharpoons 2Br(g)$ become significant at temperatures high enough for the thermal energies to be comparable with bond energy. Thus, at 1000°K diatomic bromine dissociates sufficiently that the heat of the reaction, $\Delta H = 55$ kcal, can be determined. This measured heat corresponds principally to the energy required to break the Br—Br bond. However, it is not the same as the bond energy per mole for two reasons. In the first place, the value of $\Delta H[= \Delta E + \Delta(PV)]$ includes changes in enthalpy resulting from expansion work; in the second place, there are changes in ΔE resulting from differences in translational energy of 2Br compared with Br_2, and also from the loss of excited rotational and vibrational energies of the diatomic molecule.

The difference $\Delta(PV)$ between the products (2Br) and the reactant (Br_2) is from the gas law just RT, or 2000 cal/mole at 1000°K. The contributions of molecular energies to ΔH can be obtained from calculated or measured heat capacities. As the gases are cooled, these contributions become smaller, and the bond energy corresponds to the value of ΔH^0 at 0°K, which can be written

$$\Delta H_{0°}^0 = \Delta H_{1000°}^0 - \int_{0°}^{1000°} \Delta C_P \, dT \qquad (13.42)$$

In the case $Br_2 \rightleftharpoons 2Br$, the correction represented by the integral of ΔC_P gives a value $\Delta H_{0°}^0 = 46.2$ kcal.

The thermochemical calculation outlined for bromine can be carried out for other diatomic gases; often the value of ΔH at high temperatures is determined indirectly from change of equilibrium with temperature as discussed in Section 15.4. Studies of the vibrational structure in electronic spectra can also be used to obtain the energy of dissociation, but care must be taken to identify any products of dissociation by the impinging light itself, as they may be atoms with excited electrons. Other methods are also possible, such as dissociation by high-energy electron impacts, or by high temperatures in shock pressure waves. The spectroscopic values are very accurate, provided they are not ambiguous, and the value for ΔH^0 of 45.5 kcal obtained for Br_2 is in good agreement with the thermal value of 46.2 kcal. Corresponding values of 57.1 kcal for Cl_2 and 35.6 kcal for I_2 show that the stability decreases in the order Cl_2, Br_2, I_2. This is also evidenced by comparing other properties, such as the melting or boiling points. The great stability of the hydrogen molecule is shown by its dissociation energy of 103.2 kcal.

Heats of dissociation for more complex molecules dissociating into their constituent atoms can often be obtained by suitable combinations of reactions. A simple example is dissociation of water vapor: $H_2O \rightleftharpoons 2H + O$. This reaction is not readily carried out cleanly, but the heat can be calculated from the values obtained for more accessible reactions:

$$\begin{array}{lll} H_2O(g) = H_2(g) + \tfrac{1}{2}O_2(g), & \Delta H_{0^\circ}^0 = & 58.6 \text{ kcal} \\ H_2(g) \quad = 2H(g), & \Delta H_{0^\circ}^0 = 103.2 \text{ kcal} \\ [O_2(g) \quad = 2O(g), & \Delta H_{0^\circ}^0 = 118.2 \text{ kcal}] \times \tfrac{1}{2} \end{array}$$

$$H_2O(g) = 2H(g) + O(g); \quad \Delta H_{0^\circ}^0 = \quad 58.6 + 103.2 + 59.1$$

or

$$\Delta H_{0^\circ}^0 = 220.9 \text{ kcal} \qquad (13.43)$$

Another example is the dissociation of methane to atoms: $CH_4(g) = C(g) + 4H(g)$. The energy value is known for the molecular dissociation,

$$CH_4(g) = C(s, \text{ graphite}) + 2H_2(g), \quad \Delta H_{0^\circ}^0 = 15.99 \text{ kcal} \quad (13.44)$$

To obtain the value for dissociation completely to atoms then requires use of the value 103.2 kcal for $H_2(g) = 2H(g)$, and the heat of forming gaseous carbon atoms from solid carbon in the form of graphite. This last value is troublesome, because the heat of sublimation of carbon must be known. Different values have been reported for this, the value 170.4 kcal/mole being favored by most people on the basis of present evidence. If it is used, the calculation is then

$$\begin{array}{lll} CH_4(g) = C(s) + 2H_2(g), & \Delta H_{0^\circ}^0 = & 15.99 \text{ kcal/mole} \\ C(s) \quad = C(g), & \Delta H_{0^\circ}^0 = 170.4 \quad \text{kcal/mole} \\ H_2(g) \quad = 2H(g), & \Delta H_{0^\circ}^0 = 103.2 \quad \text{kcal/mole} \times 2 \end{array}$$

$$CH_4(g) = C(g) + 4H(g), \quad \Delta H_{0^\circ}^0 = 16.0 + 170.4 + 206.4$$

or

$$\Delta H_{0^\circ}^0 = 392.8 \text{ kcal} \qquad (13.45)$$

Similar calculations can be made for more complex compounds except that often the data are lacking for correcting the values of ΔH^0 to $0°K$ (this correction requiring specific heat measurements at temperatures down to $15°K$ or lower). Even in the absence of such data, values of $\Delta H^0_{298°}$ are still frequently obtained which in most cases do not differ from the value $\Delta H^0_{0°}$ (the proper measure of energy to "atomize" the unexcited molecule) by more than 2–3 kcal/mole.

The interest in making such calculations of dissociation energies is to see to what extent they can be regarded as a sum of energies characteristic of the bonds between one atom and another in the structure. If it is possible to assign a definite value for the energy required to break a C—H, O—H, or other bond in a molecule, regardless of the other bonds present in the same molecule, then a table of such bond energies could be deduced from data for relatively few molecules, and could be used to calculate energies of dissociation and heats of formation for any other molecules containing bonds listed in the table.

By such a process, the heats of formation of all saturated hydrocarbons could be deduced from but two known values of bond energies, those of the C—H and C—C bonds. From the value of $\Delta H^0_{0°}$ for $CH_4(g) = C(g) + 4H(g)$, the breaking of four C—H bonds must require a total of 393.8 kcal, or an *average* of 98.5 kcal per C—H bond for each mole of methane. To obtain a value for C—C bonds, data for ethane can be used: $\Delta H^0_{0°}$ is calculated to be 668.9 kcal for the reaction $C_2H_6(g) = 2C(g) + 6H(g)$. Since this involves breaking one C—C and six C—H bonds, the C—C bond energy results after subtracting the energies for the six C—H bonds. Taking 98.2 kcal as the value for each C—H bond, the value for the C—C bond is $668.9 - 6 \times 98.5 = 77.9$ kcal.

The value 98.5 kcal for the energy of C—H bonds and 77.9 kcal for the energy of C—C bonds (deduced by assuming all C—H bonds to be equivalent) can be tested by comparison with experimental heats of formation of the three gaseous pentanes, C_5H_{12}. The structures of the three isomers and the corresponding values of $\Delta H^0_{0°}$ for the formation reaction $5C(s) + 6H_2(g) = C_5H_{12}(g)$ are:

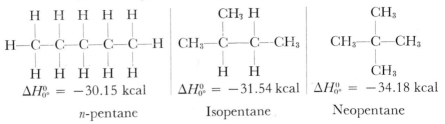

H H H H H	CH_3 H	CH_3
H—C—C—C—C—C—H	CH_3—C—C—CH_3	CH_3—C—CH_3
H H H H H	H H	CH_3
$\Delta H^0_{0°} = -30.15$ kcal	$\Delta H^0_{0°} = -31.54$ kcal	$\Delta H^0_{0°} = -34.18$ kcal
n-pentane	Isopentane	Neopentane

Since each of these isomers has four C—C bonds and twelve C—H bonds, the heats of formation would be the same for all three, if the assumption of unique bond energies for atom pairs were correct. The actual variation by more than 3 kcal shows the approximate nature of the simple bond energy concept. At the same time, the heats of formation of the isomers are not tremendously different, suggesting that at least approximate values can be deduced from suitable average bond energies.

The heat of formation for pentane from the C—C and C—H bond values is determined as follows:

Process	$\Delta H_{0^\circ}^0$ (kcal)
Forming 4 C—C bonds,	$4 \times (-77.9 \text{ kcal})$
Forming 12 C—H bonds,	$12 \times (-98.5 \text{ kcal})$

$$5C(g) + 12H(g) = C_5H_{12}(g), \qquad \Delta H_{0^\circ}^0 = -1493.6 \text{ kcal}$$

The conventional heat of formation is taken from solid carbon and molecular hydrogen. To obtain this quantity there must be added

$6H_2(g) = 12H(g),$	$6 \times (103.2 \text{ kcal})$
$5C(s) = 5C(g),$	$5 \times (170.4 \text{ kcal})$

$$5C(s) + 6H_2(g) = 5C(g) + 12H(g), \qquad \Delta H_{0^\circ}^0 = +1471.2 \text{ kcal}$$

whence results

$$5C(s) + 6H_2(g) = C_5H_{12}(g), \qquad \Delta H_{0^\circ}^0 = -22.4 \text{ kcal}$$

The value is in rather poor agreement with the observed values ranging from -30 to -34 kcal, but it must be remembered that its calculation involves a small difference between two large numbers, which magnifies any error. Also, the bond energies were taken from a specific source. Somewhat better agreement can be obtained by adopting values for average contributions of different bonds determined and selected more carefully; values chosen by K. S. Pitzer are listed in Table 13.4. This table includes values for multiple bonds as deduced from thermal and spectroscopic data for unsaturated molecules. The values given are sufficiently good that they can be used to calculate heats of formation, and hence heats of reaction, with accuracies of a few kilocalories in many cases. Values enclosed in parentheses are derived from calorimetric data for the solids.

This discussion and the examples given should make it clear that bond energies of the sort considered are somewhat empirical and at best approximate. That this is so can also be appreciated on considering the

TABLE 13.4. *Bond Energies (in kcal/mole and referred to $0°K$).*

Elements		Hydrides		Chlorides	
H—H	103.2	H—H	103.2	H—Cl	102.1
Li—Li	26	Li—H	58	Li—Cl	118.5
C—C	80.5	C—H	98.2	C—Cl	78
N—N	37	N—H	92.2	N—Cl	46(?)
O—O	34	O—H	109.4	O—Cl	49
F—F	38	F—H	135	F—Cl	59.0
Na—Na	17.8	Na—H	47	Na—Cl	97.7
Si—Si	(45)	Si—H	76(?)	Si—Cl	87
P—P	(52)	P—H	77	P—Cl	77
S—S	63(?)	S—H	87(?)	S—Cl	65(?)
Cl—Cl	57.1	Cl—H	102.1	Cl—Cl	57.1
K—K	11.8	K—H	42.9	K—Cl	101.4
Cu—Cu	—	Cu—H	62	Cu—Cl	83
Ge—Ge	(42)	Ge—H	—	Ge—Cl	—
As—As	(39)	As—H	56	As—Cl	69
Se—Se	(50)	Se—H	67	Se—Cl	59
Br—Br	45.4(53)	Br—H	86.7	Br—Cl	52.1
Rb—Rb	11.1	Rb—H	39	Rb—Cl	101.0
Ag—Ag	—	Ag—H	53	Ag—Cl	71
Sn—Sn	(35)	Sn—H	—	Sn—Cl	76
Sb—Sb	(42)	Sb—H	—	Sb—Cl	75
Te—Te	(49)	Te—H	59	Te—Cl	—
I—I	35.6(51)	I—H	70.6	I—Cl	49.6
Cs—Cs	10.4	Cs—H	41	Cs—Cl	103

Multiple Bonds

Elements	Single	Double	Triple
C—C	80.5	145	198
N—N	37	—	225.1
O—O	34	117.2	—
P—P	(52)	—	116.0
S—S	63(?)	101(?)	—
As—As	(39)	—	90.8
Se—Se	(50)	65	—
Sb—Sb	(42)	—	69
Te—Te	(49)	53	—
C—N	66	—	189
C—O	79	173	—
P—N	—	—	138(?)
S—O	—	120(?)	—
Te—O	—	62.8	—

From K. S. Pitzer, *Quantum Chemistry*, Prentice-Hall, 1953.

actual process from which the C—H bond energy was obtained. One-quarter the heat of dissociating methane into one carbon plus four hydrogen atoms would not be expected to correspond exactly to any single energy change in the sequence $CH_4 \longrightarrow CH_3 + H \longrightarrow CH_2 + 2H \longrightarrow CH + 3H \longrightarrow C + 4H$. Moreover, the best indications available as to the energies obtained from spectroscopic data for these four consecutive reactions are that all four energies are different, becoming progressively larger for removing successive hydrogens. (Notice also that molecular structure changes enter, as the structure of the methyl radical as an actual but unstable species is presumably more like ammonia than like tetrahedral methane, and the sp^3 hybridization has been lost. Thus the reaction $CH_4 \longrightarrow CH_3 + H$ to produce this radical has a different energy because of change in hybridization.)

While the limitations of bond energy values as true molecular quantities must be kept in mind, they can often be employed to advantage in thermochemical problems and in considering the stabilities of molecules. An example of the latter may be shown for benzene. If the benzene structure were ⬡, the heat of formation, using C—C, C=C, and C—H bond energies, would be approximately

$$\Delta H_{0^\circ}^0 = 3\Delta H_{0^\circ}^0(C—C) + 3\Delta H_{0^\circ}^0(C—C) + 6\Delta H_{0^\circ}^0(C—H)$$
$$+ 3\Delta H_{0^\circ}^0 [H_2(g)] + 6\Delta H_{0^\circ}^0 [C(g)]$$
$$= +66 \text{ kcal}$$

Comparison with the actual value $\Delta H_{0^\circ}^0 = +19.8$ kcal for benzene shows the increased stability of the actual structure by an amount 36 kcal as compared to a Kékulé structure. Differences of this kind are often called "resonance" energies. It is evident that normal covalent bond energies as listed in Table 13.4 do not give reliable results when they do not well represent actual structures; on the other hand, comparison of energies so calculated with actual values is often a useful way of determining possible structures and suspected resonance effects.

Problems

13.1. (a) Show that the difference between heat of reaction at constant pressure (q_P) and at constant volume (q_V) is small compared with the value of either one for such reactions as

$$2C(s) + O_2(g) = 2CO(g), \quad -\Delta H = 52.8 \text{ kcal}$$
$$2CO(g) + O_2(g) = 2CO_2(g), \quad -\Delta H = 136.0 \text{ kcal}$$

(Assume q_P is for a pressure of one atmosphere and that the volume of $C(s)$ is negligible compared to that of the gases.) (b) Show that q_P is greater than q_V if the volume increases by reaction at constant pressure, and less if it decreases.

13.2. The heat of combustion of benzoic acid has been determined with great accuracy by burning it in a bomb calorimeter. At 30°C, it was found that combustion of 1 g of benzoic acid evolved the same amount of heat as 26,424 joules of electrical energy. Calculate ΔH in kcal/mole. (Note that the reaction takes place at constant volume; correct for the effect of change of pressure.)

13.3. (a) A bomb calorimeter is calibrated by combustion of 1.0016 g of sucrose with a resulting temperature rise of 1.4835°. From the value 3950 cal/g for the heat of combustion of sucrose, calculate the quantity of heat to raise the calorimeter temperature 1°. (This quantity is called the heat capacity of the calorimeter.) (b) If the heat of combustion of another substance is to be determined, it is desirable to make the temperature rise nearly the same as in the calibration experiment, in order to minimize errors from heat loss. How many grams of benzene, with $\Delta H \sim -790$ kcal/mole, should be burned to produce a temperature rise of 1.50°?

13.4. The combustion of 1.04 g of malonic acid $CH_2(COOH)_2$ in a bomb calorimeter evolved 2.07 kcal at 25°C. What is the heat of combustion per mole at constant pressure?

13.5. (a) The heat of combustion at 25°C of n-butane is -687.982 kcal, that of hydrogen is -68.313 kcal, and that of carbon (to CO_2) is -94.052 kcal. Calculate the heat of formation of butane. (b) Show that the heat of combustion of n-butane, determined from the heats of formation of n-butane, water, and carbon dioxide is -687.982 cal.

13.6. (a) Calculate the heat of formation of methane from the heats of combustion of graphite, methane, and hydrogen at 25°C. (b) What is the error in the answer to (a) if the heat of combustion of methane is in error by 1%?

13.7. Calculate the heat of formation of propane at 25°C and (a) constant pressure, and (b) constant volume. (The heat of formation ΔH_F of water at 25°C is -68.313 kcal/mole. The heat of formation ΔH_F of carbon dioxide at 25°C is -94.052 kcal/mole. The heat of combustion ΔH, of propane at 25°C is 530 kcal/mole.)

13.8. Calculate the heats of the following gas reactions from heats of formation:

$$n\text{-}C_4H_{10} + 3H_2 = 4CH_4$$
$$\text{iso-}C_4H_{10} + 3H_2 = 4CH_4$$

13.9. (a) The heat of combustion of cyclopropane, $(CH_2)_3$, is $-\Delta H_{298} = 499.85$ kcal/mole at 25°C. Calculate the heat of formation. (b) The heat of formation of propene, CH_3CHCH_2, is $-\Delta H_{298} = 4.88$ kcal/mole. Calculate the heat of isomerizing cyclopropane to propene.

13.10. Use the following thermochemical data at 20°C to calculate the heat of formation of ammonia.

$$(COONH_4)_2H_2O(s) + 2O_2(g) = N_2(g) + 2CO_2(g) + 5H_2O(l)$$
$$-\Delta H = 189.9 \text{ kcal}$$

$$(COOH)_2(H_2O)_2(s) + \tfrac{1}{2}O_2(g) = 2CO_2(g) + 3H_2O(l) \qquad -\Delta H = 53.1 \text{ kcal}$$
$$(COONH_4)_2H_2O(s) = (COONH_4)_2H_2O(aq) \qquad -\Delta H = -11.5 \text{ kcal}$$
$$(COOH)_2(H_2O)_2(s) = (COOH)_2(H_2O)_2(aq) \qquad -\Delta H = -8.6 \text{ kcal}$$
$$(COOH)_2(H_2O)_2(aq) + 2NH_3(g) = (COONH_4)_2H_2O(aq) + H_2O$$
$$-\Delta H = 43.1 \text{ kcal}$$

$$H_2(g) + \tfrac{1}{2}O_2(g) = H_2O(l) \qquad -\Delta H = 68.4 \text{ kcal}$$

13.11. Calculate the heat of formation of $HBr(g)$ from the following data:

	$-\Delta H$ (kcal/mole)
$HBr(g) = HBr(aq)$	19.9
$\tfrac{1}{2}Br_2(g) = \tfrac{1}{2}Br_2(aq)$	0.5
$\tfrac{1}{2}H_2(g) + \tfrac{1}{2}Cl_2(g) = HCl(g)$	22.0
$HCl(g) = HCl(aq)$	17.3
$HCl(aq) + KOH(aq) = KCl(aq) + H_2O(l)$	13.7
$HBr(aq) + KOH(aq) = KBr(aq) + H_2O(l)$	13.7
$KCl(aq) + \tfrac{1}{2}Br_2(aq) = KBr(aq) + \tfrac{1}{2}Cl_2(aq)$	−11.5

13.12. (a) How much heat would be absorbed in dissolving 2 moles of ethyl alcohol in 20 moles of water? (b) What would be the heat absorbed in diluting the above solution by adding 20 additional moles of water?

13.13. The following table lists enthalpy changes $\Delta H/n_2$ in kcal/mole of $HCl(g)$ dissolved in n_1 moles of water at 25°C.

n_1	1	2	4	6	8	10
$-\Delta H/n_2$	6.268	11.688	14.628	15.748	16.308	16.608
n_1	20	50	100	200	500	(∞)
$-\Delta H/n_2$	17.155	17.514	17.650	17.735	17.811	(17.960)

(a) Make plots from these data similar to those in Fig. 13.1. Compare the extrapolation of your plot to zero molality with the value in parentheses in the table for $n_1 = \infty$. (b) Consider a reaction in which $HCl(aq)$ is a product. What is the resultant change in enthalpy after reaction if the HCl molality is 1.0, if it is very small?

13.14. (a) Calculate the value of ΔH at 25°C for the reaction

$$\tfrac{1}{2}H_2(g) + AgCl(s) = Ag(s) + H^+(aq) + Cl^-(aq)$$

The heat of formation of $AgCl(s)$ is -30.362 kcal/mole, and of $Cl^-(aq)$ is -40.023 kcal/mole at infinite dilution. (b) What difference is there in the value of ΔH if the final concentration is 1.0 molal?

13.15. 400 g of a 0.50 molal solution of acetic acid were neutralized at 20°C by an equal amount of sodium hydroxide solution of the same concentration, and the temperature rise of the calorimeter containing the solutions was 2.41°. In separate experiments it was found that 40 cal was required to raise the temperature of the empty calorimeter 1°, and that the heat capacities of the solutions were 0.989 cal/g deg and 0.970 cal/g deg. Calculate the heat of neutralization per mole of acetic acid.

13.16. What can you conclude about the relative energies of interaction of ethyl alcohol molecules with each other and with water molecules from the fact that ΔH for dilution of the alcohol with water is negative?

13.17. Calculate the heat of ionization per mole of HCN from the following: the heat of neutralization of hydrochloric acid by sodium hydroxide is $-13,600$ cal and that of hydrocyanic acid by sodium hydroxide is -2900 cal.

13.18. Calculate the heat of the reaction

$$FeO(s) + 2H^+ = H_2O(l) + Fe^{++}$$

using any of the following values you need:

$$2Fe(s) + \tfrac{3}{2}O_2(g) = Fe_2O_3(s), \qquad \Delta H = -198.5 \text{ kcal}$$
$$2FeO(s) + \tfrac{1}{2}O_2(g) = Fe_2O_3(s), \qquad \Delta H = -69.9$$
$$Fe(s) + 2H^+ = Fe^{++} + H_2(g), \qquad \Delta H = -20.6$$
$$\tfrac{1}{2}H_2 = H^+, \qquad \Delta H = 0 \text{ (by convention)}$$
$$H_2(g) + \tfrac{1}{2}O_2(g) = H_2O(l), \qquad \Delta H = -68.4$$

13.19. The heat of formation of carbon dioxide from its elements is $-94,052$ cal/mole at 25°C. What is its value at 1000°C?

For carbon $\bar{C}_P = 1.20 + 0.0050\,T - 1.2 \times 10^{-6}\,T^2$
oxygen $\bar{C}_P = 6.50 + 0.00010\,T$
carbon dioxide $\bar{C}_P = 7.40 + 0.0066\,T - 1.50 \times 10^{-6}\,T^2$

13.20. Calculate the heat of sublimation of ice at $-50°C$ from the following data:

Heat capacity of ice = 0.472 cal/g deg
Heat capacity of water = 1.000 cal/g deg
Heat capacity of water vapor = 0.445 cal/g deg
Heat of fusion of ice (0°C) = 79.7 cal/g
Heat of vaporization of water (100°C) = 539.1 cal/g

13.21. (a) From heats of formation at 25°C, calculate ΔH_{298} for the water gas reaction $H_2(g) + CO_2(g) = H_2O(g) + CO(g)$. (b) Use heat capacity data and Kirchhoff's law to calculate ΔH_{598} for the reaction.

13.22. Calculate the mean heat capacity (20°–25°) of a 4.627% by weight sodium chloride solution, using the following data:

Mean heat capacity of water (20°–25°) = 0.9993
        heat capacity of solid NaCl   = 0.208
Molar heat of solution   = -928.1 kcal at 25°C
                                     = -1043.2 kcal at 20°C

13.23. One mole of sodium chloride is dissolved in water at 20°C to make a 12.00% by weight solution. The heat absorbed is -774.6 cals. What would be the heat absorbed at 25°C? Heat capacities per gram: water = 0.9993, solid NaCl = 0.208, solution = 0.8740 (Lyssitt, Johnson, and Maas, *J. Am. Chem. Soc.*, **49**:1927, 1940).

13.24. In a paper by Kistiakowsky et al. (*J. Am. Chem. Soc.*, **57**:75, 1955) the heat of hydrogenation of ethylene at 82°C is reported to be $-32,824 \pm 50$ cal. Using ΔC_P as 4.37 calories/deg/mole, calculate the heat of hydrogenation at 25°C.

13.25. Use the value 98.2 kcal/mole for C—H bond energy with thermochemical data for propane to calculate an average C—C bond energy.

13.26. Use bond energy values from Table 13.4 to calculate the heat of formation of propene, $CH_3CHCH_2(g)$, and compare with the known value.

13.27. Calculate the heats of formation of gaseous CH_3Cl and $CHCl_3$ from bond energies, and compare with the measured values of -19.6 and -24.0 kcal/mole.

13.28. The heat of combustion of gaseous isoprene, C_5H_8 is -745.8 kcal/mole. Calculate the heat of formation and by comparison with a bond energy calculation estimate the resonance energy of isoprene.

13.29. (a) Calculate ΔH_F of $AgI(s)$ at the temperature of the experiments which gave the following data: 3.127 g of iodine and an excess of silver were added to a calorimeter containing 800 ml of 1 N KCN. A temperature rise of 0.710°C was observed. In order to determine the heat capacity of the system, an electric current was run through a heating coil immersed in the solution for 480 sec, causing a rise of 0.849°C. The potential drop in the coil and connecting wires was 8.30 V. The resistance of the heater and leads was 10.35 ohms, and of the heater alone, 10.17 ohms. Three measurements of the heat of reaction of $AgI(s)$ in the same calorimeter with the same quantity of KCN solution gave an average value of 10,251 cal/mole. (b) Check calculations of ΔH, from the tabulated data appearing in the paper by Taylor and Anderson (*J. Am. Chem. Soc.*, **43**:2014, 1921).

13.30. Kraus and Rudderhof (*J. Am. Chem. Soc.*, **56**:79, 1934) obtained the heat of solution of NaBr in $NH_3(l)$ by the method of mixtures. A capsule containing NaBr was dropped in liquid ammonia at a lower temperature and the temperature rise of the liquid calorimeter measured, as well as the amount of ammonia which evaporated. Calculate the heat of solution from these data:

Weight of NH_3	20.0000 g
Weight of NH_3 evaporated	0.5369 g
Heat of vaporization of NH_3	327.1 cal/g
Heat capacity of $NH_3(l)$	1.067 cal/g deg

Weight of NaBr	1.867 g
Heat capacity of NaBr	0.118 cal/g deg
Weight of glass container (NaBr)	0.154 g
Heat capacity of glass	0.2 cal/g deg
Water equivalent-calorimeter	5.68 g
Observed rise in temperature of calorimeter	0.34°C
Observed fall in temperature of salt and container	56.1°C

13.31. The electrical work necessary to separate 1 mole of crystalline NaCl into Na^+ and Cl^- gaseous ions can be calculated from the electrical forces in the crystal and is 183 kcal/mole. This value is strictly $-\Delta E$ at $0°K$ for the reaction $NaCl(s) = Na^+(g) + Cl^-(g)$ but is not greatly different from $-\Delta H_{298}$. The ionization energy of sodium, $Na(g) = Na^+(g) + e^-$, can be calculated from the spectrum of sodium vapor and corresponds to $-\Delta H = 118$ kcal/mole. From these data, calculate the electron affinity of chlorine, defined as the value of ΔH for the reaction $Cl(g) + e^- = Cl^-(g)$, given the following further data:

$$Na(s) = Na(g) \qquad\qquad -\Delta H = -25 \text{ kcal/mole}$$
$$Cl_2(g) = 2Cl(g) \qquad\qquad -\Delta H = -58 \text{ kcal/mole}$$
$$Na(s) + \tfrac{1}{2}Cl_2(g) = NaCl(s) \qquad -\Delta H = 98 \text{ kcal/mole}$$

Note: Electron affinities are not easily measured. The sequence of reactions in the indirect method of this problem is called the Born-Haber cycle, and can be indicated schematically as

$$NaCl(s) \longrightarrow Na^+(g) + Cl^-(g)$$
$$\uparrow \qquad\qquad\qquad\qquad \downarrow$$
$$Na(s) + \tfrac{1}{2}Cl_2(g) \longleftarrow Na(g) + Cl(g)$$

13.32. Estimate the maximum flame temperature when ethane is burned with three times the amount of air necessary for complete combustion, (a) by using room temperature heat capacities for reactants and products; (b) by estimating average heat capacities based on the temperature rise calculated in (a).

13.33. The heats of formation and of vaporization of heavy water have been measured, with the results

$$D_2(g) + \tfrac{1}{2}O_2(g) = D_2O(l) \qquad -\Delta H_{298} = 70.414 \text{ kcal/mole}$$
$$D_2O(l) = D_2O(g) \qquad\qquad \Delta H_{298} = 10.850 \text{ kcal/mole}$$

(a) Compare these values with corresponding ones from the literature for H_2O, and discuss any differences. (b) Use the data to calculate ΔH for the exchange reaction

$$D_2(g) + H_2O(g) = D_2O(g) + H_2(g)$$

13.34. (a) Show by calculation of ΔH that the water gas reaction, $C(s) + H_2O(g) = H_2(g) + CO(g)$, is endothermic at 1000°C. (b) Because the preceding reaction is endothermic, heat must be supplied to keep it running at a steady temperature, which can be done by burning an appropriate amount of carbon: $C(s) + O_2(g) = CO_2(g)$. Calculate the relative amounts burned and converted when the temperature remains constant.

13.35. The value of ΔH for $H_2O(l) = H^+(aq) + OH^-(aq)$ has been determined by Pitzer (*J. Am. Chem. Soc.*, **59**:2365, 1937) from the heat of neutralization of NaOH by HCl. Find ΔH from the following data, based on results in his paper:

$NaOH(0.052m) + HCl(1.19m) = NaCl(0.050m)$	$-\Delta H = 13.83$ kcal
$HCl(1.19m) = HCl(0.050m)$	$\Delta H = -0.35$ kcal
$HCl(0.050m) = HCl(\infty\ aq)$	$\Delta H = -0.10$ kcal
$NaOH(0.052) = NaOH(\infty\ aq)$	$\Delta H = -0.09$ kcal
$NaCl(0.050) = NaCl(\infty\ aq)$	$\Delta H = -0.07$ kcal

Suggested Readings

Any text of thermodynamics or physical chemistry contains discussions of thermochemical calculations, as for example, those suggested in Chapters 12, 14, 15, and 16. Not so readily available are discussions of experimental techniques actually used in securing thermochemical data. Two books with a wealth of material are the following: *Experimental Thermochemistry*, edited by F. D. Rossini (Interscience, New York, 1956) and *Temperature, Its Measurement and Control*, Volume 3, Part 2, *Applications, Methods, and Instruments* (Reinhold, New York, 1962).

There is a tremendous quantity of thermochemical data in the literature, much of which has been collected in various summaries and tabulations, and most textbooks of thermodynamics have condensed tables of data or equations representing them. A particularly useful book to consult is *Thermodynamics* by G. N. Lewis and M. Randall, as revised by K. S. Pitzer and L. Brewer (2nd ed., McGraw-Hill, New York, 1961); see also *Suggested Readings*, Chapter 15 (p. 461). The most extensive compilation is the series *Selected Values of Chemical Thermodynamic Properties*, prepared by a group under the supervision of F. D. Rossini and issued quarterly by the National Bureau of Standards (U.S.A.). Recent editions of the *Handbook of Chemistry and Physics* (Chemical Rubber Publishing Co., Cleveland) contain selected data from these and other tabulations.

Chapter 14

The Second Law of Thermodynamics. Entropy and Chemical Potential

STUDENTS OF SCIENCE soon learn by experience that many conceivable processes do not actually happen. So-called "practical" men have tried for centuries to obtain useful mechanical work for nothing ("perpetual motion" machines), or for less than the necessary price in the energy or heat required for the conservation of energy and by the first law of thermodynamics. None have succeeded. Others have essayed the more subtle problem of obtaining the maximum work possible from a given quantity of heat, generated by chemical reaction or otherwise, but have always achieved something less than the ideal.

The chemist is faced with somewhat similar situations—neither the direction nor the extent of chemical reaction with fixed starting materials and conditions is a matter of his free choice. A very elementary example of this is the fact that water does not spontaneously dissociate into hydrogen and oxygen, despite the fact that one can easily write the balanced equation $H_2O = H_2 + \frac{1}{2}O_2$. In other cases, reactions may proceed according to an equation as written, but reach equilibrium long before the reaction is complete. Examples are numerous, a common and important class being hydrolysis reactions, such as $NaC_2H_3O_2 + H_2O = NaOH + HC_2H_3O_2$. Such situations may be discouraging to the chemist wanting a high yield, but they exist.

Knowledge of any underlying principles governing such behavior is of major importance for predicting the actual course of chemical reactions. The second law of thermodynamics is, after the first law, the most important such principle governing possible changes in real systems of many molecules, and it has been so universally confirmed by experiment as to justify its acceptance as a law of nature which such systems must follow.

One would like also to understand the molecular origins of any such law, and to learn more in detail about the rate at which a reaction proceeds, in addition to knowing the direction of a reaction and the point at which equilibrium is reached. This requires study of the statistical consequences of molecular activity. Our discussion will suggest these origins, and the subject of rates of chemical reactions will be taken up in Chapter 22.

14.1. Le Chatelier's Principle

Intuition and experience can sometimes indicate the direction of reaction or the effect of changed conditions on the extent to which reactions occur. A useful generalization of this sort based upon experience is Le Chatelier's principle, which he stated in 1885: displacement by external forces of a system in equilibrium will result in physical or chemical changes in the direction of restoring the original equilibrium. The shift in equilibrium thus acts to absorb and reduce the changes which would occur in the absence of such a shift.

Four examples of Le Chatelier's principle follow.

1. *Effects of pressure on dissociation of a gas.* The dissociation of nitrogen tetroxide into nitrogen dioxide takes place according to the equation $N_2O_4 \rightleftharpoons 2NO_2$. At 25°C and one atmosphere pressure a sample of N_2O_4 is 19% dissociated into NO_2 at equilibrium. At 0.5 atmosphere pressure, the N_2O_4 is 26% dissociated. Thus decreasing the pressure has shifted the equilibrium in the direction which forms more moles of gas, a change which of itself would increase pressure, and so counteract the pressure decrease imposed externally.

2. *Change in equilibrium of an exothermic reaction with temperature.* Carbon monoxide will react with water vapor at high temperatures to form carbon dioxide and hydrogen in an exothermic reaction:

$$CO + H_2O \rightleftharpoons CO_2 + H_2 + 9.52 \text{ kcal}$$

If one mole each of CO and H_2O are mixed at 500°K, 0.912 moles of CO_2 and H_2 are formed, while at 700°K 0.668 moles of each product result. The reaction is exothermic ($\Delta H = -9.52$ kcal/mole), and by supplying heat to the system the equilibrium is shifted in the direction which absorbs heat.

3. *Addition of a reactant to a system in equilibrium.* If one mole of CO is added to the above equilibrium mixture of 0.088 moles each of CO and H_2O and 0.912 each of CO_2 and H_2 at 500°K, the equilibrium is reestablished with 0.992 moles of CO_2 and H_2 present, the equilibrium quantity of CO is 1.008 moles, and of H_2O, 0.008 moles. Thus 0.992 moles of CO is consumed in reaching equilibrium, 0.080 moles more than in reaching the original equilibrium. The equilibrium has shifted to consume more of the reactant added in excess of the original equilibrium amount, reducing the amount present toward that original value.

4. *Effect of pressure on equilibrium between phases.* A pressure of 200 atmospheres causes ice at $-20°C$ to melt, the equilibrium being $H_2O(s) \rightleftharpoons H_2O(l)$. Water is denser than ice, and the melting of ice therefore decreases the total volume of the system, a change which of itself would act to reduce the pressure.

Le Chatelier's principle as applied in these examples does succeed in predicting the direction of natural changes in equilibrium which take place in response to external causes. The applications described also suggest that the changes which lead again to equilibrium are related very directly to other measurable properties of the system, such as heat or reaction or change of volume. However, the principle expresses the relation only in qualitative terms, and there is no way to predict the *extent* of the changes which restore equilibrium.

14.2. Limitations of the First Law

Many attempts were made in the nineteenth century to formulate general conditions which could be used for quantitative predictions of equilibrium and extent of reaction. James Thomson in 1854 and Berthelot some years later tried to relate chemical reactivity to heats of reaction by the proposition that spontaneous reactions were exothermic. By the first law, a system undergoing an exothermic process decreases in enthalpy or internal energy. This may seem a natural direction of change; in further support of the proposition is the fact that many reactions known to take place readily at room temperature do evolve large quantities of heat.

The impossibility of any such criterion having general validity is quickly shown. In the first place, spontaneous endothermic reactions are by no means uncommon at room temperature. Moreover, equilibria reached before reaction is complete can be shifted in directions to absorb heat by suitable changes in conditions. Also significant is that examples of spontaneous endothermic reactions become more numerous at higher temperatures.

These observations are sufficient to show the inadequacy of any statement that negative changes of internal energy or enthalpy are necessary for processes approaching equilibrium under any conditions. Changes in these properties may play a significant role under some conditions, but other properties must also be involved which can be equally important or even the determining factors. An example of the last situation is the mixing of two miscible fluids, a spontaneous process. If these are ideal gases, however, neither the internal energy nor the enthalpy of the system has changed when equilibrium is reached. Further two liquids may mix with either evolution or absorption of heat, depending on the liquids chosen. The change of ΔH is evidently a secondary factor.

These considerations suggest the necessity of going beyond the concepts involved in the first law to find a valid basis for any laws governing equilibrium or processes leading to it. A suggestion of quantities which require further study is, however, found by reviewing these concepts.

In the statement of the first law ($\Delta E = q - w$), heat and work are recognized as two distinct ways of changing the state of a system. Of the two, the amount of work is determined from measured forces and the consequent changes they produce, by the application of principles of mechanics and electricity. Thus the work can be described and understood fairly explicitly.

Not so the heat change, which directly or indirectly involves the heat equivalent of work, differences in kind between heat and work being neglected. Even the specification of heat change in terms of heat capacity and temperature change results from no more than a convenient definition. Any understanding of the nature of the effect of heat changes on the system is absent. With the change in internal energy (ΔE, a thermodynamic quantity), the heat change is at best known as the sum of the change in internal energy and the external work done, and its relations to the chemical and molecular constitution of the system are missing. To understand and define the direct connection between heat and the changes in properties of the system requires further consideration of the nature of heat.

14.3. The Statistical Nature of Heat

The study of the nature of heat began long before molecular and kinetic theories of matter were established, and the developments which first led to the *second law of thermodynamics* had to be based on considerations other than those arising from these theories. A major step was the study in 1824 by a French engineer, Sadi Carnot, of the amount of work obtainable from engines supplied a definite amount of heat. His conclusions were later developed by Clausius and Lord Kelvin into far more general statements, again quite independently of molecular theory.

The historical approach is sometimes used as a basis for introducing the second law, after which a formulation suitable for chemical problems can be deduced. Rather than follow that, we shall consider the relation between heat and changes in molecular activity, from the viewpoint of kinetic and statistical theory. The latter gives some insight into the underlying molecular basis for the properties of systems expressed by the second law, even though this law can be regarded as a purely empirical statement which can be established experimentally without any reference to the molecular nature of the system.

In kinetic theory considerations, the necessity of heat as a concept to describe energy transfer arises because ordinary quantities of matter contain enormous numbers of molecules. Heat is best understood, therefore, as a statistical entity. If a chemical system contained only a few particles large enough for them and their motions to be observed, *all* the forces acting on the system could be measured and all its properties could be predicted, at least in principle. In actual systems, however, only a very limited fraction of the possible interactions between some 10^{23} molecules and their surroundings are measured in terms of mechanical and electrical forces; the net effect on the properties of the system of the overwhelming number of interactions not subject to such measurement is represented as heat.

The molecular changes produced in a system by heat and work similarly are known from experiment to only a very limited degree. The internal energy E is merely the average sum of all forms of energy possessed in some combination by the many molecules of the system. A measured addition to the internal energy is then only the increase in this sum, and this increase could be distributed in many different ways. For gases this has been discussed in Section 9.6.

Considered in terms of statistical theory, the equilibrium state of a system corresponds to the most probable distribution of energies possible among different energy states under the given external conditions. For ideal gases, the energy states will be those of the individual molecules, as discussed in Chapters 9 and 10, and the numbers of molecules with different energies E_i are proportional to the Boltzmann factor $e^{-E_i/kT}$. Fewer molecules have the higher energies, the Boltzmann factor being smaller, as indicated schematically in Fig. 14.1 (a). This Maxwell-

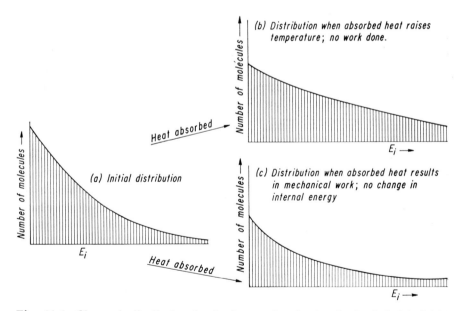

Fig. 14.1. *Changes in distribution of molecular energies when heat is absorbed:* (a) *initial distribution;* (b) *distribution when absorbed heat raises temperature, with no work done;* (c) *distribution when absorbed heat results in mechanical work; no change in internal energy.*

Boltzmann distribution can be realized by many distinct permutations of molecules among the different energy levels, and has an intrinsic probability proportional to the number of such permutations.

Consider now increasing the total energy of a system by supplying heat to it, resulting in a higher temperature. More molecules will have higher energies because of the larger Boltzmann factor (higher temperature and greater total energy). At the same time the changed distribution, suggested by Fig. 14.1 (b), corresponds to a state of increased probability because of the greater number of permutations possible in assignments of molecules to different energy levels. From this point of view, the absorption of heat has been accompanied by an increased probability of the resulting equilibrium state.

The changes just described take place when no work is done and the effect of heat is to increase internal energy and temperature. To be considered also are the changes resulting from heat absorbed producing external work (by expansion) without change in internal energy. As discussed in Section 9.5, the translational energy levels of gases are more closely spaced when the volume occupied is larger, and the effect of work done by expansion is to decrease these spacings, thus increasing the number of possible states. If the heat added supplies the loss of energy on expansion, the total amount of energy is the same as before the expansion, but is distributed among molecules occupying a greater number of energy states, as shown in Fig. 14.1 (c). This greater number of states again corresponds to an increased probability of the equilibrium state after absorption of heat.

The preceding examples are chosen to illustrate as simply as possible the general conclusion from statistical molecular theory that absorption of heat results in a characteristic change which is always related to increased probability of the final state. This amount of heat necessary for a given change in probability depends on the temperature and details of the process, but the change produced is a property of the system itself.

Internal processes in a system also produce spontaneous changes from a less probable to a more probable state without external effects. Thus mixing of gases is a change from special conditions, in which the different kinds of molecules are segregated, to a uniform mixture in which all occupy the combined volume, a state of higher probability. Equalization of temperature and pressure in a system free of other influences are further examples of spontaneous processes leading to an equilibrium state of greater probability, the reverse processes being unnatural.

14.4. The Second Law of Thermodynamics

From the preceding discussion, two facts should appear reasonable: (1) Processes involving transfer of energy as heat result in a new distribution of energies among possible energy states, which will at equilibrium be the most probable distribution consistent with the prescribed conditions of a system; and (2) spontaneous internal processes always result in a more probable state of the system—that is, one which can be realized by a larger number of internal arrangements.

The second law of thermodynamics expresses these two facts by defining a function of the state of a system, called the entropy (S), which is related to the probability of the state. This function increases upon the absorption of heat by an amount dependent upon the temperature of the process (and hence dependent upon the distribution of energies among possible states according to kinetic and statistical theory), and the function also increases by internal processes, which bring the system toward equilibrium.

The relation of entropy changes to these two kinds of change may be stated mathematically.

1. The change $(dS)_{ext}$ in entropy from the absorption of heat (q) when the system is at a temperature T is given by

$$(dS)_{ext} = \frac{q}{T} \tag{14.1}$$

(The subscript "ext" is used to emphasize absorption from outside the system.)

2. The change $(dS)_{int}$ in entropy from internal processes is given by

$$(dS)_{int} \geqq 0$$

the inequality corresponding to natural processes leading to equilibrium and the equality to changes which preserve equilibrium. (The subscript "int" is used to emphasize internal processes.)

3. The total change in entropy (dS) for any process is the sum of external and internal changes:

$$dS = (dS)_{ext} + (dS)_{int}$$

The content of these statements is conveniently combined into the following expression of the second law of thermodynamics.

For systems composed of many molecules, there exists a quantity S, called the entropy, which is a function only of the state of the system and which satisfies these conditions:

for natural processes leading to equilibrium,

$$dS > \frac{q}{T} \qquad (14.2)$$

for processes which preserve equilibrium,

$$dS = \frac{q}{T} \qquad (14.3)$$

Before proceeding to tests and uses of the second law in chemical problems, certain points should be emphasized.

1. Processes for which $dS < q/T$ are unnatural, and do not happen spontaneously.

2. The entropy S, like internal energy, E, is an extensive property of the system, i.e., its value is proportional to the quantity of matter in the system.

3. The temperature T is also defined by the statement of the second law, but the units in which it is measured are not.

4. Changes in entropy can be calculated from measurement of heat absorbed and temperature by the equation $dS = q/T$, *if and only if* the heat is absorbed or given off so as to preserve equilibrium.

Most of the discussion to this point has been to suggest the molecular and statistical properties of matter which underlie the existence of such a function as entropy possessing the properties stated by the second law, which historically developed as a concise statement of experimental fact. Unfortunately, the term entropy lacks the familiar connotations of terms such as pressure, temperature, and energy that make them seem commonplace.

The situation with respect to defining the concept of entropy is much like that in defining the concept of internal energy. The first law defines energy as a property of a system, changes in energy being determined and measured as the sum of energy changes involving the heat absorbed and work done. This is not implied at all by the familiar but unprecisely defined energy of popular usage; the first law is instead a precise statement about a statistical assembly of molecules, subject to certain restrictions of total number of molecules, volume occupied by them, and the like. The second law postulates that another quantity, entropy, exists which also is a property of such an assembly, and that changes of entropy can also be determined from experiment (in this case from measurements of the heat absorbed reversibly at a given temperature). These explanatory remarks are included to suggest to the student that what seems a quite abstract statement will prove a valuable and practical law when he learns to use it. The best demonstration of the validity of these arguments is to show that the second law as it has been stated does lead to results which are both correct and useful. This demonstration follows immediately.

14.5. Some Tests of the Second Law

Equalization of Temperatures

It is common experience that two substances exchanging energy as heat will do so in the direction to equalize their temperature; that is, heat flows from the hotter to the colder substance. Consider then two systems A and B at temperatures T_A and T_B connected to one another by a thermal conductor as shown in Fig. 14.2, but thermally isolated from any other system. If a small quantity of heat q is *lost* reversibly from A by conduction to B, the entropy change of A is $dS_A = -q/T_A$. The entropy gained by B on absorbing this same quantity of heat q reversibly is $dS_B = +q/T_B$.

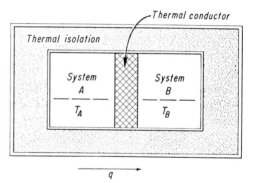

Fig. 14.2. *Heat flow between two systems thermally isolated from surroundings.*

The entropy change of A and B together is

$$dS = dS_A + dS_B = q\left(\frac{1}{T_B} - \frac{1}{T_A}\right) \tag{14.4}$$

But A and B together are thermally isolated from their surroundings, and hence $q_{A+B} = 0$. For the combined system, the second law therefore requires that

$$dS = q\left(\frac{1}{T_B} - \frac{1}{T_A}\right) \geq 0 \tag{14.5}$$

For $dS > 0$ (a natural process), T_B must therefore be *less* than T_A if q is positive (heat taken from A and added to B). The equilibrium condition that $dS = 0$ can only be realized for $T_B = T_A$; that is when there exists no difference in temperature between A and B. Both of these predictions of the second law are obviously in agreement with experience and expectations.

Effusion of a Gas

Consider the free expansion of a gas from one container, originally at some finite pressure, into a second one, originally at zero pressure, and of equal volume V_0. As discussed in Section 12.4, since no work is done on the surroundings, $w = 0$, and, if the containers are thermally insulated from their surroundings, $q - 0$. Hence $\Delta E = 0$, by the first law. The second law states that the entropy of the system increases ($\Delta S > 0$) until equilibrium is reached.

To determine the amount by which the entropy is larger for the final state of the system than for the initial, known almost intuitively to be when the gas in both containers is of equal density, an equilibrium process must be devised in which the gas volume will increase from V_0 to $2V_0$, and for each step of the process the quotient q divided by T must be determined, these quotients to be summed for the whole process. If the gas is ideal, the calculation is very simple, for it is known in this case that the condition $\Delta E = 0$ corresponds to an isothermal expansion under equilibrium conditions for which

$$q = w = P \, dV = nRT \frac{dV}{V}$$

The change dS in entropy for the infinitesimal volume change dV is then

$$dS = \frac{q}{T} = nR \frac{dV}{V} \tag{14.6}$$

and the total change ΔS for expansion from a volume V_1 to a volume V_2 is

$$\Delta S = \int_{V_1}^{V_2} nR \frac{dV}{V} = nR \ln \frac{V_2}{V_1} \tag{14.7}$$

For the present example, $V_2 = 2V_0$ and $V_1 = V_0$; hence $\Delta S = nR \ln 2$. The logarithm of any number greater than one is positive, and hence $\Delta S > 0$, as required by the second law for natural processes.

This calculation of ΔS has been carried out in detail to illustrate the way in which such calculations are made. It should be emphasized that the equilibrium process from which ΔS was determined was quite different from the nonequilibrium process which actually transpired. Because both processes lead from the same initial state to the same final state, and from the definition of entropy as a thermodynamic quantity, the change in ΔS must be the same for both. The equilibrium process used is one for which ΔS is directly calculable, and the ΔS so calculated is the same as for the nonequilibrium process.

Heating and Compression of an Ideal Gas

Another illustration of the second law is in the calculation of the entropy change of one mole of nitrogen gas on being compressed from its original state at 25°C and 1 atmosphere to a final state of 430°C and 20 atmospheres. Three different routes for this compression were described in Section 12.1:

1. Equilibrium adiabatic compression. By definition, no heat is absorbed or evolved, and $q = 0$. Since the process is at equilibrium, $dS = 0$ for every step, and the total change

$$\Delta S = \int dS = 0$$

2. Compression at 25°C to 20 atmospheres, followed by heating at constant pressure to 430°C. Heat is evolved in the first step, the iso-thermal compression, of amount $q_1 = -1780$ cal. The heat absorbed in the second step $q_2 = +2810$ cal, giving a total of $+1030$ cal for the process.

The entropy change in the first step can be calculated from Eq. 14.7:

$$\Delta S_1 [25°C, 1 \text{ atm} \longrightarrow 25°C, 20 \text{ atm}] = R \ln \frac{V_2}{V_1} = -R \ln \frac{P_2}{P_1} \quad (14.8)$$

(assuming the ideal gas law), or

$$\Delta S_1 = -2.303 \times 1.987 \log \frac{20}{1} = -5.97 \text{ cal mole}^{-1} \text{ deg}^{-1}$$

In the second step, absorbing heat at constant pressure, $q_p = C_p \, dT$ and $dS = C_p \, dT/T$. For such a process,

$$\Delta S_p = \int_{T_1}^{T_2} \frac{C_p \, dT}{T} = C_p \ln \frac{T_2}{T_1} \quad (14.9)$$

Using the value of $C_p = 6.95$ cal mole^{-1} deg^{-1} for nitrogen gives $\Delta S_2 [25°C, 20 \text{ atm} \longrightarrow 430°C, 20 \text{ atm}]$

$$= 6.95 \times 2.303 \log \frac{703}{298} = +5.97 \text{ cal mole}^{-1} \text{ deg}^{-1}$$

The total entropy change is therefore

$$\Delta S_1 + \Delta S_2 = -5.97 + 5.97 = 0$$

3. Compression isothermally at 25°C to a volume of 2.88 liters, and a pressure of 8.50 atmospheres, followed by heating of this volume to 430°C. For these two steps $q_1 = -1275$ cal and $q_2 = 2010$ cal to give $q = 375$ cal. The entropy change in the first step is from Eq. 14.7,

$$\Delta S_1 [25°C, 1 \text{ atm} \longrightarrow 25°C, 8.50 \text{ atm}]$$

$$= -R \ln \frac{P_2}{P_1} = -2.303 \times 1.987 \log \frac{8.5}{1} = -4.26 \text{ cal mole}^{-1} \text{ deg}^{-1}$$

The second step is at constant volume; hence $q_v = C_v \, dT$ and $dS = C_v \, dT/T$. The total change ΔS in heating from T_1 to T_2 is then

$$\Delta S_v = \int_{T_1}^{T_2} \frac{C_v \, dT}{T} = C_v \ln \frac{T_2}{T_1} \qquad (14.10)$$

Using $C_v = 4.96$ cal mole^{-1} deg^{-1} gives

$$\Delta S_2 [25°C, 8.5 \text{ atm} \longrightarrow 430°C, 20 \text{ atm}, V = 2.88 \text{ liters}]$$

$$= 4.96 \times 2.303 \log \frac{703}{298} = +4.26 \text{ cal mole}^{-1} \text{ deg}^{-1}$$

The total entropy change is then

$$\Delta S_1 + \Delta S_2 = -4.26 + 4.26 = 0$$

Thus for each of the three different routes from the *same* initial to the *same* final state, the entropy change is the *same*, although the amounts of heat absorbed are quite different and entropy changes enroute vary according to the particular step. The zero net change of entropy is the result of balancing two opposing effects: one of increase of temperature and the other of decrease in volume.

14.6. Thermodynamic and Ideal Gas Scales of Temperature

In the preceding discussion, a tacit assumption has been made which the reader may have noticed, namely that the thermodynamic temperature defined by the statement $dS \geq q/T$ of the second law is the same as the temperature defined for the ideal gas scale by $PV = nRT$, for gases at sufficiently low concentrations. This assumption is not hard to justify from observed properties of gases as they approach ideal behavior.

Suppose that the ideal gas temperature scale is *not* the thermodynamic one, and measurement of PV defines some other scale in which the temperature, to distinguish it from the thermodynamic second law temperature (T), is indicated by θ; that is, $PV = nR\theta$. Consider the ideal gas expanding reversibly from volume V_1 to a new volume V_2 at a particular fixed temperature θ_B (Fig. 14.3, Operation 1). Then the entropy change, for the thermodynamic temperature T_B, is

$$\Delta S_B = \frac{q}{T_B} = nR\frac{\theta_B}{T_B}\ln\left(\frac{V_2}{V_1}\right) \qquad (14.11)$$

(The origin of the ratio θ_B/T_B is apparent from the derivation of the expression for the entropy change of isothermal expansion or compression.)

At a different temperature A, the entropy change for the *same* initial and final volumes as for temperature B is

$$\Delta S_A = nR\frac{\theta_A}{T_A}\ln\left(\frac{V_2}{V_1}\right) \qquad (14.12)$$

(Fig. 14.3, Operation 2). Consider now the entropy changes on heating from A to B at constant volume V_1 and again at constant volume V_2 (Operations 3 and 4). These are given by

$\Delta S(A \longrightarrow B$, volume $V_1)$

$$= \int_{T_A}^{T_B}\left(\frac{nC_v}{T}\right)_{V_1}dT = \int_{T_A}^{T_B}\frac{n}{T}\left(\frac{\partial E}{\partial T}\right)_{V_1}dT \quad (14.13)$$

$\Delta S(A \longrightarrow B$, volume $V_2)$

$$= \int_{T_A}^{T_B}\left(\frac{nC_v}{T}\right)_{V_2}dT = \int_{T_A}^{T_B}\frac{n}{T}\left(\frac{\partial E}{\partial T}\right)_{V_2}dT \quad (14.14)$$

But for an ideal gas E is independent of volume $[(\partial E/\partial V)_T = 0]$, and $(\partial E/\partial T)_{V_1}$ must equal $(dE/dT)_{V_2}$ at any volume. Therefore the integrals must be equal. If this is so, then the entropies S_B and S_A of expansion must also be equal, because otherwise heating the gas from T_A and V_1 to T_B and V_2 would give different entropies for the two routes shown in Fig. 14.3 (Operations 2 plus 4, Operations 3 plus 1).

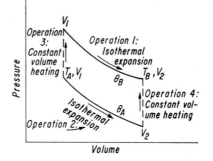

Fig. 14.3. *Isothermal and constant volume expansions of ideal gas. Identity of ideal gas temperature and thermodynamic temperature.*

The values of S_B and S_A from Eqs. 14.11 and 14.12 can only be equal if

$$\frac{\theta_A}{T_A} = \frac{\theta_B}{T_B} \qquad (14.15)$$

Thus the ideal gas scale and thermodynamic scales must be at least proportional at *all* temperatures if Eq. 14.15 is to be true for any temperature *A* and *B*. The simplest proportionality is obtained by making the two scales agree at some one temperature, and hence at all others, and this is the prescription actually used. Thus the use of the ideal gas scale as a measure of thermodynamic temperature is justified.

It is important to realize that thermodynamic temperature is no more restricted to ideal gases than is the second law. Both describe fundamental properties of any kind of substance. The thermodynamic scale of temperature could be established just as well in principle in terms of any substance, using its measured properties in conjunction with the first and second laws. The ideal behavior approached by real gases is simple to use for this purpose at ordinary temperatures. The use of real gases becomes impractical at temperatures near absolute zero, however, and under these conditions temperatures must be established by measuring changes in other properties. (Changes in magnetism of suitable salts are actually used.)

14.7. Conversion of Heat to Work: the Carnot Cycle

Setting up alternate routes between two states, as depicted in Fig. 14.3, is a device often employed in thermodynamic problems. (Compare the calculations of heats of reaction in Section 13.2 and the entropy calculations of Section 14.5.) This technique takes advantage of the fact that any thermodynamic property describing the state of a system depends only on the state. Changes in thermodynamic properties accompanying a process are determined only by the differences between the initial and final states, and are independent of the path; that is, they are the same for all of the various routes which the system may follow in proceeding from the initial to the final state.

An alternative, equivalent device is a *cyclic process:* one carrying a system through a series of steps which finally return it to its original state. For any cyclic process, the change in any property of the state of the system must be zero, for the obvious reason that—the initial and final states being identical—there has been no change in state, even though heat has been absorbed and work done for various of the individual steps comprising the route.

The use of a cyclic process can be illustrated by considering the important problem of transforming heat into useful work. Carnot, in about 1820, considered an ideal model of engines doing work through a series of cycles, in order to determine the maximum amount of work obtainable from a given quantity of heat absorbed during the absorption step of each cycle.

The *Carnot cycle* consists of four steps, indicated in Fig. 14.4. In the first two, work is done by the system. (1) Starting with a substance at temperature T_1, point A, isothermal and reversible expansion is produced by reducing pressure, and by supplying heat to the substance in amount q_1, so that the substance does work. (2) After the isothermal expansion, the substance is allowed to expand further and do more work by reducing the pressure, but perfect adiabatic conditions are assumed so that no heat is absorbed ($q = 0$),

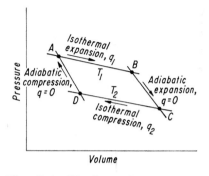

Fig. 14.4. *The Carnot Cycle.*

and the substance thus cools to a temperature T_2, point C.

The next two steps are taken to return the substance to its original state in a fashion which gives some net work for the cyclic process. (3) The cooled substance is compressed isothermally and reversibly at T_2 with absorption of heat q_2. (Actually, since in the compression the substance will give off heat rather than absorbing it, the value of the quantity q_2 will be negative.) This proceeds just to the extent that (4) reversible adiabatic compression ($q = 0$) returns the substance to its original volume and temperature T_1 (and hence to its original pressure).

The whole sequence and routes are indicated schematically as the series of changes in P and V of Fig. 14.4. In such a diagram, the total work done is proportional to the area enclosed by the four curves of the separate steps. This is because for each step the work is

$$\text{Work} = \int P \, dV,$$

and is thus proportional to the area below each curve. In the expansion steps, this work is positive (done *by* the substance), but compression work is negative (done *on* the substance) and must be subtracted from the expansion work, leaving the net work from the complete cycle represented by the area enclosed by the curves. The returning steps are at lower temperature or volume simply to give the net work a positive sign (work delivered by the substance to its surroundings). (It should be noted that this system is defined so that the only work involved is pressure-volume work. Others could be defined for any other kind of work equally well.)

Applying the first and second laws to this cyclic process gives an important result. The first law states that $\Delta E = q - w$ for any process, where q is the sum of the heats absorbed by the substance and w the work done by the substance. But for the cyclic process there is no net change in state and $\Delta E = 0$, since E is a property only of the state (a thermodynamic property). The total heat absorbed for the process is $q_1 + q_2$. Hence

$$\Delta E = q_1 + q_2 - w = 0 \qquad (14.16)$$

The second law states that the net change of entropy ΔS for the process is the sum of values of q/T, if the working substance is in equilibrium with its surroundings (reversible process). Since S is also a property only of the state, ΔS must also be zero for the cyclic process, giving

$$\Delta S = \frac{q_1}{T_1} + \frac{q_2}{T_2} = 0 \qquad (14.17)$$

or

$$\frac{q_2}{q_1} = -\frac{T_2}{T_1} \qquad (14.18)$$

(The negative sign emphasizes again that in the cyclic process one of the heats must be that evolved by the substance—q_2 in this case—and it will have a negative value.)

These equations lead very simply to an important deduction about the maximum amount of work (w) which can be done by the substance with the heat that is supplied to it (q_1). The ratio of the work done to the heat supplied (w/q_1) is called the efficiency and is, so to speak, a fractional yield in terms of energy conversion. It is a quantity of practical interest because the quantity q_1 must be supplied to the working substance (by combustion or in some other manner), regardless of how much heat q_2 is removed from the substance in the compression step. From Eq. 14.17, the *ideal efficiency*,

$$\frac{w}{q_1} = 1 + \frac{q_2}{q_1} \qquad (14.19)$$

Substitution of the second law result embodied in Eq. 14.19 gives

$$\text{ideal efficiency} = \frac{w}{q_1} = 1 - \frac{T_2}{T_1} = \frac{T_1 - T_2}{T_1} \qquad (14.20)$$

This efficiency, or work yield relative to heat absorbed, is always less than one because thermodynamic temperatures must always be positive. Only by the lower temperature of the process being absolute zero ($T_2 = 0$) could all the heat input possibly be made available as work. This expedient is obviously not too practical, and actually is not possible, because all real substances have such properties that they can be made only to approach, but never to reach, absolute zero.

For practical temperatures, the efficiencies calculated by Eq. 14.20 are considerably less than one. For example, even if superheated steam at $T_1 = 500°K$ (227°C) is supplied as the heat source, and is exhausted at $T_2 = 300°K$ (27°C), the ideal efficiency in using the inlet steam to produce work cannot exceed $1 - 300/500 = 0.40$ or 40%.

Care has been taken to call the ratio w/q_1 the *ideal efficiency*, because even this value can be realized only if the cyclic process proceeds under equilibrium (reversible) conditions at all stages. This is not a practical condition to achieve, and all actual engines therefore are still less efficient than an ideal engine. That the efficiency is reduced can be easily shown. If any departures from equilibrium occur during the cycle, there will be increases in entropy not accounted for by $q_1/T_1 + q_2/T_2$. If we indicate the sum of these additional entropy increments by $\Delta S'$, then Eq. 14.18 becomes

$$\Delta S = \frac{q_1}{T_1} + \frac{q_2}{T_2} + \Delta S' = 0 \qquad (14.21)$$

Solving for q_2/q_1 and calculating w/q_1 gives

$$\text{efficiency} = 1 - \frac{T_2}{T_1} - \frac{T_2 \Delta S'}{q_1} \qquad (14.22)$$

which is smaller than $1 - T_2/T_1$ because $T_2 \Delta S'/q_1$, containing only positive quantities, must be positive.

Thus any cyclic process between temperatures T_1 and T_2 has at best the Carnot ideal efficiency, $1 - T_2/T_1$. This conclusion follows independently of the type of substance or the kind of work done, because neither was explicitly defined in writing the several Eqs. 14.16 to 14.20, leading to the expression for the efficiency. Hence the result is general. (It is also interesting to note how simply the mathematical details work out, most of this section being devoted to the description of the process.)

The impossibility of converting energy supplied as heat wholly into work by a cyclic process often leads to referring to heat as a "degraded" form of energy. Likewise, a change in state under nonequilibrium conditions results in more heat evolution at the lower temperature and in less work being done, since for heat so absorbed $q_{\text{nonequilibrium}} <$ $T\,dS = q_{\text{equilibrium}}$. Nonequilibrium changes thus can be described as

those in which energy usable as work has instead been degraded to heat
(supplied in greater amount to the surroundings than would be the case
in an equilibrium transformation).

14.8. Thermodynamic Conditions for Equilibrium

Up to this point, the first and second laws have been stated and used
separately in applications to specific situations. The fact that the heat
(q) appears explicitly in basic equations of both laws makes possible,
however, the combination of the two into one, by eliminating q in favor
of the state properties S and T. Upon substituting $q \leq T \, dS$ from the
second law into the first, expressed as $dE = q - w$, it becomes

$$dE \leq T \, dS - w \qquad (14.23)$$

If the work which can be done is limited to expansion work, $w = P \, dV$,
giving

$$dE \leq T \, dS - P \, dV \qquad (14.24)$$

This statement embodying both laws of thermodynamics gives particularly simple conditions if V and either E or S are constant.

1. If $dS = 0$ and $dV = 0$, then $dE \leq 0$. For natural processes at
constant volume and constant entropy, the internal energy must
decrease ($dE < 0$), unless the system is already in equilibrium, in which
case internal energy has a minimum value and $dE = 0$.

2. If $dE = 0$, and $dV = 0$, then $dS \geq 0$. For natural processes, at
constant volume and constant internal energy, the entropy must
increase until it reaches a maximum at equilibrium, in which case dS
for small changes is zero.

These results show that either a decrease of internal energy or an
increase of entropy may determine the changes leading to equilibrium.
If there is no absorption of heat or internal change to create a state of
higher probability, the entropy remains constant, and equilibrium is
reached for the state of least energy. This is the situation encountered
in mechanical problems, in which changes of temperature, volume, and
internal condition are neglected, and the criterion of least energy is
appropriate. At the other extreme, the system may be isolated from
changes in internal or other energy, in which case any spontaneous
changes must be ones that increase the entropy. This situation is
approached in experiments on free expansion of gases, mixing of fluids
by diffusion, and the like.

Most experiments are conducted under quite different circumstances. Chemists usually find it very convenient to carry out chemical reactions at constant temperature. In addition, either pressure or volume is usually fixed, making the calculation of the work of expansion simple, or null. Constant pressure, such as atmospheric, is the more common, but constant volume conditions are sometimes maintained as in bomb calorimeters.

14.9. Equilibrium at Constant Temperature

When temperature is fixed, heat usually enters or leaves the system as reactions or other processes take place in it, and changes in both energy and entropy will occur in amounts depending on the nature and extent of the process. The absorption of heat in an endothermic reaction acts to increase both quantities, which is favorable for realizing higher entropy states of greater probability, but unfavorable for minimizing the energy. Exothermic reaction, on the other hand, decreases internal energy (or enthalpy, for constant pressure) but at the expense of decreased entropy. This suggests that the direction of spontaneous change will be decided by the relative importance of the opposing effects, and that the state of equilibrium will be the best compromise which the system can realize.

The Helmholtz Function (Work Function)

The criteria defining equilibrium at constant temperature may be expected from the foregoing discussion to involve both energy and entropy in some form which indicates their opposing natures influencing the direction of natural change. The form is not obvious from the fundamental Eq. 14.23,

$$dE \leqq T\,dS - w$$

because the condition to be applied is $dT = 0$, rather than dE or $dS = 0$ as in the previous section. An equation involving dT can, however, be obtained by manipulation using calculus. For if we write

$$T\,dS = d(TS) - S\,dT$$

Eq. 14.23 becomes

$$dE \leqq d(TS) - S\,dT - w$$

or

$$d(E - TS) \leqq -S\,dT - w \qquad (14.25)$$

The combination $E - TS$ is called the Helmholtz function or work function, and is denoted in American chemical literature by the symbol A. The name *work function* comes from the form of Eq. 14.25 at constant temperature. Setting $dT = 0$ gives

$$[d(E - TS)]_T = (dA)_T \leqq - w \qquad (14.26)$$

For reversible processes taking place under equilibrium conditions, the equality sign applies, and the equation states that the decrease in A $[-(dA)_T]$ is then equal to the maximum work w done by the system. For natural processes, on the other hand, there is less work done for the same decrease in A.

If only expansion work is done, then $w = P \, dV$ and

$$(dA)_T \leqq -P \, dV \qquad (14.27)$$

The simplest condition for processes carried out at constant volume and temperature results by setting $dV = 0$:

$$(dA)_{T,V} \leqq 0 \qquad (14.28)$$

Hence for equilibrium A $(= E - TS)$ must be a minimum; this is the state which goes furthest to realize both low internal energy and high entropy (the latter making the energy equivalent TS a larger number).

The Free Energy

The equation $(dA)_T \leqq -P \, dV$ could be used perfectly well to discuss equilibrium at constant pressure, but a more convenient condition for these purposes can be obtained by further manipulation to introduce both dT and dP into the equation $dE \leqq T \, dS - P \, dV$ for processes involving only expansion work. If the two differentials $T \, dS = d(TS) - S \, dT$ and $P \, dV = d(PV) - V \, dP$ are substituted, it becomes

$$dE \leqq d(TS) - S \, dT - d(PV) + V \, dP \qquad (14.29)$$

or

$$d(E - TS + PV) \leqq -S \, dT + V \, dP \qquad (14.30)$$

The function $(E - TS + PV)$, obtained by combining differentials, is called the *free energy* (F) by American chemists; others often use the name Gibbs function and symbol G for the same quantity. The usefulness of the function is greatest for processes at constant temperature and pressure, for when $dT = 0$ and $dP = 0$,

$$[d(E - TS + PV)]_{T,P} = (dF)_{T,P} \leqq 0 \qquad (14.31)$$

The free energy F is thus the thermodynamic quantity which decreases, and at equilibrium reaches a minimum value, during processes carried out at constant temperature and pressure. For small changes which preserve equilibrium, the necessary condition is that

$$(dF)_{T,P} = 0 \qquad (14.32)$$

This simple result will be used in later sections as the basis for deducing important laws of chemical equilibrium. It is the fundamental equation governing coexistence of liquid, solid, and gaseous phases, and when modified to account for electrical work, is the basis for relating this work to chemical reactions in galvanic cells. This is only a partial list of important applications, but should emphasize the key position of free energy and free energy changes in discussion of chemical equilibrium.

Much of what has been said about the dual roles of energy and entropy in determining the position of equilibrium at constant temperature applies as well to free energy for processes at constant pressure as it does to the Helmholtz function for constant volume. The difference between the two is the extra PV term in the definition of F ($F = E + PV - TS$, compared with $A = E - TS$); this added term accounts for PV work at constant pressure, which vanishes if the volume is constant. Thus natural processes at constant pressure decrease free energy, while decreases in A must be greater than the work done. This difference in statements can be expressed another way: since $E + PV = H$, the enthalpy defined in Chapter 12, the free energy F can be written

$$F = H - TS \qquad (14.33)$$

When mechanical work is done at constant pressure, the position of equilibrium is for the state which goes furthest to realize simultaneously low enthalpy and large entropy.

14.10. Physical Equilibrium and the Chemical Potential

There are many kinds of equilibria among substances, all of which must satisfy conditions of the form just described. The important types which will be considered in detail fall into two classes.

1. Physical equilibria. Among these are equilibria between different phases, whether solid, liquid, or gas. The process occurring in achieving equilibrium is a change of state such as melting or vaporization. Examples involving physical equilibria in the chemistry of solutions are the solubility of a salt and the osmotic pressure of a solvent.

2. Chemical equilibria. This is a very broad class, as it includes all

forms of chemical reaction, whether in gas, liquid, or solid phases, and also heterogeneous reactions with chemical species present in more than one phase.

Both chemical and physical equilibria represent a condition of balance for processes by which the state of a system can change even though the pressure and temperature or pressure and volume are kept fixed. They occur because of internal changes in the substance or substances involved, whether from one state of aggregation of many molecules to another, as in the melting of a solid, or from changes within the molecules themselves, as in a chemical reaction. (Processes in which the two types both occur may be broken down to consider each process separately.)

The thermodynamic conditions derived in the previous considerations must be satisfied if the system is *closed;* that is, changes are limited to heat and work, without entrance or escape of matter. To be useful, the conditions must first be expressed in terms of changes in the separate species or phases. The manner in which these changes are affected by differences in such conditions of state as pressure and temperature can then be determined. In this and the following sections, discussion of these matters is begun, and further examples and uses are included in later chapters.

Consider first the simple case of a single homogeneous chemical substance which can exist in two or more different phases—gas, liquid, or solids of different structures. Under certain limited conditions, two or more of these phases may coexist; for example, the liquid phase and vapor phase at the boiling point of the liquid and a pressure of one atmosphere, or at lower temperatures and correspondingly reduced pressures. It is also common experience that if the temperature is fixed, the pressure will remain unchanged until one or the other phase disappears.

The total free energy of a system containing two phases is the sum of the free energies of the separate phases, and any change in the total, resulting from vaporization or fusion, is the sum of the separate changes. Representing the free energy of phase α by F_α and of a second phase β by F_β, the total free energy is

$$F = F_\alpha + F_\beta$$

and a small change in dF in the total free energy is given by

$$dF = dF_\alpha + dF_\beta \tag{14.34}$$

Suppose now that the *quantity* of the substance in phase α changes by a small amount, dn_α, where n is expressed in moles. If this change is for a *closed* system, so that the *total* amount of substance is fixed, the requirement that $dF_{T,P} \leq 0$ can be imposed. For the total amount to be fixed, any change in quantity in phase β must be in the amount $dn_\beta = -dn_\alpha$. For convenience the resulting changes dF_α and dF_β are represented by partial molal quantities:

$$dF_\alpha = \left(\frac{\partial F}{\partial n_\alpha}\right)_{T,P} dn_\alpha = \bar{F}_\alpha\, dn_\alpha$$

$$dF_\beta = \left(\frac{\partial F}{\partial n_\beta}\right)_{T,P} dn_\beta = \bar{F}_\beta\, dn_\beta = -\bar{F}_\beta\, dn_\alpha \qquad (14.35)$$

where $\bar{F}_\alpha$ is used as an abbreviation for $(\partial F/\partial n_\alpha)_{T,P}$.

Inserting these changes in Eq. 14.34 yields for the total change in free energy,

$$dF = \bar{F}_\alpha\, dn_\alpha + \bar{F}_\beta\, dn_\beta$$

$$= (\bar{F}_\alpha - \bar{F}_\beta)\, dn_\alpha \qquad (14.36)$$

If dn_α is not artificially required to be zero, $dF = 0$ only if

$$\bar{F}_\alpha = \bar{F}_\beta \text{ (condition for equilibrium)} \qquad (14.37)$$

For a system not in equilibrium, $dF < 0$ for the natural, possible change. If phase α is unstable, the change will be from phase α to phase β. Then dn_α is negative, and dF can be negative (<0) only if

$$\bar{F}_\alpha > \bar{F}_\beta \text{ (phase } \alpha \text{ unstable relative to } \beta \text{ at given } T \text{ and } P) \quad (14.38)$$

Conditions of this kind are of such fundamental importance and occur so often that special names have been given the partial derivative $\bar{F} (= \partial F/\partial n)_{T,P}$; it is called the chemical potential, the molal free energy, the partial molal free energy, or simply the potential. The term *chemical potential* is particularly appropriate. The equation $\bar{F}_\alpha > \bar{F}_\beta$, stated in words, means that substances will go naturally from a state of higher chemical potential to one of lower chemical potential; the substances can exist in equilibrium in two phases only if their chemical potentials in the two phases are equal. The similarity of chemical potential to the gravitational and electrical potentials familiar and so important in physics is evident, and chemical potentials as defined by Eq. 14.35 are equally important for chemistry.

So far only the possibility of two phases in equilibrium has been considered. If we suppose a third phase γ also to be present, it is still true that $\bar{F}_\alpha = \bar{F}_\beta$ for equilibrium between α and β, but for equilibrium of phase γ with, say, phase β, it must *also* be true that $\bar{F}_\gamma = \bar{F}_\beta$. Otherwise, phase γ would either grow at the expense of β, or disappear as the substance changed to phase β. Hence three phases can simultaneously be in equilibrium only if

$$\overline{F}_\alpha = \overline{F}_\beta = \overline{F}_\gamma \text{ (three-phase equilibrium)} \qquad (14.39)$$

This kind of relation is the basis for Gibbs' celebrated phase rule governing equilibria between phases, which is discussed in Chapter 20.

The equality of the chemical potentials of a given substance in different phases, when equilibrium is established between those phases, is also true for a given substance when other substances are present. For example, if water vapor is to be in equilibrium with an aqueous solution containing salts or other liquids in any proportion, the transfer of a small amount of water from the solution to the vapor phase cannot at equilibrium change the total free energy F; that is, $dF = 0$. This can only be the case if the chemical potentials of water in vapor and in solution are the same:

$$\overline{F} \text{ (H}_2\text{O in solution) } = \overline{F} \text{ (H}_2\text{O as vapor)}$$

It should be noted that F for water in some other solution can be, and usually is, different, and likewise for the water vapor over the second solution if it is in equilibrium. In other words, the chemical potential of any species depends upon its concentration. Conditions of this kind are important in solution chemistry and will be encountered on many occasions.

14.11. Thermodynamic Relations for Chemical Potentials and Change of Phase

The necessity that the chemical potentials of two phases be equal for equilibrium limits severely the possible values of pressure and temperature at equilibrium. The chemical potentials of two phases change differently with either change in pressure or change in temperature. To make this explicit, examine the fundamental equation $dF = -S\, dT + V\, dP$ (Eq. 14.30). If both sides of the equation are differentiated with respect to the amount n_α in order to find the variation of chemical potential, $\overline{F}_\alpha = (\partial F/\partial n_\alpha)_{T,P}$, we obtain

$$d\left(\frac{\partial F}{\partial n_\alpha}\right)_{T,P} = -\left(\frac{\partial S}{\partial n_\alpha}\right)_{T,P} dT + \left(\frac{\partial V}{\partial n_\alpha}\right)_{T,P} dP \qquad (14.40)$$

The quantities $(\partial S/\partial n_\alpha)_{T,P}$ and $(\partial V/\partial n_\alpha)_{T,P}$ represent the changes in entropy and volume corresponding to changes in the quantity of substance in phase α, and are called the *partial molal entropy* and the *partial molal volume*. Let us denote them for convenience by $\bar{S}_\alpha$ and $\bar{V}_\alpha$; then

$$d\bar{F}_\alpha = -\bar{S}_\alpha \, dT + \bar{V}_\alpha \, dP$$

If temperature is fixed, $dT = 0$, and the change of $\bar{F}_\alpha$ with pressure is then given by

$$(d\bar{F}_\alpha)_T = \bar{V}_\alpha \, dP$$

or

$$\left(\frac{\partial \bar{F}_\alpha}{\partial P}\right)_T = \bar{V}_\alpha \left[= \left(\frac{\partial V}{\partial n_\alpha}\right)_{T,P} \right] \qquad (14.41)$$

The partial molal volumes of different phases are always different at any given temperature, and are of the order of 20–30 liters per mole for gases at ordinary pressure and temperatures, and of the order of only milliliters per mole for liquids and slightly less than that for the solid forms of normal substances.

Because of this difference in the pressure dependence of the chemical potential $\bar{F}$ in different phases, in general only one pressure will exist at a given temperature for which $\bar{F}_\alpha = \bar{F}_\beta$ in the two phases α and β. If the two phases happen to be the pure liquid and the vapor, this single value of the pressure permitted is evidently the *vapor pressure* discussed in Section 11.2.

Considering the changes in free energies of different phases with changing temperature if pressure is fixed ($dP = 0$), the change of $\bar{F}_\alpha$ is given from Eq. 14.40:

$$(d\bar{F}_\alpha)_P = -\bar{S}_\alpha \, dT$$

or

$$\left(\frac{\partial \bar{F}_\alpha}{\partial T}\right)_P = -\bar{S}_\alpha \left[= -\left(\frac{\partial S}{\partial n_\alpha}\right)_{T,P} \right] \qquad (14.42)$$

Since heat is absorbed when a liquid is vaporized or a solid melted, the phase stable at the higher temperature evidently has a larger entropy in amount $\Delta S = q/T$, provided the process is carried out reversibly. If phase α is gas and β liquid, $\Delta S = \bar{S}_{\text{gas}} - \bar{S}_{\text{liq}}$ and the heat (q) absorbed is just the latent heat of vaporization, $\Delta \bar{H}_{\text{vap}}$ (the bar, as always, indicates the partial molal value). Hence

$$\bar{S}_{\text{gas}} - \bar{S}_{\text{liq}} = \frac{\Delta \bar{H}_{\text{vap}}}{T} \qquad (14.43)$$

where T is the temperature at which the two phases are in equilibrium. Similarly for the melting of a solid

$$\bar{S}_{\text{liq}} - \bar{S}_{\text{solid}} = \frac{\Delta \bar{H}_{\text{fusion}}}{T} \qquad (14.44)$$

$\Delta \bar{H}_{\text{fusion}}$ being the latent heat of fusion per mole and T the equilibrium melting temperature.

In these and other phase changes at equilibrium, the entropy differences are those calculable from the heats of transition. Because the entropies of the various phases are different, the equation $(\partial \bar{F}/\partial T)_P = -\bar{S}$ shows that a change of temperature alone will cause different changes in the chemical potentials of two phases, with the result that equilibrium no longer exists. But if the pressure also changes, the changes resulting from pressure effects can compensate the different changes resulting from temperature effects, and thus restore equilibrium at a new temperature *and* pressure. The necessary relation for this to obtain follows directly from the equations already at hand.

The condition that $d\bar{F}_\alpha = d\bar{F}_\beta$, when given in terms of pressure and temperature changes, is

$$-\bar{S}_\alpha \, dT + \bar{V}_\alpha \, dP = -\bar{S}_\beta \, dT + \bar{V}_\beta \, dP$$

or, on rearranging,

$$(\bar{V}_\alpha - \bar{V}_\beta) \, dP = (\bar{S}_\alpha - \bar{S}_\beta) \, dT$$

The ratio dP/dT of the pressure and temperature changes necessary to preserve equilibrium is therefore

$$\frac{dP}{dT} = \frac{\bar{S}_\alpha - \bar{S}_\beta}{\bar{V}_\alpha - \bar{V}_\beta} \qquad (14.45)$$

Since the entropy difference $\bar{S}_\alpha - \bar{S}_\beta$ is equal to the latent heat $\Delta \bar{H}$ divided by the temperature, and $\bar{V}_\alpha - \bar{V}_\beta$ is the difference of molal volumes of the two phases, this can also be written

$$\frac{dP}{dT} = \frac{\Delta \bar{H}}{T \, \Delta \bar{V}} \qquad (14.46)$$

which is often called Clapeyron's equation. (For processes involving only changes of state of pure substances, partial molal quantities become identical with molal quantities and the Clapeyron equation is often seen written $dP/dT = \Delta H / T \, \Delta V$.)

The magnitudes and significance of the various quantities in Clapeyron's equation can be illustrated by two examples. First consider the vaporization of ammonia at $-33.3°C$ and 1 atmosphere: $\Delta \bar{H} = 327.4 \times 17.0 = 5580$ cal/mole, $\Delta \bar{V} = 19.12 - 0.025 = 19.1$ liters/mole, and $T = 240°K$. In order to use these numbers to obtain a recognizable value of dP/dT, the units must be consistent. If dP is to be in atmospheres, with V in liters, H must be in liter-atmospheres, and so the value of $\Delta H = 5580$ cal mole^{-1} $\times$ (0.082 1 atm deg^{-1} mole^{-1}/1.987 cal deg^{-1} mole^{-1}) $= 230$ 1 atm mole^{-1} must be used. This gives

$$\frac{dP}{dT} = \frac{230}{240 \times 19.1} = 0.050 \text{ atm deg}^{-1}$$

The equation thus shows that a vapor pressure increase of 0.050 atmospheres per degree rise in temperature is necessary to maintain equilibrium conditions between liquid and gaseous ammonia. The measured value is 0.053 atm deg^{-1}.

The necessary pressure changes accompanying changes in temperature for solid-liquid equilibria are very much higher, because of the much smaller volume differences between the two phases. Glacial acetic acid, for example, melts at 16.6°C (289.8°K) with a latent heat of fusion of 44.7 cal g^{-1} $\times$ 60.1 g mole^{-1} $= 2790$ cal mole^{-1}, and the molal volume increases by 0.96 cm^3 mole^{-1}, giving

$$\frac{dP}{dT} = \frac{2790(0.082/1.097)}{289.8 \times 0.96} = 41.5 \text{ atm deg}^{-1}$$

Thus an increase of 41.5 atm in pressure is necessary to raise the melting point one degree. Similar values are found for other solids, and are large enough that for many purposes change of melting point with ordinary pressure variation in the laboratory can be neglected.

For the vaporization of a liquid it is possible to obtain from the Clapeyron equation a simple approximate equation for the slope of the vapor pressure curve. This is done by making three assumptions: (a) the vapor is an ideal gas, (b) the volume of the liquid is negligible in comparison with that of gas, and (c) the heat of vaporization does not change with temperature.

From the first two assumptions, $\overline{V}_{gas} - \overline{V}_{liquid} \cong RT/P$; hence

$$\frac{dP}{dT} = \frac{P \Delta H}{RT^2}$$

or

$$\frac{dP}{P} = \frac{\Delta H}{R} \frac{dT}{T^2} \qquad (14.47)$$

The assumption that ΔH is independent of T makes integration simple. For the limits (T_1, P_1) and (T_2, P_2), the result is

$$\ln \frac{P_2}{P_1} = \frac{\Delta H}{R} \left(\frac{1}{T_2} - \frac{1}{T_1} \right) \qquad (14.48)$$

which can also be written

$$\ln P = -\frac{\Delta H}{R}\frac{1}{T} + \text{constant} \qquad (14.49)$$

This equation has precisely the form of that given in Section 11.2 to describe the vapor pressure curve, and the slope of the plot of $\log P$ against $1/T$ is $\Delta H/2.303R$ (the factor 2.303 to convert from ln to log). The value for ΔH obtained in this manner is evidently both approximate and an average over the temperature range of the data plotted. For example of ethyl ether given in Section 11.2, the equation obtained was $\log P = -(1479/T) + 7.680$. Hence $\Delta \bar{H} = 2.303 \times 1.987 \times 1479 = 6770$ cal/mole, as compared with the measured value of 6210 cal/mole at 35°C.

14.12. Reaction Equilibria

The phase equilibrium condition just discussed can be likened in a sense to a very simple form of chemical reaction: one in which a single homogeneous substance changes from one state to another. Consider now the more general conditions for equilibrium when chemically different substances react to form new substances as products. A reaction may be written in general terms as

$$aA + bB = cC + dD \qquad (14.50)$$

by which is meant that a moles of substance A react with b moles of B to form c moles of C and d moles of D. Starting with arbitrary amounts of each of the four substances, the changes in each of the amounts during the reaction will affect the thermodynamic state of the system in which the reaction occurs. If the pressure and temperature are kept constant, the most convenient thermodynamic quantity for describing the situation is the free energy, F.

The total change in the free energy as a result of reaction in a system containing all the reactants and products is

$$(dF)_{T,P} = \left(\frac{\partial F}{\partial n_A}\right)_{T,F} dn_A + \left(\frac{\partial F}{\partial n_B}\right)_{T,P} dn_B + \left(\frac{\partial F}{\partial n_C}\right)_{T,P} dn_C$$

$$+ \left(\frac{\partial F}{\partial n_D}\right)_{T,P} dn_D$$

$$= \bar{F}_A \, dn_A + \bar{F}_B \, dn_B + \bar{F}_C \, dn_C + \bar{F}_D \, dn_D \qquad (14.51)$$

Each term represents the effect of the change in amount of a particular substance; the subscripts indicate that temperature and pressure are constant, in addition to the amounts of all other substances.

For constant temperature and pressure, however,

$$(dF)_{T,P} \leqq 0$$

if the system is a closed one. To apply this condition to Eq. 14.51 for a closed system, only changes in n_A and dn_A that are consistent with the reaction given by Eq. 14.50 are allowed. If the number of moles of A reacting is written as $dn_A = -a\,dx$, then for stoichiometric balance dn_B must equal $-b\,dx$, $dn_C = c\,dx$, and $dn_D = d\,dx$; the minus signs indicate that for reactions to the right with dx positive, dn_A and dn_B are negative. Combining those expressions with Eq. 14.51 gives

$$(dF)_{T,P} = [(c\bar{F}_C + d\bar{F}_D) - (a\bar{F}_A + b\bar{F}_B)]\,dx \leqq 0 \qquad (14.52)$$

If dx is positive, as in formation of C and D, then the sum of chemical potentials $c\bar{F}_C + d\bar{F}_D$ for the products must be less than the corresponding sum $a\bar{F}_A + b\bar{F}_B$ of reactants. If dx is negative, with A and B formed at the expense of C and D, the opposite holds. In either case, the direction of natural change is that which results in a net decrease in the total free energy, and it is governed by the chemical potentials and their stoichiometric weights.

The condition of equilibrium, $dF = 0$, can only be realized (if dx is not artificially required to be zero, permitting no reaction) if the chemical potentials satisfy the equation

$$c\bar{F}_C + d\bar{F}_D = a\bar{F}_A + b\bar{F}_B \qquad (14.53)$$

This expression is the fundamental equation for reaction equilibrium. Because the chemical potential of each substance present varies in its own individual way with temperature, pressure, and concentrations, the equation can be satisfied only by particular values of these quantities, and not by any one of a number of choices. In order to apply Eq. 14.53 to specific reactions, it is therefore necessary to find ways of determining how the chemical potentials vary for different chemical species and states of aggregation. This is undertaken in chapters following, and makes possible a logical discussion of "ideal laws" of chemical equilibrium, the reasons why they are not exact, and the significance of various kinds of equilibria.

Problems

14.1. For each of the following pairs of states identify the equilibrium state and describe a spontaneous process by which it is reached, indicating the nature of work done and flow of heat. What is the reverse process? Is it unnatural?

State A	State B
Iron rust	Iron plus oxygen
Water at $-10°C$	Ice at $-10°C$
Methanol	$CO + 2H_2$
Bomb with air at high pressure connected to atmosphere through a capillary	Atmospheric pressure in bomb

14.2. For each of the final states you gave in Problem 14.1, devise a *reversible* process for returning the system to its original state, and indicate the nature of heat flow and work done. Compare with the spontaneous process.

14.3. An explosive bomb is dropped from high altitude into water, and after impact and explosion a quiet state is ultimately reached. Discuss the transformations of energy, the heat and work effects, and the entropy change of the system.

14.4. A 200-g metal block at 90°C is dropped into 300 cm³ of water at 20°C in a container of negligible heat capacity, which is well enough insulated that heat loss to the surroundings can be neglected. The heat capacities of water and the metal are 1.00 and 0.13 cal/g deg. (a) What is the final temperature of the system? (b) What is the change in entropy of the water? of the copper? (c) Discuss the reversibility of the process.

14.5. (a) A thermostat is maintained at 50°C in a room at 20°C by supplying electrical energy to a heater at the rate of 50 cal/min. If no reaction or other effect occurs in the thermostat, what is its entropy change in one minute? How much does the entropy of the room change as a result of one minute of operation? (b) If the heater is now turned off, by how much does the entropy of the thermostat change in one minute, assuming that heat loss to the room is at the same rate and that the bath temperature changes only slightly in this time?

14.6. One mole of nitrogen is expanded from 2.0 atm at 25°C to a final pressure of 1.0 atm. When done by reversible adiabatic expansion the final temperature is $-29°C$, as calculated by using $\bar{C}_P = 7.0$ cal/mole deg. (a) What is the entropy change of the gas? (b) A different reversible route is cooling to $-29°C$ at 2.0 atm, followed by isothermal expansion to 1.0 atm. Calculate the entropy change of each step and the total. (c) A third route is cooling the gas to $-29°C$, keeping the initial volume unchanged, and again expanding the gas isothermally to 1.0 atm. Calculate the two entropy changes and the total change.

14.7. (a) Calculate the entropy increase of 2.0 moles of ammonia heated from $300°K$ to $400°K$ at constant pressure, assuming that $\bar{C}_P = 8.61$ cal/mole deg, the value at room temperature. (b) The assumption that $\bar{C}_P$ is constant is not a good one for ammonia, better values being given by the equation $\bar{C}_P = 6.70 + 0.0063T$. Repeat the calculation using this expression for $\bar{C}_P$. What are absolute and percentage differences in the entropy change by the new calculation?

14.8. (a) Show that the increase in entropy per mole of an ideal gas which is taken from pressure P_1 and temperature T_1 to new values P_2 and T_2 if $\bar{C}_P$ is assumed constant, is given by

$$\Delta S = \bar{C}_P \ln \frac{T_2}{T_1} - R \ln \frac{P_2}{P_1}$$

(b) If $\bar{C}_P$ is not satisfactorily constant, but can be represented by $\bar{C}_P = A + BT$, where A and B are empirical constants, derive an improved expression for ΔS.

14.9. Calculate the ideal efficiencies of obtaining work from heat by an engine working under the following conditions: (a) Inlet steam at $100°C$, exhaust at $35°C$. (b) Steam at $100°C$, exhaust at $20°C$. (c) Superheated steam at $400°C$, exhaust at $35°C$. What considerations about operating temperatures do the answers suggest?

14.10. The heat pump as a device for home heating is essentially an engine driven by an electric motor which takes heat from the ground at a temperature T_2 and delivers heat to the home at the desired higher temperature T_1. (a) Show that for ideal efficiency, the necessary work w to deliver heat q_1 at temperature T_1 is

$$w = q_1 \left(1 - \frac{T_2}{T_1}\right)$$

(b) If the driving electric motor has practically 100% efficiency, which is the more efficient way of heating a home—by electric heaters or by a heat pump? (This is not the only consideration in choosing a heating plant. Suggest others.)

14.11. Refrigerators are essentially engines run backwards, with the objective of extracting heat q_2 from a region at a lower temperature T_2, in the course of which heat q_1 is given off to the room at temperature T_1 and work w must be done *on* the system by a compressor. (a) Show that the work w to remove q_2 calories is ideally (i.e., at least)

$$w = q_2 \left(\frac{T_1}{T_2} - 1\right)$$

(b) How much work, in calories and in watt hours, must be done to freeze 1.0 kg of ice in a refrigerator?

14.12. Calculate the values of q, w, ΔE, ΔH, ΔS, and ΔF for vaporization of one mole of each of the following at its boiling point:

Liquid	Boiling Point (°C at 760 mm)	Heat of Vaporization (cal/g)
Helium	−268.9	5.0
Ethane	−52.6	117.2
Carbon disulfide	46.2	84.0
Water	100.0	539.3
Mercury	356.7	70.4

How well do the liquids satisfy Trouton's rule (Chapter 11)?

14.13. What does the approximate validity of Trouton's rule for "normal" liquids imply about differences in entropy and order on vaporizing these liquids?

14.14. Calculate the values of q, w, ΔE, ΔH, ΔS, and ΔF for fusion of 1 mole of benzene (freezing point 5.5°C, latent heat of fusion 30.1 cal/g) and cyclo-hexane (freezing point 6.5°C, latent heat of fusion 7.6 cal/g).

14.15. The heat of fusion of ice at 0°C is 79.7 cal/g and the heat capacities of water and ice are 1.00 and 0.48 cal/g. (a) Calculate by Kirchhoff's law the heat of fusion of ice at −10°C. (b) Devise a process of reversible steps for transforming ice at −10°C to (supercooled) water at −10°C, and calculate the entropy change in this transformation from the sum of the entropy changes of the steps. (c) Use the second law and your answers to (a) and (b) to show that melting of ice at −10°C is an unnatural process.

14.16. (a) Show that for any phase change (e.g., fusion, sublimation, vaporization) the change ΔA per mole is $\Delta A = -P\Delta V$, where ΔV is the change in molar volume on change of phase. (b) Calculate the change in ΔA for fusion of ice (specific volume of ice = 1.08 cm³/g) and for vaporization of water at 100°C (specific volume for water = 1.00 cm³/g). (c) Is the normal change ΔA of fusion positive or negative?

14.17. In Section 14.11, a value of the heat of vaporization ΔH_v for diethyl ether was deduced from an approximate vapor pressure equation and the Clausius-Clapeyron equation. A more accurate value can be obtained from Eq. 14.48 if sufficiently accurate vapor pressures P_2 and P_1 are known for two neighboring temperatures T_2 and T_1. For diethyl ether, $P = 400$ mm at 17.9°C and 760 mm at 34.6°C. Calculate ΔH_v and compare with the measured value at the boiling point.

14.18. The heat of fusion of ice is 79.7 cal/g and the specific volumes of ice and water are 1.08 and 1.00 cm³/g. (a) Calculate the slope dT/dP of the melting point curve for pressures in atmospheres. (b) What is the melting point of ice at a pressure of 100 atm?

14.19. The heat of vaporization of a liquid is found to be 79.1 cal/g at the boiling point, 211°C. The vapor pressure is 400 mm at 186°C. Calculate the molecular weight of the vapor.

14.20. Show that ΔF is positive for melting of ice at $-10°C$, obtaining the necessary data from Problem *14.15*.

14.21. Show that steam at 760 mm pressure and 90°C (supersaturated steam) is unstable with respect to liquid water by showing that ΔF for the reaction $H_2O(g) = H_2O(l)$ is negative at 90°C and 760 mm pressure.

14.22. According to the Debye theory of heat capacities of solids (Chapter 10), the heat capacity at temperatures a few degrees above absolute zero has the form $\bar{C}_P = AT^3$, where T is in °K and A is a constant. (a) Show that the entropy increase from 0°K to such a temperature T_1 is given by

$$S(T_1) - S(0°) = \tfrac{1}{3}AT_1^3 = \tfrac{1}{3}\bar{C}_P(T_1)$$

(b) The heat capacity of solid SO_2 at 15.2°K is 0.86 cal/mole deg. By how much does the entropy at 15.2°K exceed that at 0°K? (Calculations of this kind are needed for entropy determination at higher temperatures, as discussed in Section 15.8).

14.23. A bomb of volume V_1 contains n_1 moles of one gas, and a second bomb of volume V_2 contains n_2 moles of a different gas, at the same temperature T. A valve in a connecting line is opened to allow the gases to mix and occupy the common volume $V_1 + V_2$. (a) Neglecting interactions of the gases and assuming both behave ideally, show that the sum of the entropy changes of the two gases is

$$\Delta S = n_1 R \ln \frac{V_1 + V_2}{V_1} + n_2 R \ln \frac{V_1 + V_2}{V_2}$$

(b) This kind of entropy change is called entropy of mixing. Show by the second law and the formula you have derived for the given conditions (identical temperatures, ideal behavior) that the process is spontaneous.

14.24. Another form of mixing two gases (besides the one in Problem *14.23*) is as follows. Two gases initially at the same concentration, n moles of each in containers of the same volume V, and temperature T, are mixed by forcing one gas into the other container, so that both are finally in one container of volume V. (a) If the process is isothermal to prevent entropy changes with temperature, what is the total entropy change? (b) Is this process necessarily irreversible or not? Explain your answer, using the second law.

14.25. A form of refrigerator cycle is used in a commercial nitrogen liquefier; that is, heat removed from the gas at temperature T_2 cools it according to $q_2 = -n\bar{C}_p\,dT_2$ if the pressure remains constant and q_2 is the amount removed, and the necessary work is given by the formula in Problem *14.11*. By integrating this equation from 300°K to the boiling point of nitrogen (78°K), find the total amount of work to cool 50 moles of nitrogen to its boiling point. Find the necessary further work to liquefy the gas, and the total amount to liquefy 50 moles initially at 300°K. The latent heat of vaporization of N_2 is 1330 cal/mole deg at 78°K.

14.26. The assumption that the heat of vaporization ΔH_v is independent of temperature, made in deriving the approximate vapor pressure equation

$$\ln P = -\frac{\Delta H_v}{R}\frac{1}{T} + \text{constant}$$

becomes increasingly poor at higher temperatures. A better expression for ΔH_v is of the form $a - bT$. (a) Show that the corresponding vapor pressure equation

$$\ln P = -\frac{A}{R}\frac{1}{T} - b \ln T + \text{constant}$$

(b) Explain the origin of a term of the form $-bT$ in $\Delta H_v = a - bT$. Would you expect the negative sign, corresponding to smaller ΔH at higher temperatures?

14.27. Actually, the simple vapor pressure equation, $\ln P = -(A/T) + \text{constant}$ can often, by suitable choice of A, be made to fit vapor pressure data better than one would expect from the result of the preceding problem. What other approximation is made in deriving the Clausius-Clapeyron equation? Consider whether errors in these approximations would be in the direction to cancel the error in assuming ΔH is constant.

14.28. A gas at pressure P_1 and temperature T_1 expands into a container maintained at a lower pressure P_2. Neglecting heat exchanges so that the process can be considered adiabatic, calculate the entropy change of one mole of gas in undergoing this expansion. Is the process reversible? (Hint: Review the solution of Problem *12.18*.)

14.29. Two containers at the same temperature hold gas at pressures P_1 and P_2. Show that when connected gas flows spontaneously in the direction to equalize the pressure.

14.30. Two containers, one with 0.3 moles of He at 30°K and 1 atm and the other with 0.7 moles at 100°K and 1.5 atm, are connected and the gases allowed to mix adiabatically. Calculate the final temperature and pressure and the entropy change of the system, assuming $\bar{C}_P = 5.0$ cal/mole deg independent of temperature. (Hint: See Problem *14.23* on entropy of mixing.)

Suggested Readings

The references at the end of Chapter 12 can be recommended for their treatments of the present subject matter. Another very readable account is *Introduction to Chemical Thermodynamics* by E. F. Caldin (Oxford, London, 1958). Two advanced texts emphasizing concise deduction from principles are distinctive: *Thermodynamics* (2nd ed.) by E. A. Guggenheim (Interscience, New York, 1950) and *Chemical Thermodynamics*, written by I. Oppenheim from notes of lectures by J. G. Kirkwood (McGraw-Hill, New York, 1961).

The statistical treatment of entropy is given in texts on statistical mechanics. Of the many available, one of the most elementary mathematically is *Statistical Mechanics* by R. W. Gurney (McGraw-Hill, New York, 1949). Other texts have been cited in Chapter 10.

Chapter 15

Equilibrium in Gas Reactions

IN THIS CHAPTER, some of the many possible applications of thermodynamics to equilibrium are discussed. The specialization of the general laws to particular systems naturally begins with substances in the form with the simplest behavior—the ideal gas state.

For reaction mixtures of ideal gases, the condition for equilibrium proves to be the ideal equilibrium law of mass action, and thermodynamics gives a sound basis for understanding both the underlying significance of ideal expressions and the reasons underlying their approximate character. Moreover, thermodynamics provides ways of predicting equilibrium conditions for many gas reactions from other measurable quantities.

The study of equilibrium and chemical potentials for gases is equally important as a preliminary to the consideration of equilibrium of substances in other phases (solids or solutions) because much of what can be said about other states depends upon first appreciating and being able to make use of the properties of these substances as gases.

15.1. Chemical Potentials and Pressure of Ideal Gases

In Section 14.12, the basic thermodynamic condition for equilibrium of the reaction $aA + bB = cC + dD$ was shown to be

$$\Delta F = c\overline{F}_C + d\overline{F}_D - a\overline{F}_A - b\overline{F}_B = 0 \qquad (15.1)$$

That is, at equilibrium the stoichiometric sum of chemical potentials for products must equal the corresponding sum for reactants. In order to use this condition, we first determine the manner of variation of the chemical potentials of the separate species with such determining factors as concentration and temperature. In this section, we consider first the effect of concentration on the simplest state, that of an ideal gas.

The effect of concentration (and for a gas of pressure) on the chemical potential of a single gas is readily obtained from Eq. 14.41:

$$\left(\frac{\partial \overline{F}}{\partial P}\right)_T = \overline{V} \tag{15.2}$$

where $\overline{V}$ is the partial molal volume of the gas. If the gas is ideal, $PV = nRT$ and $\overline{V} = (\partial V/\partial n)_{T,P} = RT/P$, giving

$$\left(\frac{\partial \overline{F}}{\partial P}\right)_T = \frac{RT}{P} \tag{15.3}$$

The difference between potentials at pressure P and any other pressure P_0 at the same temperature then can be found by integration:

$$\overline{F}(P) - \overline{F}(P_0) = \int_P^P \frac{RT}{P} \, dP = RT \ln \frac{P}{P_0}$$

For convenience, chemical potentials are customarily referred to a standard pressure P_0, usually taken to be one atmosphere. Then

$$\overline{F}(P) = \overline{F}(P_0) + RT \ln \left(\frac{P}{P_0}\right) \tag{15.4}$$

The standard chemical potential $\overline{F}(P_0)$ defined at pressure $P_0 = 1$ atmosphere is denoted by $\overline{F}^0$, and thus the equation can be written more simply as

$$\overline{F}(P) = \overline{F}^0 + RT \ln P \tag{15.5}$$

This result can be expressed equally usefully in terms of the concentration $C(= n/V)$, instead of pressure. For an ideal gas, $P = CRT$, and so

$$\overline{F}(C) = \overline{F}^0 + RT \ln CRT \tag{15.6}$$

Equation 15.5 or 15.6 is valid for a single ideal gas, but gas reactions involve a mixture of several different gases. For these, it is required to know the potential of any gas i as a function of its concentration C_i or partial pressure P_i, in the gas mixture. One would expect, however, that the value would be the same as that of the gas present by itself, if its *concentration* is unchanged and if the mixture is dilute enough to behave ideally, since in the latter case the properties of each species are unchanged by the presence of other species.

Under these ideal conditions, for each gas i present in the mixture one can write

$$\overline{F}_i = \overline{F}_i^0 + RT \ln C_i RT \tag{15.7}$$

Since $c_i RT = P_i$, the partial pressure of gas i, this also can be written as

$$\overline{F}_i = \overline{F}_i^0 + RT \ln P_i \tag{15.8}$$

The difference between Eqs. 15.5 and 15.8 is important. In a mixture, the potential of a gas is determined by its *partial* pressure, and hence concentration, *not* by the total external pressure resulting from all gases present. The quantity $\overline{F}_i^0$ must also be understood to be the value for the gas i when its partial pressure $P_0 = 1$ atmosphere, not when the total pressure is one atmosphere. Using Eq. 15.7 or 15.8 to express the chemical potential, the change in free energy accompanying a reaction can be expressed in terms of concentrations or partial pressures. Using partial pressure expressions in Eq. 15.1 gives

$$\Delta F = c\overline{F}_C^0 + d\overline{F}_D^0 - a\overline{F}_A^0 - b\overline{F}_B^0$$
$$+ RT(c \ln P_C + d \ln P_D - a \ln P_A - b \ln P_B)$$

The sum of logarithms can be rewritten more conveniently as the logarithm of the products and quotients of the partial pressures, with the result

$$\Delta F = (c\overline{F}_C^0 + d\overline{F}_D^0 - a\overline{F}_A^0 - b\overline{F}_B^0) + RT \ln \frac{P_C^c P_D^d}{P_A^a P_B^b}$$

The quantity in brackets is an important one. Each of the chemical potentials $\overline{F}^0$ is a standard value characteristic of the individual gas at the temperature T and pressure P_0. The sum of values of the standard free energy for products less the sum for reactants is thus a *standard free energy difference*, which depends only on these standard values and is independent of the actual concentration of the gases or changes in their values. At the same time, however, the relative amounts of the gases consumed or produced by the reaction are represented by the values of the stoichiometric coefficients a, b, c, d. For an ideal gas reaction, therefore, this stoichiometric summation of the standard free energies is characteristic of the gases which can take part in the reaction, and at a given temperature has some definite fixed value. Denoting this value by $\Delta \overline{F}^0$. the equation reduces to

$$\Delta F = \Delta \overline{F}^0 + RT \ln \left(\frac{P_C^c P_D^d}{P_A^a P_B^b} \right) \tag{15.9}$$

Consider now the difference in this equation between an equilibrium and nonequilibrium condition. The partial pressure P_A, P_B, P_C, P_D may have values which will make ΔF greater or less than zero, depending on whether the product $P_C^c P_D^d / P_A^a P_B^b$ is large or small. But for equilibrium ΔF must be zero, and only for special values of the partial pressures will this be true. These special values are equilibrium pressures, and from Eq. 15.9 it is obvious that if $\Delta F = 0$, they must be in such a relation that

$$\Delta \overline{F}{}^0 = -RT \ln \left(\frac{P_C^c P_D^d}{P_A^a P_B^b} \right)_{equil} \tag{15.10}$$

where the subscript "equil" indicates that the pressures are such as to satisfy equilibrium conditions. If the pressures of products are too small relative to those of the reactants, the ΔF for the reaction for the formation of C and D will be negative. Thus the forward reaction $aA + bB \longrightarrow cC + dD$ will increase the partial pressures of products until the value for ΔF for the reaction is no longer negative, and Eq. 15.10 is satisfied. If, instead, the pressures of products are too large, ΔF will be positive for forward reaction (as written) and the reaction will hence proceed to the left until ΔF becomes zero at equilibrium.

Equation 15.10 is the thermodynamic basis for the *ideal law of equilibrium* as determined for reactions of ideal gases. Since $\Delta \overline{F}{}^0$ is independent of concentrations and hence constant at any fixed temperature, then so also must be the product of partial pressures at equilibrium. This constant value of this product at any one temperature is appropriately called the equilibrium constant K_P, the subscript P indicating that the constant is expressed in terms of partial pressures. Hence, for reactions of ideal gases,

$$\left(\frac{P_C^c P_D^d}{P_A^a P_B^b} \right)_{equil} = K_P \tag{15.11}$$

a constant depending only on temperature. The thermodynamic connection of the equilibrium constant with free energy (chemical potential) of the gases is, from Eq. 15.10, given by

$$\Delta \overline{F}{}^0 = -RT \ln K_P \tag{15.12}$$

In applying Eq. 15.11 to actual situations, the circumstances under which K_P is constant should be recognized. From the derivation, K_P is constant only when the temperature is fixed, for the standard free energy change $\Delta \overline{F}{}^0$ which determines K_P according to Eq. 15.12, depends on temperature, and in addition, T is a proportionality constant between $\Delta \overline{F}{}^0$ and $\ln K_P$. Shifts of equilibrium with temperature thus require a study of how $\Delta \overline{F}{}^0$ depends on temperature, which will be considered in Section 15.4.

15.2. Examples of Gas Equilibria

Formation of Hydrogen Iodide

The gas reaction $H_2 + I_2 = 2HI$ has been carefully studied at 425°C, where at moderate pressures both reactants and products exist in appreciable concentrations. The partial pressures of the reactants and product have been determined at equilibrium, starting with different initial amounts of H_2 and I_2, and also with varying amounts of HI initially present, with results shown in Table 15.1. For this reaction, Eq. 15.11 becomes

$$\frac{P_{HI}^2}{P_{H_2}P_{I_2}} = K_P, \qquad (15.13)$$

and the value of K_P calculated from the measured partial pressures should be constant. The last column in Table 15.1 gives the values for the constant, and within experimental error it is in fact independent of the different combinations of pressures produced during the course of the experiment.

TABLE 15.1.   *Equilibrium Pressures for the Reaction $H_2 + I_2 = 2HI$ at 425°C. (Pressures given in atmospheres.)*

P_{H_2}	P_{I_2}	P_{HI}	K_P (Eq. 15.13)
0.1645	0.09783	0.9447	55.46
0.2583	0.04429	0.7763	55.19
0.1274	0.1339	0.9658	54.67
0.1034	0.1794	1.0129	55.31
0.02703	0.02745	0.2024	55.19
0.06443	0.06540	0.4821	55.28
			Mean 55.18

The importance of the equilibrium equation lies in its predictive value, for once K_P is known for a given temperature, the equilibrium pressures realized from other starting conditions at the same temperature can be calculated. Suppose, for example, that the extent of decomposition of HI at 425°C and a total pressure of one atmosphere is wanted. This sort of problem is best solved by using the mole fractions of different species to specify the overall composition. Let x = mole fraction of HI at equilibrium. If only HI were present initially, the mole fractions of H_2 and I_2 must have the same value, which will be $(1 - x)/2$. The partial pressures of the gases in terms of the total pressure and the mole fraction of HI present are

$$P_{HI} = xP$$

and

$$P_{H_2} = P_{I_2} = (1 - x)P/2$$

Substitution in Eq. 15.12 gives

$$\frac{x^2 P^2}{\left(\dfrac{1 - x}{2}\right)^2 P^2} = \frac{4x^2}{(1 - x)^2} = K_P \qquad (15.14)$$

Solving for x, we find

$$\frac{x}{1 - x} = \sqrt{\frac{K_P}{4}}$$

and

$$x = \frac{\sqrt{K_P/4}}{1 + \sqrt{K_P/4}}$$

Substituting the value 55.2 for K_P yields

$$x = \frac{\sqrt{13.8}}{1 + \sqrt{13.8}} = 0.79$$

Thus 21% of the original HI is decomposed to H_2 and I_2.

The solution resulting from less simple starting conditions is more complicated. Suppose, for example, that hydrogen and iodine are mixed in a two to one ratio and allowed to react until equilibrium is reached. If the initial number of moles of I_2 is s and of this a fraction y reacts, leaving $s(1 - y)$ moles, then the $2s$ moles of H_2 initially present will decrease to $2s - sy$ moles with the formation of $2sy$ moles of HI. The total moles of gas present at equilibrium will be $s(2 - y) + s(1 - y) + 2sy = 3s$. The mole fractions and partial pressures of the gases at equilibrium are

$$N_{H_2} = \frac{s(2 - y)}{3s}, \qquad P_{H_2} = \frac{2 - y}{3} P$$

$$N_{I_2} = \frac{s(1 - y)}{3s}, \qquad P_{I_2} = \frac{1 - y}{3} P \qquad (15.15)$$

$$N_{HI} = \frac{2sy}{3s}, \qquad P_{HI} = \frac{2y}{3} P$$

Substitution in Eq. 15.11 gives

$$\frac{4y^2}{(2 - y)(1 - y)} = K_P$$

This gives a quadratic equation in y, for which the solution by the familiar algebraic formula is

$$y = \frac{3K_P \pm [9K_P^2 - 8K_P(K_P - 4)]^{1/2}}{2(K_P - 4)}$$

Substituting $K_P = 55.2$, the possible solutions are $y = 2.29$ or 0.938. Only one of these can be physically possible and the choice of solution in all situations like this can be made by considering the significance of the quantity. In the present case, y is the fraction of I_2 which reacts, and must be between zero and one to have meaning. Hence $y = 0.938$ is the solution, and 93.8% of the quantity of the I_2 present initially has reacted when equilibrium is established.

The results of these calculations illustrate an aspect of equilibrium qualitatively predictable by Le Chatelier's principle, that the presence of one reactant in excess results in the reaction going further "toward completion." For equal amounts of H_2 and I_2, the first calculation showed that 79% of I_2 reacts while for an amount of H_2 which is twice the stoichiometric amount of I_2, 93.8% of the I_2 reacts. (Thus if one reactant essential to a given reaction is dear or in short supply, more of the products can be formed with a given initial amount of the given reactant if the other reactants are present in excess.)

A second aspect of the calculations for the reaction $H_2 + I_2 = 2HI$ is that the total pressure has no effect on the extent of this particular reaction: the total pressure P cancels out of the equilibrium equation written for partial pressures, regardless of the way the partial pressures are varied by starting conditions. These pressures appear as the same total powers in numerator and denominator for K_P, corresponding to the fact that there is no change in number of moles of gas during the reaction. The independence with respect to pressure is what one would expect from Le Chatelier's principle.

Decomposition of Nitrogen Tetroxide

The effect of pressure upon a reaction in equilibrium where there is a change in number of moles during reaction can be illustrated by the dissociation of nitrogen tetroxide: $N_2O_4 = 2NO_2$. If (as in Section 8.5) h moles of N_2O_4 are introduced into a bulb of known volume V, a fraction

z decomposes to form $2hz$ moles of NO_2 at equilibrium, leaving $h(1 - z)$ moles of N_2O_4. The total number of moles present at equilibrium is $n = h(1 - z) + 2hz = h(1 + z)$.

The mole fractions and partial pressures of the reactant and product are

$$N_{N_2O_4} = \frac{h(1 - z)}{h(1 + z)}, \qquad P_{N_2O_4} = \frac{1 - z}{1 + z} P$$

$$N_{NO_2} = \frac{2hz}{h(1 + z)}, \qquad P_{NO_2} = \frac{2z}{1 + z} P$$

Substitution in the appropriate expression of K_P gives

$$K_P = \frac{P_{NO_2}^2}{P_{N_2O_4}} = \frac{[2z/(1 + z)]^2 P^2}{[(1 - z)/(1 + z)]P}$$

or

$$K_P = \frac{4z^2}{1 - z^2} P \tag{15.16}$$

Because of the change in number of moles in the course of reaction, the expression for K_P, which must remain constant, has the factor P. If the pressure is larger, the factor $4z^2/(1 - z^2)$ must be correspondingly smaller, which is only true if z^2, and hence z, is smaller. This increase in pressure shifts the equilibrium in the direction of less decomposition, as expected by Le Chatelier's principle. This example both demonstrates the prediction of Le Chatelier's principle and gives a quantitative expression by which the *amount* of shift can be calculated. To be explicit, consider the following problem. The measured density of the equilibrium mixture of N_2O_4 at 760 mm and 25°C is 3.176 g/liter. What is the degree of dissociation at this pressure, and also at a pressure of 300 mm?

The degree of dissociation at 1 atm is obtained as in Section 8.5. The density $w/V = hM/V$, if h and M refer to the initial amount and molecular weight of N_2O_4. By the ideal gas law, $n = (1 - z)h = PV/RT$. Hence $w/V = MP/(1 + z)RT$. Therefore, the fraction dissociated is

$$z = \frac{MP}{RT(w/V)} - 1 = \frac{92 \times 1}{.0821 \times 298 \times 3.176} - 1$$

or

$$z = 0.185$$

To find the degree of dissociation at 300 mm ($= 0.395$ atm), the value of K_P must first be found. Since $z = 0.185$ for $P = 1$ atm,

$$K_P = \frac{4(0.185)^2 \times 1}{1 - (0.185)^2} = 0.141$$

Then, at 300 mm,

$$\frac{z^2}{1-z^2} = \frac{K_P}{4P} = \frac{0.141}{1.580}$$

or

$$z = 0.286$$

Thus the degree of dissociation is increased from 18.5% to 28.6% by reducing the pressure from 1.00 to 0.395 atm.

Decomposition of Nitrosyl Bromide

A slightly more complicated example of a decomposition equilibrium is is the reaction $2NOBr \rightleftharpoons 2NO + Br_2$. If the initial number of moles of NOBr is g and the fraction decomposed at equilibrium (degree of dissociation) is x, then substitution in Eq. 15.11 leads to the result, which the reader should verify, that

$$K_P = \frac{\left(\frac{x}{1+\frac{1}{2}x}\right)^2\left(\frac{\frac{1}{2}x}{1+\frac{1}{2}x}\right)}{\left(\frac{1-x}{1+\frac{1}{2}x}\right)^2}P = \frac{x^3}{\left(1+\frac{x}{2}\right)(1-x)^2}\frac{P}{2} \qquad (15.17)$$

Formation of Water Gas

For the water gas reaction, $CO_2 + H_2 \rightleftharpoons CO + H_2O$, the equilibrium constant expression in terms of partial pressures is

$$\frac{P_{CO}P_{H_2O}}{P_{CO_2}P_{H_2}} = K_P \qquad (15.18)$$

It is equally feasable to express the variables as concentrations instead of as partial pressures. If we write $P_{CO} = C_{CO}RT$, and so on, and substitute, we obtain

$$\frac{C_{CO}C_{H_2O}}{C_{CO_2}C_{H_2}}\frac{(RT)^2}{(RT)^2} = K_P$$

Thus the stoichiometric product of concentrations at any temperature constant is

$$\frac{C_{CO}C_{H_2O}}{C_{CO_2}C_{H_2}} = K_c \qquad (15.19)$$

independent of total concentration. In the particular case of the water gas reaction, and for any gas reaction without change in number of moles, the concentration product (K_C) and partial pressure product (K_P) are evidently identical. For reactions in which the number of moles changes with reaction, this is no longer true, but the values of K_C and K_P are related. For the reaction $2SO_2 + O_2 \rightleftharpoons 2SO_3$, for example, K_P is given by

$$K_P = \frac{P_{SO_3}^2}{P_{SO_2}^2 P_{O_2}}$$

Substitution of the appropriate expressions for the partial pressures gives

$$\frac{C_{SO_3}^2}{C_{SO_2}^2 C_{O_2}} \frac{1}{RT} = K_P$$

or

$$K_C = \frac{C_{SO_3}^2}{C_{SO_2}^2 C_{O_2}} = (RT)K_P$$

The value for either K_P or K_C at any temperature will define the possible equilibrium conditions for ideal gas reactions; which one is used is a matter of convenience. As will be shown later, K_P is a somewhat more convenient choice when changes in temperature are of interest. In any case, however, the existence of a constant value K for the product of concentration or of pressure provides a representation for the effects of the concentration of different species on the position of equilibrium. It should be emphasized that the reason the *products* of concentrations appear combined in the equilibrium expression is that, for ideal gases, *changes of chemical potential* are proportional to the *ratio* of concentrations or pressures, as shown by Eqs. 15.7 and 15.8.

Before considering other aspects of reaction equilibria, it is of interest to examine the effect of different amounts of CO_2 and H_2 on the water gas equilibrium. If n_1 moles of CO_2 and n_2 of H_2 are initially present, and at equilibrium $n_1 x$ moles of CO_2 have reacted, then the equilibrium condition is

$$\frac{(n_1 - n_1 x)(n_2 - n_1 x)}{(n_1 x)(n_1 x)} = K_P \, (= K_C)$$

which can be rewritten

$$\frac{(1 - x)\left(\dfrac{n_2}{n_1} - x\right)}{x^2} = K_P \qquad\qquad (15.20)$$

The value of x, and hence the equilibrium composition, thus depends only on the ratio n_2/n_1—of reactants in this case.

15.3. Deviations from Ideal Behavior at High Pressure

The equilibrium condition for gas reactions in the form so far discussed depends for its validity upon the mixture's following ideal gas behavior. This is evident because the derivation is based on the use of $\overline{V} = RT/P$ in the expression $(\partial \overline{F}/\partial P)_T = \overline{V}$, giving the dependence of the chemical potential on pressure. The discussion of Chapter 8 showed that the ideal gas law is only a limiting approximation to behavior of real gases, and is reasonably accurate for pressures of not more than a few atmospheres at most. The mass action expression is to this extent only an approximation, and hence it may fail at higher pressures. This is indeed the case, as experimental studies have shown.

The classic example of this deviation from ideal behavior is the direct synthesis of ammonia, $N_2 + 3H_2 \rightleftharpoons 2NH_3$, for which the ideal equilibrium expression is

$$\frac{P_{NH_3}^2}{P_{N_2}P_{H_2}^3} = K_P \qquad (15.21)$$

a constant at any given temperature. In terms of mole fractions, this becomes

$$\frac{N_{NH_3}^2}{N_{N_2}N_{H_2}^3}\frac{1}{P^2} = K_P \qquad (15.22)$$

To test the validity of these equations at high pressures, yields of ammonia have been determined for 3 to 1 ratios of H_2 and N_2 at various pressures, and values of K_P calculated for these conditions. The results at 450°C for pressures to 1000 atm are listed in Table 15.2. The change from 10 to 30 atm produces only a small difference (about 5%) in K_P, but at higher pressures the effects are more marked. At 1000 atmospheres K_P has nearly 13 times its value at pressures of a few atmospheres.

TABLE 15.2.   *Values of K_P for the Reaction $N_2 + 3H_2 \rightleftharpoons 2NH_3$ at High Pressures and 450°C.*

P (atm)	10	30	50	100	300	1000
$10^6 K_P$ (calc)*	43.4	45.7	47.6	52.6	78.1	542

*The notation $10^6 K_P = 43.4$ means that $K_P = 43.4 \times 10^{-6}$.

The failure of K_P to remain even approximately constant at high pressures is of more than academic interest, because the yield is substantially improved at high pressures. While this would be true even if

K_P were essentially constant (because of the factor P^2 in the denominator of Eq. 15.22), the yield is enhanced by the deviations from ideality which make K_P increase with pressure. As a result, the yield at 450°C increases from 16% at 100 atm to nearly 70% at 1000 atm.

Unfortunately, there are no general rules or formulas adequate for predicting the changes in the equilibrium constant with pressure under a set of desired conditions. A variety of rules using empirical equations of state data for the individual gases have been proposed; the more successful of these work very well under some conditions, but none can be trusted under all circumstances. (Detailed discussion of such prescriptions for using real gas behavior to predict equilibrium conditions may be found in the literature.) The present discussion will be confined to examples showing that real gases at high pressures have chemical potentials significantly different from the ideal values, and that these lead to deviations from the simple equilibrium law expressed in terms of pressure or concentration.

The basic equation for calculating chemical potential is Eq. 15.2,

$$\left(\frac{\partial \bar{F}_i}{\partial P}\right)_T = \bar{V}_i$$

where $\bar{V}_i = (\partial V/\partial n_i)_{T,P}$ is the partial molal volume of the species i at the particular temperature and pressure. For a single substance, $\bar{V}$ is identical with the volume of one mole of the substance and is hence determined by its equation of state. For gases at pressures not too high, deviations from ideal gas behavior were shown in Section 8.7 to be given reasonably well by $P\bar{V} = PV/n = RT + BP$, where B is the second virial coefficient. Under these conditions,

$$\bar{V} = \frac{RT}{P} + B$$

Taking this as the dependence of $\bar{V}$ on pressure, Eq. 15.2 can be integrated to give

$$\bar{F}(P) - \bar{F}(P_0) = RT \int_{P_0}^{P} \frac{dP}{P} + B \int_{P_0}^{P} dP$$

or

$$\bar{F}(P) - \bar{F}(P_0) = RT \ln \frac{P}{P_0} + B(P - P_0) \qquad (15.23)$$

The term $B(P - P_0)$ thus represents the correction for nonideal behavior. Its magnitude compared to the ideal gas term $RT \ln (P/P_0)$ depends on the value of B, which can be positive or negative. For nitrogen at 450°C, for example, B is approximately 28 cc/mole. The correction at 300 atm is then 8300 cc atm or 200 cal/mole, as compared to the ideal free energy change $RT \ln P/P_0 = 8200$ cal/mole, and hence amounts to about 2%. At 1000 atm, the correction is proportionately larger, amounting to 670 cal, almost 7% of the value 9850 cal/mole for $RT \ln P/P_0$.

A way of representing deviations from ideal behavior which proves useful was devised by Lewis and Randall. They proposed that the ideal gas form of chemical potential be modified by introducing numerical factors multiplying the pressures in the term $RT \ln P$ so that the ideal gas equation,

$$\overline{F}(P) = \overline{F}(P_0) + RT \ln \frac{P}{P_0} \text{ (ideal gas)} \qquad (15.24)$$

is for real gases replaced by

$$\overline{F}(P) = F(P_0) + RT \ln \frac{(\nu P)}{(\nu_0 P_0)} \text{ (real gas)} \qquad (15.25)$$

The fugacity coefficient ν is chosen to give the correct value for $\overline{F}(P)$. This alternative to writing an extra term in the equation, such as $B(P - P_0)$ in the example previously considered, is used simply because it proves to be more convenient for many purposes. The two procedures are obviously related, because the difference $RT \ln (\nu/\nu_0)$ between Eqs. 15.24 and 15.25 must be the same as the correction $B(P - P_0)$; the two terms are simply different ways of representing the same thing. Hence if the second virial coefficient B represents the real gas adequately, then

$$\ln (\nu/\nu_0) = \ln \nu - \ln \nu_0 = B(P - P_0)/RT$$

This equation will only hold for different pressures P or P_0 if $\ln \nu = (B/RT)P$ for any pressure, including P_0. Hence the variation of ν with pressure is given by

$$\nu = e^{BP/RT} \qquad (15.26)$$

when $\overline{V} = (RT/P) + B$.

From Eq. 15.25, the quantity νP represents the pressure an ideal gas would have to be equivalent to the real gas at its actual pressure. The fictitious, but convenient, pressure is often called the *fugacity f* and so by definition

$$f = \nu P$$

For the example of nitrogen at 450°C, the fugacity at 300 atm is

$$f = e^{BP/RT}P = e^{200/1446} \times 300 \text{ atm}$$

or

$$f = 1.15 \times 300 = 345 \text{ atm}$$

Thus in these terms, nitrogen at 450°C and 300 atm is equivalent to a hypothetical "ideal" nitrogen at a pressure 15% higher. For hydrogen at the same temperature and pressure, similar calculations give a fugacity 9% higher, while for ammonia, the fugacity is 9% *less*. (This decrease results because ammonia has a higher critical temperature, making B negative at 450°C, corresponding to the greater intermolecular attractive forces.)

These differences between real and ideal behavior make understandable changes in the equilibrium for formation of ammonia. At higher pressures, both nitrogen and hydrogen have higher chemical potentials than if they were ideal and consequently are less stable, but ammonia has a lower potential and is more stable. The three changes in chemical potential at high pressure are all such as to increase the yield.

It might be supposed that changes in equilibrium constant with pressure could be calculated simply by inserting fugacity coefficients as multipliers for partial pressures in the equation for K_P. While this is possible in principle, knowledge of the proper values is difficult when the gases are present as components of a mixture rather than singly. A possible assumption is that the fugacity coefficient of the gas is the same when it is present in the mixture as it is alone at the total pressure of the mixture. This appears justified in some cases, but is obviously based on the hopeful reasoning that if one gas is partly replaced by a different one, the remaining gas is unaffected; this and other devices useful for special purposes have been discussed in greater detail in Chapter 8. The important point to be recognized here is that the failure of the ideal law of mass action is the result of effect upon the chemical potentials of deviations from ideal gas behavior.

A final point to be considered is the fact that actual gases do not behave quite ideally even at the pressure of one atmosphere chosen as the standard state for the ideal law of equilibrium. This difference is reflected in the failure of v to be exactly unity for the pressure P_0. When $P_0 = 1$ atm, the virial coefficient B gives a good account of the non-ideality, and Eq. 15.26 can be used to calculate v. For representative values $B = 30$ cc/mole and $T = 300°K$; taking R as 82 cc atm/mole/° gives

$$v = e^{30/82 \times 300} = 1.0012$$

The difference of the chemical potential from that expected for ideal behavior corresponds in this case to a pressure difference of 0.12%. In precise work such a difference will be significant, but for most purposes the difference between a real gas at one atmosphere pressure and the equivalent ideal gas can be neglected. If the accuracy of the experimental measurements and the purposes of their use justify the distinction, for the real case, it is usually made by taking the standard state and corresponding chemical potential to be that for the gas at a pressure to result in unit fugacity, rather than at a pressure of one atmosphere.

15.4. The Effect of Temperature on Equilibrium

The consideration of equilibrium conditions satisfying the fundamental Eq. 15.1 for chemical potentials has so far been confined to the effects of differences in gas concentration (partial pressures) at a fixed temperature. The dependence of equilibrium on temperature is reflected in the fact that equilibrium constants K_P for gas reactions change substantially with temperature. A few examples listed in Table 15.3 show in particular how temperature differences of a hundred degrees can change K_P by orders of magnitude. It is also evident that K_P may either increase or decrease as the temperatures increase.

It was noted in Section 14.3 that the direction of shift in equilibrium is related to the thermicity of reaction, and can be deduced from Le Chatelier's principle. Here this will be justified by thermodynamics; moreover, the change in K_P with temperature will be related quantitatively to the heat of reaction.

From the formulation of the condition for equilibrium in terms of chemical potentials, the problem is the determination of the variation of free energy and chemical potential with temperature. For a closed system, the basic free energy equation, $dF = -S\,dT + V\,dP$, gives for changes with temperatures at constant pressure

$$(dF)_P = -S\,dT$$

and on writing $(dF)_P = (\partial F/\partial T)_P\,dT$, we have

$$\left(\frac{\partial F}{\partial T}\right)_P = -S$$

This equation determines the change of F with temperature if the entropy S is known. An alternative form for $(\partial F/\partial T)_P$ results from the definition $F = H - TS$, which on substitution for S gives

$$\left(\frac{\partial F}{\partial T}\right)_P = \frac{F - H}{T} \qquad (15.27)$$

Another relation which is particularly useful for studying the variation

TABLE 15.3.   *Temperature Dependence of Equilibrium Constants of Gas Reactions.*

(a) $SO_2 + \frac{1}{2}O_2 = SO_3$

$$\ln K_P = \frac{22,600}{RT} - \frac{21.36}{R} \ (700°K–1200°K)$$

T	$\ln K_P$	K_P	$K_P^{1/2}$
700	11.5	1.0×10^5	320
800	7.0	1.1×10^3	33.4
900	3.8	4.5×10^1	6.7
1000	1.3	3.8	1.9

Moore.

(b) $CO_2 + H_2 \rightleftharpoons CO + H_2O$

$T°K$	K_P
673	0.08
873	0.41
1073	0.93
1273	1.66

Hammett.

(c) Dehydrogenation of benzyl alcohol to
       benzaldehyde:
       $C_6H_5CH_2OH \rightleftharpoons C_6H_5CHO + H_2$

$t°C$	K_P (atm)
200	0.177
250	0.558
300	2.14

Paul.

(d) $CO + 2H_2 \rightleftharpoons CH_3OH$

$t°C$	K_P (atm^{-2})
225	.00608
250	.00232
275	.00088

Paul.

L. P. Hammett, *Introduction to the Study of Physical Chemistry* (McGraw-Hill, New York, 1952).

W. J. Moore, *Physical Chemistry*, 3rd ed. (Prentice-Hall, New York, 1962).

M. A. Paul, *Principles of Chemical Thermodynamics* (McGraw-Hill, New York, 1951).

of K_P with temperature can be obtained by further rearrangement and manipulation of this result:

$$\left(\frac{\partial F}{\partial T}\right)_P - \frac{F}{T} = -\frac{H}{T}$$

Observing that

$$\left[\frac{\partial}{\partial T}\left(\frac{F}{T}\right)\right]_P = \frac{1}{T}\left(\frac{\partial F}{\partial T}\right) - \frac{F}{T^2}$$

it is apparent that

$$\left[\frac{\partial}{\partial T}\left(\frac{F}{T}\right)\right]_P = -\frac{H}{T^2} \tag{15.28}$$

These equations can also be applied to changes of free energy occurring as the quantity of material is changed, if the quantities S and H refer to the corresponding changes of entropy and enthalpy. For example, if F is replaced by $\bar{F}_i$, the partial of chemical potential $(\partial F/\partial n_i)_{P,\,T,\,\text{all other } n}$ and S is replaced by $\bar{S}_i = (\partial S/\partial n_i)_{P,\,T,\,\text{all other } n}$, then

$$\left(\frac{\partial \bar{F}_i}{\partial T}\right)_P = -\bar{S}_i$$

and

$$\left[\frac{\partial}{\partial T}\left(\frac{\bar{F}_i}{T}\right)\right]_P = -\frac{\bar{H}_i}{T^2} \tag{15.29}$$

This process replaces the quantities F, S, H, and V, which depend on total amounts of substances present, by the corresponding partial molal quantities which are the *rates* of change of the parameter with amount of substance. The partial molal quantities are valuable in representing the effects of changing conditions of temperature, pressure, and composition without specifying whether there are a few milligrams or many tons of reaction mixture. The free energy change of especial interest is the standard free energy change $\Delta \bar{F}^0$, because of the ideal equilibrium condition that $RT \ln K_P = -\Delta \bar{F}^0$. If $\Delta \bar{F}^0$ is substituted for F, then H and S must be replaced by the corresponding standard changes $\Delta \bar{H}^0$ and $\Delta \bar{S}^0$. The quantity $\Delta \bar{H}^0$ is of interest as the change of enthalpy by reaction, equal to the standard heat of reaction at constant pressure already familiar from thermochemistry (Chapter 13). With this in mind, we can rewrite

$$\left[\frac{\partial}{\partial T}\left(\frac{F}{T}\right)\right]_P = -\frac{H}{T^2}$$

in the form

$$\frac{d}{dT}\left(\frac{\Delta \bar{F}^0}{T}\right) = -\frac{\Delta \bar{H}^0}{T^2} \tag{15.30}$$

(The ordinary derivative may be used because the change $\Delta \bar{F}^0$ is for a standard state not involving changes in pressure, and hence stipulating that the pressure is fixed is unnecessary.)

Substituting $\Delta \bar{F}^0/T = -R \ln K_P$ gives

$$\frac{d}{dT}(\ln K_P) = \frac{\Delta \bar{H}^0}{RT^2} \tag{15.31}$$

It is evident that the variation of K_P with temperature is directly related to the heat of reaction, and Eq. 15.31 is a quantitative expression of the result expected from the Le Chatelier prediction of the direction of the shift of equilibrium accompanying a change in temperature. If a reaction is exothermic, as is apt to be the case at low temperatures, $\Delta \bar{H}^0$ is negative and $\ln K_P$ must decrease with increasing temperature, since $d(\ln K_P)/dT$ is negative. This means that the reaction will shift in the direction of less products—that is, to the left—to satisfy the condition that $\ln K_P$, and hence K_P itself, decreases.

The reader should avoid the confusion which is possible when $\ln K_P$ is negative: if $\ln K_P$ decreases, this means that it becomes more negative, and not that $\ln K_P$ is a smaller number. That is, -3.0 is less than -2.5, just as a temperature of $-30°C$ is surely lower than $-25°C$.

In order to appreciate the numerical values and magnitudes involved in the various factors, consider a reaction with a representative value for $\Delta \bar{H}^0 = -30$ kcal/mole at $300°K$. Then

$$\frac{d}{dT}\ln K_P = \frac{-30,000}{1.99 \times (300)^2} = -0.167$$

For one degree rise in temperature, $\log K_P$ must change by $-0.167/2.303 = -0.0724$; K_P is then smaller by a factor 0.844, corresponding to a decrease of almost 16%.

For changes over larger intervals of temperature, Eq. 15.31 must of course be integrated, if possible taking into account the manner in which $\Delta \bar{H}^0$ varies with temperature. For a simple approximate result usable if the temperature difference is not too large, the heat of reaction can be assumed constant. Making this assumption, the integration of Eq. 15.31 from temperature T_1 to T_2 gives

$$\int_{K_P(T_1)}^{K_P(T_2)} d\ln K_P \cong \frac{\Delta \bar{H}^0}{R} \int_{T_1}^{T_2} \frac{dT}{T^2}$$

or

$$\ln \frac{K_P(T_2)}{K_P(T_1)} = \ln K_P(T_2) - \ln K_P(T_1) \cong -\frac{\Delta \bar{H}^0}{R}\left(\frac{1}{T_2} - \frac{1}{T_1}\right) \tag{15.32}$$

(The symbol $\cong$ is used to indicate approximate equality, since the assumption that $\Delta\overline{H}^0$ is a constant independent of temperature is never precisely true.)

The Ammonia Synthesis

As an example of the use of this equation, consider the ammonia synthesis,

$$\tfrac{1}{2}N_2 + \tfrac{3}{2}H_2 = NH_3$$

at a pressure sufficiently low for K_P to be independent of pressure. To estimate how K_P depends on temperature, take the heat of reaction as $\Delta\overline{H}^0 = -12.7$ kcal/mole and $K_P = 0.0066$ atm^{-1} at 450°C. Then

$$\log K_P(T_2) \cong \log 0.0066 + \frac{12,700}{2.3 \times 1.99}\left(\frac{1}{T_2} - \frac{1}{723}\right)$$

$$= -218 + \frac{2,770}{T_2} - 3.84$$

or

$$\log K_P(T_2) = -6.02 + \frac{2,770}{T_2} \qquad (15.33)$$

At 350°C, for example, the approximate value for K_P is then obtained by $\log K_P$ (623°K) $\cong -6.02 + \frac{2770}{623} = -6.02 + 4.45 = -1.57$, or $K_P \cong 0.0268$, as compared with the measured value $K_P = 0.0266$ at 10 atm.

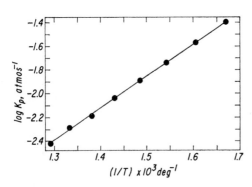

Fig. 15.1. *Log K_P versus $1/T$ for ammonia synthesis (pressure = 10 atmospheres),* $\tfrac{1}{2}N_2(g) + \tfrac{3}{2}H_2(g) = NH_3(g)$. *[Data of A. T. Larson and R. L. Dodge J. Am. Chem. Soc.* **45**: 2918 (1923).]*

From Eqs. 15.32 and 15.33, it is evident that measured values of $\log K_P$ plotted against $1/T$ should fall along a straight line, if $\Delta\overline{H}^0$ is constant over the range of temperatures involved; the slope of this line will be $\Delta\overline{H}^0/2.303R$. Figure 15.1 shows the plot for the ammonia reaction data in the range 325–500°C, and from the slope of the line we obtain

$\Delta\overline{H}^0 = -12.3$ kcal/mole. This agrees fairly well with the determined value $\Delta\overline{H}^0 = -12.7$ kcal/mole at 450°C. Over larger ranges of temperature, this will not hold; for example, $\Delta \bar{H}^0$ at 20°C is -11.01 kcal/mole, nearly 15% smaller.

The example of the ammonia reaction is interesting and important, since it was the study of this equilibrium that led the German chemist Haber to his process for nitrogen fixation (as ammonia) just prior to World War I. The successful use of Haber's process prolonged the war, by supplying the nitrate that Germany lacked, and later led to enormous new chemical industries. The conditions for high ammonia yield are of obvious practical importance; it is evident that low temperature is desirable to increase K_P, with the resulting higher equilibrium concentration of ammonia, and the discussion in Sections 15.2 and 15.3 show the advantages of high pressure as well. From these considerations alone, one can deduce that equilibrium yields would be vastly better at room temperature than at temperatures above 300°C, but at the lower temperatures no way has yet been found to make the reaction proceed at a reasonable rate and reach equilibrium in a reasonable time. This situation illustrates an important consideration, that the *rate* of a reaction is of as great practical importance as the direction and possible yield. The rules of thermodynamics were neither derived from nor do they contain information about reaction times or rates, and hence can make no predictions in these regards. The study of such important aspects of chemical reactions comprises what is called chemical kinetics, which will be taken up in Chapter 22.

Water Gas Reaction

The more refined calculations necessary to account for the variation of the heat of reaction with temperature can be illustrated by the reaction: $CO_2 + H_2 = CO + H_2O$. At 800°K the value of K_P is 0.196. The value of $\Delta \bar{H}^0$ through the range including 800°K can be determined from the known heat of reaction at 298°K, or $\Delta \bar{H}^0_{298°} = 9.83$ kcal/mole, and empirical heat capacity equations for the four gases over a temperature range up to 1500°K:

$$\bar{C}_P(CO) = 6.42 + 1.7 \times 10^{-3}T - 0.3 \times 10^{-6}T^2$$
$$\bar{C}_P(H_2O) = 7.26 + 2.3 \times 10^{-3}T + 0.2 \times 10^{-6}T^2$$
$$\bar{C}_P(CO_2) = 6.21 + 10.4 \times 10^{-3}T - 3.5 \times 10^{-6}T^2$$
$$\bar{C}_P(H_2) = 6.95 - 0.2 \times 10^{-3}T + 0.5 \times 10^{-6}T^2$$

The difference of heat capacities for products and reactants is then

$$\Delta \bar{C}_P = 0.52 - 6.2 \times 10^{-3}T + 2.9 \times 10^{-6}T^2$$

and the heat of reaction at a temperature T is

$$\Delta \bar{H}^0_T = \Delta \bar{H}^0_{298°} + \int_{298°}^{T} \Delta \bar{C}_P \, dT$$

$$= 9830 + 0.52(T - 298) - 3.1 \times 10^{-3}(T^2 - 298^2)$$
$$+ 1.0 \times 10^{-6}(T^3 - 298^3)$$

or

$$\Delta \bar{H}^0_T = 9923 + 0.52T - 3.1 \times 10^{-3}T^2 + 1.0 \times 10^{-6}T^3$$

Substitution in the equation giving the temperature dependence of K_P yields

$$\frac{d}{dT} \ln K_P = \frac{\Delta \bar{H}^0}{RT^2} = \frac{4990}{T^2} + \frac{0.26}{T} - 1.56 \times 10^{-3} + 0.5 \times 10^{-6}T$$

which, on integrating between 800°K and T, gives

$$\ln K_P(T) = \ln K_P(800) - 4990 \left(\frac{1}{T} - \frac{1}{800} \right) + 0.26(\ln T - \ln 800)$$

$$- 1.56 \times 10^{-3}(T - 800) + 0.25 \times 10^{-6}(T^2 - 800^2)$$

or, using $K_P(800) = 0.196$ (or $\ln K_P = -1.63$),

$$\ln K_P(T) = 3.96 - \frac{4990}{T} + 0.26 \ln T - 1.56 \times 10^{-3}T + 0.25 \times 10^{-6}T^2$$

In this example, the reaction as written is endothermic ($\Delta \bar{H}^0 > 0$), and K_P increases with T as it should, the dominant term being $(-4990/T)$.

In applying the various equations given in this section, one must be sure that the proper significance is attached to $\Delta \bar{H}^0$. Since this is the standard enthalpy change of a given reaction, it corresponds strictly to the heat absorbed for the reaction as written when all reactants and products are under standard conditions. Measurements complying with this stipulation often are inconvenient and occasionally impractical or impossible; fortunately they are unnecessary in most cases. This is because measured values of $\Delta \bar{H}$ are essentially independent of concentrations if the concentrations are sufficiently small—that is, the system is sufficiently dilute to approach ideal behavior.

15.5. Heterogeneous Equilibria Involving Gases

So far only homogeneous gas reactions, in which all species reacting or forming are gaseous under the conditions of reaction, have been considered. When one or more species is present as a solid or liquid phase, the situation is changed because the chemical potential of a species at any fixed temperature in a condensed phase can no longer change freely. Its concentration is essentially fixed, either in the condensed phase or as gas in equilibrium with the solid or liquid.

The only possible changes in potential of such a species at a fixed temperature result when changing pressure produces a significant change in the solid or liquid state. The effect of pressure on the chemical potential is expressed by the derivative $(\partial \bar{F}/\partial P)_T = \bar{V}$, the partial molal volume. For liquids or solids $\bar{V}$ is but a few milliliters per mole, and is insignificant in comparison with partial molal volumes of gases at ordinary pressures. Hence the change in chemical potential with changing pressure is very small. Since for a given species the chemical potential must be the same in all phases in which the species is present, this means that the partial pressure, or concentration, must remain essentially constant in the vapor phase just as it does in the condensed phase.

This restriction applies to reactions such as the following:

$$NH_4HS(s) = NH_3(g) + H_2S(g)$$
$$C(s) + CO_2(g) = 2CO(g)$$
$$CaCO_3(s) = CaO(s) + CO_2(g)$$

where the phase in which each component is present in quantity is indicated in parentheses. (A liquid, or indeed a solid such as carbon, $C(s)$, will have some molecules in the gas phase in equilibrium.) Thus $NH_4HS(s)$ refers to solid ammonium hydrosulfide. If the presence of ammonium hydrosulfide as a solid phase were overlooked, one would write

$$\frac{P_{NH_3}P_{H_2S}}{P_{NH_4HS}} = K'_P$$

as the equation for equilibrium. But since NH_4HS *is* present as solid, its partial pressure in the gas phase (which must be in equilibrium with solid NH_4HS), whether small or large, cannot change with variation of the total pressure on the system, or with the concentration of NH_3 or H_2S. Regardless of such changes, $P_{NH_4HS} = $ constant; hence there is no point in writing this pressure as a variable under these circumstances. Instead, the equilibrium expression for this reaction is written

$$P_{NH_3} \times P_{H_2S} = \text{constant} \times K'_P = K_P$$

The equilibrium expression for the other two reactions are similarly respectively written

$$\frac{P^2_{CO}}{P_{CO_2}} = K_P$$

when carbon C is solid, and

$$P_{CO_2} = K_P$$

when both $CaCO_3$ and CaO are solids.

Another simplification in these and many examples is that the vapor pressures of the solids may be neglected because they are insignificantly small. Thus for ideal gas behavior there will be no significant error in writing the total pressure for the ammonium hydrosulfide equilibrium as $P = P_{NH_3} + P_{H_2S}$ (neglecting P_{NH_4HS}). For the other two, the total pressures can be written as

$$P = P_{CO} + P_{CO_2}$$

neglecting P_C, and

$$P = P_{CO^2}$$

neglecting P_{CaCO_3} and P_{CaO}.

As an example of a heterogeneous gas equilibrium illustrating the foregoing, consider the oxidation of iron by steam. If the reaction is written

$$3Fe(s) + 4H_2O(g) = Fe_3O_4(s) + 4H_2(g) \qquad (15.34)$$

the equilibrium condition is that

$$\frac{P_{H_2}^4}{P_{H_2O}^4} = K_P \quad \text{or} \quad \frac{P_{H_2}}{P_{H_2O}} = K_P' \, (= K_P^{1/4}) \qquad (15.35)$$

Measured partial pressures of hydrogen and water for the equilibrium at 900°C are listed in Table 15.4, and the constancy of the quotient P_{H_2}/P_{H_2O} indicates the validity of Eq. 15.35.

TABLE 15.4.   *Oxidation of Iron by Steam at 900°C.*

P_{H_2} (mm)	P_{H_2O} (mm)	P_{H_2}/P_{H_2O}
13.5	8.8	1.53
26.0	17.4	1.49
54.1	35.4	1.53
71.8	49.3	1.46

G. Prenner, *Z. Phys. Chem.* **47**:385 (1904).

This example has been chosen deliberately to make another point. Iron oxide in the lower oxidation state corresponding to FeO could be formed by the reaction

$$Fe(s) + H_2O(g) = FeO(s) + H_2(g) \qquad (15.36)$$

The equilibrium for the formation of FeO by this reaction should then satisfy the constant

$$\frac{P_{H_2}}{P_{H_2O}} = K_P$$

But since $P_{H_2}^4/P_{H_2O}^4$ (and hence also P_{H_2}/P_{H_2O}) for the reaction given by Eq. 15.34 is a constant, the equilibrium expression for the formation of Fe_3O_4 is thus indistinguishable from that for the formation of FeO. In this case equilibrium measurements alone give no basis for determining which of two possible reactions will take place, or which product will be formed. Actually, formation of FeO is increasingly important at higher temperatures but this can not be inferred from equilibrium pressure data alone.

A simple form of heterogeneous gas equilibrium was discussed in Section 14.10—the vaporization of a liquid—and it is interesting to consider this further by the techniques developed above. For a substance A which vaporizes simply and without dimerization, dissociation, or other complications, the equilibrium is

$$A(l) \rightleftharpoons A(g)$$

and the equilibrium expression is

$$P_A = K_P \ (= \text{constant at fixed temperature})$$

This merely asserts that the vapor pressure P_A cannot change unless the temperature does, and so is a rather trivial result. If we try further to determine the temperature dependence of P_A by Eq. 15.31, we get

$$\frac{d}{dT} \ln K_P = \frac{d}{dT} \ln P_A = \frac{\Delta \overline{H}^0}{RT^2}$$

But $\Delta \overline{H}^0$ for this equilibrium is the latent heat of vaporization, $\Delta \overline{H}_v$, and so

$$\frac{d}{dT} \ln P_A = \frac{\Delta \overline{H}_v}{RT^2}$$

which is no more than the Clausius-Clapeyron equation already deduced by approximation in Section 14.11.

This method of treating phase changes as simple equilibria can be applied to other phase equilibria. If ideal (or dilute) equilibrium expressions are used, the results will be approximate just as the Clausius-Clapeyron equation is approximate (because ideal gas conditions and negligible liquid volume are assumed). The use of the equilibrium constant often gives such results more quickly, but derivations starting with the fundamental governing equations have advantages in making the necessary approximations more obvious, and in providing a more direct means of obtaining more accurate results by the elimination of the approximations made.

15.6. Free Energy Changes and Free Energy Tables

The illustrations and applications of the conditions for equilibrium which have been discussed are but a few of the many possible. They should, however, suffice to show the importance of the knowledge of equilibrium conditions.

The number of known and conceivable reactions in chemistry is enormous, and ideally one would like to be able to predict the possible states of equilibrium for all of them. Although the present knowledge of chemistry falls far short of realizing this ideal, many reactions have been studied under conditions suitable for determining the necessary information, and the number about which this information is available is steadily increasing. All such information obviously must be tabulated in conveniently usable form, and it is necessary to consider the ways in which this is done.

The thermodynamic justification of the equilibrium constant expressions for ideal gas reactions is, as has been shown, a consequence of the relation $\Delta \bar{F}^0 = -RT \ln K_P$. From this relation it is evident that known values of K_P could equally well be expressed as standard free energy changes $\Delta \bar{F}^0$. Before the practical advantages of this alternative expression for equilibrium constants are taken up, a few examples will be cited as typical of numerical relations between K_P and $\Delta \bar{F}^0$.

1. For formation of NO at 1800°K by the reaction

$$N_2 + O_2 \rightleftharpoons 2NO, \qquad K_P = 1.21 \times 10^{-4} \text{ atm}$$

and hence

$$\Delta \bar{F}^0_{1800°} = -1.99 \times 1800 \times 2.3 \log 1.21 \times 10^{-4}$$
$$= +32,300 \text{ cal/mole} = 32.3 \text{ kcal/mole}$$

The large positive value of the free energy change, corresponding to K_P much less than one, means that reaction to form NO from N_2 and O_2 will not be spontaneous if all three gases have partial pressures of one atmosphere. Instead, the reverse process of forming N_2 and O_2 from NO is the spontaneous process under these conditions; for the reverse reaction, $2NO \longrightarrow N_2 + O_2$, the standard free energy change must be the negative of that for $N_2 + O_2 \longrightarrow 2NO$, or $\Delta F^0 = -32.3 \text{ kcal/mole}$, and K_P is the reciprocal of the former expression

$$K_P(\text{reverse}) = \left(\frac{P_{N_2}P_{O_2}}{P_{NO}^2}\right)_{\text{equil}} = \frac{1}{1.21 \times 10^{-4}} = 8.36 \times 10^3.$$

2. What are the values of $(\Delta F^0)'$ and K_P' for the reaction $\frac{1}{2}N_2 + \frac{1}{2}O_2 \rightleftharpoons NO$? As this represents half the quantity of reaction for $N_2 + O_2 = 2NO$, then $(\Delta F^0)'$ is half as great as ΔF^0, or $(\Delta F^0)' = 16.15$ kcal/mole. In the equation $\ln K_P' = -(\Delta F^0)'/RT$, $\ln K_P'$ must be one-half $\ln K_P$, and so $K_P' = K_P^{1/2}$. This is also evident on comparing

$$K_P' = \frac{P_{NO}}{P_{N_2}^{1/2}P_{O_2}^{1/2}} \quad \text{with} \quad K_P = \frac{P_{NO}^2}{P_{N_2}P_{O_2}}$$

3. The equilibrium constant for dissociation of phosphorus penta-chloride, $PCl_5(s) = PCl_3(s) + Cl_2(g)$ is $K_P = P_{Cl_2} = 1.78$ atm at 250°C, and ΔF^0 is therefore

$$\overline{F}_{523°}^0 = -1.99 \times 523 \times 2.3 \log 1.78$$
$$= -600 \text{ cal/mole}$$

The negative value means that reaction is spontaneous to the right for reactants and products initially at one atmosphere, and that appreciable dissociation will occur at ordinary pressures. The value of ΔF^0 is, however, not large compared to the value for RT of 1040 cal/mole, and dissociation will be far from complete except at very low pressures.

The examples cited illustrate consequences of the fact that the change in the standard free energy (ΔF^0) is a free energy change for particular conditions. The value of ΔF^0 determines possible equilibrium conditions for which the actual change ΔF of a reaction will be zero. Since ΔF must decrease for spontaneous processes approaching equilibrium, negative values of the difference between the free energy of reactants and products at standard conditions mean that forward reaction is the possible one to reach the condition that $\Delta F = 0$ between reactants and products. If by coincidence $\Delta F^0 = 0$, the standard state is one of equilibrium, while if ΔF^0 is a large positive or negative number, the possible states of equi-librium lie further to left or right, respectively, of the equilibrium state for the reactants and products at their standard conditions.

An important advantage of using ΔF^0 to express the conditions for equilibrium results from the fact that free energies, like all proper thermodynamic functions, have values which depend only on the state of the system, and not on the particular processes which led to it. Because this is as true of free energy as it is of enthalpy and entropy, the free energy change of any reaction can be expressed as the sum of changes for any sequence of reactions leading from the same initial to the same final state as the direct reaction.

The additive property of free energies, and in particular the additivity of the change in standard free energies $(\Delta \overline{F}{}^0)$, can be illustrated by the reaction previously considered for the equilibrium involving the transformation of carbon dioxide and hydrogen into carbon monoxide and steam. The equilibrium is ordinarily represented by the water gas equation,

$$(1) \quad CO_2(g) + H_2(g) = CO(g) + H_2O(g), \qquad K_1 = \frac{P_{CO}P_{H_2O}}{P_{CO_2}P_{H_2}}$$

These species, however, can also undergo the familiar reactions:

$$(2) \qquad CO_2(g) = CO(g) + \tfrac{1}{2}O_2(g); \qquad K_2 = \frac{P_{CO}P_{O_2}^{1/2}}{P_{CO_2}}$$

and

$$(3) \qquad H_2(g) + \tfrac{1}{2}O_2(g) = H_2O(g); \qquad K_3 = \frac{P_{H_2O}}{P_{H_2}P_{O_2}^{1/2}}$$

The reactions are evidently not independent, for the possible sequence of CO_2 dissociating by reaction (2) followed by reaction (3) of the oxygen formed with hydrogen gives exactly reaction (1). The free energy changes of (2) plus (3) must therefore equal that of (1):

$$(\Delta \overline{F}{}^0)_1 = (\Delta \overline{F}{}^0)_2 + (\Delta \overline{F}{}^0)_3$$

and so if any two values are known, the third can be calculated. Of the three values, $(\Delta \overline{F}{}^0)_1$ for the water gas reaction is best known at the temperatures in the range 1200–1500°C, and at 1565°K $(\Delta \overline{F}{}^0)_1 = -3300$ cal/mole, corresponding to $K_1 = 2.8$. The values for the other two standard free energy differences at this temperature have been estimated to be $(\Delta \overline{F}{}^0)_2 = 35,300$ cal/mole $(K_2 = 1.14 \times 10^{-5}$ atm$^{1/2})$ and $(\Delta \overline{F}{}^0)_3 = -38.800$ cal/mole $(K_3 = 2.5 \times 10^5$ atm$^{-1/2})$; they are less accurate because the dissociations of CO_2 and H_2O are small and also difficult to measure. The sum $(\Delta \overline{F}{}^0)_2 + (\Delta \overline{F}{}^0)_3 = -3500$ cal/mole is in as good agreement with the measured $(\Delta \overline{F}{}^0)_3 = -3300$ cal/mole as could be expected, and indicates fair consistency of the experimental values.

The combination of interdependent chemical equilibria as illustrated by use of free energies can also be treated by the corresponding equilibrium constants. Since $(\Delta \overline{F}{}^0)_2 + (\Delta \overline{F}{}^0)_3 = -RT \ln K_2 - RT \ln K_3$, and $(\Delta \overline{F}{}^0)_1 = -RT \ln K_1$, we have

$$RT \ln \frac{K_1}{K_2 K_3} = 0$$

or

$$K_1 = K_2 K_3$$

From experimental values, $K_2 K_3 = 1.14 \times 10^{-5}$ atm$^{1/2}$ $\times$ 2.5×10^5 atm$^{-1/2}$ = 2.85, while the value of K_1 is 2.80.

The necessary relation $K_1 = K_2 K_3$ also follows, as it must, from writing K_2 and K_3 in terms of partial pressures:

$$K_2 K_3 = \frac{P_{CO} P_{O_2}^{1/2}}{P_{CO_2}} \frac{P_{H_2O}}{P_{H_2} P_{O_2}^{1/2}} = \frac{P_{CO} P_{H_2O}}{P_{CO_2} P_{H_2}} = K_1$$

The fact that free energy differences can be added or subtracted for combinations and sequences of reactions to give the value for the resultant reaction makes them as useful for calculations of equilibrium as are enthalpy values for heats of reaction and thermochemical calculations. Results of equilibrium measurements are usefully collected and made available by compilations of tables of standard free energies of formation. Just as heats of reaction are deducible from standard heats of formation is these are known, so also can a standard free energy difference of an unknown reaction be calculated from the sum of $\Delta \bar{F}^0$ values for the products less the sum of $\Delta \bar{F}^0$ values for the reactants. (The sequence of reactions is thus the hypothetical one of dissociating reactants to the elements and reassembling the elements to the products.)

Although determination of free energies of formation presents serious problems for many substances, an enormous amount of work, using various alternative or indirect approaches discussed in later sections, has resulted in extensive tables of known values. A selection of such values at the reference temperature of 25°C is given in Table 15.5; the values are taken from National Bureau of Standards compilations cited at the foot of the table. The values for a given compound refer to the difference at 25°C between its free energy in its standard state and that of the elements in their standard states—these states being a pressure of one atmosphere for gases—and the stable crystalline form for solids, which is noted.

As an example of the use of these tables, consider the gas reaction to form ethanol from ethylene and water vapor at 25°C. For the reaction $C_2H_4(g) + H_2O(l) = C_2H_5OH(l)$, the standard free energy change is

$$\Delta \bar{F}_{298°}^0 = \Delta \bar{F}_{298°}^0(C_2H_5OH) - \Delta \bar{F}_{298°}^0(C_2H_4) - \Delta \bar{F}_{298°}^0(H_2O)$$

TABLE 15.5. *Free Energy of Formation at 25°C.* ($\Delta \overline{F}°$ *in kcal mole^{-1}*)

Elements and Inorganic Compounds

$O_3(g)$	39.06	C $(s,\text{ diamond})$	0.6850
$H_2O(g)$	-54.6357	$CO(g)$	-32.8079
$H_2O(l)$	-56.6902	$CO_2(g)$	-94.2598
$HCl(g)$	-22.769	$PbO_2(s)$	-52.34
$Br_2(g)$	0.751	$PbSO_4(s)$	-193.89
$HBr(g)$	-12.72	$Hg(g)$	7.59
$HI(g)$	0.31	$AgCl(s)$	-26.224
S (monoclinic)	0.023	$Fe_2O_3(s)$	-177.1
$SO_2(g)$	-71.79	$Fe_3O_4(s)$	-242.4
$SO_3(g)$	-88.52	$Al_2O_3(s)$	-376.77
$H_2S(g)$	-7.892	$UF_6(g)$	-485
$NO(g)$	20.719	$UF_6(s)$	-486
$NO_2(g)$	12.390	$CaO(s)$	-144.4
$NH_3(g)$	-3.976	$CaCO_3(s)$	-269.78
$HNO_3(l)$	-19.100	$NaF(s)$	-129.3
$P(g)$	66.77	$NaCl(s)$	-91.785
$PCl_3(g)$	68.42	$KF(s)$	-127.42
$PCl_5(g)$	-77.59	$KCl(s)$	97.592

Organic Compounds

Methane, $CH_4(g)$	-12.140	Propylene, $C_3H_6(g)$	14.990
Ethane, $C_2H_6(g)$	-7.860	1-Butene, $C_4H_8(g)$	17.217
Propane, $C_3H_8(g)$	-5.614	Acetylene, $C_2H_2(g)$	50.000
n-Butane, $C_4H_{10}(g)$	-3.754	Formaldehyde, $CH_2O(g)$	-26.3
iso-Butane, $C_4H_{10}(g)$	-4.296	Acetaldehyde, $C_2H_4O(g)$	-31.96
n-Pentane, $C_5H_{12}(g)$	-1.96	Methanol, $CH_3OH(l)$	-39.73
n-Hexane, $C_6H_{14}(g)$	0.05	Ethanol, $C_2H_6O(l)$	-41.77
n-Heptane, $C_7H_{16}(g)$	2.09	Formic acid, $CH_2O_2(l)$	-82.7
n-Octane, $C_8H_{18}(g)$	4.14	Acetic acid, $C_2H_4O_2(l)$	-93.8
Benzene, $C_6H_6(g)$	30.989	Oxalic acid, $C_2H_2O_4(s)$	-166.8
Benzene, $C_6H_6(l)$	29.756	Carbon tetrachloride, $CCl_4(l)$	-16.4
Ethylene, $C_2H_4(g)$	16.282	Glycine, $C_2H_5O_2N(s)$	-88.61

From Daniels and Alberty. These data have been obtained from Rossini, Wagman, Evans, Levine, and Jaffe, "Selected Values of Chemical Thermodynamic Properties," Circular of the National Bureau of Standards 500, U.S. Government Printing Office, Washington, D.C., 1952, and Rossini, Pitzer, Taylor, Ebert, Kilpatrick, Beckett, Williams, and Werner, "Selected Values of Properties of Hydrocarbons," Circular of the National Bureau of Standards C461, U.S. Government Printing Office, Washington, D.C., 1947.

Using values from Table 15.5, we obtain

$$\Delta \overline{F}^0_{298°} = -41.77 - 16.28 - (-56.69)$$
$$= -1.36 \text{ kcal/mole}$$

The reaction equilibrium thus lies on the side of products, but not sufficiently so to make yields at 25°C and ordinary pressures possible

Additional values of the standard free energy of formation ($\Delta \overline{F}^0$) can
be deduced by combining new previously unavailable measurements of
reaction equilibria together with values already at hand. Thus the value
of $\Delta \overline{F}^0_{298°} = -0.29$ kcal/mole for the hydrolysis of urea,

$$CO(NH_2)_2(s) + H_2O(g) \rightleftharpoons CO_2(g) + 2NH_3(g)$$

can be combined with $\Delta \overline{F}^0$ values of NH_3, CO_2, and H_2O to give $\Delta \overline{F}^0_{298°}$
for the formation of urea. The free energy change for the hydrolysis is

$$\Delta \overline{F}^0 = -0.29 = \Delta \overline{F}^0(CO_2) + 2\Delta \overline{F}^0(NH_3) - \Delta \overline{F}^0(H_2O) - \Delta \overline{F}^0(\text{urea})$$

By substituting values from Table 15.5, the standard free energy of formation of urea may be evaluated:

$$\Delta \overline{F}^0(\text{urea}) = 0.29 + \Delta \overline{F}^0(CO_2) + 2\Delta \overline{F}^0(NH_3) - \Delta \overline{F}^0(H_2O)$$
$$= 0.29 + (-94.26) + 2(-3.98) - (-54.64)$$
$$= -47.29 \text{ kcal/mole}$$

The choice of 25°C as the temperature for which standard free energy
values are tabulated is no more than a matter of agreement among
scientists to refer data to a single convenient temperature, and by no
means implies any special significance or desirability of this temperature
for reaction equilibria. On the contrary, most reactions can proceed
more favorably at other temperatures, and it is therefore important to
be able to calculate standard free energies and thence equilibrium conditions at any desired temperature. Several ways of doing this are possible, provided adequate data are available. The first to be considered is
based on the same thermodynamic equation as the calculations of the
temperature dependence of K_P, in Section 15.4. This equation,

$$\frac{\partial}{\partial T}\left(\frac{\Delta F}{T}\right)_P = -\frac{\Delta H}{T^2} \tag{15.37}$$

is equally valid for the standard changes $\Delta \overline{F}^0$ and $\Delta \overline{H}^0$:

$$\frac{d}{dT}\left(\frac{\Delta \overline{F}^0}{T}\right) = -\frac{\Delta \overline{H}^0}{T^2} \tag{15.38}$$

Hence if $\Delta \overline{F}^0$ is known at any one temperature T_1, its value at any other
temperature T can be found by integration, provided $\Delta \overline{H}^0$ is known
over the temperature range from $T_1 \longrightarrow T$:

$$\frac{\Delta \overline{F}^0_T}{T} - \frac{\Delta \overline{F}^0_{T_1}}{T_1} = -\int_{T_1}^{T} \frac{\Delta \overline{H}^0}{T^2} dT$$

As an example of the use of this equation, consider the formation of methane from carbon and hydrogen: $C(s) + 2H_2(g) = CH_4(g)$. The standard free energy at $T_1 = 298°K$ from Table 15.5 for the reaction is $\Delta F^0_{298°} = -12.14$ kcal. At room temperature the reaction could thus give useful yields under equilibrium conditions. Unfortunately, however, the reaction is immeasurably slow at room temperature, and no catalyst to accelerate it has been found. As an alternative, the feasibility of higher temperatures and presumably faster rates can be considered. To determine the equilibrium condition at, say, $1000°K$ requires knowledge of the values of $\Delta \overline{H}^0$ over the range $298°K–1000°K$, for which an approximate equation is

$$\Delta \overline{H}^0_T = -14.40 - 14.28 \times 10^{-3}T + 8.85 \times 10^{-6}T^2$$
$$- 1.07 \times 10^{-9}T^3 \text{ (kcal/mole)}$$

Inserting this and $\Delta F^0_{298°} = -12.1$ kcal/mole in Eq. 15.35, and then integrating, we get

$$\Delta \overline{F}^0_{1000°} = 1000 \left[\frac{-12.1}{298} - 14.40 \left(\frac{1}{1000} - \frac{1}{298} \right) - 14.28 \times 10^{-3} \ln \frac{1000}{298} \right.$$
$$\left. + 8.85 \times 10^{-6}(1000 - 298) - 0.54 \times 10^{-9}(1000^2 - 298^2) \right]$$

or

$$\Delta \overline{F}^0_{1000°} = +5.0 \text{ kcal/mole}$$

The value of $+5.0$ kcal/mole at $1000°K$ is a sufficiently large positive free energy to be unfavorable for appreciable yields. The calculation thus shows the very limited extent to which reaction is possible at the higher temperature; the unfavorable result is in the direction expected when $\Delta \overline{H}^0$ is negative (exothermic). On a thermodynamic basis, therefore, lower temperatures are necessary for favorable yield in this reaction, but thermodynamics gives us no indication of the rate of reaction (or of what may be a suitable catalyst to increase this rate). For other reactions for which $\Delta \overline{H}^0$ is less negative, or perhaps becomes positive, the conditions will be more favorable at high temperatures.

15.7. Determination of $\Delta \overline{F}^0$

The applications of the laws of thermodynamics to problems of equilibrium show their great value in predicting the effects of the variation of conditions on possible states of equilibrium. In order to make these predictions, however, a certain amount of information about the particular reaction or process of interest must first be supplied.

Thus, to use the methods of preceding sections, we must know the position of equilibrium for some particular set of conditions before those resulting from others can be calculated from thermochemical and equation of state data. The convenience of expressing the necessary information in terms of standard free energies of formation has just been discussed, but these useful values are not numbers contained in the laws of thermodynamics. They are instead obtained from experimental measurements, or from molecular theory if the system is simple or the accuracy needed not too great (or from a combination of both). The present section outlines some of the more important and useful methods for obtaining standard free energy values.

Direct Equilibrium Measurements

The most immediate and direct way to determine the standard free energy change of a reaction is by determining the pressure or concentrations of the reactants and products *when it is known that equilibrium has been reached*. Then one may calculate an equilibrium constant such as K_P from the equilibrium pressures, after which the value $\Delta \bar{F}^0 \ (= \ -RT \ln K_P)$ may be immediately obtained. The same procedure can be modified to suit reaction equilibria in solution and in other nongaseous systems, and would therefore seem capable of supplying any values which are needed.

Actually, however, the method falls far short of what one would like in many cases. The determination of *equilibrium* pressures or concentrations is often difficult. Carbon (as graphite) and hydrogen in stoichiometric proportions to form methane may be left together indefinitely at room temperature without reaction, and the measured pressure of hydrogen (which will be constant) does *not* determine an equilibrium constant because the system is not in equilibrium. This example is an extreme case of a potentially serious error in any direct equilibrium measurements. To guard against it, two precautions are taken: measurements are made by starting with varying amounts and proportions of reactants, and procedures are set up to approach equilibrium from both directions—that is, by starting with the products to let the reaction proceed in the reverse direction of the reaction for the equation as written. If the same value for the equilibrium constant is calculated under the different circumstances, there is then some reason for confidence that this value has been obtained for true equilibrium conditions.

Rather than make a direct determination of an equilibrium constant, one often would like to predict the outcome of a reaction from properties of the separate species without running the reaction at all, or at least without having to make difficult equilibrium measurements for it. Less direct methods of determining $\Delta \overline{F}^0$ than by equilibrium measurement are therefore of great value; two which have important uses will now be considered.

Calculations from Enthalpy and Entropy Values

From the definition $F = H - TS$, the standard free energy difference of any reaction at any temperature can be written as

$$\Delta \overline{F}^0 = \Delta \overline{H}^0 - T\Delta \overline{S}^0,$$

where $\Delta \overline{H}^0$ is the standard enthalpy difference and $\Delta \overline{S}^0$ the standard entropy difference. From this, values of $\Delta \overline{F}^0$ for desired reactions can be obtained from known values for $\Delta \overline{H}^0$ and $\Delta \overline{S}^0$ at the same temperature. The value of $\Delta \overline{H}^0$ is equal to heat absorbed during the reaction under standard conditions and furthermore (as discussed in Chapter 13) can be calculated for many reactions from known tabulated heats of formation of reactants and products.

To obtain the necessary values for $\Delta \overline{S}^0$ presents more difficulties. The direct determination of this quantity is no easier than that of $\Delta \overline{F}^0$ itself, since both are quantities governed by the second law, and must be calculated from quantities measured under equilibrium conditions (reversible absorption of heat, equilibrium pressures, or concentrations). The quantity $\Delta \overline{S}^0$ is simply the difference in the entropies of the products and reactants when these are in their standard states at the temperature specified; that is, for the general type reaction $aA + bB \rightleftharpoons cC + dD$, $\Delta \overline{S}^0$ is given by

$$\Delta \overline{S}^0 = c\overline{S}_C^0 + d\overline{S}_D^0 - a\overline{S}_A^0 - b\overline{S}_B^0$$

The determination of the required value $\Delta \overline{S}^0$ can thus be made from values of $\overline{S}^0$ for all species if these are known or can be measured. Experimental and theoretical studies of entropies and entropy changes of pure substances have led to two methods of obtaining such values of $\overline{S}^0$ for a considerable number of substances. A calorimetric method involving the "third law" of thermodynamics is the first to be considered, and later a method involving knowledge concerning spectroscopic energy levels will be taken up.

15.8. The Third Law of Thermodynamics and Entropy Calculations

Entropy has statistical significance as a measure of the manner in which the total energy of the system is distributed among the possible energy levels of the system. The number of energy levels involved is very large indeed, as already shown in Chapter 10, and both the number and spacing of the levels depends on the kind of molecules and their state of aggregation—solid, liquid, or gaseous. At ordinary temperatures the total energy of any substance is sufficient to involve many energy levels; the resultant entropy is considerable in amount and will have different values for different substances. For all but the simplest substances the entropy is impossible to calculate by statistical methods, because not enough is known about the number and spacing of the possible energy states.

On the basis of molecular and statistical theories, the variety of entropy values at high temperatures can be expected to become simpler at lower temperatures, because with less and less total energy the number of energy states of sufficiently low energy to be available for occupancy steadily decreases. Ultimately, in fact, only the lowest energy state or states (if more than one have the same energy or must be considered) will be used by the system.

From this point of view, the entropies of all substances show a much simpler behavior as the absolute zero of temperature is approached, and the assertion of the validity of this assumption is commonly called *the third law of thermodynamics*. Because the state of a substance at the absolute zero of temperature is so simple and essentially unique, it is a particularly logical state of reference with which to compare entropy of substances in other states. Since only entropy *differences* of substances enter into calculations of equilibrium conditions, the entropy of this reference state can be assigned any value whatever without affecting the result. The simple and convenient assigned value of zero entropy at zero temperature makes the entropies of all substances positive at temperatures above absolute zero (as well as entropies of less perfectly ordered substances at absolute zero). With this convention, the third law states that

$$\overline{S}_{0^\circ}^0 = 0 \text{ for a perfectly ordered crystalline phase}$$
$$\overline{S}_{0^\circ}^0 > 0 \text{ for a less ordered state} \qquad (15.39)$$

Most substances satisfy the first condition, and the exceptional cases result from various special circumstances. The nature of these is best illustrated by examples:

1. Some liquids, such as glycerol, supercool readily and at sufficiently low temperatures ultimately become vitreous or glassy without crystallizing. The amorphous solid, failing to crystallize, is left in some less ordered arrangement and this less well defined state is characterized by $\bar{S}_{0°}^0 > 0$.

2. Some pairs of substances, AgCl and AgBr for example, are sufficiently similar that cooling a melt of the two produces a mixed crystal with a single structure, containing both substances distributed through it in some one of many possible arrangements. The lack of definiteness in this situation even at absolute zero again leads to $\bar{S}_{0°}^0$ being greater than the value zero assigned to a unique, perfectly regular arrangement.

3. Other examples where $\bar{S}_{0°}^0 > 0$, for similar reasons are mixtures of isotopes of a single element, which freeze into some random arrangement, and crystals of such substances as CO, NO, and NNO. (Such molecules are so symmetrical that they fit equally well into the structure if turned end-for-end. Some are turned one way, some the other, but thermal measurements can never distinguish any one combination from all those that otherwise have the same structure.)

Exceptions of the kinds cited have values $\bar{S}_{0°}^0$ which are more or less definite, but must be determined by some other considerations than the third law alone. For the majority of simply behaved substances, the assignment $\bar{S}_{0°}^0 = 0$ permits calculation of entropy $\bar{S}_T^0$ at any temperature T if heat capacity data are available for the range from very low temperatures to the desired one. By the second law for heat (q) absorbed reversibly, $dS = q/T$. As long as there is no phase change, $q = \bar{C}_P \, dT$ per mole of substance at constant pressure, and for $P = 1$ atm, $dS = d\bar{S}^0$, whence

$$d\bar{S}^0 = \frac{\bar{C}_P \, dT}{T}$$

and the entropy $\bar{S}^0$ at temperature T is

$$\bar{S}_T^0 = \bar{S}_{0°}^0 + \int_0^T \frac{\bar{C}_P \, dT}{T} \tag{15.40}$$

$$= \int_0^T \frac{\bar{C}_P \, dT}{T}$$

if $\bar{S}_{0°}^0 = 0$.

This equation shows clearly the reason for the many investigations of heat capacities down to liquid hydrogen and liquid helium temperatures

(15°K and 4°K). To make strict use of it requires that $\overline{C}_P$ be known to $T = 0°K$. Fortunately $\overline{C}_P$ is very small, and moreover approaches zero rapidly at low temperatures, following the T^3 law given for solids in Section 10.10.

The small contribution of C_P/T to the integral in the range $0°K \longrightarrow 15°K$ can be estimated with sufficient accuracy from theory or by extrapolation, and experimental values at higher temperatures then can be used to calculate desired values of $\overline{S}_T^0$ by Eq. 15.40. This calculation is the only one necessary for solids, but for the liquid and gaseous states the increases in entropy upon melting and vaporization must be considered, as well as that from the further increase in temperature. These are also measurable, since $\Delta \overline{S}_{\text{fusion}}^0 = \Delta \overline{H}_f/T_f$ and $\Delta \overline{S}_{\text{vap}}^0 = \Delta H_v/T_v$. For heating of the liquid

$$\Delta \overline{S}^0(\text{liquid}) = \int_{T_1}^{T_2} \frac{\overline{C}_P(\text{liquid})\, dT}{T}$$

and similarly for the gaseous state. An actual case will be illustrated by the example of chlorine. Measured values of $\overline{C}_P$ are shown in the upper plot of Fig. 15.2, and heats absorbed in melting and vaporization are also indicated. The lower plot shows values of C_P/T, and the area under the curves from 0°K to 298.1°K, plus the entropies of melting and vaporization, will evaluate the standard entropy $\overline{S}_{298°}^0$. From this plot, the importance of the entropy values for the liquid and solid forms in determining the total is obvious, and it can also be seen that the values of C_P/T fall off rapidly below 40°K. The contributions itemized in Table 15.6 for the several steps lead to the total $\overline{S}_{298°}^0 = 53.3$ cal/mole deg for gaseous chlorine at 298°K and 1 atmosphere pressure.

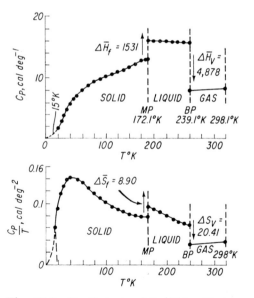

Fig. 15.2. *Specific heat and C_P/T for chlorine.*

Calculations based on measurements of this kind and the third law

TABLE 15.6.   *Third-Law of Entropy of Chlorine.*

Change	Calculation	Contribution
0–15°K, solid	Debye T^3 law	0.33 cal mole^{-1} deg^{-1}
15–172°K, solid	$\int_{15°}^{172°} \dfrac{\bar{C}_P(s)}{T}\,dT$	16.57
Melting at 172°K,	$\dfrac{\Delta H_f}{T_f} = \dfrac{1531}{172.1}$	8.90
172–239.1°K, liquid	$\int_{172°}^{239°} \dfrac{\bar{C}_P(l)}{T}\,dT$	5.23
Boiling at 239.1°K	$\dfrac{\Delta H_v}{T_v} = \dfrac{4878}{239.1}$	20.41
239.1–298.2°K, gas	$\int_{239°}^{298°} \dfrac{\bar{C}_P(g)}{T}\,dT$	1.88*
Entropy $\bar{S}^0_{298°}$		= 53.32 cal mole^{-1} deg^{-1}

After Giauque and Powell, *J. Am. Chem. Soc.* **61**: 1970 (1939).
* A correction to ideal gas behavior, or unit fugacity rather than 1 atm, makes a difference of 0.12 cal mole^{-1} deg^{-1} in this number and in the value of $\bar{S}^0_{298°}$.

TABLE 15.7.   *Spectroscopic and Third Law Entropies.*

Substance	Spectroscopic $\bar{S}^0_{298°}$	Third Law $\bar{S}^0_{298°}$
Ne(g)	34.948 cal/mole deg	35.0 cal/mole deg
Ar(g)	36.983	37.0
HCl(g)	44.617	44.5
HBr(g)	47.437	47.6
Cl$_2$(g)	53.286	53.32
CO$_2$(g)	51.061	51.1
H$_2$(g)	31.210	29.7
CO(g)	47.301	46.2
N$_2$O(g)	52.58	51.44
H$_2$O(g)	45.106	44.23

are available for a considerable and increasing number of substances; values of $\bar{S}^0_{298°}$ for some important ones are listed in Table 15.7. The use of standard entropy values combined with heats of formation to calculate standard free energies (ΔF^0) can be illustrated by the reaction of methane and formaldehyde to give ethanol: $CH_4(g) + HCHO(g) \rightleftharpoons C_2H_5OH(l)$. From Tables 15.5 and 15.7,

$$\Delta\bar{H}^0_{298^\circ} = \Delta\bar{H}_f(C_2H_5OH) - \Delta\bar{H}_f(CH_4) - \Delta\bar{H}_f(HCHO)$$
$$= -66.36 - (-17.89) - (-27.7)$$
$$= -20.88 \text{ kcal/mole}$$
$$\Delta\bar{S}^0_{298^\circ} = \bar{S}^0(C_2H_5OH) - \bar{S}^0(CH_4) - \bar{S}^0(HCHO)$$
$$= 38.4 - 44.5 - 52.3$$
$$= -58.4 \text{ cal/mole deg}$$

The value of $\Delta\bar{F}^0$ is therefore

$$\Delta\bar{F}^0 = \Delta\bar{H}^0 - T\Delta\bar{S}^0 = -20.880 - 298.2(-58.4)$$

or

$$\Delta\bar{F}^0 = -3.47 \text{ kcal/mole}$$

The negative value means that reaction of methane and formaldehyde at one atmosphere to give liquid ethanol is the possible spontaneous reaction. The equilibrium condition, $\Delta\bar{F}^0 = -RT \ln K_P$, gives

$$\log K_P = \frac{3470}{2.3RT} - 2.52$$

or

$$K_P = 330$$

This value is for pressures measured in atmospheres and at the temperature $298^\circ K$, since for each species $\Delta\bar{F}^0$ is defined at one atmosphere and $298^\circ K$. The equilibrium constant expression for the reaction is therefore

$$\frac{1}{P_{CH_4}P_{HCHO}} = K_P = 330 \text{ atm}^{-2}$$

(Only gas phase pressures appear in the expression for K_P, because the reaction gives as product liquid ethanol at $25^\circ C$; this is consistent with the values of $\Delta\bar{H}_f$ and $\bar{S}^0$ used in the calculation being for liquid ethanol.)

15.9. Spectroscopic Entropies

A second way of calculating the entropies of pure substances is based on a knowledge of the energy states of the molecules in the gas phase. These states arise (as explained in Chapter 10) from the translations, rotations, and vibrations of molecules having discrete quantum differences of energy. The distribution of molecules in different energy states at a given temperature can be calculated using the Maxwell-Boltzmann function discussed in Chapters 9 and 10, provided the number of energy levels as well as their differences in energy are known. From this, the principles of statistical mechanics make possible a calculation of the entropy, defined statistically in terms of this distribution. A proper development of the necessary formulas requires a detailed treatment of statistical mechanics, and only an indication of the possibilities and outcome of such calculations can be given here.

For such calculations even to be possible, it is necessary to know what energy levels are available and the energy differences between them. Part of this information is supplied accurately by calculations based on quantum theory, but some cannot be calculated accurately enough and must be obtained by experiment. The spectra of molecules result from transitions between molecular energy levels, and the arrangement and spacings of the levels can sometimes be deduced from the observed spectra.

To date, this analysis has been possible only for some three hundred molecules but, when successful, it gives very accurate entropy values indeed. Spectroscopic entropies of this kind for ideal gases are often accurate to four significant figures and sometimes to five. A comparison of values for a number of molecules with those obtained independently from specific heat data and the third law is given in Table 15.7. The agreement for all but the last group is to about 0.1 cal/mole deg or better; the last are examples of the exceptional cases for which $\bar{S}_0^0 > 0$ and show differences of 0.9 to 1.1 cal/mole deg. The third law entropies are all too small because the residual entropies $\bar{S}_0^0$ are not zero at the absolute zero of temperature, and are not measured by heat capacity experiments, whereas the spectroscopic entropies take into account all forms of molecular contributions to the actual entropy of the gas, and make no assumption about the state at $0°K$.

That the entropy from heat capacity data will be too small can be seen in another way. Suppose a gas is cooled from $298°K$ to very low temperatures, and all heat capacities and latent heats measured. If the final state is crystalline order, heat will be lost at some low temperature in the process of crystallization and there will be a measured entropy decrease which makes the value of $\bar{S}_0^0 = 0$. If it does not crystallize or does so to an incomplete state of order, all or part of this change on crystallization will not take place or be measured as q/T, and the total change will be correspondingly smaller.

Problems

15.1. For each of the following reactions, write the expression for K_P in terms of partial pressures and in terms of composition and total pressure. Also indicate for each the direction in which the equilibrium will shift with increased pressure.

$$CH_4(g) + 2H_2S(g) = CS_2(g) + 4H_2(g)$$
$$CO_2(g) + H_2S(g) = OCS(g) + H_2O(g)$$
$$2COF_2(g) = CF_4(g) + CO_2(g)$$
$$CrCl_2(s) + H_2(g) = Cr(s) + 2HCl(g)$$
$$CoO(s) + CO(g) = Co(s) + CO_2(g)$$
$$NH_4OCONH_2(s) = 2NH_3(g) + CO_2(g)$$

15.2. The reaction $2SO_2(g) + O_2(g) = 2SO_3(g)$ is industrially important and has been extensively studied. Bodenstein found the following equilibrium partial pressures in atmospheres for different starting conditions, all at $1000°K$:

P_{SO_2}	0.273	0.309	0.456	0.564
P_{O_2}	0.402	0.353	0.180	0.102
P_{SO_3}	0.325	0.338	0.364	0.333

(a) Calculate K_P for each mixture. To what precision are the values the same?
(b) What error in measurement of the pressure of SO_2, for example, would account for the deviations of K_P from constancy?

15.3. When hydrogen iodide gas at 1.00 atm is passed through a furnace at $1200°K$ the partial pressure of hydrogen in the equilibrium exit mixture is 0.185 atm. Calculate K_P.

15.4. Obtain the relation between the equilibrium constant K_1 of the water gas reaction $CO_2(g) + H_2(g) = CO(g) + H_2O(g)$ and the equilibrium constants K_2 and K_3 of the reactions

$$NiO(s) + CO(g) = Ni(s) + CO_2(g)$$
$$NiO(s) + H_2(g) = Ni(s) + H_2O(g).$$

15.5. The equilibrium constant K of the gas reaction $I_2 + Cl_2 = 2ICl$ can be calculated from the equilibrium constants of the gas reactions

$$2NO + Cl_2 = 2NOCl$$
$$2NO + 2ICl = 2NOCl + I_2$$

as well as from direct measurements. (a) Discuss how pressure measurements could be used to obtain equilibrium constants of the reactions involving NO. (b) What advantage can you see in this procedure to obtain K for $I_2 + Cl_2 = 2ICl$ instead of determining it from direct measurements.

15.6. The reaction $CH_3OH(g) + NOCl(g) = CH_3ONO(g) + HCl(g)$ has been studied as follows. At 50°C, CH_3OH was admitted to a vessel of volume 200 cm³ until the pressure was 38 mm. $NOCl$ was then introduced until the pressure was 80 mm. $NOCl$ absorbs light at 4000 Å but the other gases do not; from the measured absorption and calibration with known pressures of $NOCl$, the partial pressure of $NOCl$ in the equilibrium mixture was found to be 21 mm. Calculate K_P for the reaction.

15.7. (a) Introduction of 0.46 g of SO_2 and 0.54 g of Cl_2 in a 500 cm³ flask results in an equilibrium pressure of 650 mm Hg. Determine the equilibrium constant of the gas reaction $SO_2 + Cl_2 = SO_2Cl_2$ at 102°C. Express your answer in mm Hg and in atmospheres. (b) From your answer to (a), calculate the degree of dissociation and the final pressure if 2.00 g of SO_2Cl_2 are introduced in an evacuated 500-cm³ flask at 102°C.

15.8. The equilibrium constant for the reaction $PCl_5(g) = PCl_3(g) + Cl_2(g)$ at 250°C is $K_P = 1.78$ atm. (a) Calculate the degree of dissociation of PCl_5 when the total pressure is 1.00 atm. (b) Repeat for a pressure of 0.5 atm.

15.9. An amount 0.30 moles of PCl_5 is introduced into a 500-cm³ flask, and 0.10 mole of Cl_2 is then added. Calculate the degree of dissociation and the pressure before and after the addition of chlorine, using $K_P = 1.78$ atm for dissociation of PCl_5 at 250°C.

15.10. Will the dissociation of a fixed initial amount of PCl_5 be increased or reduced on addition of Cl_2 or PCl_3 under conditions which keep the total pressure constant?

15.11. At 400°C, the equilibrium constant for formation of phosgene by the reaction $CO(g) + Cl_2(g) = COCl_2(g)$ is $K_P = 22.5$ atm⁻¹. (a) How much phosgene will be formed if equal numbers of moles of CO and Cl_2 reach equilibrium at $P = 1$ atm? (b) How much will be formed if $P = 5$ atm? (c) How much phosgene will be formed if the initial numbers of moles of CO and Cl_2 are in the ratio 2:1 and $P = 1$ atm?

15.12. From the values of $\Delta \bar{F}^0_{298°}$ for the reactions below, calculate the equilibrium constants K_P at 25°C:

$2SO_3(g)$	$= 2SO_2(g) + O_2(g)$	$\Delta \bar{F}^0 = \quad 31.8$ kcal
$2H_2(g) + O_2(g)$	$= 2H_2O(g)$	$\Delta \bar{F}^0 = -109.2$ kcal
$N_2(g) + 3H_2(g)$	$= 2NH_3(g)$	$\Delta \bar{F}^0 = - \quad 7.82$ kcal
$C_2H_4(g) + H_2(g)$	$= C_2H_6(g)$	$\Delta \bar{F}^0 = - \quad 24.0$ kcal

Which of these reactions are possible in the standard state?

15.13. (a) Use free energies of formation to calculate $\Delta \bar{F}^0$ and K_P for the reaction $CO(g) + 2H_2(g) = CH_3OH(l)$ at 25°C. (b) Is a good yield thermodynamically possible at moderate pressure? (c) Calculate $\Delta \bar{H}^0$ for the reaction. Are better yields thermodynamically possible at higher temperatures?

15.14. The free energies of formation of methane, benzene, and toluene at 500°K are -8.05, 38.7, and 41.2 kcal/mole. Calculate $\Delta \bar{F}^0$ for preparing toluene from methane and benzene. Does this value indicate substantial yield if a suitable catalyst is found?

15.15. (a) Using values of K_P for the four reactions listed in Table 15.3, make plots of log K_P against $1/T$. (b) From the slopes of these plots, calculate average values of ΔH over the temperature ranges of the data.

15.16. The equilibrium constant K_P for the reaction $H_2(g) + I_2(g) = 2HI(g)$ is 67 at 350°C and 50 at 450°C. (a) Calculate an average heat of reaction over this range of temperature. (b) Using the answer to (a), calculate K_P at 300°C and the degree of dissociation of HI at 300°C.

15.17. (a) From $\Delta \bar{F}^0$ and $\Delta \bar{H}^0$ for the formation of nitric oxide at 25°C, calculate an approximate value of $\Delta \bar{F}^0$ at 300°C, assuming $\Delta \bar{H}^0$ is constant. (b) From heat capacity data, estimate an average $\Delta \bar{H}^0$ for the reaction over the range 25–300°C. How much difference will use of this value make in the calculated value of $\Delta \bar{F}^0$ at 300°C?

15.18. Using the value of $\Delta \bar{F}^0$ from Problem *15.17*, calculate the amount of nitric oxide in air at 300°C and 1 atm, assuming that air is 80 mole percent nitrogen and 20 mole percent oxygen.

15.19. (a) From appropriate thermodynamic data for ethane, ethylene, and hydrogen, calculate K_P for the reaction $C_2H_6(g) = C_2H_4(g) + H_2(g)$ at 25°C and at 200°C. (b) From these results, calculate the degree of dissociation of ethane at 25°C and 1 atm and at 200°C and 1 atm.

15.20. The density of acetic acid vapor at 110°C and 500 mm corresponds to an apparent molecular weight of 93 and at 150°C and 500 mm to a molecular weight of 75. Assuming that this is due to the dimerization $2CH_3COOH(g) = [CH_3COOH]_2(g)$, calculate (a) the fraction of acetic acid molecules at each temperature existing in dimers, (b) the average heat of dimerization.

15.21. The standard entropies $\bar{S}^0_{298°}$ of hydrogen, bromine, and hydrogen bromide are 31.2, 58.7, and 47.5 cal/mole deg. (a) From these values and from $\Delta \bar{H}^0_{298°}$ for $\frac{1}{2}H_2(g) + \frac{1}{2}Br_2(g) = HBr(g)$, calculate $\Delta \bar{F}^0_{298°}$. (b) Using empirical heat capacity formulas, calculate $\Delta \bar{F}$ for^0 the reaction at 1000°K.

15.22. The entropy of solid benzene at the melting point (5.5°C) has been found from heat capacity data to be 30.79 cal/mole deg. Use the following data to calculate $\bar{S}^0_{298°}$ for benzene as an ideal gas at 1 atm pressure:

$\bar{C}_p$ of liquid benzene $= 32.0$ cal/mole deg

Vapor pressure of benzene at $298°K = 95$ mm Hg

Heat of vaporization at $298°K = 8.09$ kcal/mole

15.23. The dissociation of $N_2O_4(g)$ near room temperature is assumed to be by the reaction $N_2O_4(g) = 2NO_2(g)$, but the reaction $N_2O_4(g) = 2NO(g) + O_2(g)$ also occurs under suitable conditions. (a) What difference would it make in observed gas densities at different pressures if both reactions occurred, rather than just the first? (b) The standard free energy of formation of $N_2O_4(g)$ is $\Delta F^0_{298°} = 23.4$ kcal/mole. Use these and other thermodynamic data to calculate K_P for the reaction to form NO and O_2. How much N_2O_4 would dissociate by this reaction alone at 25°C and 1 atm?

15.24. (a) Show that for reactions of ideal gases $K_P = K_C(RT)^{\Delta n}$ at temperature T, where Δn is the increase in number of moles of gases in the stoichiometric formula. (b) Show that

$$\frac{d}{dT} \ln K_C = \frac{\Delta \bar{E}^0}{RT}$$

where $\Delta \bar{E}^0$ is the standard internal energy change of the reaction (the equivalent for internal energy of $\Delta \bar{H}^0$ for enthalpy).

15.25. At high temperatures the dissociation of HI is followed by partial dissociation of I_2 to atomic iodine. (a) Assuming n_0 moles of hydrogen iodide are introduced into a flask of volume V, set up equations for the amounts of HI, H_2, I_2, and I present at equilibrium in terms of the equilibrium constant K_1 for $2HI = H_2 + I_2$ and K_2 for $I_2 = 2I$. (b) At 1000°C, $K_1 = 39$, and $K_2 = 0.17$ atm. Calculate the amounts of HI, I_2, and I at a total pressure of 1 atm. (This kind of problem is best solved by successive approximations, first neglecting any species present in small quantity.)

15.26. (a) Show, for the reaction $COCl_2 = CO + Cl_2$, that if a moles of $COCl_2$ and b moles of Cl_2 are introduced in a volume V, the amount x of CO present at equilibrium is given by

$$K_P = \frac{x(x + b)}{a - x} \frac{RT}{V}$$

(b) Show from this equation, by calculus or otherwise, that in a constant volume the dissociation of $COCl_2$ is decreased by addition of chlorine—i.e. that x must decrease if b is increased.

15.27. (a) For the reaction $AB = A + B$, show that if the fraction α of AB originally introduced which is dissociated is small, the fraction is given by $\alpha = (K_P/P)^{1/2}$. (b) If at the other extreme the gas AB is almost entirely dissociated, so that α is nearly one, show that $\alpha = 1 - (P/2K_P)$.

15.28. If oxygen is not in excess over solid carbon, the reactions $C(s) + \frac{1}{2}O_2(g) = CO(g)$ and $C(s) + O_2(g) = CO_2(g)$ may both occur. Discuss how the relative amounts of CO and CO_2 will depend on temperature and pressure.

15.29. Heat capacity data in cal mole^{-1} deg^{-1} for solid SO_2 to the melting point at 198°K are as follows:

$T°K$	15	25	35	50	75
$\bar{C}_P$	0.84	2.80	4.82	7.32	9.92
$T°K$	100	125	150	175	198
$\bar{C}_P$	11.42	12.64	13.81	15.19	16.44

(a) By a plot of $\bar{C}_P/T$ against T and graphical integration, calculate the entropy at the melting point. (See Problem *14.22*.) (b) The heat of fusion of SO_2 is 1.77 kcal/mole, and the average $\bar{C}_P$ of liquid SO_2 to the boiling point at 263°K is 20.8 cal/mole deg. Use these and other needed data from tables to calculate $\bar{S}^0_{298°}$ for $SO_2(g)$.

15.30. Nernst proposed an empirical equation for the equilibrium constant K_P of gas reactions at different temperatures which has the form

$$\log K_P = -\frac{\Delta H}{4.57\,T} + 1.75\,\Delta n \log T + (cK_C + dK_D - aK_A - bK_B)$$

In this equation, ΔH is the heat of reaction in cal/mole, Δn is the difference in number of moles of products and reactants. The coefficients a, b, c, d are the stoichiometric coefficients in the type equation $aA + bB = cC + dD$ (hence $\Delta n = c + d - a - b$), and the K's are empirical constants for each species which are for most substances close to 3 in value. What thermodynamic basis can you give for different terms appearing in this equation?

Suggested Reading

An extensive discussion is given by E. A. Moelwyn-Hughes in *Physical Chemistry* (Pergamon, New York, 1957). Examples of equilibrium calculations and a wealth of problems drawn from literature data will be found in *Problems in Physical Chemistry* by L. G. Sillén, P. W. Lange, and C. O. Gabrielson (Prentice-Hall, New York, 1952).

Sources of thermodynamic data are listed at the end of Chapter 13.

Chapter 16

Heterogeneous and Solution Equilibria

THE DISCUSSION in this chapter will concern chemical reactions and changes in state when one or more of the reacting substances is present as a solid or is in a solution, possibly with a non-reacting solvent. When more than one phase is present, heterogeneous equilibrium is involved, and there are of course many equilibria of this kind. The study of heterogeneous equilibrium is so large and involves so many problems important to chemists that many volumes have been written about our knowledge to date, and a great deal of work is yet to be done.

Fortunately, much of the mass of information available can be brought into perspective and coordinated by patterns of related behavior. The laws of thermodynamics are important aids in realizing these objectives, and much of the development of our understanding of equilibrium depends on thermodynamics. This prominent role should not, however, obscure the fact that only detailed molecular considerations can account for properties related by thermodynamic equations.

16.1. Chemical Potentials and Reaction Equilibria in Solution

In this section the thermodynamic requirement for equilibrium in solution will be developed and applied to some of the simpler kinds of reaction. Since the fundamental condition for equilibrium is that the free energy change in terms of chemical potentials must be zero, it is first necessary to determine how chemical potentials of different species in solution depend on their concentrations. This information can be found in a variety of ways, which may be based quite directly on experimental measurements or in simpler cases may be based upon theory and simplified models.

An important method, which is particularly appropriate for ideal or dilute solutions, is based on the equality of the chemical potential of any component in solution to the potential of this component in any other phase in which it is present. The other phase may be vapor, another solution, or a solid form, and all three possibilities can yield useful information.

Consider first an equilibrium of solution and vapor, for which the chemical potentials of any component i must satisfy

$$\overline{F}_i(\text{solution}) = \overline{F}_i(\text{vapor})$$

If the vapor is at low enough pressure to be considered an ideal gas, which is often the case, substitution for its chemical potential from Eq. 15.8 gives

$$\overline{F}_i(\text{solution}) = \overline{F}_i^0(\text{vapor}) + RT \ln P_i \qquad (16.1)$$

This equation is useful because the chemical potential in solution can be given in terms of solution composition, since vapor pressure can be related to solution concentration in a simple way for ideal or dilute solutions.

Ideal Solutions

For the simplest case of ideal solutions, the vapor pressure P_i of any species is (from Section 11.12) related to its mole fraction N_i in solution by Raoult's Law, $P_i = P_i^0 N_i$, where P_i^0 is the vapor pressure of the pure liquid i. Hence, for any component in an ideal solution,

$$\overline{F}_i(\text{solution}) = \overline{F}_i(\text{vapor}) + RT \ln P_i^0 N_i$$

Since P_i^0 is a constant at any given temperature, the equation is conveniently rewritten

$$\overline{F}_i(\text{solution}) = [\overline{F}_i^0(\text{vapor}) + RT \ln P_i^0] + RT \ln N_i$$

As the term in brackets is just the potential of pure i liquid at pressure P_i^0, designated $\overline{F}_i^0(l)$, the concentration dependence of chemical potential is given by

$$\overline{F}_i(\text{solution}) = \overline{F}_i^0(l) + RT \ln N_i$$

Although we have written $\overline{F}_i^0(l)$ to indicate the standard state of pure liquid, the (l) is usually omitted for simplicity and the equation written

$$\overline{F}_i(\text{solution}) = \overline{F}_i^0 + RT \ln N_i \qquad (16.2)$$

We shall do this for convenience, but it should be remembered that $\overline{F}_i^0$ so defined is for pure liquid and not the same as $\overline{F}^0$ for vapor at unit pressure, or strictly speaking, unit fugacity. The relation between the two is obviously $\overline{F}_i^0(l) = \overline{F}_i^0(\text{vapor}) + RT \ln P_i^0$.

With Eq. 16.2 for the potential of components in solution, the equilibrium expression for ideal solution reactions is easily derived in the same way that the expression for ideal gas reactions was obtained in the preceding section. If the reaction in solution is written as $aA + bB = cC + dD$, the equilibrium condition for $\Delta F = 0$, requiring that

$$c\overline{F}_C + d\overline{F}_D = a\overline{F}_A + b\overline{F}B$$

becomes, on substituting values for $\overline{F}_i$ by Eq. 16.2,

$$c\overline{F}_C^0 + d\overline{F}_D^0 - a\overline{F}_A^0 - b\overline{F}_B^0 = -RT \ln \frac{N_C^c N_D^d}{N_A^a N_B^b}$$

The difference of the standard values, $\overline{F}^0$, is constant for any one temperature regardless of concentration (just as for gases), and the product of mole fractions, *at equilibrium*, is therefore a constant in the same sense that K_P is. Denoting the product by K_N (the subscript N indicates that mole fractions are the units of concentrations), we then obtain

$$\Delta\overline{F}^0 = -RT \ln K_N$$

$$K_N = \frac{N_C^c N_D^d}{N_A^a N_B^b} = \text{equilibrium constant} \qquad (16.3)$$

As already remarked in Section 11.12, not many solutions behave ideally or even approximately so, and hence there are not many reactions in solution to which this simplest equilibrium result applies. A classic example is the esterification of acetic acid with ethanol:

$$CH_3COOH + C_2H_5OH \rightleftharpoons CH_3COOC_2H_5 + HOH$$

This equilbrium was extensively studied by Berthelot and St. Gilles in 1862. Some of their data obtained by analysis of the equilibrium solution resulting after reactions with varying initial proportions of acetic acid and ethanol are listed in Table 16.1. The ratio

$$\frac{N_{CH_3COOC_2H_5} N_{H_2O}}{N_{CH_3COOH} N_{C_2H_5OH}} = K_N$$

should be constant for this solution, which closely approximates ideality. The calculated K_N values given in Table 16.1 scatter somewhat but have no systematic trend, and examination of the calculations shows the probable reason for the scatter.

TABLE 16.1.   *Data of Berthelot and St. Gilles for Esterification of Acetic Acid with Ethanol.*

| INITIAL MOLES | | EQUILIBRIUM MOLES | |
Acetic Acid	Ethanol	(Ester or Water)	K_N
1.0	0.18	0.171	3.9
1.0	0.33	0.293	3.3
1.0	0.50	0.414	3.4
1.0	1.00	0.667	4.0
1.0	2.00	0.858	4.6
1.0	8.00	0.966	3.9

M. Berthelot and L. P. de St. Gilles, *Annales de Chimie et Physique* (3) **65:** 385 (1862), and later papers in this journal.

Consider the first set of conditions for which 0.171 moles of ester is obtained. The number of moles (n) of the different species are at equilibrium:

$$n_{CH_3COOH} = 1.00 - 0.171 = 0.829$$
$$n_{C_2H_5OH} = 0.180 - 0.171 = 0.009$$
$$n_{CH_3COOC_2H_5} = n_{H_2O} = 0.171$$

and therefore the equilibrium constant can be written

$$K_N = \frac{(0.171)^2}{(0.829)(0.009)} = 3.92$$

Notice that dividing the number of moles of a single component by the total number of moles present (1.18) to obtain mole fractions is unnecessary in this particular case because the total number of moles cancels out.

If the number of moles of ester found at equilibrium had been 2% less—0.168 instead of 0.171—the calculated K_N would be

$$K_N = \frac{(0.168)^2}{(0.832)(0.012)} = 2.81$$

This is smaller by 28% than that calculated previously; the scatter could thus easily be the result of experimental error. Other investigations have shown that K_N is virtually independent of concentration, the best value being very nearly 4.0 at room temperature.

Dilute Solutions

The reader will recall from Section 11.12 that solutions approach a simple limiting behavior at sufficient dilution: Henry's Law relates concentration and vapor pressure of solutes, and Raoult's Law applies similarly to the solvent. In the case of a solute in dilute solution, the vapor pressure (P) is given by $P = k \times$ concentration. For a dilute solution, concentration is conveniently expressed as molarity or molality and the value for k must be for the units chosen. Designating the concentration by C, then the vapor pressure is given by $P = kC$. Substitution in Eq. 16.1 gives for the chemical potential

$$\overline{F} = \overline{F}^0(\text{vapor}) + RT \ln kC$$
$$= \overline{F}^0(\text{vapor}) + RT \ln k + RT \ln C$$

Since the first two terms are constant, they may be combined into a standard value $\overline{F}^*$ characteristic of the dilute solution, giving

$$\overline{F} = \overline{F}^* + RT \ln C \text{ (dilute solute)} \tag{16.4}$$

For a reaction involving only dilute solutes, the use of this expression for the free energies in the fundamental equation gives, similarly to Eq. 16.3,

$$\Delta \overline{F}^* = -RT \ln K_C$$

and

$$K_C = \frac{C_C^c C_D^d}{C_A^a C_B^b} = \text{constant for equilibrium} \tag{16.5}$$

In the first equation it is to be noted that $\Delta \overline{F}^*$ is a standard free energy difference characteristic of the solutes present in dilute solution at the particular temperature of interest. It is *not* the same as the standard difference $\Delta \overline{F}^0$ of potentials for pure liquids because (1) it applies only for Henry's Law behavior of dilute solutions, which is seldom the same as ideal behavior, and (2) molarity rather than mole fraction is the unit for the concentration. The most precise interpretation of $\Delta \overline{F}^*$ is that it is a constant characteristic of the particular reaction and is determinable by suitable measurements.

An example of an equilibrium in dilute solution is the bromination of phenanthrene in carbon tetrachloride as solvent:

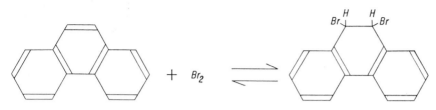

The equilibrium expression in terms of concentration is

$$\frac{C_{C_{14}H_{10}Br_2}}{C_{C_{14}H_{10}}C_{Br_2}} = K_C$$

Equations of this kind are more conveniently written by enclosing the chemical formula of a substance within brackets to represent its concentration:

$$\frac{[C_{14}H_{10}Br_2]}{[C_{14}H_{10}][Br_2]} = K_C \qquad (16.6)$$

This designation will be employed frequently in later discussions.

Price, in studying this equilibrium, started with known concentrations of phenanthrene and bromine, and analyzed colorimetrically for bromine at equilibrium. From the change in bromine concentration, the amounts of dibromide and phenanthrene could then be computed and used to calculate K_C by Eq. 16.6. A typical measurement at 25°C gave the following results:

$$\text{initial } [C_{10}H_{14}] = .00845 \text{ moles/liter}$$
$$\text{initial } [Br_2] = .00431 \text{ moles/liter}$$
$$\text{equilibrium } [Br_2] = .00184 \text{ moles/liter}$$
$$\overline{\text{loss of } [Br_2]} = .00247 \text{ moles/liter}$$

From these values, the other equilibrium concentrations were

$$\text{equilibrium } [C_{10}H_{14}] = .00845 - .00247 = .00598$$
$$\text{equilibrium } [C_{10}H_{14}Br_2] = .00431 - .00184 = .00247$$

The calculated equilibrium constant is then

$$K_C = \frac{(.00247)}{(.00598) \times (.00247)} = 224$$

Similar values for other initial concentrations are listed in Table 16.2, and show satisfactory constancy of K_C.

TABLE 16.2.   *Bromination of Phenanthrene in CCl_4 Solution at 25°C.*

Initial $[C_{10}H_{14}]$	Initial $[Br_2]$	$K_C = [C_{10}H_{14}Br_2]/[C_{10}H_{14}][Br_2]$
(moles/l)	(moles/l)	(liters/mole)
0.00845	0.00431	224
0.00845	0.00824	230
0.00845	0.01495	225
0.03405	0.00889	223
0.03405	0.02268	219
0.03405	0.02997	241

From C. C. Price, *J. Am. Chem. Soc.*, **58**, 1835 (1936).

This bromination reaction illustrates well the distinction between stoichiometric equations for reaction and the actual reaction steps. The simultaneous addition of two bromine atoms from molecular Br_2 across the double bond to give the dibromide directly is not a plausible molecular process, even though the overall reaction quantitatively agrees with the equation $C_{10}H_{14} + Br_2 \rightleftharpoons C_{10}H_{14}Br_2$.

Instead, evidence from kinetic studies indicates a probable role involving free bromine atom attack to form the unstable radical

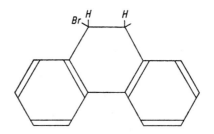

which reacts with Br_2 to give the dibromide and a bromine atom. The need for such distinction between the overall reaction and the molecular steps accounting for it is the rule, rather than the exception, and will receive attention in Chapter 22.

Role of the Solvent

The solution equilibria so far discussed have been for ideal solutions, in which no distinction need be made between solutes and solvent, or else they have involved only reaction of solutes. In many equilibria, however, the solvent takes part in the reaction, and when such reactions are run in dilute solution, simplification of the equilibrium expression by omitting the solvent concentration is possible. This results because any possible change in solvent concentration is negligible when the amount of solute available for reaction is much smaller than the quantity of solvent present. The chemical potential of the solvent will therefore change only slightly, and for approximate calculations that change can be neglected.

A system of interest in which this approximation can be made is the ionization of carbonic acid in water:

$$H_2CO_3 + H_2O \rightleftharpoons H_3O^+ + HCO_3^-$$

The equilibrium expression, including all reacting species, would be

$$\frac{[H_3O^+][HCO_3^-]}{[H_2CO_3][H_2O]} = K$$

Carbonic acid, however, is only weakly ionized in water and concentrations of $[H_3O^+]$ are of the order 10^{-3} moles/liter or less. These correspond to changes of the same amount in the concentration of the water present in the mixture. However, the concentration of water itself before ionization is approximately that of pure water,

$$H_2O = \frac{1000}{18} \text{ moles/liter} = 55.5 \text{ moles/liter}$$

and a change of 10^{-3} moles/liter evidently alters the concentration by less than one part in 50,000. This is insignificant relative to the water concentration, and it is unnecessary to consider it in the equilibrium expression. In practice a simpler equilibrium constant K_1 can be used with validity:

$$\frac{[H_3O^+][HCO_3^-]}{[H_2CO_3]} = K_1 \qquad (16.7)$$

where $K_1 = K[H_2O]$.

Similar approximations can be made in considering other reactions involving the solvent whenever the solutes are present in low concentrations. This is appropriate for water at solute concentrations as large as 1 molar, since loss of 1 mole of water per liter corresponds to a change in solvent concentration of less than 2%.

That solvent concentration can be omitted for dilute solution equilibria does not mean that the solvent plays no role. On the contrary, the nature and extent of such solution reactions are as much a function of solvent as of solutes. The nature of the solvent is also often significant for solute equilibria even when it does not appear in the reaction equation. Both these facts are reflected in the numerical value of the equilibrium constant, which for any given reaction can be expected to depend markedly on the solvent medium. Thus values of K_C determined for a solution reaction in one solvent will not hold for the equilibrium in another solvent.

Before turning to solution equilibria in which the solvent chemical potential must be considered explicitly, a few remarks about the ionization of carbonic acid are appropriate. Carbon dioxide gas is known to be appreciably soluble in water, and there is good evidence that it is only partly hydrolyzed; that is, there is an equilibrium:

$$CO_2 + H_2O \rightleftharpoons H_2CO_3.$$

This can formally be described by an equilibrium constant K_2 which, omitting $[H_2O]$ as before, is

$$K_2 = \frac{[H_2CO_3]}{[CO_2]}. \qquad (16.8)$$

In the chemical analysis for carbon dioxide, the ordinary procedures remove carbon dioxide in any form from solution; that is, H_2CO_3 is removed by decomposition to H_2O and CO_2, according to the above equilibrium. Thus a gross concentration $C = [CO_2] + [H_2CO_3]$ is determined. Since only this value is measured, the only equilibrium expression which can be calculated from measured hydrogen ion and total CO_2 concentration is

$$K_{app} = \frac{[H_3O^+][HCO_3^-]}{C}$$

where the subscript "app" indicates an apparent rather than the true equilibrium.

This value is, however, different from the true ionization constant K_1 for the reaction $H_2CO_3 \rightleftharpoons H_3O^+ + HCO_3^-$, as is apparent from

$$C = [CO_2] + [H_2CO_3]$$
$$= [H_2CO_3](1 + 1/K_2),$$

from Eq. 16.8. Hence

$$K_{app} = \frac{[H_3O^+][HCO_3^-]}{[H_2CO_3]} \frac{1}{1 + 1/K_2},$$

or

$$K_{app} = K_1 \frac{1}{1 + 1/K_2}. \qquad (16.9)$$

Since K_1 and K_2 are both constants that hold in dilute solution, there is no way from concentration studies to determine either separately, and only the ratio $K_1/(1 + 1/K_2)$ is measurable by ordinary methods. Thus the value of K_{app} in such a situation, simultaneously involving *two* equilibria, does not represent merely the ease with which H_2CO_3 ionizes, the equilibrium with dissolved CO_2 being also a factor. However, the value of K_{app} is usable to calculate ion concentrations if the gross concentration $C = [CO_2] + [H_2CO_3]$ is known.

16.2. Freezing Point of Solutions

The nature of solutions can usefully be studied by their equilibrium with solid solvent. If pure solvent freezes out when the solution is cooled sufficiently, an equilibrium between solvent crystals and solvent in solution is realized. The condition for this equilibrium is necessarily that the chemical potential of the solvent substance be the same in the two phases. Otherwise, it would prefer the phase of lower potential, and the other phase would disappear. Thus, at the freezing point,

$$\overline{F}_1(\text{solution}) = \overline{F}_1(\text{solid}),$$

where the subscript 1 indicates the solvent.

The dependence of the chemical potential of the solvent in solution, $\overline{F}_1(\text{solution})$, on the solvent concentration can be found in much the same way as it is in the case of solutes. If the equilibrium vapor pressure of solvent over the solution is P_1, then—since the chemical potentials of the solution and the solvent vapor must be equal—

$$\overline{F}_1(\text{solution}) = \overline{F}_1^0(\text{vapor}) + RT \ln P_1.$$

(It is assumed that the vapor behaves ideally.) But for dilute solutions Raoult's Law, $P_1 = P_1^0 N_1$, enables us to express P_1 in terms of the mole fraction N_1 of solvent in solution, giving

$$\overline{F}_1(\text{solution}) = \overline{F}_1^0(\text{vapor}) + RT \ln P_1^0 + RT \ln N_1$$

or

$$\overline{F}_1(\text{solution}) = \overline{F}_1^0(\text{liquid}) + RT \ln N_1 \qquad (16.10)$$

where $\overline{F}_1^0(l)$ is the potential for pure solvent.

Substitution of this value in the condition for equilibrium between solvent in solution and solid solvent gives

$$\overline{F}_1^0(\text{liquid}) + RT \ln N_1 = \overline{F}_1(\text{solid})$$

For pure solvent, $N_1 = 1$, and this reduces $\overline{F}_1^0(\text{liquid}) = \overline{F}_1(\text{solid})$; that is, the chemical potentials of pure liquid solvent and its solid form are equal. This will be the case at the freezing point of the solvent. But if solute is present, the potential of the solvent is lowered by the decrease in concentration. [$N_1 = (1 - N_2) < 1$, and $RT \ln N_1$ will be negative.] Unless some change occurs, the solvent is now more stable in solution than in the crystal, and solid solvent will dissolve, decreasing the total free energy of the system. A change tending to restore equilibrium is a decrease in temperature, because this makes the solid phase increasingly stable compared to the liquid phase. At some lower temperature, then, the values of N_1 and the chemical potentials will satisfy the equation

$$R \ln N_1 = \frac{\overline{F}_1(\text{solid}) - \overline{F}_1^0(\text{liquid})}{T}$$

or

$$R \ln N_1 = -\frac{\Delta \overline{F}^0}{T}$$

where $\Delta \overline{F}^0 = \overline{F}^0(\text{liquid}) - \overline{F}(\text{solid})$ is the free energy difference of pure liquid and solid solvents at the new temperature.

The amount by which $\ln N_1$ changes with temperature, which is the effect of solvent dilution on the freezing point, can be related to measured quantities by Eq. 15.30,

$$\frac{d}{dT}\left(\frac{\Delta \overline{F}^0}{T}\right) = -\frac{\Delta \overline{H}^0}{T^2}$$

Substituting $\Delta \overline{F}^0/T = -R \ln N_1$ gives

$$\frac{d}{dT} \ln N_1 = \frac{\Delta \overline{H}^0}{RT^2}$$

or

$$\frac{1}{N_1}\frac{dN_1}{dT} = \frac{\Delta H^0}{RT^2}$$

The quantity $\Delta \overline{H}^0$, however, is the enthalpy change involved when solvent solid changes to solvent liquid in solution, and so is equal to the heat of fusion $\Delta \overline{H}_f$ of the solvent. Using $\Delta \overline{H}_f$,

$$\frac{1}{N_1}\frac{dN_1}{dT} = \frac{\Delta \overline{H}_f}{RT^2}$$

For small changes of the solvent mole fraction (N_1), the corresponding change dT of the freezing point of the solution is thus

$$dT = \left(\frac{RT^2}{\Delta \overline{H}_f}\right)\frac{dN_1}{N_1} \tag{16.11}$$

Since dN_1 is negative when solute is added to the solution, this equation predicts a lowering or depression of the freezing point, as expected.

For many purposes, the freezing point depression is most conveniently expressed in terms of solute molality, m. This conversion follows from the observation that for a binary solution, any change of mole fraction of solute dN_2 is related to the solvent change dN_1 by $dN_1 = -dN_2$. (This follows from the statement, $N_1 + N_2 = 1$.) The change in mole fraction dN_2 when solute is added to give molality m, is for dilute solutions approximated with sufficient accuracy by $dN_2 =$ moles of solute/moles of solvent $= m/(1000/M_1)$, where M_1 is the solvent molecular weight. Using $dN_1 = -(M_1/1000)m$ in Eq. 16.11 and setting $N_1 = 1$ (an adequate approximation for dilute solutions), we obtain

$$dT = -\frac{M_1 R T^2}{1000 \Delta H_f} m \qquad (16.12)$$

The magnitude of the freezing point depression for a given solute molality thus depends on the *solvent* heat of fusion and molecular weight. For water, with $\Delta H_f = 1435$ cal/mole, $M_1 = 18.0$, and $T = 273°K$ (the normal freezing point),

$$dT = -\left(\frac{18.0 \times 1.99 \times 273^2}{1000 \times 1435}\right) m = -1.86m \qquad (16.13)$$

Thus the freezing point of a one-molal aqueous solution should be lowered by 1.86° from that of pure water, or $-1.86°C$, if the assumption of dilute behavior is valid for $m = 1$.

Deviations from the behavior predicted by Eq. 16.13 are usually evident at lower molalities. This is shown by the examples of aqueous solutions of urea and of aniline given in Table 16.3, where measured values

TABLE 16.3.   *Freezing Point Depressions of Solutions of Urea and Aniline.*

A. Urea

$m\left(\dfrac{\text{Formula wt.}}{\text{per kg } H_2O}\right)$	0.324	0.432	0.646	1.521
dT	−0.595	−0.789	−1.169	−2.673
$-dT/m$	1.837	1.829	1.811	1.757

B. Aniline

$m\left(\dfrac{\text{Formula wt.}}{\text{per kg } H_2O}\right)$	0.050	0.204	0.276	0.437
dT	−0.0910	−0.355	−0.466	−0.700
$-dT/m$	1.82	1.74	1.69	1.60

A. Caldwell and Politi, *J. Am. Chem. Soc.*, **60:** 1291 (1938). B. From Lewis and Randall, *Thermodynamics* (McGraw-Hill, New York, 1923, p. 290.)

of dT are listed for various molalities of the solutes, together with the ratio $-dT/m$, which from Eq. 16.13 should have the value 1.86 at sufficiently low molality. This value is evidently approached as m decreases, but small deviations are noticeable for aniline solutions even at $m = 0.050$.

With sufficient care the freezing point of a liquid can be measured with good precision, and since it is sensitive to solute impurities, the value of the freezing point is sometimes used as a measure of purity. If the freezing point can be measured reproducibly to .001°C, solute impurities of 10^{-3} molal or less can be detected. Impurities introduce another effect on freezing phenomena, which is also useful as a test of purity: namely, the solvent freezing out of a solution leaves the remaining solution more concentrated, and hence with a lower freezing point. Thus the temperature of a solution becomes progressively lower as freezing continues, in contrast to a pure liquid, in which, once freezing begins, it continues at the same temperature (the true freezing point) until no liquid remains. The change in freezing point during the freezing of an impure solvent can be made an index to the presence of impurity, and, by suitable analysis based on Eq. 16.11, its amount.

Freezing points are also useful in the determination of the state of aggregation of a solute in a particular solution. The calculated molalities used in the freezing point equation are based on an assumed molecular weight, and represent the actual number of solute particles only if the assumed value of the molecular weight is the actual molecular weight of the species present in solution. In the examples given in Table 16.3, the use of the formula weights for urea and aniline gives the correct value of dT/m for dilute aqueous solutions; this thus indicates that both solutes exist in water as single molecules corresponding to the given chemical formulas, at least at low concentrations. This is not always the case, and a particularly significant class of exceptions is found in aqueous solutions of salts and strong acids. Many precise measurements of freezing point depressions have been made, and ratios of the depressions to formula weight molality for a few solutes are listed in Table 16.4.

It is evident that all values of $-dT/m$ are much larger than 1.86, and moreover vary significantly from one substance to another even at formula molalities as low as 10^{-3}. Study of the data suggests a pattern of behavior, however, as the ratios for similar solute types become closer together at low concentration; they all are plausibly approaching values of $2 \times 1.86 = 3.72$, or $3 \times 1.86 = 5.58$. Van't Hoff first pointed this out, suggesting the hypothesis that one formula weight of the acid or salt

TABLE 16.4.   *Freezing Point Constants for Salts in Water.*

(The values of $-dT/m$ listed are computed from measured depressions dT and the number of formula weights per kilogram of water.)

Gram Formula Wts. per kg H_2O	HCl	NH_4Cl	$COCl_2$	K_2SO_4
0.002	3.69		5.35	5.27
0.005	3.64	3.62	5.21	5.15
0.010	3.60	3.58	5.11	5.01
0.050	3.53	3.49	4.92	4.56
0.10	3.52	3.44	4.88	4.32
1.00	3.94	3.33	6.31	

dissociates to produce two or three moles of solute particles and with the corresponding lowering of freezing point greater by a factor two or three than the value expected in the absence of dissociation.

The hypothesis that salts and strong acids in water are dissociated, forming charged ions, has of course been abundantly verified by a variety of evidence. The variations in behavior evident even at molalities of 10^{-3} present further problems requiring explanation, and this will be considered in Section 16.7 and in later chapters.

16.3. Other Solvent Phase Equilibria

There are a number of other equilibria between solvent in solution and another solvent phase. These also yield data which substantiate the points already made or provide further understanding. Among such observable properties are increased boiling point, lowering of solvent vapor pressure, and the phenomenon of osmosis occurring when solvent, but not solute, can pass through a membrane from one solution to another. These are all classified as colligative properties.

Solvent Vapor Pressure Lowering

If solute is added to a solution, the vapor pressure of solvent is lowered because of its decreased mole fraction. So also is the total pressure of the vapor in equilibrium with the solution, if the solute has negligible vapor pressure of its own; that is, it is a "nonvolatile" solute. The relation of solvent vapor pressure (P_1) to mole fraction (N_1) of solvent is, for dilute solutions, merely Raoult's Law:

$$P_1 = P_1^0 N_1$$

where P_1^0 is vapor pressure of pure solvent. The decrease in vapor pressure occurring upon the addition of solute to pure solvent is then

$$dP = P_1 - P_1^0 = -P_1^0(1 - N_1)$$

Since $N_2 = 1 - N_1$ for a binary solution, and for dilute solutions is approximately $= (M_1/1000)m$, the vapor pressure lowering in dilute solutions is given by

$$dP = -\left(\frac{M_1 P_1^0}{1000}\right) m \qquad (16.14)$$

The usefulness of this formula depends on the particular situation, and it is subject to the possible difficulty that small changes in vapor pressure have to be measured with considerable precision. For example, water at 25°C has a vapor pressure $P_1^0 = 23.76$ mm Hg, and the decrease in vapor pressure occurring over a 0.10 molal solution is

$$dP = -\left(\frac{18 \times 23.76}{1000}\right) 0.10 = -0.043 \text{ mm Hg}$$

Despite the difficulty in measuring such small pressure differences, the vapor pressure method has been used successfully in studies of aqueous salt solutions, and has given valuable information. (Solvent vapor pressure lowering can be considered also in terms of free energy changes, as will be recognized from previous treatments.)

Boiling Point Elevation

Since the vapor pressure of a solution is lower than that of pure solvent if the solute is nonvolatile, it is obvious that a solution will boil at the same pressure as pure solvent only if the temperature is higher. The necessary increase in temperature is called the boiling point elevation. This phenomenon is much like freezing point depression, as in both cases the solvent is made more stable by the addition of solute. The differences between the two processes lie in the temperatures at which they take place and the presence of the pure solvent as vapor rather than solid.

If these differences are taken into account, the relation between boiling point rise and solute molality can be derived in the same way as the freezing point formula of Section 16.2,

$$dT = \frac{-M_1 R T^2}{1000 \Delta H_f} m$$

To fit the boiling point situation, the temperature T must be the boiling, rather than freezing, temperature, and the quantity ΔH_f must be replaced by the heat of vaporization, ΔH_v. Here one must remember that heat is absorbed in amount ΔH_v per mole of solvent vaporized, rather than in amount $-\Delta H_f$ when it freezes; hence $-\Delta H_f$ must be replaced by ΔH_v. The boiling point equation, valid for dilute solutions of non-volatile solutes, is then

$$dT = \frac{M_1 R T^2}{1000 \Delta H_v} m \qquad (16.15)$$

Since all quantities on the right are positive, the equation gives positive values of dT; that is, the boiling point is increased by the addition of solute.

For water, $T = 373°\mathrm{K}$, $\Delta H_v = 9700$ cal/mole, and $M_1 = 18.0$; the equation becomes

$$dT = 0.513\, m \qquad (16.16)$$

The molal boiling point elevation is thus comparable to the freezing point depression, but is smaller because of the much larger heat for the vaporization process. The equation can be employed in much the same way, and is sometimes used to determine unknown solute molecular weights (for example, by comparing molality calculated from $m = dT/0.513$ in water with the weight of solute in grams per kilogram of water.) There are several difficulties, however.

1. The boiling point is quite sensitive to atmospheric pressure, which must therefore be controlled closely for accurate results.

2. Superheating of the liquid may result in unreliable boiling temperatures.

3. Any appreciable solute vapor pressure will change the boiling point, even to the point of decreasing it from that of pure solvent.

4. The solute must be stable and not decompose at the solvent boiling point.

Any of these factors can be troublesome, and boiling point measurements as a result have limited application.

Osmotic Pressure

The phenomenon of osmosis occurs when solvent, but not solute, is free to pass through some sort of barrier from one solution to another. This barrier is usually accomplished by placing a membrane porous only to solvent between two solutions of different solute concentrations. A variety of natural and synthetic films capable of this discrimination for suitable solute and solvent combinations are available, such as animal and plant tissues for aqueous solutions, palladium foil for permeability to hydrogen but not to gases of larger molecules, and, again for aqueous solutions, colloidal dispersions on copper ferrocyanide, $Cu_2Fe(CN)_6$. They are often called "semipermeable" membranes.

The osmotic effect can be illustrated by the arrangement shown in Fig. 16.1. The two closed containers A and B are separated by the

Fig. 16.1. *Osmosis:* (A) *closed containers;* (B) *open tubes.*

solvent-permeable membrane M, with a dilute solution of solvent mole fraction N_1 in A and pure solvent in B. The chemical potential of solvent in A will be approximately

$$(\overline{F}_1)_A = (\overline{F}_1^0)_A + RT \ln N_1$$

and hence less than the value $(\overline{F}_1^0)_A$ of pure solvent at the same pressure and temperature. If the pure solvent in B is at the same conditions of pressure and temperature, its potential is equal to $(F_1^0)_A$, and the direction of solvent flow through the membrane is from B to solution A of lower potential. This flow will continue until by some opposing effect the potentials $(\overline{F}_1)_B$ and $(\overline{F}_1)_A$ are equalized.

The value $(\overline{F}_1)_A$ will increase to equal $(\overline{F}_1)_B$ because in this case the transport of solvent into the closed container A results in increased pressure. If the solution compartments should be open, as in Fig. 16.1, B, the transport of solvent results in a greater solution pressure at the membrane which is proportional to the difference between the levels of the two free liquid surfaces. This difference of pressure is not necessarily small, as pressures of several hundred atmospheres sufficient to support a column of solution several thousand feet high can be developed, provided the difference in concentrations is sufficiently great and that the membrane is strong enough to withstand the consequent stress. (Needless to say, these are measured by more suitable methods than the difference in height of two columns of liquid.)

That an increase of solution pressure increases solvent potential, and hence counteracts the decrease produced by pressure of solute, is shown from Eq. 14.47, with notation corresponding to the present situation:

$$d\bar{F}_1' = \bar{V}_1\, dP$$

where dP is a small increase in pressure and $\bar{V}_1 = (\partial V/\partial n_1)$ is the change of the volume of the solution resulting from the addition of dn_1 moles of solvent at fixed pressure and temperature. (Constant temperature is assumed.)

For a pressure increase dP sufficient to restore equilibrium, its effect must balance the lowering of solvent potential produced by the change of concentration. For the change dN_1 (which is negative when solute is added), this lowering is

$$d\bar{F}_1'' = d(RT \ln N_1) = RT\, dN_1/N_1$$

If equilibrium is to be maintained, the total change in free energy must be zero; therefore the sum $dF_1 = dF_1' + dF_1''$ must be zero, and

$$\bar{V}_1\, dP = -RT\frac{dN_1}{N_1}$$

Introducing solute mole fraction N_2 rather than N_1, $dN_1 = -dN_2$, we get

$$dP = \frac{RT}{\bar{V}_1 N_1}\, dN_2$$

The pressure increase on the solution necessary to maintain equilibrium with pure solvent is called the *osmotic pressure*, denoted by the symbol Π. The partial molal volume of solvent in solution, $\bar{V}_1$, does not differ greatly from the molar solvent volume V_1, and is $V_1 = M_1/1000d_1$ liters mole^{-1}, where M_1 and d_1 are the solvent molecular weight and density in g ml^{-1}. Making these substitutions, the equation for the osmotic pressure of a solution of concentration N_2 is

$$\Pi \cong RT\frac{N_2}{(M_1/1000d_1)\, N_1}$$

(Note that comparing a solution of concentration N_2 to pure solvent with $N_2 = 0$ results in $dN_2 = N_2$.) Since the molality $m = n_2/(M_1n_1/1000) = N_2/(M_1N_1/1000)$,

$$\Pi \cong RT\, d_1 m \qquad\qquad (16.17)$$

where m is the molality of the solution.

The osmosis of sugar solutions against water has been studied extensively. Measured pressures for various molalities at 20°C and 60°C are listed in Table 16.5, together with values calculated from the approximation that $\Pi = RTm$. (The density d_1 of water is assumed to differ insignificantly from 1 g/cm³.) The agreement is good at lower molalities, but systematic departures become evident at higher ones. These become increasingly large, and for a 5 molal solution at 30°C the observed value is 187 atm as compared to the calculated 125 atm. The difference is partly the result of mathematical approximations in the derivation of the formula (a 5 molal solution differs more than slightly in concentration from pure solvent, and 187 atm is not an infinitesimal pressure difference dP); the more serious error is, however, in the initial assumption that the change in chemical potential of the pure solvent is $RT \ln N_1$ at these high concentrations.

TABLE 16.5.   *Measured and Calculated Osmotic Pressures of Sucrose Solutions in Water at 20°C and 60°C.*

Molality (moles/ 1 kg H₂O)	Π (20°C) (atm)	RTm (20°C) (atm)	Π (60°C) (atm)	RTm (60°C) (atm)
0.1	2.59	2.40	2.72	2.74
0.2	5.06	4.80	5.44	5.48
0.4	10.14	9.60	10.87	10.96
0.7	18.13	16.8	19.40	19.1
1.0	26.6	24.0	28.4	27.4

Berkeley and Hartley, *Phil. Trans. Roy. Soc.*, **206A**: 486 (1906); **209A**: 177 (1909). Frazer et al., *J. Am. Chem. Soc.*, **38**: 1907 (1916); **43**: 2497 (1921).

In recent years osmotic pressure measurements have found considerable use in studying the molecular weights of high polymers in solution. Vinyl chloride (CH_2CHCl), polymerized in suitable solvents, will yield long chain polymers:

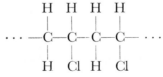

A measure of the extent of the polymerization of these chains can be obtained from values for the average molecular weight of the polymer. This is given by comparison of the molality deduced from osmotic pressure with the measured weight of polymer in solution. For example, the osmotic pressure of a solution of 0.40 g of polymer dissolved in 105 g of dioxane is 0.00064 atm at 27°C. From Eq. 16.17 the calculated molality is

$$m = \frac{\Pi d_1}{RT} = \frac{0.00064 \times 1.04}{.082 \times 300} = 2.70 \times 10^{-5} \text{ moles/kg}$$

and may be compared with the number of grams of polymer per kilogram of solvent,

$$w = 0.40 \times (1000/105) = 3.81 \text{ g/kg},$$

to give a "number average" molecular weight of

$$M = w/m = 3.81/2.70 \times 10^{-5} = 141,000$$

16.4. Solute Phase Equilibria

The equilibrium between a solution and a second phase containing the same substances is not confined to the solvent component. The effects for solvents discussed in the preceding sections have more or less close analogues for solutes, and the more useful and important of these will now be considered.

Solubility

The upper limit of the range of possible stable concentrations of many solutes in solvents is established by a maximum concentration called the *solubility*. The solubility is defined as the concentration of a solution which is or could be in equilibrium with the pure solute, either gas, liquid, or solid. For solid solutes the equilibrium of the saturated solution may be considered similar to that of freezing, as in both cases one component is in equilibrium with its solid form. The distinction is in the fact that this component is the solute for solubility, and the solvent for freezing phenomena.

For nonideal solutions, the distinction between solute and solvent is real and leads to differences of significance in the very similar thermodynamic equations for equilibrium. These require that the solute potential in solution equal that in the solid phase:

$$\overline{F}_2(\text{solution}) = \overline{F}_2(s)$$

where the subscript 2 indicates solute. For a dilute solution of a single solute, use of Eq. 16.4 for $\bar{F}_2$(solution) gives

$$F_2^* + RT \ln C = \bar{F}_2(s)$$

This is the condition which obtains when a solid solute is in equilibrium with a solution. Since $\bar{F}_2^*$ and $\bar{F}_2(s)$ are fixed by the temperature, and are independent of the concentration of solution, there is only one concentration, namely C_{sat}, which will satisfy the equation. Smaller molality evidently makes $\bar{F}_2$(solution) smaller than $\bar{F}_2(s)$, and the solution becomes the more stable phase. Attempts to increase the concentration beyond the saturation value make the solution unstable, relative to the solid, and equilibrium is re-established only if the added solute becomes solid—that is, precipitates out.

The actual saturation concentrations (C_{sat}) of different substances vary widely according to both the solute and solvent. In ideal or nearly ideal systems, solute and solvent are miscible in all proportions, as demonstrated by certain pairs of liquids in Chapter 11; less similar liquid pairs may be miscible only to a limited extent. Most salts have very limited solubility in solvents with dielectric constants much less than that of water, and some salts are virtually insoluble even in water. Actual solubility values are obviously of great importance for analytical and separatory purposes, but unfortunately they are beyond the power of purely thermodynamic reasoning to predict. The determination of such values and the understanding of the underlying molecular forces of solution phenomena are thus matters for molecular theory and laboratory experiment.

Among important aspects of solubility equilibria about which thermodynamics gives useful information is the temperature dependence of solubility. This must satisfy the basic equation

$$\frac{\partial}{\partial T}\left(\frac{\Delta \bar{F}_2}{T}\right) = -\frac{\Delta \bar{H}_2}{T^2}$$

If $\Delta \bar{F}_2$ is the standard potential difference $\bar{F}_2 - \bar{F}_2(s)$ between solution and solid, then $\Delta \bar{F}_2 = -RT \ln C_{\text{sat}}$ from Eq. 16.4, and substitution gives

$$\frac{d}{dT}\ln C_{\text{sat}} = \frac{1}{C_{\text{sat}}}\frac{dC_{\text{sat}}}{dT} = \frac{\Delta \bar{H}_2}{RT^2}$$

The value of $\Delta \bar{H}_2$ is the heat absorbed when solid solute dissolves into dilute solution (the heat of solution), and $\Delta \bar{H}_2 = \bar{H}_2^* - \bar{H}_2(s)$. This may be positive in value, in which case the solubility increases with temperature (analogous to freezing point consideration). Negative values are also possible, and in this respect solubility differs from freezing phenomena: a melting solvent goes to a solution largely made up of the same kind of molecules, but a dissolving solute goes from its solid form into a liquid that is largely composed of a different species of molecules of the solvent, which may have a quite different affinity for solute molecules than do other molecules of solute. The great variability of solubility with temperature and solvent, and the related differences in heats of solution for different solvents are thus understandable.

Distribution of Solute between Solvents

There is a rough analogue of solvent osmosis in the equilibrium distribution of a solute between two immiscible solvents. If two such solvents are in intimate contact—by shaking them together for example—an added solute will distribute itself between the two until at equilibrium its chemical potentials in the two solutions are equal. Thus for a solute (2) in two immiscible (or partially miscible) solvents, forming solutions A and B,

$$(\overline{F}_2)_A = (\overline{F}_2)_B$$

From the dilute solution expression of Eq. 16.4,

$$(\overline{F}_2^*)_A + RT \ln C_A = (\overline{F}_2^*)_B + RT \ln C_B$$

or

$$RT \ln \left(\frac{C_A}{C_B}\right) = (\overline{F}_2^*)_B - (\overline{F}_2^*)_A$$

Since the standard potentials $\overline{F}_2^*$ are constant, this requires that the ratio C_A/C_B of concentration in the two solvents must be constant at a given temperature, regardless of magnitude of either concentration separately (provided of course that neither concentration is so large that the assumption of simple dilute behavior is not valid).

This prediction is well borne out within the limitations set. For example, iodine is soluble in both carbon tetrachloride and water, which are virtually immiscible liquids. Varying amounts of I_2 shaken with the two solvents give the equilibrium concentrations listed in Table 16.6, and although these vary in magnitude by a factor four, their ratio is constant.

The distribution of solute between immiscible solvents is the basis of extraction procedures often employed in organic chemistry. Many compounds soluble in both an organic solvent and water have a lower

TABLE 16.6. *Distribution of Iodine between Carbon Tetrachloride and Water.*

$[I_2]_{CCl_4}$ moles/liter	0.020	0.040	0.060	0.080
$[I_2]_{H_2O}$ moles/liter	0.000235	0.000470	0.000704	0.000931
$[I_{2CCl_4}/[I_2]_{H_2O}$	85.1	85.2	85.4	86.0

chemical potential in organic solvents, as evidenced by their greater solubility in them. Ether is often used as the organic solvent, and shaking an aqueous solution with ether transfers most of the solute to the ether layer. This extraction from the aqueous solution can be repeated with a fresh supply of ether, removing more solute from the aqueous phase, from which virtually all the solute can be removed by a sufficient number of extractions. This can be equally well or better accomplished by a suitable continuous process for passing the organic solvent through the aqueous solution.

EXAMPLE

The distribution ratio for H_2S in benzene and water is about 6.0, or $[H_2S]_{C_6H_6}/[H_2S]_{H_2O} = 6$. If 100 cc of a 0.050 molar solution in water is shaken with 200 cc of benzene, the final concentration must satisfy $[H_2S]_{C_6H_6} = 6[H_2S]_{H_2O}$. The number of moles of H_2S in benzene and in water are then $n_{C_6H_6} = 0.2[H_2S]_{C_6H_6}$ and $n_{H_2O} = 0.1[H_2S]_{H_2O}$, and the sum must be the total amount present initially in the aqueous solution. Hence

$$0.2[H_2S]_{C_6H_6} + 0.1[H_2S]_{H_2O} = 0.1 \times 0.05$$

Substituting $[H_2S]_{C_6H_6} = 6[H_2S]_{H_2O}$ gives

$$(6 \times 0.2 + 0.1)[H_2S]_{H_2O} = 0.1 \times 0.05$$

or

$$[H_2S]_{H_2O} = \frac{0.0050}{1.3} = 0.0038 \text{ moles/liter}$$

Thus the concentration of H_2S in water is one-thirteenth its original value, and over 90% has been extracted by benzene. It should be noticed that the greater volume of benzene increases the amount of H_2S extracted. Using only 100 cc would have resulted in

$$[H_2S]_{H_2O} = \frac{0.1 \times 0.050}{0.7} = 0.0071 \text{ moles/liter}$$

or one-seventh its original concentration in water; less than 86% would have been extracted. It is also obvious that two successive extractions with 100 cc quantities of benzene are far more effective than a single extraction with the same total quantity.

If the solute associates or dissociates in one of the solvents, the distribution ratio is no longer a constant. For example, when benzoic acid is shaken with benzene and water, the fraction found in the benzene layer is progressively larger at higher concentrations, as shown by the data in Table 16.7. Benzoic acid is a weak enough acid in water that ionization is small at the given concentrations, and it exists almost wholly as single molecules of molecular weight, corresponding to the formula C_6H_5COOH.

TABLE 16.7.   *Distribution of Benzoic Acid between Benzene and Water at 20°C. (Concentration of benzoic acid in benzene is denoted by C_B, in water by C_W.)*

C_B	0.242	0.412	0.970
C_W	0.0150	0.0195	0.0289
C_B/C_W	16.1	21.2	33.6
C_B/C_W^2	1070	1090	1160

There is still less ionization for benzoic acid in benzene solution, and a variety of evidence indicates the existence of a double molecule (a dimer) in equilibrium with the single molecule (monomer):

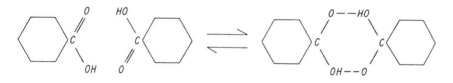

The complete equilibrium equations for the distribution of benzoic acid between water and benzene are

$$C_6H_5COOH \overset{K_d}{\rightleftharpoons} C_6H_5COOH \overset{K_c}{\rightleftharpoons} \tfrac{1}{2}(C_6H_5COOH)_2$$
water layer   benzene layer

The monomeric benzoic acid in the benzene layer must be in equilibrium with that in the water layer, but at the same time there must be sufficient benzoic acid present as the dimer in the benzene layer to satisfy the equilibrium with the monomer. There will therefore be a greater total quantity of benzoic acid in the benzene layer than there would be if it were present only as monomer. The effect will be greater for greater concentrations, and the greater the equilibrium constant, K_c, becomes relative to the distribution constant, K_d.

The equilibria may be treated quantitatively according to the usual principles. Let the total concentration of benzoic acid (monomer and dimer) in the benzene layer be C_B, expressed as moles/liter of monomer. (This is the total weight of acid present per liter of benzene solution, divided by the molecular weight of the monomer.) In terms of the concentrations of monomer and dimer,

$$C_B = [C_6H_5COOH]_B + 2[(C_6H_5COOH)_2]_B$$

For the dimerization, the equilibrium constant,

$$K_C = \frac{[(C_6H_5COOH)_2]_B^{1/2}}{[C_6H_5COOH]_B}$$

and

$$[(C_6H_5COOH)_2]_B = K_C^2[C_6H_5COOH]_B^2$$

Representing the concentration in the water layer $[C_6H_5COOH]_W$ by C_W, the equilibrium constant K_d for the monomers distributed between the water and benzene layers is

$$K_d = \frac{[C_6H_5COOH]_B}{C_W}$$

and

$$[C_6H_5COOH]_B = K_dC_W$$

It is seen from above that

$$[(C_6H_5COOH)_2]_B = K_c^2K_d^2C_W^2$$

and

$$C_B = K_dC_W + 2K_c^2K_d^2C_W^2$$

Dividing by C_W^2, for the overall equilibrium one obtains

$$\frac{C_B}{C_W^2} = \frac{K_d}{C_W} + 2K_c^2K_d^2$$

The first term is small relative to the second if K_c is large and C_W, K_d are not too small. For this case of considerable dimerization,

$$\frac{C_B}{C_W^2} \simeq 2K_c^2K_d^2 = \text{a constant}$$

For Table 16.7, the constancy of C_B/C_W^2 indicates this to be the case. On the other hand, if K_C is small (little dimerization), the second term is negligible relative to the first at low concentrations, and

$$\frac{C_B}{C_W} \simeq K_d$$

This equation holds then for very dilute solutions, or in cases where the dimerization is very limited.

The data showing the approximate constancy of C_B/C_W^2 is thus consistent with the assumption of dimerization. An additional consideration is necessary at lower concentrations, as the ionization of benzoic acid in water becomes significant, and the constant for the further equilibrium

$$C_6H_5COO^- + H^+ \rightleftharpoons C_6H_5COOH$$
water layer

must be incorporated in the overall equilibrium expression.

16.5. Ionic Equilibria and Chemical Potential

An important class of equilibria in solutions is that in which the solute dissociates into ionic species. The outstanding examples of systems in which this is important are those of salts and acids in water, and in other solvents of high dielectric constant, such as hydrogen cyanide, formamide, and ammonia. While there are not many such solvents with sufficiently polar molecules for significant ionization at ordinary concentrations, the case of water alone is important enough to justify special consideration of the properties of ionized solutes.

An enormous amount and variety of evidence supports the hypothesis that many solutes exist in water largely as ions, and that many others are at least partially ionized. The ability of electrolyte solutions to carry electric currents is direct evidence of ionization, and processes in electrochemical cells or electrolysis have reasonable explanations only in terms of ions. Less direct, but equally impressive, evidence comes from study of any of the equilibrium properties of electrolyte solutions. Much of this was unavailable when Arrhenius in 1887 made the then radical postulate that many solutes exist wholly or in part as ions when in solution, and the hypothesis was a controversial one for years. Since then, however, even the most confirmed skeptics have been convinced by the weight of accumulated evidence, and the postulate has long since been generally accepted as fact.

Because solutions usually exhibit most simple and regular properties when they are dilute, the behavior of ionizable solutes at low concentration will be considered first. Let the solute represented by the molecular formula RX dissociate according to the equilibrium

$$RX \rightleftharpoons R^+ + X^-$$

If complications resulting from the charges on the ions are disregarded for the present, the equilibrium can be treated as a reaction of ordinary solutes, and in sufficiently dilute solution should ultimately conform to the expression

$$\frac{[R^+][X^-]}{[RX]} = K_i$$

If C moles of solute dissolved per liter of solution result in C_i moles each of R^+ and X^-, leaving $(C - C_i)$ moles of unionized solute, the equilibrium is

$$\frac{C_i^2}{C - C_i} = K_i$$

The consequences of this condition for small concentrations C can be seen if the expression is rearranged to give an equation in C and the ratio C_i/C of ion to total concentrations:

$$C - C_i = \frac{C_i^2}{K_i}$$

or

$$\frac{C_i}{C} = 1 - \left(\frac{C_i^2}{CK_i}\right)$$

The concentration C_i of either ion cannot exceed the concentration of solute as initially added, provided it is the only source of ions, hence the ratio C_i/C will always be less than one. As C decreases, the term $(C_i/C)^2(C/K_i)$ must also decrease. The equation thus shows that the ratio C_i/C must be essentially unity at low concentrations, that is, the limiting state of the solute in dilute solution is complete dissociation into ions.

This conclusion from the mass action equilibrium expression is to be expected for any dissociative equilibrium. It is also reasonable from a molecular viewpoint, as the possibilities for ion recombination, if each ion concentration is halved, will be reduced by a factor four (other things being equal), while the possibility of the combined ion species RX dissociating is reduced only by a factor two when the concentration is halved. If the solute is a salt existing as an ionic crystal in its solid form, it is still more reasonable that dissolving the salt in water should in the first place result in ions as solute particles, which may or may not then combine to the associated form.

From all these points of view, one reasonably postulates that for dilute ionic solutions, ionization becomes essentially complete at low concentrations, provided the ionization is significant at any concentration; in fact, any other assumption is unreasonable. Equilibrium of dilute solutions should therefore be expressed in terms of the potentials of the separate ions at concentrations assuming complete ionization. For a concentration C of salt RX producing ions R^+ and X^-,

$$\overline{F}(R^+) = \overline{F}^*(R^+) + RT \ln [R^+] = \overline{F}^*(R^+) + RT \ln C$$
$$\overline{F}(X^-) = \overline{F}^*(X^-) + RT \ln [X^-] = \overline{F}^*(X^-) + RT \ln C$$

For equilibria which produce or consume the completely ionized solute, the potential of RX must therefore be expressed by the sum of the ion potentials:

$$\overline{F}(R^+) + \overline{F}(X^-) = \overline{F}^*(R^+) + \overline{F}^*(X^-) + RT \ln [R^+][X^-]$$

The sum $\overline{F}^*(R^+) + \overline{F}^*(X^-)$ is usually referred to as the standard potential of the solute RX, and abbreviated $\overline{F}^*(RX)$. Then for $[R^+] = [X^-] = C$ (the case for strong electrolytes),

$$\overline{F}(R^+) + \overline{F}(X^-) = \overline{F}^*(RX) + RT \ln C^2$$

the product C^2 in the concentration term resulting from two kinds of ions, each at concentration C.

Similar solution potentials can be written for solutes dissociating into several ions with differing charges, the only difference being in the relation of ion to formula concentrations. For the case of Na_2SO_4 dissociating according to $Na_2SO_4 \longrightarrow 2Na^+ + SO_4^{2-}$, the ion potentials are, just as before,

$$\overline{F}(Na^+) = \overline{F}^*(Na^+) + RT \ln [Na^+]$$
$$\overline{F}(SO_4^{2-}) = \overline{F}^*(SO_4^{2-}) + RT \ln [SO_4^{2-}]$$

A difference, however, appears when $[Na^+]$ and $[SO_4^{2-}]$ are expressed in terms of formal concentration C of Na_2SO_4. For if ionization is complete, $[Na^+] = 2C$ and $[SO_4^{2-}] = C$; hence

$$\overline{F}(Na^+) = \overline{F}^*(Na^+) + RT \ln 2C$$
$$\overline{F}(SO_4^{2-}) = \overline{F}^*(SO_4^{2-}) + RT \ln C$$

For equilibria producing Na_2SO_4 as $2Na^+ + SO_4^{2-}$, the sum of chemical potentials representing the ionized solute must be

$$\overline{F}(Na_2SO_4) = 2\overline{F}(Na^+) + \overline{F}(SO_4^{2-})$$
$$= [2\overline{F}^*(Na^+) + \overline{F}^*(SO_4^{2-})] + 2RT \ln 2C + RT \ln C$$

If we write the sum $[2\overline{F}^*(Na^+) + \overline{F}^*(SO_4^{2-})] = \overline{F}^*(Na_2SO_4)$ and combine the logarithms, we obtain

$$\overline{F}(Na_2SO_4) = \overline{F}^*(Na_2SO_4) + RT \ln 4C^3$$

the appearance of $4C^3$ resulting because 2 moles of Na^+ ions and 1 mole of SO_4^{2-} ions are obtained from one mole of Na_2SO_4.

Ion potentials and their combinations to represent the potential of a completely ionized solute find important applications to any ionic equilibria. Equilibrium expressions in terms of ion concentrations are only approximate for actual solutions, because dilute behavior is assumed; these equations must be modified if ion concentrations are large or if accurate calculations are necessary. To introduce the discussion of ionic solutions, two examples of ionic equilibria will be considered which illustrate both the significance of complete ionization at low concentrations, and the deviations from dilute behavior with increasing concentration.

16.6. Solubility of Salts in Water

The deduction in Section 16.4—that a solute has a fixed solubility for a particular solvent at a given temperature—is so simple as to be mathematically trivial when the substance does not ionize in solution. If the solute is a slightly soluble *salt*, however, the situation is different in characteristic and important ways.

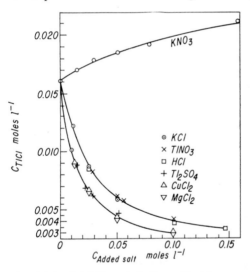

Fig. 16.2. *Solubility of thallous chloride as a function of concentration of salts with common ion and of potassium nitrate.*

Some of the classic early investigations of electrolytes are the studies by A. A. Noyes and co-workers from 1892 to 1905 on solubility of thallium chloride in water, both alone and when other salts are also present. Its solubility of 16.1×10^{-3} moles/liter at 25°C is increased appreciably on adding such salts as KNO_3 and CH_3COONa in concentrations of the order of 0.01–0.02 moles/liter, as shown by the data of Table 16.8 and Fig. 16.2. This effect is reasonably ascribed to the change in solvent conditions for the TlCl, and on this basis one might expect similar increases when more soluble thallium or chloride salts, such as $TlNO_3$ or KCl, are added to modify the solvent. The actual effect for these and other salts is instead a great decrease in the solubility of TlCl.

Thus, from Table 16.8, its solubility in a 0.025 molar KCl solution is 8.72×10^{-3} moles/liter, or about half its solubility in water.

TABLE 16.8.   *Solubility of Thallium Chloride in Aqueous Solutions at 25°C.*

Added Salt	Moles Salt/liter	Solubility	[Tl$^+$]	[Cl$^-$]	[Tl$^+$][Cl$^-$]
None	—	16.1×10^{-3}	16.1×10^{-3}	16.1×10^{-3}	259×10^{-6}
KNO$_3$	0.015	17.0	17.0	17.0	289
	0.030	17.9	17.9	17.9	320
	0.07887	19.2	19.2	19.2	369
	0.1574	21.2	21.2	21.2	449
NaCH$_3$COO	0.15	16.8			282
	0.30	17.2			296
	0.787	18.5			342
	0.1574	19.6			384
KCl	0.25	8.72	8.72	33.7	294
	0.50	5.93	5.93	55.9	331
	0.100	3.99	3.99	104	415
HCl	0.0283	8.36	8.36	36.7	306
	0.0560	5.65	5.65	61.6	348
	0.100	3.84	3.83	104	399
	0.1468	3.16	3.16	150	474
TlNO$_3$	0.0283	8.3	36.6	8.3	304
	0.0560	5.71	61.7	5.71	352
	0.1468	3.32	150	3.32	498
TlSCN	0.0107	11.9	22.6	11.9	269
CuCl$_2$	0.0125	9.05	9.05	34.1	308
	0.025	6.14	6.14	56.1	344
	0.050	4.22	4.22	104	439
Tl$_2$SO$_4$	0.0142	8.86	37.5	8.86	332
	0.028	6.24	62.2	6.24	388
	0.05	4.63	104	4.63	481

From Seidell, *Solubilities*, 3rd ed. (Van Nostrand, New York, 1940).

Similar effects are found for other uniunivalent (1–1) salts such as NaCl, and even more marked are the decreases for unibivalent (1–2) and biunivalent (2–1) salts such as Na$_2$SO$_4$, CuCl$_2$, and other salts listed in Table 16.8 and plotted in Fig. 16.2.

The decrease in solubility when a salt with an ion in common is added is the familiar appropriately named *common ion effect*, and it can be understood very simply on the basis of the chemical potentials of ionic solutes. For if the solubility equilibrium of thallium chloride is written

$$TlCl \text{ (solid)} \rightleftharpoons Tl^+ + Cl^-$$

then at constant temperature the *sum* of ion potentials must be constant in the saturated solution, since it is in equilibrium with the solid. If the solution is sufficiently dilute that ion concentrations may be used (the dilute solution laws hold), one may write for the solution,

$$\overline{F}(TlCl) = \overline{F}^*(TlCl) + RT \ln [Tl^+][Cl^-] = \text{constant}$$

This can be true only if

$$[Tl^+][Cl^-] = \text{constant} = K_{SP} \tag{16.18}$$

the constant K_{SP} being called the solubility product constant.

From Eq. 16.18, the reason for the common ion effect becomes obvious on realizing that the concentrations $[Tl^+]$ and $[Cl^-]$ are based upon the total quantities of the respective ions present, regardless of their source. That is, when KCl in concentration C moles of salt per liter and TlCl in concentration S are both present, the ion concentrations are $[K^+] = C$, $[Tl^+] = S$, and $[Cl^-] = C + S$. The solubility product for TlCl is then

$$K_{SP} = S(C + S)$$

and *not* $K_{SP} = S^2$, as for TlCl when no added common ion is present. Evidently an increase in C must be compensated by a corresponding decrease in S in order that $[Tl^+][Cl^-] = S(C + S)$ remain at least approximately constant.

The pronounced decreases in solubility which are encompassed by the common ion effect thus are understandable as a result of increased concentration of one or the other ion of the salt added from another source. No such explanation would be possible if either or both salts were non-ionized. A further point of importance is the fact that, as shown by Fig. 16.2, the effect is very similar for all 1–1 salts, and larger, but again similar, for all 1–2 or 2–1 salts.

A quantitative test of the dilute solution approximation to the ion potentials can be made by calculating the solubility products $S(C + S)$ for the various salt pairs in Table 16.8. The resultant values listed in the table are evidently not very constant, as they increase considerably for higher concentrations of the added salt. This is not surprising in view of the increased solubility when a salt without a common ion such as KNO_3 is added. The plot of the K_{SP} values against equivalent concentrations (equivalency is used in order to account for numbers of ions added by 2–1 and 1–2 salts) in Fig. 16.3 demonstrates that the increases of solubility product with ion concentration are much the same, whether or not one of the added ions is common to Tl^+ or Cl^-. The failure of K_{SP} to remain constant is thus reasonably to be ascribed to the fact that the solution into which TlCl dissolves contains electrically charged

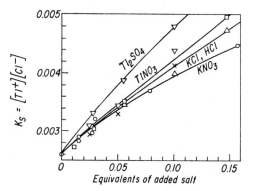

Fig. 16.3. *Ion product of thallous chloride as a function of salt concentration.*

ions and is a different medium than water. This difference brought about by the presence of charged ions, to be discussed further in later chapters, is important in all electrolyte solutions.

The increase in solubility product resulting from higher total ion concentrations is called the *salt effect* and in the examples is significant even at concentrations of 0.02 moles/liter. Because of the salt effect, dilute solution approximations in the case of ionic equilibria give valid results only at much lower concentrations than for nonelectrolytes, and this limitation must be kept in mind for any calculations where accuracy is required. Despite the difficulty, however, the approximate expressions are very useful for a qualitative understanding of ionic solutions, in a fashion impossible without explicitly recognizing ions as actual species in solutions. Calculations with tolerable errors for many purposes can be made very easily with their aid.

16.7. Freezing Points of Electrolytes

A second example of effects which are characteristic of ions in solution is the change in freezing temperature with concentration. As emphasized in Section 16.2, if the solid phase is pure solvent, the equilibrium embraces only the solvent as modified by solute and the solid solvent (for example, ice for aqueous solution). The effect of the ionization of solute is a greater molal depression of freezing point than that calculated or measured when there is no solute ionization.

The obvious explanation is that a wholly ionized salt, such as KCl, when dissolved in water produces equal concentration of both K^+ and Cl^- ions, and hence twice the concentration of solute particles present in the absence of ionization (calculated from the formula weight of the salt). On this basis, then, if the solute molality is m, assuming no ionization, the effective molality should be $2m$ for a 1–1 salt, or im for any salt giving i ions per molecule of salt. On this basis, the freezing point formula for dilute salt solutions should be

$$dT = i\left(\frac{M_iRT}{1000\,\Delta\overline{H}_f}\right)m \qquad (16.19)$$

or, if water is the solvent,

$$dT = 1.858im$$

This result can be tested by calculating the values of the coefficient i which actually give agreement with measured values of dT and m, and the results of this for KCl solutions are given in Table 16.9. The measurements for concentrations from 0.050 molal down to 0.001 molal give values of i from 1.883 to 1.978, which are thus much closer to the value of 2.00 expected for completely ionized solute than to the value of 1.00 for no solute ionization. At the same time, however, the values are measurably different in all cases from the value 2.00 expected if ionization is complete, and merely approach this value slowly even at 0.001 molal concentration.

TABLE 16.9.   *Freezing Point Depression of KCl Solutions.*

m (moles/kg)	$-dT$ (°C)	i
0.001	0.00368	1.978
0.002	0.00732	1.969
0.005	0.01815	1.953
0.010	0.03599	1.933
0.020	0.07122	1.917
0.050	0.17490	1.883

From Scratchard and Prentiss, *J. Am. Chem. Soc.*, **55**: 4355 (1933).

Deviations of the kind found for KCl solutions are characteristic of all salt solutions and are more pronounced for higher valence type salts. Attempts often have been made to account for them in terms of incomplete ionization, and hence an equilibrium of ions and unionized salt. It is now generally agreed, however, that the deviations result directly from the ionic character of the solute and the electrical forces between charged ions, rather than from the presence of neutral salt molecules in significant quantity at the low concentrations involved. The explanation of dilute electrolyte behavior in terms of interionic forces will be considered in the next and later chapters; here it will only be observed that the deviations change too slowly over too great a range of concentrations to be accounted for simply by ion association effects.

16.8. The Activity and Activity Coefficients

In the discussion of solution equilibria so far, principal attention has been devoted to those features which are primarily dependent on the concentration—that is, on the relative numbers of solute and solvent molecules. Many equilibria are of this type and give rise to such effects as freezing and boiling point changes and vapor and osmotic pressure differences, which are called *colligative properties*. In sufficiently dilute solutions the chemical potentials assume the simple forms used in the preceding sections, and lead to equilibrium conditions involving concentrations as products and ratios in the simple mass action form.

At higher concentrations, departures of the actual behavior from that described by the simple expressions become evident for all but the rare cases of ideal solutions, as the various examples have shown. The nature and magnitude of these deviations are important both for better understanding of chemical processes in solution and for many calculations involving solution equilibria. Realizing either objective requires quantitative expressions for the difference between ideal or dilute and actual behavior, and the purpose of this section is to introduce the forms of such expression which chemists have found most useful.

The quantitative treatment of equilibrium in concentrated solutions was originally developed by G. N. Lewis and his associates at the University of California over a period of years after 1900. Lewis introduced the idea of adding a multiplying factor for the concentration terms in the expressions for the equilibria of dilute solutions. The values for this factor were such that the equation gave correct values for the chemical potential at higher concentrations.

Thus, if concentration is expressed by the mole fraction N of solute, the dilute solution expression $\overline{F} = \overline{F}_N^* + RT \ln N_2$ is modified to read

$$\overline{F} = \overline{F}_N^* + RT \ln \gamma_N N \qquad (16.20)$$

and the quantity γ_N is called the *activity coefficient* of the solute (the subscript N specifies mole fraction units). If weight molality m is used to express solute concentration, the equation is written

$$\bar{F} = \bar{F}_m^* + RT \ln \gamma_m m \qquad (16.21)$$

(Both of these formulas represent the same chemical potential $\bar{F}$ of the solute in solution, but the quantities F^* and γ used to do this will have different values because of the difference in using mole fraction or molality to express concentration. Thus a 0.50 molal solution in water has a solute mole fraction 0.0089, and both the standard states and the deviation from ideal behavior are described in terms of different numbers according to the units chosen to represent concentration.)

The activity coefficient thus introduced is an empirical quantity, its value depending on the nature of the solute and solvent and the concentration of the solution. The values of the coefficient are definite if the reasonable requirement is made that the modified equation must become identical with the corresponding dilute solution expression at low concentrations. This requires that γ must have the value unity at great dilution. The necessary values of activity coefficients to give the correct chemical potentials at higher concentrations are then either larger or smaller, depending on the nature of the deviation from dilute behavior, and their magnitudes are determined from experimental measurements or from adequate theories of the underlying molecular interactions.

Another description of solutes in solution equilibria deriving from the above discussion is a closely related quantity called the *activity a*, the product of the activity coefficient and the concentration, $\gamma_N N$ or $\gamma_m m$. Thus defined, the activity can replace the concentration term, accounting accurately for actual behavior. It therefore describes both the direct effect of different numbers of molecules and ions, and the indirect effect of different amounts and kinds of interaction between them.

With these definitions of activity and activity coefficients, the equilibrium conditions for solutes previously used can be extended with validity to higher concentrations if the concentration C is replaced wherever it appears by the activity a, or the product $a = \gamma C$. This will be useful only if the differences between activity and concentration at appreciable concentrations can be predicted from the nature of the species present or determined from equilibrium measurements. Many different approaches to these problems have been devised and applied with varying degrees of success. The most useful lines of attack depend considerably on the nature of the solution in question and its observed behavior, and so are best considered for specific cases.

The activity coefficient of a solute is easily calculated from its vapor pressure, and such measurements can be useful provided the solute has a sufficiently large vapor pressure—that is, if the solute is sufficiently volatile. The calculation will be illustrated by data for solutions of 1-propanol in water, for which vapor pressures of the solute (1-propanol) at 25°C have been measured. When the solute is in equilibrium with its vapor, the chemical potentials in the two phases must be equal, giving (with mole fraction as the units of concentration),

$$\overline{F}^*(\text{PrOH}) + RT \ln \gamma N_{\text{PrOH}} = \overline{F}^0(\text{PrOH}) + RT \ln P_{\text{PrOH}}$$

or, since $\overline{F}^0$ and $\overline{F}^*$ are fixed standard values,

$$\frac{\gamma_N N_{\text{PrOH}}}{P_{\text{PrOH}}} = \text{constant} = \frac{1}{K_N} \qquad (16.22)$$

where the constant K_N includes quantities not depending on concentration. In order to determine γ_N at different concentrations from the equation, the value of this constant must be found. This is possible because of the stipulation that $\gamma \longrightarrow 1$ as $N \longrightarrow 0$. Thus we must have

$$\lim_{N \to 0} (P_{\text{PrOH}}/N_{\text{PrOH}}) = K_N$$

For the data in Table 16.10, the plot of $(P_{\text{PrOH}}/N_{\text{PrOH}})$ against N_{PrOH} in Fig. 16.4 gives $K_N = 284$ mm. Then values of γ_N can be computed from Eq. 16.22 in the form

$$\gamma_N = \frac{(P_{\text{PrOH}}/N_{\text{PrOH}})}{K_N} = \frac{(P_{\text{PrOH}}/N_{\text{PrOH}})}{284}$$

TABLE 16.10.   *Vapor Pressure and Activity Coefficients of 1-Propanol in Water at 25°C.*

N_{PrOH}	P_{PrOH} (mm Hg)	$P_{\text{PrOH}}/N_{\text{PrOH}}$	γ_N	m_{PrOH} (moles/kg)	$P_{\text{PrOH}/m}$	γ_m
0.010	2.68	268	0.95	0.56	4.79	0.95
0.020	5.05	253	0.90	1.13	4.57	0.90
0.050	10.8	216	0.77	2.92	3.70	0.73
0.10	13.2	132	0.47	6.17	2.14	0.42
0.20	13.6	68	0.24	13.9	0.98	0.19
0.40	14.2	35.5	0.13	37.0	0.38	0.075

Vapor pressure data from Butler, Thomson, and Maclennan, *J. Chem. Soc.*, **1933**: 674.

Values calculated in this way are listed in Table 16.10 and plotted in Fig. 16.4. It is evident that the solution deviates considerably from dilute behavior for mole fractions greater than 0.01.

The difference between γ_N and γ_m can be illustrated by calculating values of γ_m in the same fashion. The values of (P_{PrOH}/m) in Table 16.10, when plotted against m, give

$$\lim_{m \to 0} (P_{\text{PrOH}}/m) = K_m = 5.10 \text{ mm}/(\text{mole/kg})$$

and hence

$$\gamma_m = \frac{(P_{\text{PrOH}}/m)}{5.10}$$

The values of γ_m so obtained and listed in Table 16.10 do not differ greatly from those of γ_N at the same concentration (but N is different from m), and the difference in definition of molality and mole fraction makes γ_m smaller than γ_N at the higher concentrations. It is of course necessary that γ_N of a 0.1 mole fraction solution be different than γ_m of a 0.1 molal solution, because these are very different solutions.

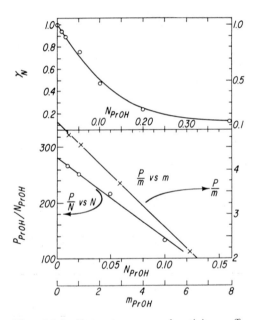

A further point of importance is the fact that either value of γ is close to unity and changes nearly linearly for solutions which would be considered moderately concentrated on a molality basis. Thus a 0.56 molal solution has $\gamma = 0.90$, from which we can be reasonably sure that γ is essentially unity below, say, 0.1 molal. This type of behavior is usually found in moderately dilute solutions of nonelectrolytes, *but not for electrolytes*.

Fig. 16.4. *Vapor pressure and activity coefficient of 1-propanol at various concentrations in water at 25°C.*

The convention adopted for solutes that $\gamma \longrightarrow 1$ as concentration approaches zero is not the only possible one. It is perfectly possible, for example, to require that γ becomes unity for the pure component as $N \longrightarrow 1$, rather than as $N \longrightarrow 0$ or $m \longrightarrow 0$. The activity coefficient then has a different significance, because it measures the deviation from limiting behavior of the solute when it is the component in excess, rather than the deviation from its behavior when it is present at very low concentrations.

Although either standard state—pure solute or very dilute solute—can be chosen in principle, practical considerations usually dictate one or the other.

If the solute and solvent can be mixed in any proportion, discussing both in terms of the pure liquid has experimental meaning and is useful for analyzing vapor pressure measurements. But many solutes have a solubility limit, and the limiting state of pure solute is then an imaginary, unmeasurable one. Under these conditions, comparison of actual and limiting dilute behavior is both necessary and more appropriate. To avoid confusion, further discussion will be confined to the latter choice, but the reader should be aware of the other possibility, which is discussed in texts on thermodynamics.

16.9. Activity of Ionic Solutes

The discussion of electrolyte solutions in Section 16.6 showed that departures from simple concentration laws are significant even at concentrations of 10^{-3} molal in water, and the need to describe deviations from dilute behavior quantitatively is thus particularly great for ionic solutions.

The importance of ions naturally suggests that activity coefficients be defined for ions and ion concentrations. Thus for NaCl in water, we are led to write

$$\overline{F}(Na^+) = \overline{F}^*(Na^+) + RT \ln \gamma_{Na^+} m_{Na^+}$$
$$\overline{F}(Cl^-) = \overline{F}^*(Cl^-) + RT \ln \gamma_{Cl^-} m_{Cl^-}$$

if molality is used as the unit of concentration. The chemical potential of salt, as ions, is then

$$\overline{F}(NaCl) = \overline{F}(Na^+) + \overline{F}(Cl^-)$$

or

$$\overline{F}(NaCl) = \overline{F}^*(NaCl) + RT \ln (\gamma_{Na^+} \gamma_{Cl^-})(m_{Na^+} m_{Cl^-})$$

At this point it is important to recognize that concentrations of ions in solutions are not independently variable. Both Na^+ and Cl^- ions in the same concentration result from dissolving common salt in water, but there is no known way of injecting either one separately without at the same time adding ions of opposite sign as well, in exactly the amount that there will be no net charge. In other words, all solutions are *electrically neutral*, and sodium or chloride ion concentrations can be made different only when other ions are also added. Thus if NaCl is added to water, the ion concentrations are $m_{Na^+} = m_{Cl^-} = m_{NaCl}$, the molality of the salt itself. The substance Cl^- does not exist as a solid or liquid alone in nature and cannot be added as such to the solution, but KCl can be added to give a molality m_{KCl}, and increase the concentration of both K^+ and Cl^- ions. The solute ion concentrations are then

$$m_{Na^+} = m_{NaCl}$$
$$m_{K^+} = m_{KCl}$$
$$m_{Cl^-} = m_{NaCl} + m_{KCl}$$

Relations of this kind always exist, no matter how many different ions are present or however they are introduced.

The importance of the condition of electroneutrality is the fact that it prevents us from measuring the separate effects of one ion alone on solution behavior. The quantities γ_{Na^+} and γ_{Cl^-} represent such separate effects and so cannot be measured separately. Thus the freezing of NaCl solutions can give information about $\overline{F}(NaCl)$, and solubility of TlCl in water as affected by other salts and ions give information about $\overline{F}(TlCl)$, but neither can determine anything about one of the ions alone. This fundamental limitation means that products $\gamma_{Na^+}\gamma_{Cl^-}$ and $\gamma_{Tl^+}\gamma_{Cl^-}$ can be obtained from experiment, but γ_{Na^+}, γ_{Tl^+}, γ_{Cl^-} separately cannot. To emphasize this, it is customary to represent such products by

$$\gamma_{Na^+}\gamma_{Cl^-} = \gamma_{\pm}^2$$

This is simply a definition of a new quantity $\gamma_{\pm}$ called the *mean ionic activity coefficient*. It is defined as $\gamma_{\pm}^2$ for 1–1 salts in order to express deviations from dilute behavior on an ionic basis rather than the unrealistic molecular basis implied if γ were used instead of $\gamma_{\pm}^2$, and m instead of m^2 (when $m_{Na^+} = m_{Cl^-} = m$). With this definition, the chemical potential of NaCl, as the sole solute in an aqueous solution, is written

$$\overline{F}(NaCl) = \overline{F}^*(NaCl) + RT \ln \gamma_{\pm}^2 m^2 \qquad (16.23)$$

The ionic character of other valence type solutes is recognized in a similar way best illustrated by example. Consider $BaCl_2$, which dissolves in water yielding free ions according to

$$BaCl_2(s) \longrightarrow Ba^{2+} + 2Cl^-$$

By rearranging the expression for the chemical potentials, $\overline{F}(\text{BaCl}_2) = \overline{F}^*(\text{BaCl}_2) + RT \ln \gamma_{\text{Ba}^{2+}} m_{\text{Ba}^{2+}} \gamma_{\text{Cl}^-}^2 m_{\text{Cl}^-}^2$. In this case $\gamma_\pm$ is defined by $\gamma_\pm^3 = \gamma_{\text{Ba}^{2+}} \gamma_{\text{Cl}^-}^2$, corresponding to *three* moles of ions per formula weight of salt. For salt molality m we have $m_{\text{Ba}^{2+}} = m$ and $m_{\text{Cl}^-} = 2m$, and the equation for BaCl_2 is

$$\overline{F}(\text{BaCl}_2) = \overline{F}^*(\text{BaCl}_2) + RT \ln \gamma_\pm^3 (4m^3) \qquad (16.24)$$

Although the weight molality m has been used here to express concentrations, since it is the one more commonly employed, the molarity C in moles per liter is also used. Activity coefficients may be defined analogously when m is replaced by C, and of course the values of the standard state and of $\gamma_\pm$ will be different because of the change in units. (In the case of aqueous solutions the differences are small, because molality and molarity are so nearly the same for dilute solutions.) Thus in terms of molarity

$$\overline{F}(\text{NaCl}) = \overline{F}^*(\text{NaCl}) + RT \ln \gamma_\pm^2 C^2$$

Values of $\gamma_\pm$ differing appreciably from unity are necessary to describe the effects of interionic forces in salt or strong acid solutions at concentrations of 10^{-3} molal or less. The effect of increased ion concentrations on the solubility of sparingly soluble salts such as TlCl or AgCl can be used to determine the dependence of activity coefficients on ion concentrations. The latter is an especially good example to illustrate the behavior because silver chloride is very slightly soluble in water $(C_s = 1.273 \times 10^{-5}$ moles/liter) and changes in solubility on adding other salts such as KNO_3, $\text{Ba(NO}_3)_2$, or $\text{La(NO}_3)_3$ have been measured with considerable accuracy. The equilibrium of AgCl in solution with its solid phase requires that

$$\overline{F}(\text{AgCl}) = \overline{F}^*(\text{AgCl}) + RT \ln \gamma_\pm^2 C_s^2 = \text{constant} \qquad (16.25)$$

if C_s is the saturation concentration. Since solubility C_s increases significantly when other ions are added in any appreciable concentration, the solubility product $K_{\text{SP}} = C_s^2$ is not constant. The effect of changing solution conditions is represented in the values of $\gamma_\pm$ required to make the quantity $\gamma_\pm^2 C_s^2$ strictly constant and Eq. 16.25 true for all concentrations. This constant value is called the true equilibrium constant, K^0, whence

$$\gamma_\pm^2 C_s^2 = K^0$$

The value of K^0 and the reference state of the system is fixed by the condition that $\gamma_\pm \longrightarrow 1$ as the ion concentrations approach zero. A plot of C_s^2 against concentration of added salt (Fig. 16.5), however, shows complications in determining exactly what this value is for zero ion concentration. There is appreciable curvature, and C_s^2 varies most rapidly at low concentration. This is troublesome because K^0 should be evaluated by taking account of the concentrations of Ag^+ and Cl^- ions as well as those of the added salt, and even concentrations of 10^{-5} correspond to a solution not quite ideal in behavior. The values of $\gamma_\pm$ are thus not quite unity even when the total concentration is no more than $C_s = 1.27 \times 10^{-5}$.

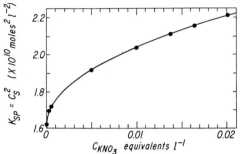

Fig. 16.5. *Variation of solubility product of silver chloride with added potassium nitrate.*

The accentuated curvature shown in Fig. 16.5 is characteristic of the behavior of equilibrium quantities for ionic solutions at low concentrations, and many expedients have been tried to avoid the difficulties it causes in extrapolation to zero concentration. The most successful, later justified by theories of interionic forces (see Section 17.14), is to plot the quantity against square root of concentration, rather than concentration itself. Moreover, the sum of the concentrations of both salts is used in order to account for all the sources of ions. The reason for using the square root of the total is evident from the resulting plot in Fig. 16.6, as the original increasing curvature is replaced by a nearly linear plot which can be extrapolated safely to zero concentration. The intercept at zero concentration is the value of K^0, since from Eq.

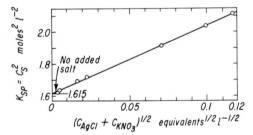

Fig. 16.6. *Solubility product of silver chloride vs. square root of total salt concentration with added potassium nitrate.*

16.25, K^0 equals the value C_s^2 for the hypothetical solution with $\gamma_s = 1$, where there is no deviation from ideal dilute behavior.

Such a solution is hypothetical because the equation involves the solubility product for ion interactions, when no ions are present (concentration zero), which we have no way of measuring. This does not, however, prevent the deduction of what the value would be by an extrapolation as shown in Fig. 16.6 or by other methods, and using the result to calculate $\gamma_\pm$ at the ion concentrations in the actual solution. Thus the value $K^0 = 1.615 \times 10^{-10}$ is found, and hence,

$$\gamma_\pm^2 C_s^2 = 1.615 \times 10^{-10}$$

or

$$\gamma_\pm = \frac{1.271 \times 10^{-5}}{C_s}$$

Values calculated for $\gamma_\pm$ from this equation are listed in Table 16.11 and plotted against concentration in Fig. 16.7. The initial rapid decrease of $\gamma_\pm$ with decreasing concentration, followed by relatively little change, is typical of ionic solutes, and is even more marked for higher valence-type salts. The significance of this behavior is that ions in solution have lower chemical potentials, and are correspondingly more stable, than nonionized solutes which never show such marked initial deviations. The difference

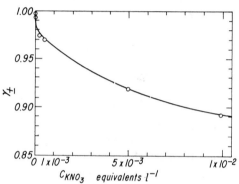

Fig. 16.7. *Activity coefficient γ for silver chloride in aqueous solution with added potassium nitrate.*

TABLE 16.11.   *Calculation of $\gamma_\pm$ for AgCl in Aqueous Solution with Various Concentrations of Added KNO_3.*

C_{KNO_3} (equiv/liter)	C_{AgCl} (equiv/liter; $\times 10^5$)	$C_{KNO_3} + C_{AgCl}$ (equiv/liter)	$\gamma_\pm$ ($= 1.271 \times 10^{-5}$ per C_B)
0	1.273	1.273×10^{-5}	0.998
1.28×10^{-5}	1.280	2.56×10^{-5}	0.993
2.61×10^{-4}	1.301	2.74×10^{-4}	0.975
5.09×10^{-4}	1.311	5.22×10^{-4}	0.970
4.97×10^{-3}	1.385	4.98×10^{-3}	0.918
9.93×10^{-3}	1.427	9.93×10^{-3}	0.892
1.37×10^{-2}	1.453	1.37×10^{-2}	0.878
1.64	1.469	1.64	0.868
2.01	1.488	2.01	0.858

must be ascribed to the electrical charges on the ions. The underlying basis for the effects of these charges will be taken up in Chapters 17 and 18, following the discussion of other properties of electrolytes.

Problems

16.1. (a) The standard free energies (25°C, gas at 1 atmosphere) of benzene and toluene are 30.99 kcal/mole and 29.23 kcal/mole. From the vapor pressures, calculate $\bar{F}^0(l)$ for each pure liquid. (b) Calculate the total free energy of one mole of an equimolar mixture of benzene and toluene.

16.2. In a study of esterification of acetic acid with ethanol, various amounts of acid are added to one mole of alcohol and the amount of acid esterified is determined, with the following results:

Initial moles of acid	2.00	1.00	0.67
Moles esterified	0.84	0.66	0.52

Calculate K_N for each case.

16.3. Halogen reactions such as $Br_2 + Cl_2 = 2BrCl$, in solution with CCl_4 and other inert solvents, conform closely to the ideal solution equilibrium expression. At 25°C, $K_N = 3.2$ for the bromine-chlorine reaction (a) Calculate the percentage of Br_2 and Cl_2 reacting if their initial mole fractions are each 0.1. (b) Repeat for $N_{Br_2} = 0.2$, $N_{Cl_2} = 0.1$, and for $N_{Br_2} = N_{Cl_2} = 0.2$.

16.4. Naphthalene (A) and m-dinitrobenzene (B) form an addition compound in dilute solution in nonpolar solvents, corresponding to $A + B = AB$. Concentrations of the species have been inferred by spectroscopic absorption measurements at different concentrations. From these the values $\Delta \bar{H}^° = 1500$ cal/mole deg and $\Delta \bar{S}^° = 7$ cal/mole deg have been calculated for standard states of unit concentration (1 mole/liter. Calculate K_C at 20° and 40° and the amount of addition compound formed at each temperature if $C_A = C_B = 0.01$ moles/liter initially.

16.5. From the values of K_C listed in Table 16.2, calculate the amounts of bromine at equilibrium for the second and last set of conditions. What percentage error in determination of these amounts would cause an error of 5% in K_C?

16.6. The ionization of dilute solutions of CO_2 in water at 25°C has been determined by conductivity measurements (see Chapter 18). From the total concentrations C of $CO_2 + H_2CO_3$ and ion concentrations $C_i = [H_3^+O^+] = [HCO_3^-]$ listed below, calculate values of K_{app} to test the dilute solution equilibrium expression.

$C \times 10^3$ (moles/liter)	1.87	10.89	21.40	32.20
$C_i \times 10^3$ (moles/liter)	0.0286	0.0692	0.0972	0.1194

16.7. The dissociation of N_2O_4, a familiar gas equilibrium, was also studied in 1890 in dilute solutions in chloroform at 0°C. (a) From the following equilibrium concentrations of N_2O_4 and NO_2 calculate K_C values as a test of the dilute solution equilibrium expression:

$[N_2O_4]$ (mole/liter)	0.129	0.227	0.3247	0.405
$[NO_2]$ (mole/liter)	0.00117	0.00161	0.00185	0.00213

(b) Calculate K_C for the gas reaction $N_2O_4(g) = 2NO_2(g)$ and compare with the solution values. Is there a solvent effect?

16.8. Freezing point depressions of ethanol in water for various molalities m are as follows:

m (moles/kg)	.0742	.0952	.1094	.1348	.2307
$-dT$ (°C)	.1371	.1755	.2017	.2482	.4253

Calculate the ratios $-dT/m$ as a test of the freezing point depression formula.

16.9. The ratio $-dT/m$, often called the freezing point or cryoscopic constant K_f, has the unusually large value 40 for camphor, which when pure freezes at 172°C. (a) What other unusual property of camphor must be associated with the large value? (b) How many milligrams of solute of molecular weight 150 must be added to 1.00 g of camphor to lower the freezing point 1.00°?

16.10. A weighed amount solute of known molecular weight is added to a known weight of solvent and the freezing point depression determined. The heat of fusion of this weight of solvent is also determined in a separate experiment. Can the molecular weight of the solvent be determined from these data?

16.11. Freezing point depressions by nitric acid in water are given below for gram formula weights of nitric acid per kilogram of water:

wt/kg	.002	.005	.010	.020	.050	.100
$-dT$	.0073	.0181	.0360	.0713	.176	.349

Analyze these data in the same way as for aqueous salt solutions in water (Section 16.2).

16.12. The molecular weight of a substance soluble in water is suspected to be about 200. A freezing point experiment in water is to be made to obtain a better value, and, to avoid errors from failure of Eq. 16.13 at high molalities, the molality is not to be greater than 0.01. How accurately must the change in freezing point on adding the solute be measured if the molecular weight is to be determined to 1%?

16.13. (a) Look up necessary data to calculate the freezing point constant $K_f = -dT/m$ for bromoform. (b) A formula weight molality 0.210 of phenol in bromoform lowers the freezing point by 2.20°C. What is the apparent molecular weight? (c) Assuming that dimerization is the only reason for the answer to (b), what percentage of phenol molecules are associated?

16.14. It is suspected that a solute A is partially dimerized in water: $A = \frac{1}{2}A_2$. (a) If the formula weight molality is m, obtain an expression for the solution molality in terms of m and the equilibrium constant K_m for the dimerization. (b) From this obtain a formula for the freezing point depression $-dT$ as a function of m and K_m. How could you analyze a series of freezing point measurements to test the assumption of dimerization and obtain a value for K_m if the test is satisfied?

16.15. The freezing point depression of an aqueous solution is 0.102°C. Assuming that the solute is nonvolatile, calculate the vapor pressure of the solution at 25°C and its boiling point.

16.16. Sulfur dioxide boils at -10.0°C and its vapor pressure changes by 33.7 mm Hg per degree at this temperature. What is the boiling point constant for SO_2 solutions?

16.17. Molecular weights of synthetic rubbers can be studied by osmotic pressures of solutions with a solvent such as toluene for which semipermeable membranes have been found. For 0.20 g of such a rubber in 100 g of toluene at 25°C, the difference of solution and solvent levels in an open-tube osmosis arrangement was 0.50 cm. Calculate an average molecular weight of the rubber, assuming that the solution density is the same as that of the solvent, 0.87 g/cm³.

16.18. (a) A 1.65 molal solution of sucrose in water at 0°C has an osmotic pressure of 43.8 atm, and a 2.36 molal solution a pressure of 67.7 atm. How well do solutions of these concentrations conform to the approximate osmotic pressure Eq. 16.17? (b) The actual partial molal volumes $\bar{V}_1$ of water at these two concentrations are 17.81 cm³/mole and 17.76 cm³/mole. How significant is the error introduced by setting $\bar{V}_1 \cong V_1$ in deriving Eq. 16.17?

16.19. A salt of molecular weight 150 has a solubility 0.060 moles/liter in water at 25°C and 0.075 moles/liter at 30°C. What is the heat of solution at these temperatures?

16.20. The heat absorbed on solution of succinic acid in a large excess of water at 5°C is $\Delta \bar{H}_2 = 6{,}500$ cal/mole. Van't Hoff found that the solubility increased by 20.0% from 0°C to 5°C. How well do these values agree with the solubility equation developed in Section 16.4?

16.21. Mercuric bromide distributes itself between benzene and water, which are immiscible, such that at 25°C the concentration in benzene is 1.10 times that in water. What volume of benzene is needed to extract 90% of the $HgBr_2$ in 1 liter of 0.1 molar aqueous solution?

16.22. Compare the amounts of $HgBr_2$ extracted from 50 cm³ of 0.1 molar aqueous solution (a) by shaking it with 300 cm³ of benzene and (b) by three successive extractions, using 100 cm³ of benzene each time.

16.23. Phenol exists almost entirely as single molecules in water, but association is suspected in solutions in chloroform. To study this, the distribution between the solvents is measured for several concentrations, with the following results at 25°C:

C in $CHCl_3$	.00685	.0157	.0489
C in H_2O	.00905	.0137	.0242

Can these data be explained by assuming dimerization of phenol in chloroform?

16.24. Equilibrium concentrations for distribution of aniline between water and toluene at 25°C are as follows:

C in H_2O	.023	.048	.102
C in C_7H_8	.181	.413	1.01

Assuming no association or ionization in water, analyze these data for the state of aniline in toluene. (Hint: Plot $C_{C_7H_8}/C_{H_2O}^2$ against C_{H_2O}.)

16.25. The solubility product constant of silver bromate in water is 5.8×10^{-5} at 25°C. Calculate its solubility in (a) water, (b) 0.005 molar KNO_3, (c) 0.005 molar $KBrO_3$. Neglect activity coefficient corrections.

16.26. The solubility of Ag_2CrO_4 in water is 8.2×10^{-5} moles/liter at $-25°C$. Calculate (a) the value of K_{SP}, (b) the solubility in 0.01 molar K_2CrO_4, (c) the solubility in 0.01 molar $AgNO_3$.

16.27. (a) The solubility of CaF_2 in water at 25°C is 2.7×10^{-4} moles/liter. What is the solubility in 0.01 molar NaF solution? (b) The solubility product of $CaCO_3$ is 8.7×10^{-9}. What is the solubility in water and in 0.01 molar Na_2CO_3 solution?

16.28. Show that the solubility S of Ag_2CO_3 for large added amounts of silver ion is given to a good approximation by $S = K_{SP}/C^2$, where C is the concentration of silver ion added.

16.29. Write expressions for the chemical potential in terms of concentrations of the following solutes in water: Na_2SO_4, Na_3PO_4, $Ca_3(PO_4)_2$. (These are examples of 1–2, 1–3, and 2–3 electrolytes.)

16.30. The solubility S of silver acetate in water at 25°C for different molalities m of added KNO_3 are:

m (moles/Kg H_2O)	0	0.2001	0.4010	0.8021
S (moles/liter)	.0664	0.0755	0.0798	0.0845

(a) Calculate the values of K_{SP} at each concentration and plot against the square root of *total* ion concentration (neglecting the distinction between molarity and molality) to obtain K_s at infinite dilution. (b) From this value, calculate $\gamma \pm$ of silver acetate for each concentration.

16.31. Data (Henry's law) for the partial pressures of ammonia above solutions of ammonia in water at 25°C are as follows:

C_{NH_3} (moles/liter)	.0618	.1883	.339	.601	1.005	1.242
P_{NH_3} (mm Hg)	.79	2.41	4.41	7.96	13.46	16.94

Calculate molar activity coefficients of ammonia in water by a procedure similar to that used in Section 16.8.

16.32. Freezing point depressions for solutions of sodium sulfate in water are as follows:

m	.00050	.00100	.00200	.00500	.0100
dT (°C)	.00271	.00536	.01057	.02574	.05013

(a) Calculate ratios dT/m. What can you conclude about the state of sodium sulfate in water? (b) The Debye-Hückel theory predicts that in dilute solution the value of i $= -dT/1.858m$ will vary linearly with $m^{1/2}$. Test the prediction with the data above.

16.33. Freezing point depressions of lanthanum nitrate solutions in water are:

m	.002	.005	.010	.020
dT (°C)	.014	.033	.062	.117

Calculate the van't Hoff factors i and discuss your results.

16.34. A variety of evidence indicates that aliphatic alcohols ROH in nonpolar solvents form dimers and chain polymers by hydrogen bonds, which are sufficiently stable to be identified spectroscopically, and correspond to the series of equilibria:

$$\text{ROH} + \text{ROH} = (\text{ROH})_2$$
$$(\text{ROH})_2 + \text{ROH} = (\text{ROH})_3$$
$$\cdots\cdots\cdots\cdots\cdots\cdots\cdots\cdots\cdots\cdots$$
$$(\text{ROH})_n + \text{ROH} = (\text{ROH})_{n+1}$$

(a) Show that the concentrations C_1, C_2, $\cdots$, C_n of monomer, dimer, and higher polymers are related to the total formula concentration C as ROH by

$$C = C_1 + 2C_2 + \cdots + nC_n + \cdots$$

(b) If the equilibrium constant K_C is assumed to be the same for each addition of an ROH molecule, show that

$$C_{n+1} = K_C C_1 C_n = (K_C C_1)^n C_1$$

(c) Combine these results to show that the ratio C_1/C, which can be measured, should then satisfy the relation

$$\frac{C_1}{C} = (1 - K_c C_1)^2$$

Hint: The following series expansion is legitimate for $x < 1$:

$$\frac{1}{(1 - x)^2} = 1 + 2x + 3x^2 + (n + 1)x^n + \cdots$$

16.35. (a) For ideal solutions, which mix without heat changes, the heat of solution of the solute is equal to a heat of fusion $\Delta \overline{H}_f$ of the pure solute appropriate to the temperature as inferred from Kirchhoff's law.

Show that the solubility equation, where N_{sat} is the saturation mole fraction of the *solute*, is then

$$\frac{d}{dT} \ln N_{\text{sat}} = \frac{\Delta \overline{H}_f}{RT^2}$$

(b) If this heat of fusion can be taken as independent of temperature and equal to the value $\Delta \overline{H}_f$ at the melting point T_m of the pure solute, show that the solubility at temperature T is

$$\ln N_{\text{sat}} = \frac{\Delta \overline{H}_f}{R} \left(\frac{1}{T_m} - \frac{1}{T} \right)$$

(c) Phenanthrene melts at 100°C, an appropriate average $\Delta \overline{H}_f$ from Kirchhoff's laws is 4500 cal/mole, and it forms nearly ideal solutions in benzene. What is the solubility of phenanthrene in benzene at 25°C?

16.36. The solubility of silver chloride in water is increased by addition of ammonia. (a) Show that this can be explained if the silver ion forms a complex ion with ammonia. (b) If virtually all the silver complexes to form $Ag(NH_3)_2^+$, show that the solubility C_{AgCl} is related to the concentration C of ammonia by the expression $C/C_{AgCl} = $ constant. (c) If chloride ion is added in excess to the solution, so that the total concentrations of chloride ion and silver are C_{Cl^-} and C_{Ag}, show that $C^2/C_{Cl^-}C_{Ag} = $ constant.

16.37. Hydrogen gas dissolves in some solid metals at high temperatures. In nickel at 1100°K, the moles dissolved per mole of nickel at various gas pressures P are as follows:

P (atm)	0.419	0.588	0.767	1.05
n_{H_2}	.000137	.000166	.000187	.000214

Show that the state of dissolved hydrogen is not reasonably as molecules, but that the assumption of atomic hydrogen as the form of the solute is consistent with these data.

16.38. Henry's law studies of the solubility of NH_3 in water at various gas pressures gave the following results at 25°C and 40°C:

	At 25°C	P_{NH_3} (mm)	369	754	1120	1557
		C_{NH_3} (moles/liter)	.0497	.1010	.1499	.2050
	At 40°C	P_{NH_3} (mm)	432	879	1315	1798
		C_{NH_3} (moles/liter)	.0426	.0858	.1260	.1722

(a) How closely do these data conform to Henry's law? (b) The vapor pressure of pure ammonia is 9.86 atm at 25°C and 15.34 atm at 40°C. Are the deviations from ideal behavior positive or negative? (c) From your results for (a), is the heat of solution of ammonia positive or negative? Calculate approximate values for this heat, and for the heat of vaporization of pure liquid ammonia. How do the values compare?

16.39. The freezing point formula for solutions,

$$dT = -\frac{M_1 RT}{1000 \, \Delta \bar{H}_f} m$$

is valid only for small molalities m and freezing point depressions dT. (a) Show, by integrating the equation

$$\frac{1}{N_1}\frac{dN_1}{dT} = \frac{\Delta \bar{H}_f}{RT^2}$$

with the assumption $\Delta \bar{H}_f = A - BT$, that a more accurate expression has the form

$$\ln N_1 = \frac{A}{R}\left(\frac{1}{T_o} - \frac{1}{T}\right) - \frac{B}{R}\ln\frac{T_o}{T}$$

where N_1 is the mole fraction of solvent at T, and T_o is the freezing point of pure solvent. (b) Show for T nearly the same as T_0 and N_1 nearly unity that this gives the approximate formula. (Hints: Write $N_1 = 1 - N_2$ and $T = T_o - dT$, and use the result $\ln(1 - x) \cong -x$ where x is small.

16.40. The freezing point of a solvent containing some impurity decreases as more solvent freezes because the remaining solution has increasing concentrations of impurity. Express the freezing temperature as a function of the amount of solvent frozen out from the original solution, and show how estimates of both the original amount of impurity and the freezing point of pure solvent can be deduced from this relation. (Hint: Express your equation in terms of the reciprocal of the amount of solvent in solution.)

Suggested Reading

All textbooks of physical chemistry or chemical thermodynamics contain some discussion of the subjects of this chapter. The references for Chapter 15 can be recommended for the illustrative material they contain, as can the text *Thermodynamics* by G. N. Lewis and N. Randall, revised by Pitzer and Brewer (2nd ed., McGraw-Hill, New York, 1961).

More detailed treatments of solution behavior are given by J. H. Hildebrand and R. L. Scott in *Solubility of Nonelectrolytes* (3rd ed., Reinhold, New York, 1950) and by J. S. Rowlinson in *Liquids and Liquid Mixtures* (Academic Press, New York, 1959).

Chapter 17

Electrochemical Reactions and Galvanic Cells

THE ELECTRICAL CHANGES accompanying chemical reaction under suitable conditions have been important almost from the time electricity itself was first studied as a natural phenomenon accessible to experiment rather than being regarded as a supernatural manifestation. Thus, although Benjamin Franklin's 1747 theory of electricity as a fluid transferred from one phase to another has no direct chemical implications, Galvani in 1791 discovered electrical potential differences in animal nerves, set up as we now know by electrochemical processes. Soon afterward another Italian, Volta, made his voltaic pile of zinc and silver plates separated by cloth soaked in salt solution, and produced the first electrolytic cell.

The basic laws of electrolysis were discovered by Faraday in 1834 as a result of brilliantly conceived experiments, and he was quick to realize their importance in relation to chemical reaction. Although Faraday saw in electrochemical processes strong evidence for the atomic nature of matter, a full understanding of the relations involved required much further research and development of atomic theory.

Study of electrolyte solutions and of reactions at electrodes in solution became an important phase of chemistry in the nineteenth century. There is considerable justice in the statement that physical chemistry as an important field of science began in about 1890, with electrochemical studies by such workers as Ostwald, Arrhenius, Kohlrausch, and van't Hoff in Europe, and A. A. Noyes in the United States.

The pioneer work on solubilities of salts has been mentioned in Section 16.6; the subject of electrolytic conduction, first investigated systematically by Kohlrausch, will be taken up in Chapter 18. In this chapter the principal subject will be the relation of reaction at electrodes and in electrolyte solutions to potential differences and electrical work. These subjects are, however, inherently so closely related to other solution properties—notably solubility, ionic transference, and conductance— that there will be frequent occasion to refer to what has been said about them and to anticipate further discussions later.

17.1. Electrode Reactions

Reduced to its essentials, any galvanic cell consists of two metal electrodes in an electrolytic solution or solutions and an external metallic circuit through which an electric current can pass from one electrode to the other. In this section we shall be interested first of all in the cell acting as the source of energy to drive current through the external circuit. In order to measure the electrical effects—potential difference between the terminals and current passed from one to the other—a voltmeter and ammeter may be connected with a resistance, motor, or other load to the terminals, as shown in Fig. 17.1.

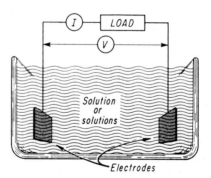

Fig. 17.1. *A galvanic cell as a source of electric current.*

In arrangements of this kind, the external circuit is almost invariably metallic, and any current through it is carried by electrons. The processes of interest are therefore ones in which electrons are delivered to adjacent solution at one electrode and taken up from solution at the other. For a steady current to flow, the two numbers of electrons must be exactly equal, as electrical charge cannot be created or destroyed, nor can it accumulate in any one place without some change in current.

It has been realized almost from the beginning of electrochemistry that the supply and uptake of electrons in cell reactions is by changes in number or kind of ions in solution adjacent to the electrodes. Some important examples of such processes are described below.

Active Metal Electrodes

If a copper electrode is immersed in copper sulfate solution as shown in

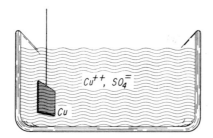

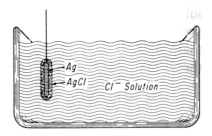

Fig. 17.2. *A copper electrode in cupric sulfate solution.*

Fig. 17.3. *The silver-silver chloride electrode.*

Fig. 17.2, copper ion Cu^{2+} can take up two electrons from the electrode and deposit metallic copper on the electrode by the reaction

$$Cu^{2+}(\text{solution}) + 2e^- \text{ (from electrode)} \longrightarrow Cu \text{ (on electrode).}$$

In the reverse reaction copper ion in solution is formed from metallic copper of the electrode,

$$Cu \longrightarrow Cu^{2+} + 2e^-$$

with the electrode taking up the two electrons. Similar electron supply or consumption occurs for other metal electrodes in suitable electrolytes —for example silver electrode in silver nitrate solution. $Ag \longrightarrow Ag^+ + e^-$, or zinc electrode in zinc sulfate solution, $Zn \longrightarrow Zn^{2+} + e^-$. (The reactions in reverse are of course also possible.)

Silver–Silver Chloride Electrode

Metal electrodes can also be arranged to serve as a source of supply or means for discharge of negative ions. An important example is the silver–silver chloride electrode, which can be used for chloride ion reactions and depends for its action on the very low solubility of silver chloride in water. It consists of a platinum wire, for connection to the external metallic circuit, on which metallic Ag and solid AgCl are deposited (Ag by electrolysis or by reduction of silver oxide at high temperature and AgCl by precipitation or electrolysis).

When this electrode is put in aqueous solution, as shown in Fig. 17.3, AgCl will dissolve until saturation is reached. If electrons are removed by the metal, the oxidation process is initially $Ag(s) \longrightarrow Ag^+(aq) + e^-$, but the silver ion is supplied to a solution saturated with $AgCl(Ag^+ + Cl^-)$. The excess silver ion therefore reacts with chloride ion to form $AgCl(s)$, and the overall process is the sum:

$$Ag(s) \longrightarrow Ag^+ + e^-$$
$$Ag^+ + Cl^- \longrightarrow AgCl(s)$$
$$\overline{}$$
$$Ag(s) + Cl^- \longrightarrow AgCl(s) + e^-$$

Thus the oxidation at this electrode is of chloride ion, because increase in silver ion concentration is prevented by the limited solubility of AgCl. This saturation concentration of Ag^+ is very small, being 1.33×10^{-5} in water and still less in chloride solutions (Section 16.6); hence it has very little effect on solutions in which the Ag–AgCl electrode may be inserted.

Calomel Electrode

This electrode is widely used as a reference electrode to supply or take up chloride ions, and is like the Ag–AgCl electrode in depending for its action on limited solubility of a chloride salt, in this case calomel (Hg_2Cl_2). As shown in Fig. 17.4, it consists of a pool of mercury covered

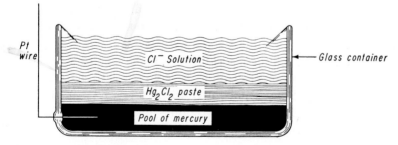

Fig. 17.4. *The calomel electrode.*

with a paste of Hg_2Cl_2 and immersed in an electrolyte containing chloride ion, connection being made to the external circuit by a platinum wire in the mercury. Usually a $0.1N$, $1.0N$, or saturated solution of KCl in water is used as electrolyte for connection to the rest of the cell, especially for pH measurements, but aqueous HCl or other chloride ion solutions can also be used for other purposes.

The oxidation reaction at this electrode is represented as

$$\text{Hg}(l) \longrightarrow \tfrac{1}{2}\text{Hg}_2^{2+} + e^-$$

followed by

$$\tfrac{1}{2}\text{Hg}_2^{2+} + \text{Cl}^- \longrightarrow \tfrac{1}{2}\text{Hg}_2\text{Cl}_2$$

to give the overall reaction

$$\text{Hg}(l) + \text{Cl}^- \longrightarrow \tfrac{1}{2}\text{Hg}_2\text{Cl}_2 + e^-$$

(Mercurous chloride is written as $\tfrac{1}{2}\text{Hg}_2\text{Cl}_2$ rather than HgCl and mercurous ion as Hg_2^{2+}; note that HgCl is an "odd" molecule with 97 electrons and is unstable.)

Often this electrode is used in connection with a second, different electrolyte and electrode. A common way of making this connection is by a salt bridge, as illustrated in Fig. 17.5. The intermediate solution

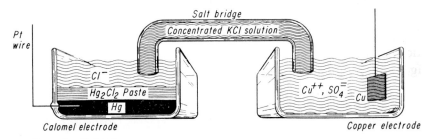

Fig. 17.5. *A salt bridge.*

usually contains KCl at high concentrations, to minimize potential differences set up at boundaries between solutions. These extraneous effects, called *junction potentials*, are discussed further in Section 17.12, and may change measured cell potentials by several thousandths of a volt (millivolts).

The potential of a cell incorporating a calomel electrode also depends on the concentration of electrolyte in contact with it, changing by 0.092 v (volts) or 92 mv (millivolts) when $0.1N$ KCl is replaced by saturated ($\sim$3.5N) KCl solution. (Values for different conditions are given in Table 17.3.)

Passive Electrodes

Electrons can also be delivered to or taken from electrodes when they otherwise have no direct part in the reaction. An important example is the hydrogen electrode, involving formation of hydrogen ion in aqueous solution from hydrogen gas by the reaction

$$\tfrac{1}{2}H_2(g) \longrightarrow H^+(aq) + e^-$$

This reaction can proceed readily if hydrogen gas is bubbled over the surface of a suitably prepared platinum wire in solution containing hydrogen ions, as indicated in Fig. 17.6; the electron set free at the metal surface can be taken up by the metal. In this process the platinum is neither reactant nor product, but does serve an essential function in making the reaction possible.

An electrode can also perform the function of taking up or supplying electrons for change in valence of ions in solution. Thus an electrode in solution containing both ferrous and ferric ion, for example by dissolving $FeCl_2$ and $FeCl_3$, can supply or receive electrons of the reaction:

$$Fe^{2+} \longrightarrow Fe^{3+} + e^-$$

17.2. Some Cell Conventions

The preceding examples are but a few of the many possible ionic reactions at an electrode surface. In all of them, electrons are either added or removed by the electrode. By general agreement, certain terms are conventionally used.

1. The removal of electrons is *oxidation*. The electrode at which it occurs is called the *anode*.

2. The addition of electrons is *reduction*. The electrode at which it occurs is called the *cathode*.

If an electrode is placed in solution, neither of the possible directions of reaction can continue for long unless something is done to remove excess electrons given it by oxidation or to make up the deficiency of electrons used in reduction. In a complete galvanic cell, this is accomplished by connecting the two electrodes by an external circuit for electron transfer from one electrode to a second one. Thus if any number of electrons is taken from the circuit by cathode reduction, exactly this number is supplied to it by oxidation at the anode, thus balancing electrons in both the external circuit and in the complete cell reaction.

An important aspect of cells to be discussed more fully later is that ion currents must flow in the electrolyte from one electrode to the other if current flows in the outside circuit. The ions present must move in the direction to prevent accumulation of net positive or negative charge;

otherwise further reaction will be counteracted, and soon blocked, by any such accumulation. At the anode, positive ions liberated must therefore travel away from the electrode toward the cathode, and negative ions must move from cathode to anode. The migration also brings ions into the opposite electrode region in just the amount to match the changes of concentration of the ions of opposite charge—by their production at the electrode and migration from it.

17.3. Examples of Complete Galvanic Cells

The fundamental processes just discussed all take place when electrodes, a solution (or solutions), and an external circuit are combined to form an operating galvanic cell. How they operate in combination, and their relation to the conventions used in describing them, are best appreciated by specific examples.

Hydrogen and Ag–AgCl Electrodes in HCl Solution

A cell incorporating two electrodes already described is shown schematically in Fig. 17.6. The left electrode is a hydrogen gas electrode, the

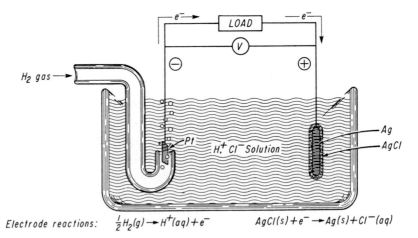

Electrode reactions: $\frac{1}{2}H_2(g) \rightarrow H^+(aq) + e^-$ $AgCl(s) + e^- \rightarrow Ag(s) + Cl^-(aq)$

Fig. 17.6. *Hydrogen: silver-silver chloride cell: a spontaneous galvanic cell.*

right an Ag–AgCl electrode, and an aqueous HCl solution provides H^+ and Cl^- ions for conduction between them. Electrons can flow in either direction in the external circuit, by oxidation at one electrode and

equivalent reduction at the other. Thus the platinum wire of the hydrogen electrode can receive electrons from the reaction

$$\tfrac{1}{2}H_2(g) \longrightarrow H^+(aq) + e^-$$

but the Ag–AgCl electrode can also supply electrons to the metal circuit
in an opposing sense by the reaction

$$Ag(s) + Cl^-(aq) \longrightarrow AgCl(s) + e^-$$

For actual flow of electrons from one electrode to the other, one reaction
must be in the reverse direction—reduction rather than oxidation—and
the direction taken is decided by which of the two is more effective as a
source of electrons.

Which is the oxidation electrode can be answered experimentally by
electrical measurements in the external circuit. For by convention, *electrons are negative charges which flow spontaneously from a point of lower to one
of higher (more positive) potential.* The anode, from which electrons flow,
must thus be more negative than the cathode (which takes up electrons
by the reduction reaction) when the cell is the source of energy to drive
electrons in the outside circuit.

In our present example, the hydrogen electrode is found to be more
negative (by about 0.46 v for a 0.01m HCl solution), and the actual
reactions are

$$\tfrac{1}{2}H_2(g) \longrightarrow H^+(aq) + e^- \text{ (oxidation at anode)}$$
$$AgCl(s) + e^- \longrightarrow Ag(s) + Cl^-(aq) \text{ (reduction at cathode).}$$

The total chemical change is the sum of these processes, and the complete
reaction is thus

$$\tfrac{1}{2}H_2(g) + AgCl(s) \longrightarrow Ag(s) + H^+(aq) + Cl^-(aq)$$

Thus the writing of separate electrode reactions—one an oxidation and
the other an equivalent reduction—and of the overall process as their
sum is typical of the analysis of cells. The overall process, called the cell
reaction, is the source of the energy necessary to drive electrons in the
external circuit, and from electrical measurements of this energy we
can learn something about the reaction, as discussed in Section 17.6.

The directions of electrode reaction, electron flow, and ion currents
for the present example are shown in Fig. 17.6, which the reader should
study to make sure he understands the consistency of the separate processes and their relations to the conventions adopted in describing them.

The Daniell Cell

A second example of a simple galvanic cell is shown in Fig. 17.7, in which zinc and copper electrodes in $ZnSO_4$ and $CuSO_4$ solutions are externally connected. If this cell is to deliver current continuously, contact must also be made between the two solutions; otherwise ion currents

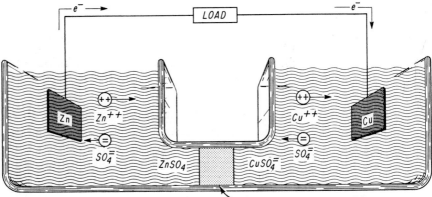

Fig. 17.7. *The Daniell cell.*

are unable to flow and compensate the charge accumulation which would block electrode reaction. This contact is accomplished in the cell shown by a plate porous to solution through which ions can flow, but which prevents the solutions from becoming mixed. If set up with equal concentrations of electrolyte the zinc electrode is more negative and hence is the oxidation electrode. The reactions producing the electron flow from zinc to copper are

$$Zn(s) \longrightarrow Zn^{2+}(aq) + 2e^-$$
$$Cu^{2+}(aq) + 2e^- \longrightarrow Cu(s)$$
$$\overline{\qquad\qquad\qquad\qquad\qquad}$$
$$Cu^{2+} + Zn \longrightarrow Cu + Zn^{2+}$$

Since the spontaneous reaction plates out copper, one realizes that zinc oxidizes more readily than copper and that Cu^{2+} ion is instead reduced at the cathode. The corresponding directions of ion flow are shown in Fig. 17.7.

17.4. Current Flow in Cells; Electrolysis

The relations of potential difference and charge transferred to chemical reaction in cells are important in understanding their operation and in learning something about the reactions. The potential difference between the two electrodes of a cell is easily found experimentally to depend on both the current—that is, on the rate at which charge is transferred—and on the size and spacing of the electrodes, even though the electrode materials and solutions are the same.

The way in which the potential difference changes is shown by the plots in Fig. 17.8 of measured potential difference when different

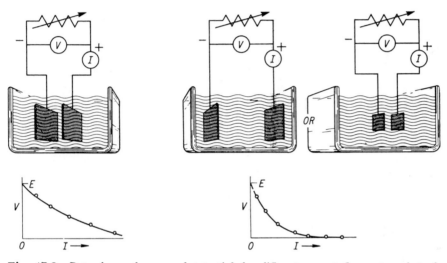

Fig. 17.8. *Dependence of measured potential for different current flows upon electrode spacing or size.*

currents are drawn (by changing a load resistance across the cell for example) and for two different sizes and spacings of electrodes. In both cases the potential difference indicated by the voltmeter decreases with increased current, and more rapidly when the electrodes are smaller or further apart.

The reason for the difference is that available energy by electrode reactions must drive current through both the external resistances and through the solution. If the solution resistance is high, as for smaller or more widely spaced electrodes, a greater potential drop V_S must occur *in the solution* for a given current by Ohm's law, $V_S = R_S I$, where R_S is the resistance of the solution. If this is true, the potential difference V between the electrodes, which is measured by the voltmeter, drops correspondingly; only if no current is drawn can the measured value depend on the electrode reactions alone. The existence of such a value is indicated by the intercepts marked $\mathcal{E}$ on the plots of voltage against current.

The value ε, for no current, cannot be measured accurately by ordinary voltmeters, all of which draw some current in order to give a reading proportional to voltage,

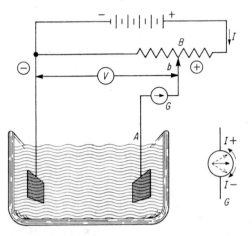

but this difficulty can be avoided in two ways. The first is by using a potentiometer circuit, which compares the potential difference between cell terminals with the voltage drop along a series of resistances, as shown in Fig. 17.9; a galvanometer or sensitive ammeter is used to indicate when points A and B are at the same potential. The second method employs a vacuum tube circuit (electronic voltmeter) which draws extremely small currents (10^{-11} amp or less) and changes a cell potential very slightly on being connected.

Fig. 17.9. *A potentiometer circuit in the measurement of cell potential.*

If the potential for no current drawn is independent of time and of whether current was previously drawn from or supplied to the cell, there is reason to believe that this potential is characteristic of the cell reaction at equilibrium with the external circuit. The value for such equilibrium conditions is called the EMF of the cell.

Before discussing the relation of cell EMF to cell reaction, the consequences of making the external potential difference greater than the EMF should be considered (see Fig. 17.10). When this is done, as by connecting a battery of greater potential difference, the direction of current flow in the cell reverses and all the cell processes are driven in the opposite sense. This reversed operation

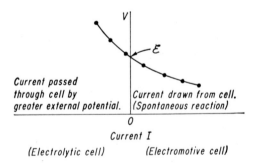

Fig. 17.10. *Current versus potential for electrolytic and electromotive cells.*

of a cell is called *electrolysis*, and is one in which electrical energy is supplied to produce chemical changes, rather than one in which chemical changes do electrical work. That is, electrical work is done on the cell by the external source of energy rather than by the cell on the external circuit, and the roles of the electrodes in oxidation-reduction are reversed.

An example of the reversal of cell processes, the direction of cell reaction, and current flow in the cell with hydrogen electrode, HCl solution, and Ag–AgCl electrode is shown in Fig. 17.11, when this cell is connected to a battery with potential difference greater than the cell EMF. Electrons must flow *from* the Ag–AgCl electrode, which is now the anode, *to* the hydrogen electrode acting as cathode, and the electrode reactions and ion currents are all reversed.

In electrolysis, the reactions of electrode reactions, polarities, and currents are always of the kind shown in Fig. 17.11. The reader should study this carefully and compare it with Fig. 17.6 to be sure that the distinction between electrolysis and spontaneous galvanic cell reaction is understood.

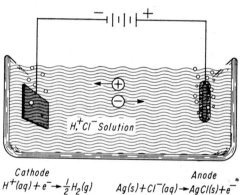

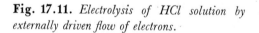

For a considerable number of cell reactions, the relation of potential to current is simple and reproducible, whether the cell is being charged or discharged. Often, however, one finds that considerable voltages

Cathode
$$H^+(aq) + e^- \rightarrow \tfrac{1}{2}H_2(g)$$

Anode
$$Ag(s) + Cl^-(aq) \rightarrow AgCl(s) + e^-$$

Fig. 17.11. *Electrolysis of HCl solution by externally driven flow of electrons.*

(0.2 v or more) in excess of equilibrium values are necessary for electrolysis. This *overvoltage* is important in commercial application of electrolysis (electroplating), and is a serious difficulty in obtaining reproducible values of EMF characteristic of equilibrium in the cell reaction. Difficulties of this kind can arise from failure of electrode reactions to supply the necessary electrons because they take place too slowly, and from failure of ion concentrations at the electrodes to reach equilibrium rapidly enough.

17.5. Faraday's Laws of Electrolysis

As already discussed, the rate of electrolysis or of current delivered by a cell depend on the external potential difference and the cell construction. The quantity of chemical reaction for a fixed amount of charge transferred depends, however, only on the chemical reactions at the electrodes. This fact is implicit in the equations of electrode reactions, and is stated in *Faraday's laws of electrolysis*. These laws, it will be remembered, are embodied in two statements.

1. The weight of substance produced or consumed by electrode reaction is always proportional to the total electrical charge passing through the cell.

2. The weights for different substances and the same total charge are proportional to the equivalent weights of the substances.

Both these laws are natural consequences of the ionic theory of electrode processes in solution. Thus, the equation $Ag^+(aq) + e^- \longrightarrow Ag(s)$ connotes that one electron reduces a single silver ion to metallic silver, and one mole (Avogadro's number) of electrons likewise involves one mole of material. Distinguishing equivalents and formula weights is of course necessary when the ions involved gain or lose more than one electron. Thus the reaction $Cu^{2+} + 2e^- \longrightarrow Cu$ requires two moles of electrons per gram atomic weight of copper. If referred to fixed quantity of charge, one-half gram atom of copper is the equivalent weight for reaction with one mole of electrons. The equivalent weight defined in terms of electron changes is thus the gram atomic weight divided by the change in valence.

The standard quantity of charge in cell reactions is taken to be the charge carried by one mole of electrons, and is called the *faraday* ($\mathcal{F}$). With the values $e = 1.60207 \times 10^{-19}$ coulombs and $N_0 = 0.60231 \times 10^{24}$ the quantity of charge is

$$1\mathcal{F} = 96{,}494 \text{ coul}$$

The weights of substance by electrode reactions are thus related to the quantity of charge dQ transferred by

$$dQ = \mathcal{F} \times \text{number of equivalents}$$

If n is the change in number of electrons and dx the number of gram atoms or gram moles which react, then

$$dQ = n\mathcal{F}\, dx \qquad\qquad (17.1)$$

where $n = 1$ for $Ag \longrightarrow Ag^+ + e^-$, $n = 2$ for $Cu \longrightarrow Cu^{2+} + 2e^-$, and so on.

For Q expressed in coulombs,

$$dQ(\text{coulombs}) = 96{,}494n\, dx \qquad\qquad (17.2)$$

This relation of charge to amount of chemical reaction is fundamental to the study of the relations between electrical potential differences and chemical energy changes.

17.6. EMF and Free Energy Change

A chemical reaction occurring in a galvanic cell is distinguished from one in solution without electrodes and external circuit by the fact that electrical work is done by the cell in addition to expansion work by volume changes. The amount of this electrical work (w_{el}) for a quantity of charge dQ transferred through an electrical potential difference V is

$$w_{el} = V \, dQ \tag{17.3}$$

By the standard convention of American chemists, both V and dQ are considered positive when electrons are driven from anode to the more positive cathode by spontaneous cell reaction, and w_{el} is then also positive.

The amount of work and the potential difference for a given quantity of charge dQ vary with the current—that is, the rate at which charge is transferred. As already discussed, V is smaller when the current is large, and hence $w_{el} = V \, dQ$ is also smaller. The external work done by the cell is therefore greatest when the cell discharges at a rate so slow that the current and its irreversible heating of the solution in the cell are negligible and there are no irreversible chemical changes. The equilibrium potential difference is then the EMF, ε, and corresponds to the maximum electrical work possible:

$$(w_{el})_{max} = \varepsilon \, dQ.$$

For dx moles of reaction, Eq. 17.3 gives

$$(w_{el})_{max} = n\mathfrak{F}\varepsilon \, dx, \tag{17.4}$$

where n is the number of moles of electrons per mole of reaction. If $\mathfrak{F}$ (the faraday) is expressed in coulombs/equivalent ($\mathfrak{F} = 96{,}494$ coulombs/equivalent) and ε in volts, the work done by the cell is in units of *joules* (number of joules = volts × coulombs).

This maximum work must come as the result of the reaction, and so must be related to the thermodynamic changes in the cell. To find the relation, we may return to the first and second laws of thermodynamics. From the first law,

$$dE = q - w,$$

where q is the heat absorbed by the cell and w is the *total* work done by the cell. Electrical work, as well as expansion work $P\,dV$, must be included, and hence

$$w = P\,dV + w_{el}$$

and

$$dE = q - P\,dV - w_{el}$$

This result is as far as the first law can go. The second law, $q \leq T\,dS$, gives

$$dE \leq T\,dS - P\,dV - w_{el} \qquad (17.5)$$

Since most cell reactions are studied at fixed temperature and pressure, the free energy F is more useful than E or S as a thermodynamic function. By the definition $F = E - TS + PV$, and the differential $dF = dE - T\,dS - S\,dT + P\,dV + V\,dP$, Eq. 17.5 becomes, on substitution,

$$dF \leq -S\,dT + V\,dP - w_{el}$$

Hence for cell reactions at constant temperature and pressure

$$dF_{T,P} \leq -w_{el} \qquad (17.6)$$

This result thus differs from the requirement $dF_{T,P} \leq 0$ when no electrical work is done by exactly the amount of this work. It may be stated thus: the external electrical work done is equal to the *decrease* in free energy by reaction if this is under equilibrium conditions (for then $w_{el} = -dF_{T,P}$), or is less than the decrease in free energy if irreversible processes occur (for then $w_{el} < -dF_{T,P}$).

The relation of w_{el} to $-dF$ suggests the reason for calling F a "free energy"; as for constant T and P, the amount of work obtained in addition to expansion work is at most equal to the amount of free energy lost.

The smaller work done externally when irreversible processes occur corresponds to the potential V being less than the equilibrium EMF, $\mathcal{E}$. When this happens, part of the free energy change is used internally, for example to drive current through the solution. The result in this case is heating of the solution by the current and this heat is given off to the surroundings. Thus less heat is absorbed and less work is done by the cell for a given amount of reaction when the reaction is not under equilibrium conditions.

Under equilibrium conditions, the equality sign applies and the work is the maximum value $(w_{el})_{max} = n\mathfrak{F}\mathcal{E}\,dx$. Hence

$$dF_{T,P} = -n\mathfrak{F}\mathcal{E}\,dx$$

If the cell reaction is written symbolically as $aA + bB = cC + dD$ with free energy change $dF_{T,P} = (c\bar{F}_c + d\bar{F}_d - a\bar{F}_a - b\bar{F}_b)\,dx = \Delta\bar{F}\,dx$, then

$$\Delta \overline{F} = -n\mathfrak{F}\mathcal{E} \tag{17.7}$$

where $\Delta \overline{F}$ is the free energy per mole of reaction producing n moles of electron transfer.

The simple relation of Eq. 17.7 is basic in thermodynamics for electrochemical equilibrium, and is important because it relates free energy and equilibrium to measured EMF. The significance of $\Delta \overline{F}$ is the same as for any reaction, and the expression of $\Delta \overline{F}$ in terms of standard chemical potentials and concentrations is done in exactly the same way. The difference when electrical work can be done is that $\Delta \overline{F}$ is not zero for equilibrium. Instead, $\Delta \overline{F} = -n\mathfrak{F}\mathcal{E}$ represents the fact that the chemical potential difference is exactly matched by the electrical potential difference $\mathcal{E}$ at equilibrium, and no electric current flows. The equilibrium conditions in a cell are thus different than when there is no electrical work, unless $\mathcal{E}$ happens to be zero, and the equilibrium concentrations for an EMF $\mathcal{E}$ are correspondingly different from those for $\mathcal{E} = 0$ or $\Delta \overline{F} = 0$.

17.7. Relation of EMF to Concentrations in Simple Cells

Effect of Electrolyte Concentration

Of the two examples of cells discussed in Section 17.1, the hydrogen, Ag–AgCl electrode cell is useful for a first illustration of the equation $\Delta \overline{F} = -n\mathfrak{F}\mathcal{E}$, relating EMF and chemical change. For oxidation at the hydrogen electrode, the cell reaction is $\frac{1}{2}H_2(g) + AgCl(s) = Ag(s) + HCl(aq)$, the free energy change $\Delta \overline{F}$ is then

$$\Delta \overline{F} = \overline{F}_{HCl} + \overline{F}_{Ag} - \tfrac{1}{2}\overline{F}_{H_2} - \overline{F}_{AgCl}.$$

Since HCl is a strong electrolyte in water, its chemical potential should be written as a sum of ionic potentials, as discussed in Section 16.9:

$$\overline{F}_{HCl} = \overline{F}^0_{HCl} + RT \ln \gamma_\pm^2 m^2$$

the activity coefficient $\gamma_\pm$ being included to represent the chemical potential at appreciable molality m. The chemical potential for the hydrogen gas is

$$\overline{F}_{H_2} = \overline{F}^0_{H_2} + RT \ln P_{H_2},$$

and the potentials for Ag(s) and AgCl(s) are constant at any chosen temperature because these species are solids. Hence the free energy change $\Delta \overline{F}$ is given by

$$\Delta \overline{F} = [\overline{F}^0_{HCl} + \overline{F}^0_{Ag} - \tfrac{1}{2}\overline{F}^0_{H_2} - \overline{F}^0_{AgCl} + RT \ln \gamma_\pm^2 m^2 - \tfrac{1}{2}RT \ln P_{H_2}]$$

or

$$\Delta \bar{F} = \Delta \bar{F}^0 + RT \ln \frac{\gamma_\pm^2 m^2}{P_{H_2}^{1/2}},$$

where $\Delta \bar{F}^0 = \bar{F}_{HCl}^0 + \bar{F}_{Ag}^0 - \tfrac{1}{2}\bar{F}_{H_2}^0 - \bar{F}_{AgCl}^0$ is the standard free energy change for the reaction.

The EMF of the cell is then

$$\varepsilon = -\frac{\Delta \bar{F}}{n\mathfrak{F}} = -\left(\frac{\Delta \bar{F}^0}{n\mathfrak{F}}\right) - \left(\frac{RT}{n\mathfrak{F}}\right) \ln \frac{\gamma_\pm^2 m^2}{P_{H_2}^{1/2}}$$

Since the quantity $(-\Delta \bar{F}^0/n\mathfrak{F})$ for this reaction is independent of concentrations or pressures, it can be called a standard EMF, denoted by ε^0.

In order to express ε in volts, R must be in joules rather than calories and F in coulombs. For the reaction as written, $n = 1$ (one mole of electrons transferred), and for the EMF at 25°C, using $T = 298°K$ and common logarithms, we obtain

$$\varepsilon_{298°} = \varepsilon_{298°}^0 - \frac{8.317 \times 298 \times 2.303}{1 \times 98,494} \log \frac{\gamma_\pm^2 m^2}{P_{H_2}^{1/2}}$$

or

$$\varepsilon_{298°} = \varepsilon_{298°}^0 - 0.05915 \log \frac{\gamma_\pm^2 m^2}{P_{H_2}^{1/2}} \qquad (17.8)$$

The cell EMF thus decreases for larger HCl molality m, and increases if the hydrogen gas pressure is larger. The effect of changing molality m on measured EMF when gas pressure is kept constant at one atmosphere is shown in the plot of ε against m in Fig. 17.12, but this plot does not show clearly the rapid rise of ε at low molalities. From Eq. 17.8, for $P_{H_2} = 1$, the variation of ε with m is of the form

$$\varepsilon = \varepsilon^0 - 0.1185 \log \gamma_\pm - 0.1183 \log m \qquad (17.9)$$

Thus, except for deviations from dilute behavior represented by $\log \gamma_\pm$ when $\gamma_\pm$ is not unity, a plot of ε against $\log m$ should give a straight line of slope -0.1183. This plot is shown in Fig. 17.12 and it is seen that the dashed straight line drawn with this slope approximately fits the measured points. The fit is not exact, however, and the deviations are

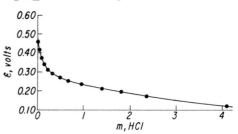

Fig. 17.12. ε of cell $Pt:H_2, HCl(m), AgCl:Ag$ versus $m(HCl)$. [Data from Harned and Ehlers, J. Am. Chem. Soc. **54:** 1350 (1932); **55:** 2179 (1933).]

real ones, corresponding to departures from dilute behavior ($\gamma_\pm = 1$).

From this example, it is evident that setting $\gamma_\pm = 1$ at all concentra-

tions can be used to predict approximate values of ε for different molalities if ε^0 is known. This value, from Fig. 17.13, is the intercept of the
dashed line with the ordinate
$\log m = 0$; hence, within the
accuracy of the plot, $\varepsilon^0 =$
0.2224 v and the variation
of EMF with molality is approximately given by $\varepsilon =$
$0.2224 - 0.1183 \log m_{\text{HCl}}$. The
form of the equation involving
$\log m$ rather than m shows
that changes in EMF, like
changes in free energy, are proportional to *ratios* of concentrations rather than differences.
That is, the EMF changes by
approximately 0.118 v from a
1 molal to a 0.1 molal solution
and from a 0.01 molal to a

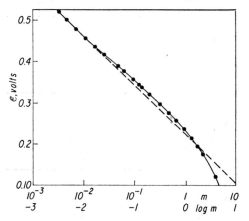

Fig. 17.13. ε *of cell Pt:H₂, HCl(m), AgCl:Ag
versus log m (HCl). [Data from Harned and
Ehlers, J. Am. Chem. Soc.* **54:** 1350 (1932);
55: 2179 (1933).]

0.001 molal solution, the concentration ratio being a factor 10 in each
case. It will be noticed also that the value $\varepsilon^0 \cong 0.2224$ volts also determines the standard free energy of the reaction:

$$\Delta \overline{F}^0 = n\mathfrak{F}\varepsilon^0 = -1 \times 96{,}500 \times 0.2224$$
$$= -21{,}460 \text{ joules/mole}$$

or

$$= -5.129 \text{ kcal/mole}$$

The deviations of HCl solutions from ideal dilute behavior have been
studied by EMF measurements of this cell in order to determine accurate
values of $\gamma_{\pm}$ for different molalities. Very careful measurements of the
EMF by several workers have given results in agreement to about
0.0001 v (0.1 mv), and representative values for several molalities m of
HCl are given in Table 17.1. The precision is great enough to justify a
more refined analysis than is possible by plotting ε against $\log m$. Accordingly, we can rearrange Eq. 17.9 to read

$$\varepsilon + 0.1183 \log m = \varepsilon^0 - 0.1183 \log \gamma_{\pm}$$

thereby putting only known, measured quantities (ε and m) on the left.
The sum ($\varepsilon + 0.1183 \log m$) would be constant and equal to ε^0 if $\gamma_{\pm}$
were unity at all molalities m. The actual values listed in Table 17.1
show that this is not exactly true, for $\gamma_{\pm}$ is not unity and $\log \gamma_{\pm} \neq 0$.

TABLE 17.1.   *EMF of the Cell Pt(H₂): HCl(m), AgCl, Ag at 25°C.*

Molality of HCl (m)	ε (v)	$\varepsilon + 0.1183 \log m$
0.003215	0.52053	.22563
.004488	.50384	.22609
.005619	.49257	.22637
.007311	.47948	.22680
.009138	.46860	.22738
.011195	.45861	.22782
.013407	.44974	.22820
.01710	.43783	.22878
.02563	.41824	.23000
.05391	.38222	.23217
.1238	.34199	.23472

A plot of the values of $(\varepsilon + 0.1183 \log m)$ against m gives the upper curve of Fig. 17.14. The increasing curvature of this plot at low molalities makes extrapolation to a reliable value for ε^0 at $m = 0$ very uncertain, and is reminiscent of the situation for dependence of silver chloride solubility on ion concentrations, discussed in Section 16.9. As in that case, the behavior is more usefully represented if $(\varepsilon + 0.1183 \log m)$ is plotted against $m^{1/2}$ rather than m, as shown by the lower curve and scale of Fig. 17.14. The smooth curve obtained becomes more nearly linear at low concentrations and with further refinement of the analysis can be extrapolated to the value $\varepsilon^0 = 0.2225$ v, as indicated by the dashed line and intercept in Fig. 17.14.

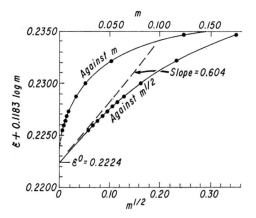

Fig. 17.14. $(\varepsilon + 0.1183 \log m)$ *versus m and versus $m^{1/2}$ for cell Pt:H₂ (1 atmosphere), AgCl:Ag.*

The conclusions possible from the measurements of the cell are thus that the observed EMF shows deviations from that expected for no ionic effects $(\gamma_\pm = 1)$, and that at low concentrations the difference from ideal behavior varies more and more nearly as $m^{1/2}$. Hence if accuracy in EMF concentration studies of better than 0.01 v—corresponding to about 20% change in concentration in this case—is desired, these deviations must be taken into account. The ways in which this can be done and the origins of the variations as $m^{1/2}$ will be taken up in Section 17.11.

Effect of Gas Pressure

The previous example of cell reaction and EMF was discussed only from the point of view of changes in solution concentration when the pressure of gas for the hydrogen electrode is kept fixed. A change in this pressure also affects the EMF, as shown by Eq. 17.8 for example, and another cell reaction will now be considered from this point of view. The effect of hydrogen pressure on hydrogen electrode reaction has been studied to pressures of 1000 atm employing a $0.1\,N$ HCl solution and a calomel electrode, rather than Ag–AgCl. The electrode and cell reactions are

$$\tfrac{1}{2}H_2(P) = H^+(0.1\,N) + e^- \qquad \text{(oxidation)}$$
$$\tfrac{1}{2}Hg_2Cl_2(s) + e^- = Hg(s) + Cl^-(0.1\,N) \quad \text{(reduction)}$$

$$\tfrac{1}{2}Hg_2Cl_2 - \tfrac{1}{2}H_2(P) = Hg(s) + HCl(0.1\,N) \quad \text{(cell reaction)}$$

The EMF of the cell, then, when all species in standard states are included in ε^0, is given by

$$\varepsilon = \varepsilon^0 - \frac{RT}{n\mathfrak{F}} \ln \frac{\gamma_\pm^2 m^2 (0.1\,N)}{P_{H_2}^{1/2}}$$

Since $n = 1$ and $\gamma_\pm$ and m are fixed at the values for a $0.1\,N$ solution, the effect of pressure on EMF is given by

$$\varepsilon = \left[\varepsilon^0 - \frac{2.303 RT}{\mathfrak{F}} \log \gamma_\pm^2 m^2 \right] + \frac{2.303 RT}{2\mathfrak{F}} \log P_{H_2}$$

or

$$\varepsilon = \varepsilon' + \frac{2.303 RT}{2\mathfrak{F}} \log P_{H_2}$$

$$(17.10)$$

where ε' represents the constant term in brackets. Some of the measured values of ε for pressures P up to 1000 atm at 25°C are listed in Table 17.2 and the complete set of results is plotted in Fig. 17.15. Up to log $P = 2$ ($P = 100$ atm), the EMF increases linearly with log P and the

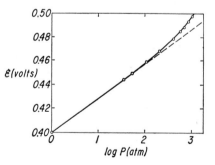

Fig. 17.15. *ε versus log P_{H_2} for the cell $Pt(H_2)$: $HCl(m)$; Hg_2Cl_2: Hg.*

slope $2.303 RT/2\mathfrak{F} = 0.02958$, from Eq. 17.10, is shown by the dashed line.

At high pressures the EMF increases more rapidly, primarily because

TABLE 17.2.   *Variation of EMF with Hydrogen Electrode Gas Pressure for the Cell $Pt(H_2)$: $HCl(0.1\ N)$; $Hg_2Cl_2(s)$, $Hg(s)$.*

P (atm)	1.0	37.8	110.2	204.7	556.8	1035.2
ε (v)	0.3990	.4456	.4596	.4683	.4844	.4975

From D. A. MacInnes, *Principles of Electrochemistry*, New York, Reinhold, 1939, p. 116.

the chemical potential of hydrogen gas is not given by $\overline{F}_{H_2} = \overline{F}^0_{H_2} + RT$ ln P, since hydrogen shows deviations from ideality at these pressures. In other words, the pressure should be replaced by fugacity to account for nonideal behavior, as discussed in Section 15.3. When this change is made by using $PV = RT + BP$, the corrected EMF curves agree closely with calculations to 600 atm; they are dubious at higher pressures only because effects of pressure on the solid phases have not been considered. (The entire cell was subjected to the hydrostatic pressure.) It is clear, however, that the simple expression Eq. 17.10 accounts accurately for pressure effects up to 100 atm.

17.8. Electrode Reactions and Potentials

The examples of cell reactions discussed in Section 17.6 were chosen to give simple illustrations of important features common to all cell reactions, and because accurate EMF measurements are available for them. Many other combinations of electrodes and solutions have been studied, with results of varying accuracy. In this section we consider the question of expressing the results for different electrode processes in compact, convenient form for application to problems of chemical equilibrium.

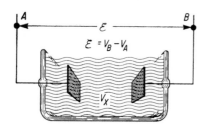

Fig. 17.16. *Cell EMF as derived from EMF_s of electrodes.*

Definition of Electrode Potential

Every cell reaction must involve oxidation at one electrode and reduction at the other, as only in this way can electrons be transferred by conduction through an external circuit. Since the overall reaction must be the net result of both electrode reactions, it is natural to represent the cell EMF similarly, as a difference of two electrode potentials relative to solution.

Thus in Fig. 17.16 the cell EMF, ε, is measured as the difference of potentials between points A and B in the external circuit; that is, $\varepsilon = V_B - V_A$. If the potential of the solution is some value V_x (which for no current flow must be the same everywhere except at the electrodes or on crossing a boundary between solutions), then ε can also be written as

$$\varepsilon = (V_x - V_A) - (V_x - V_B)$$

Written in this form, each term is the potential of solution relative to that of the electrodes, and the EMF is their difference.

The differences $(V_x - V_A)$ and $(V_x - V_B)$ are defined as the electrode EMF's, ε_A and ε_B, of the two electrodes, or

$$\varepsilon = \varepsilon_A - \varepsilon_B \qquad (17.11)$$

With this definition of electrode EMF, greater ease of oxidation at an electrode is represented by a more positive electrode potential. For if A is the oxidation electrode, ε must be positive ($V_B > V_A$), which can only be if ε_A is more positive than ε_B. Conversely, negative values of ε referred to electrode A arise if ε_B is more positive than ε_A, which corresponds to oxidation at B being the actual process. Measured EMF values of cells thus represent the difference in readiness of oxidation of the two electrode reactions for the conditions in the cell.

Cell EMF in Terms of Electrode Potentials

Electrode EMF's are important and useful quantities, as by their use cell EMF's can be represented as a difference of electrode EMF's, in direct correspondence to writing the cell reaction as electrode reactions of oxidation and reduction. For any electrode process, the electrode EMF is therefore written as $-\Delta F/n\mathfrak{F}$ for the oxidation electrode reaction. Thus for the hydrogen electrode reaction

$$\tfrac{1}{2}H_2(g) \longrightarrow H^+(aq) + e^-$$

the free energy change is

$$\Delta \bar{F}_{H_2,H^+} = \Delta \bar{F}^0_{H_2,H^+} + RT \ln \frac{\gamma_{H^+} m_{H^+}}{P_{H_2}^{1/2}}$$

and the electrode EMF is

$$\varepsilon_{H_2,H^+} = -\left(\frac{\Delta \bar{F}^0_{H_2,H^+}}{\mathfrak{F}}\right) - \frac{RT}{\mathfrak{F}} \ln \frac{\gamma_{H^+} m_{H^+}}{P_{H_2}^{1/2}}$$

On defining $(-\Delta \bar{F}^0_{H_2,H^+}/\mathfrak{F}) = \varepsilon^0_{H_2,H^+}$ as the *standard* electrode EMF, this becomes

$$\varepsilon_{H_2,H^+} = \varepsilon^0_{H_2,H^+} - \frac{RT}{\mathfrak{F}} \ln \frac{\gamma_{H^+} m_{H^+}}{P_{H_2}^{1/2}} \qquad (17.12)$$

In a similar way, the Ag–AgCl and calomel electrode oxidations and electrode EMF's are

$$Ag(s) + Cl^- \longrightarrow AgCl(s) + e^-$$

$$\mathcal{E}_{Ag,AgCl} = \mathcal{E}^0_{Ag,AgCl} - \frac{RT}{\mathfrak{F}} \ln \frac{1}{\gamma_{Cl^-} m_{Cl^-}} \qquad (17.13)$$

$$Hg + Cl^- \longrightarrow \tfrac{1}{2} Hg_2 Cl_2(s) + e^-$$

$$\mathcal{E}_{Hg,Hg_2Cl_2} = \mathcal{E}^0_{Hg,Hg_2Cl_2} - \left(\frac{RT}{\mathfrak{F}}\right) \ln \frac{1}{\gamma_{Cl^-} m_{Cl^-}}$$

As a further example, the two-electron oxidation of metallic zinc,

$$Zn(s) \longrightarrow Zn^{2+} + 2e^-$$

has the electrode EMF

$$\mathcal{E} = \mathcal{E}^0 - \frac{RT}{2\mathfrak{F}} \ln \gamma_{Zn^{2+}} m_{Zn^{2+}}$$

The procedure illustrated by these particular examples is followed in writing any electrode EMF.

For the reaction *written as an oxidation*, the electrode EMF is a standard value $\mathcal{E}^0 - RT/n\mathfrak{F} \times$ the logarithm of (concentrations for the reaction products ÷ concentrations for reactants), each concentration being raised to the power of its stoichiometric coefficient.

The products in the logarithmic term include all variable concentrations, as in writing the product for free energy change. All fixed concentrations, as for solids and substances in standard states, are omitted from the logarithmic term, and the standard EMF, $\mathcal{E}^0$, therefore refers to all such species in their standard state.

If these conventions are consistently followed, the measured EMF of a cell reaction is correctly given by Eq. 17.11: $\mathcal{E} = \mathcal{E}_A - \mathcal{E}_B$, where $\mathcal{E}_A$ is the EMF for oxidation at the electrode A to which $\mathcal{E}$ is referred and $\mathcal{E}_B$ the EMF for electrode B.

EXAMPLE

If A is a hydrogen electrode in HCl solution and B a Ag–AgCl electrode, the EMF is given by combining Eqs. 17.12 and 17.13. The result is

$$\mathcal{E} = \mathcal{E}_{H_2,H^+} - \mathcal{E}_{Ag,AgCl}$$

$$= (\mathcal{E}^0_{H_2,H^+} - \mathcal{E}^0_{Ag,AgCl}) - \frac{RT}{\mathfrak{F}} \ln \gamma_{H^+} \gamma_{Cl^-} \frac{m_{H^+} m_{Cl^-}}{P_{H_2}^{1/2}}$$

or

$$\mathcal{E} = \mathcal{E}^0 - \frac{RT}{\mathfrak{F}} \ln \left(\frac{\gamma_\pm^2 m^2}{P_{H_2}^{1/2}} \right) \qquad (17.14)$$

where $\mathcal{E}^0 = \mathcal{E}^0_{H_2,H^+} - \mathcal{E}^0_{Ag,AgCl}$ is the standard cell potential.

Scales of Electrode Potentials

The value of electrode potentials is that they can express cell EMF's, and hence the conditions of cell reaction equilibria, in terms of electrode EMF values for the oxidations involved. If standard values $\mathcal{E}^0$ of these are known, the EMF and free energy changes are then readily written down, and tabulations of such values are compact and convenient representations of oxidation processes.

The only ambiguity about this otherwise straightforward procedure is in assigning numerical values to separate electrode EMF's. The ambiguity arises because there is no direct way of measuring the potential difference V_x between a solution and an electrode. One might at first suppose that a metallic probe inserted in the solution could be used to measure V_x, but any such probe would itself act as an electrode (which might or might not be reversible) and only the potential of the probe metal relative to the other electrode could be measured. This kind of limitation is a fundamental one, which makes assignment of absolute electrode EMF values by potential difference measurements impossible.

By general agreement, standard electrode potentials are defined as values of oxidation potentials relative to that for the standard hydrogen electrode. Thus the standard potential for the Ag–AgCl electrode used by general agreement and denoted by $\mathcal{E}^0_{Ag,AgCl}$ is really the value of $\mathcal{E}^0_{Ag,AgCl} - \mathcal{E}^0_{H_2,H^+}$. The numerical value for this particular $\mathcal{E}^0$ is obtained immediately from the H_2, HCl, Ag–AgCl cell measurements discussed in Section 17.7, because the standard EMF of this cell is $\mathcal{E}^0_{cell} = 0.2225$ v $= \mathcal{E}^0_{H_2,H^+} - \mathcal{E}^0_{Ag,AgCl}$, and hence the standard potential, written as $\mathcal{E}^0_{Ag,AgCl}$, is given by

$$\mathcal{E}^0_{Ag,AgCl} = -0.2225 \text{ v at } 25°C.$$

Other standard potentials are obtained by suitable comparisons of measured EMF's of reversible cell reactions. Many such measurements have led to a considerable number of known standard electrode potentials, some of which are listed in Table 17.3.

Determination of Electrode EMF Values

The values in Table 17.3 have been obtained by a wide variety of methods. A few, like the value $\mathcal{E}^0_{Ag,AgCl} = -0.2225$ v, are obtained by straightforward, exceedingly careful measurements with allowance for activity coefficient effects, and can be trusted to 10^{-4} v (0.1 mv).

TABLE 17.3.   *Standard Electrode Potentials.*

(The values are at 25°C for oxidation in aqueous solution and relative to the standard hydrogen electrode.)

Electrode Reaction	$\mathcal{E}_H^0$ v
ACID SOLUTIONS	
$Li = Li^+ + e$	3.045
$K = K^+ + e$	2.925
$Cs = Cs^+ + e$	2.923
$Ba = Ba^{2+} + 2e$	2.90
$Ca = Ca^{2+} + 2e$	2.87
$Na = Na^+ + e$	2.714
$Mg = Mg^{2+} + 2e$	2.37
$Al = Al^{3+} + 3e$	1.66
$Zn = Zn^{2+} + 2e$	0.763
$Fe = Fe^{2+} + 2e$	0.440
$Cr^{2+} = Cr^{3+} + e$	0.41
$Cd = Cd^{2+} + 2e$	0.403
$Sn = Sn^{2+} + 2e$	0.136
$Pb = Pb^{2+} + 2e$	0.126
$Fe = Fe^{3+} + 3e$	0.036
$D_2 = 2D^+ + 2e$	0.0034
$H_2 = 2H^+ + 2e$	0.000
$H_2S = S + 2H^+ + 2e$	−0.141
$Sn^{2+} = Sn^{4+} + 2e$	−0.15
$Cu^+ = Cu^{2+} + e$	−0.153
$2S_2O_3^{2-} = S_4O_6^{2-} + 2e$	−0.17
$Cu = Cu^{2+} + 2e$	−0.337
$2I^- = I_2 + 2e$	−0.5355
$Fe^{2+} = Fe^{3+} + e$	−0.771
$Ag = Ag^+ + e$	−0.7991
$Hg = Hg^{2+} + 2e$	−0.854
$Hg_2^{2+} = 2Hg^{2+} + 2e$	−0.92
$2Br^- = Br_2(l) + 2e$	−1.0652
$Mn^{2+} + 2H_2O = MnO_2 + 4H^+ + 2e$	−1.23
$2Cr^{3+} + 7H_2O = Cr_2O_7^{2-} + 14H^+ + 6e$	−1.33
$Cl^- = \frac{1}{2}Cl_2 + e$	−1.3595
$Ce^{3+} = Ce^{4+} + e$	−1.61
$Co^{2+} = Co^{3+} + e$	−1.82
$2SO_4 = S_2O_8^= + 2e$	−1.98
$2F^- = F_2 + 2e$	−2.65
BASIC SOLUTIONS	
$2OH^- + Ca = Ca(OH)_2 + 2e$	3.03
$3OH^- + Cr = Cr(OH)_3 + 3e$	1.3
$4OH^- + Zn = ZnO_2^{2-} + 2H_2O + 2e$	1.216
$2OH^- + CN^- = CNO^- + H_2O + 2e$	0.97
$2OH^- + SO_3^{2-} = SO_4^{2-} + H_2O + 2e$	0.93
$H_2 + 2OH^- = 2H_2O + 2e$	0.828
$2OH^- + Ni = Ni(OH)_2 + 2e$	0.72
$OH^- + Fe(OH)_2 = Fe(OH)_3 + e$	0.56
$O_2 + 2OH^- = O_3 + H_2O + 2e$	−1.24

From W. M. Latimer, *Oxidation Potentials*, 2nd ed., (Prentice-Hall, New York, 1952.)

Others required indirect methods, for example the value for a metallic sodium electrode,

$$\mathcal{E}^0_{Na,Na^+} = 2.714 \text{ v}$$

This was not obtained from a cell using a sodium wire as one electrode for steady equilibrium potential measurements against a suitable reference electrode, for reasons obvious to anyone who has seen the violent reaction of sodium with water. Instead, a cell was devised which employed sodium and sodium amalgam electrodes in a solution of sodium iodide in ethylene. This arrangement permitted comparison of the sodium electrode with the less reactive amalgam electrode in a solution not reacting with either. Then the more stable amalgam electrode was used in a cell with a calomel electrode and aqueous NaCl solution. Since the EMF of the first cell involves the reaction $Na(s) \longrightarrow Na(Hg)$ and the second the reaction $Na(Hg) \longrightarrow Na^+(aq) + e^-$, the desired potential results by combining the two EMF measurements.

Less satisfactory expedients have been necessary in other cases, and the best available standard potentials may be in error by 0.1 v or more. These unfortunate inaccuracies reflect the fact that cells have not been devised in which the oxidation process of interest takes place reversibly and cleanly without complications of side reactions and extraneous sources of potential differences of uncertain magnitude. (One such source is a boundary between different solutions giving rise to a "junction potential" difference; see Section 17.13.) As a result, tabulated standard electrode potentials, such as those in Table 17.3, have limitations which must be remembered in using them for their many valuable applications.

17.9. Some Uses of Electrode Potentials

Ease of Oxidation

The table of standard potentials for ions in aqueous solution provides a quantitative scale expressing relative ease with which different species lose electrons—that is, become oxidized. (The term oxidation for the process is really a misnomer. Oxygen is merely one of many electron acceptors, although it played a central role in the historical development of molecular concepts. This led to its name being used for other processes which also remove electrons from a substance and so "oxidize" it.) Thus, from Table 17.3 one deduces immediately that metallic lithium ($\mathcal{E}^0 = +3.045$ v) is very readily oxidized, and reactions to form Li^+

will be displaced strongly to the right by this readiness. At the opposite extreme, fluoride ion F^- ($\varepsilon^0 = -2.65$ v) holds the electrons strongly and is very difficult to oxidize to gaseous F_2.

Since a more positive EMF means a greater readiness to assume the oxidized form, questions such as whether zinc will displace copper in solution are readily answered. The value $\varepsilon^0_{Zn,Zn^{2+}} = -0.763$ v, as compared to $\varepsilon^0_{Cu,Cu^{2+}} = -0.337$ v, evidently means that Zn^{2+} is a more stable ion than Cu^{2+}, and addition of metallic zinc to $CuSo_4$ solution deposits solid copper. Moreover the ε^0 values go further than this, as they can be used to predict the extent to which such reactions proceed. For the oxidation reactions and corresponding EMF's are

$$Zn(s) \longrightarrow Zn^{2+}(m_{Zn^{2+}}) + 2e^-$$
$$Cu(s) \longrightarrow Cu^{2+}(m_{Cu^{2+}}) + 2e^-$$
$$\overline{Zn(s) + Cu^{2+}(m_{Cu^{2+}}) \longrightarrow Zn^{2+}(M_{Zn^{2+}}) + Cu(s)} \qquad (17.15)$$
$$\varepsilon = (\varepsilon^0_{Zn,Zn^{2+}} - \varepsilon^0_{Cu,Cu^{2+}}) - \frac{RT}{2\mathcal{F}} \ln \frac{m_{Zn^{2+}}}{m_{Cu^{2+}}}$$

or

$$\varepsilon = 1.10 - 0.295 \log \frac{m_{Zn^{2+}}}{m_{Cu^{2+}}} \qquad (17.16)$$

The reaction of Eq. 17.15 could be set up in a suitable cell, in which case ε would have the value given by Eq. 17.16 for the ratio of ion concentrations $m_{Zn^{2+}}$ and $m_{Cu^{2+}}$ and the cell, if ionic effects represented by activity coefficients $\gamma_{Zn^{2+}}$ and $\gamma_{Cu^{2+}}$ are neglected. Since $\gamma_{Zn^{2+}}$ and $\gamma_{Cu^{2+}}$ are nearly the same because both ions are divalent, the correct ratio $\gamma_{Zn^{2+}}m_{Zn^{2+}}/\gamma_{Cu^{2+}}m_{Cu^{2+}}$ is very nearly the same as $m_{Zn^{2+}}/m_{Cu^{2+}}$ or $[Zn^{2+}]/[Cu^{2+}]$.

Equation 17.16 is also useful for the reaction when it occurs with no electrodes in ordinary solution. Under these conditions, $\Delta\bar{F} = 0$ and $\varepsilon = 0$ at equilibrium; hence Eq. 17.16 becomes

$$\varepsilon = 0 = 1.10 - 0.295 \log \left(\frac{m_{Zn^{2+}}}{m_{Cu^{2+}}} \right)$$

or

$$\log \left(\frac{m_{Zn^{2+}}}{m_{Cu^{2+}}} \right) = \frac{1.10}{0.0295} = 37.2$$

The ratio of concentrations of zinc and copper ion concentrations at equilibrium is thus $m_{Zn^{2+}}/m_{Cu^{2+}} = 10^{37.2}$; that is, zinc displaces copper to all but a negligible extent.

The same result can be reached by an alternative route which is often convenient. Since $\varepsilon^0 = -\Delta\bar{F}^0/n\mathcal{F}$ and $\Delta\bar{F}^0 = -RT \ln K$, the equilibrium constant K is given by

$$\ln K = \frac{n\mathcal{F}\mathcal{E}^0}{RT}$$

For the present example this gives

$$\ln K = \frac{2 \times 96,500 \times 1.10}{2.303 \times 4.19 \times 1.987 \times 298} = 37.2.$$

But K for the reactions $Zn(s) + Cu^{2+} \longrightarrow Zn^{2+} + Cu(s)$ is $m_{Zn^{2+}}/m_{Cu^{2+}}$; hence

$$\log \left(\frac{m_{Zn^{2+}}}{m_{Cu^{2+}}}\right) \cong \log \frac{[Zn^{2+}]}{[Cu^{2+}]} = 37.2$$

The difference of oxidation potentials by more than a volt in the example is seen to correspond to virtually complete oxidation of zinc with reduction of copper and to a large standard free energy decrease $\Delta F^0 = -n\mathcal{F}\mathcal{E}^0 = -50.9$ kcal/mole. For potentials differing by a few millivolts, the reaction will be much less complete; thus if $\mathcal{E}^0 = 0.0050$ v for transfer of one electron, $\log K = 0.85$, or $K = 7.1$.

Oxidation-Reduction Reactions

Equilibrium between different valence states of ions is also represented by corresponding electrode potentials. For example, the ferrous-ferric ion potential $\mathcal{E}^0_{Fe^{2+}, Fe^{3+}} = -0.771$ v represents the fact that reduction is favored for equal initial concentrations of the two ions. Whether reduction or oxidation occurs in the overall reaction depends on the competing second process necessary for a complete reaction. This might, for instance, be the thallous-thallic ion equilibrium $Tl^+ \longrightarrow Tl^{3+} + 2e^-$, with $\mathcal{E}^0 = -1.211$ v. Reduction is evidently also favored, but two electrons are lost rather than one as in the ferrous-ferric ion equilibrium. To determine the outcome, for two electrons transferred we have

$$
\begin{array}{ll}
2Fe^{2+} \longrightarrow 2Fe^{3+} + 2e^- & \mathcal{E}^0 = -0.771 \\
Tl^+ \longrightarrow Tl^{3+} + 2e^- & \mathcal{E}^0 = -1.211 \\
\hline
2Fe^{2+} + Tl^{3+} \longrightarrow 2Fe^{3+} + Tl^+ & \mathcal{E}^0 = +0.540 \text{ v}
\end{array}
$$

If the ion concentrations are expressed as molalities, and deviations from ideality are neglected (not a very accurate approximation in this case because of the high ion charges), the EMF of the reaction is

$$\mathcal{E} = 0.540 - 0.0295 \log \frac{[Fe^{3+}]^2[Tl^+]}{[Fe^{2+}]^2[Tl^{3+}]}$$

Hence for equilibrium with $\mathcal{E} = 0$,

$$K = \left(\frac{[Fe^{3+}]^2[Tl^+]}{[Fe^{2+}]^2[Tl^{3+}]}\right)_{eq} = 10^{0.54/0.0295} = 10^{18.3}$$

For equal initial concentrations of all four ions, the equilibrium evidently lies far to the right—that is, ferrous ion is oxidized and thallic ion reduced.

In this example both oxidations were written for two moles of electrons in order that the number of electrons would balance and cancel on taking the difference. The EMF of the oxidation $2Fe^{2+} \longrightarrow 2Fe^{3+} + 2e^-$ is given by

$$\mathcal{E}_{2Fe^{2+},2Fe^{3+}} = \mathcal{E}^0_{2Fe^{2+},2Fe^{3+}} - \frac{RT}{2\mathcal{F}} \ln \frac{[Fe^{3+}]^2}{[Fe^{2+}]^2}$$

and so results in appearance of the ferric and ferrous ion concentrations as squares in the equilibrium constant product. At first sight, this expression may seem different from the EMF written for $Fe^{2+} \longrightarrow Fe^{3+} + e^-$

$$\mathcal{E}_{Fe^{2+},Fe^{3+}} = \mathcal{E}^0_{Fe^{2+},Fe^{3+}} - \frac{RT}{\mathcal{F}} \ln \frac{[Fe^{3+}]}{[Fe^{2+}]}$$

The two expressions must, however, be the same, because they refer to the same electrode situation regardless of the quantity of charge transferred. That they are the same if $\mathcal{E}^0$ is the same follows from the fact that

$$\tfrac{1}{2} \ln [Fe^{3+}]^2/[Fe^{2+}]^2 = \ln [Fe^{3+}]/[Fe^{2+}]$$

Combination of Electrode Potentials

The standard potentials in Table 17.3 may be used to obtain values for other valence changes than the ones listed. For example, the value of $\mathcal{E}^0$ for $Fe \longrightarrow Fe^{3+} + 3e^-$ is not given, but can be obtained from two which are; namely,

$$Fe \longrightarrow Fe^{2+} + 2e^-, \qquad \mathcal{E}^0 = \quad 0.440 \text{ v}$$
$$Fe^{2+} \longrightarrow Fe^{3+} + e^-, \qquad \mathcal{E}^0 = -0.771 \text{ v}$$

Because these two reactions add to give $Fe \longrightarrow Fe^{3+} + 3e^-$, the temptation is strong to add their electrode EMF values to obtain the desired EMF. There is a fallacy concealed in this argument, however, because it is assumed implicitly that electrode EMF's may be added like thermodynamic energy changes. This is not true, for the reason that electrode EMF's describe the work and free energy change per unit quantity of charge—namely, one mole of electrons, rather than per mole of reaction. Adding EMF values under such circumstances is then an improper combination of incommensurate quantities, but addition of the corresponding free energies per mole of reaction gives a meaningful result from which the desired EMF can be obtained. Thus one can write

$$\text{Fe} \longrightarrow \text{Fe}^{2+} + 2e^-, \qquad \Delta\overline{F}^0 = -2\mathcal{F}(0.440)$$
$$\text{Fe}^{++} \longrightarrow \text{Fe}^{3+} + e^-, \qquad \Delta\overline{F}^0 = -\mathcal{F}(-0.771)$$

$$\text{Fe} \longrightarrow \text{Fe}^{3+} + 3e^-, \qquad \Delta\overline{F}^0 = -2\mathcal{F}(0.440) - \mathcal{F}(-0.771)$$

Since $\Delta\overline{F}^0 = -3\mathcal{F}\mathcal{E}^0$ for the resulting oxidation, the value of $\mathcal{E}^0$ is given by

$$-3\mathcal{F}\mathcal{E}^0_{\text{Fe,Fe}^{3+}} = -2\mathcal{F}(0.440) - \mathcal{F}(-0.771)$$

or

$$\mathcal{E}^0_{\text{Fe,Fe}^{3+}} = \frac{2 \times 0.440}{3} - \frac{0.771}{3}$$
$$= 0.036 \text{ v}$$

This correct value is quite different from the erroneous sum $0.440 - 0.771 = -0.331$ v, obtained by adding EMF values without attention to the numbers of electrons.

Solubilities from EMF measurements

As discussed in Section 17.3, the Ag–AgCl electrode differs from an Ag electrode in unsaturated solution of a silver salt because the concentration of silver ion is fixed by the solubility of AgCl. The electrode EMF values differ for this reason, and the difference can be used to determine the solubility of AgCl. That this is so becomes apparent on writing the electrode reactions.

$$\text{Ag} + \text{Cl}^- \longrightarrow \text{AgCl}(s) + e^-, \qquad \mathcal{E}^0 = -0.2225 \text{ v}$$
$$\text{Ag} \longrightarrow \text{Ag}^+ + e^-, \qquad \mathcal{E}^0 = -0.7991 \text{ v}$$

The difference of the two electrode reactions gives the cell reaction,

$$\text{Ag}^+ + \text{Cl}^- \longrightarrow \text{AgCl}(s), \qquad \mathcal{E}^0 = 0.5766 \text{ v}$$

The resulting value of $\mathcal{E}^0$, thus corresponds to the standard free energy $\Delta\overline{F}^0$ for AgCl in equilibrium between solid and solution. Hence one has

$$\Delta\overline{F}^0 = -\mathcal{F}\mathcal{E}^0 = -RT \ln \frac{1}{[\text{Ag}^+][\text{Cl}^-]}$$

where $[\text{Ag}^+][\text{Cl}^-]$ is the solubility product for AgCl. Since $\mathcal{E}^0 = 0.5766$ volts is obtained from accurate measurements as a limiting value for infinite dilution, the value of $[\text{Ag}^+][\text{Cl}^-]$ is the thermodynamic value K^0_{sp}, and is given by

$$\log K^0_{sp} = \frac{-\mathfrak{F}\mathcal{E}^0}{2.303RT} = -\frac{96{,}490 \times 0.5766}{2.303 \times 4.182 \times 1.987 \times 298.2} = -9.755$$

or

$$K^0_{sp} = 1.76 \times 10^{-10}$$

Similar calculations can be made for other slightly soluble salts if the appropriate pairs of electrode potentials are available. The indirect calculation illustrates the usefulness of EMF measurements for obtaining equilibrium values which are very difficult to obtain by direct measurement, such as the minute solubility of 1.33×10^{-5} for AgCl in the example.

17.10. EMF, Temperature, Heats, and Entropies of Reaction

Thus far we have not considered explicitly how the EMF of a cell varies with temperature. The question is worth asking, both for practical problems when the temperature is other than the standard value of 25°C, and because we shall show that measured cell EMF's at different temperatures can be used to give information about the underlying cell reaction.

The EMF of a cell can, from the results of Section 17.6, be written in the form

$$\mathcal{E} = \mathcal{E}^0 - \frac{RT}{n\mathfrak{F}} \ln \left[\frac{\text{product of activities of resultant species}}{\text{product of activities of reactant species}} \right]$$

where it is understood that each activity in the products is raised to the power of its coefficient in the reaction.

This expression depends directly on temperature because of the factor $(RT/n\mathfrak{F})$. For $n = 1$, the value is 0.0591 v, or 59.1 mv at 25°C (a handy figure to remember), and at 50°C the value is 64.1 mv for $n = 1$. Hence the EMF $\mathcal{E}$ will change with temperature because of this factor alone, even when activities—or, approximately, concentrations—are kept constant.

An equally important source of temperature effects is the fact that $\mathcal{E}^0$, the standard EMF, also depends on temperature. The variations of $\mathcal{E}$ and $\mathcal{E}^0$ with temperature can both be related to thermodynamic properties of the cell by considering the basic equation $\Delta \overline{F} = -n\mathfrak{F}\mathcal{E}$, and the thermodynamic equations relating free energy $\Delta \overline{F}$ to enthalpy $\Delta \overline{H}$ and entropy $\Delta \overline{S}$. In Section 15.4 we showed that $(\partial/\partial T)(\Delta \overline{F})_P = -\Delta \overline{S}$. Taking the temperature derivative of the basic equation thus gives

$$\Delta \bar{S} = n\mathfrak{F} \left(\frac{\partial \mathcal{E}}{\partial T} \right)_P$$

or

$$\left(\frac{\partial \mathcal{E}}{\partial T} \right)_P = \frac{\Delta \bar{S}}{n\mathfrak{F}} \qquad (17.17)$$

From this result, the change of EMF with temperature is proportional to the entropy change $\Delta \bar{S}$ of the cell reaction. If this is known from thermochemical data, $(\partial \mathcal{E}/\partial T)_P$ can be calculated, and so $\mathcal{E}$ for different temperatures T; conversely, $\Delta \bar{S}$ can be obtained from $(\partial \mathcal{E}/\partial T)_P$.

Another useful relation, the Gibbs-Helmholtz equation, is obtained by combining the equations above with the thermodynamic equation $\Delta \bar{F} = \Delta \bar{H} - T\Delta \bar{S}$. From this we obtain

$$\Delta \bar{H} = \Delta \bar{F} + T\Delta \bar{S} = -n\mathfrak{F}\mathcal{E} + n\mathfrak{F}T \left(\frac{\partial \mathcal{E}}{\partial T} \right)_P$$

or

$$\Delta \bar{H} = -n\mathfrak{F} \left[\mathcal{E} - T \left(\frac{\partial \mathcal{E}}{\partial T} \right)_P \right] \qquad (17.18)$$

Thus measurements of EMF and its temperature coefficient $(\partial \mathcal{E}/\partial T)_P$ enable one to calculate the thermodynamic changes $\Delta \bar{F}, \Delta \bar{H}, \Delta \bar{S}$ in the cell reaction. These equations can also be used for the standard values $\mathcal{E}^0, \Delta F^0, \Delta H^0, \Delta S^0$ of the cell reaction, and for the corresponding quantities in the separate electrode reactions.

EXAMPLE

Calculate the change in EMF with temperature of the full charged lead-acid storage cell

$$Pb:H_2SO_4 \ (40 \ wgt \ \%):PbO_2$$

The entropy change $\Delta \bar{S} = 650$ cal mole^{-1} deg^{-1} for the cell reaction $PbO_2(s) + Pb(s) + 2H_2SO_4 = 2PbSO_4(s) + 2H_2O$.

Hence $\dfrac{\partial \mathcal{E}}{\partial T} = -\dfrac{\Delta S}{n\mathfrak{F}} = -\dfrac{4.19 \times 650}{2 \times 96500} = -0.014 \ v/^\circ C$

and the cell EMF decreases by 0.014 v for 1°C rise in temperature.

EXAMPLE

EMF values for the cell $Pt(H_2):H_2SO_4;HgSO_4:Hg$ at several temperatures t are here listed:

$t(^\circ C)$	5	15	25	35	45
$\mathcal{E}^0(v)$	0.6310	0.6231	0.6151	0.6070	0.5990

Calculate the heat of the cell reaction $H_2 + Hg_2SO_4 \longrightarrow H_2SO_4 + 2Hg$.

The EMF is fitted by the equation

$$\mathcal{E}_P^0 = 0.6351 - .00080t$$

for temperatures t in the range 5° to 45°C. At 25°C, $\mathcal{E}^0 = 0.6151$ and $(\partial \mathcal{E}^0 / \partial T)_P = -0.00080$ v/°C. (Note that $(\partial \mathcal{E}^0 / \partial T)_P = (\partial \mathcal{E}^0 / \partial t)_P$.) Hence

$$\Delta H_{25°C}^0 = -n\mathfrak{F}\left[\mathcal{E} - T\left(\frac{\partial \mathcal{E}}{\partial T}\right)_P\right] = -2 \times 96500[0.6151 + 0.2384]$$

$$= -176.7 \times 10^3 \text{ joules/mole} = -42.23 \text{ kcal/mole}$$

17.11. pH Measurement

Hydrogen ion concentration (pH) is a tremendously important factor in many chemical and biological processes in solution, and suitable electrodes for supply or removal of hydrogen ions are valuable tools for studying such processes. Although the hydrogen gas electrode is the standard of reference for electrode potentials, it is, like other gas electrodes, inconvenient for routine use. Two more convenient ones often used are the quinhydrone and glass electrodes.

Quinhydrone Electrode

Quinhydrone is the 1:1 compound of quinone and hydroquinone:

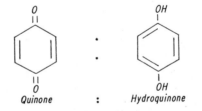

| Quinone | : | Hydroquinone |

which are abbreviated as Q for $C_6H_4O_2$ (quinone) and QH_2 for $C_6H_4(OH)_2$ (hydroquinone). Oxidation of hydroquinone in aqueous solution evolves hydrogen ion at an inert electrode by the reaction

$$QH_2 \longrightarrow Q + 2H^+ + 2e^-$$

The electrode EMF for the oxidation (setting $\gamma H^+ = 1$ as an approximation) is

$$\mathcal{E}_{QH_2,Q} = \mathcal{E}_{QH_2,Q}^0 - \frac{RT}{2\mathfrak{F}} \ln \frac{[Q][H^+]^2}{[QH_2]}$$

The usefulness of the compound $Q:QH_2$ for EMF measurements lies in the fact that it is very slightly soluble in water and produces *equal* con-

centrations of Q and QH$_2$. Hence for a saturated solution with quinhydrone and inert metal electrode, the EMF is approximately

$$\mathcal{E} = \mathcal{E}^0_{QH_2,Q} - \frac{RT}{2\mathfrak{F}} \ln [H^+]^2$$

or

$$\mathcal{E} = \mathcal{E}^0_{QH_2,Q} - 0.00592 \log [H^+] \qquad (17.19)$$

Comparison with a chlorine reference electrode in aqueous HCl solution
gives $\mathcal{E}^0 = -0.700$ v. This value being known, the EMF expression of
Eq. 17.19 can be used to determine the hydrogen ion concentration of a
solution in which a quinhydrone electrode is immersed. For example, a
calomel half-cell and solution of unknown hydrogen ion concentration

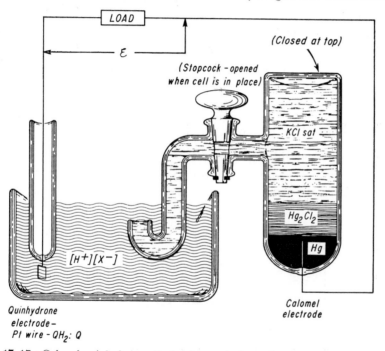

Quinhydrone
electrode –
Pt wire - QH$_2$: Q

Fig. 17.17. *Calomel-quinhydrone cell of unknown hydrogen ion concentration.*

with quinhydrone may be combined, as shown in Fig. 17.17. If junction
potentials are neglected, the cell EMF at 25°C is

$$\mathcal{E} = \mathcal{E}_{Q,QH_2} - \mathcal{E}_{cal(sat)}$$
$$= -0.700 + 0.592 \log [H^+] + 0.242$$

which gives

$$\log [H^+] = \frac{\mathcal{E} + 0.458}{0.0592}$$

This expression for log [H$^+$], and hence pH ($= -$log [H$^+$]), is approximate because ion activity and function potential effects are neglected. As a result the values of log [H$^+$] may easily be in error by 0.05 (12% difference in [H$^+$]), despite the fact that EMF values may be measurable to 0.0001 v, corresponding to a change of only .0017 in log [H$^+$]. This distinction between precision and accuracy in pH measurement is of common occurrence and must be kept in mind.

The quinhydrone electrode is useful but has definite limitations, because hydroquinone is a weak acid which may supply enough H$^+$ ions to change the pH of the solution and because quinone is unstable in alkaline solutions with pH greater than about 7.

A second type of limitation is the fact that the quinhydrone electrode, like the hydrogen gas electrode, can alter the composition of the solution in which it is immersed if active oxidizing or reducing agents are present which react directly with the species in the electrode reaction. This difficulty is avoided in the most generally usable electrode for pH measurements—the glass electrode.

Glass Electrode

The glass electrode is a device of the form indicated in Fig. 17.18, in which an electrode and its solution—usually Ag–AgCl or calomel in KCl solution—are separated from the solution to be studied by a thin-

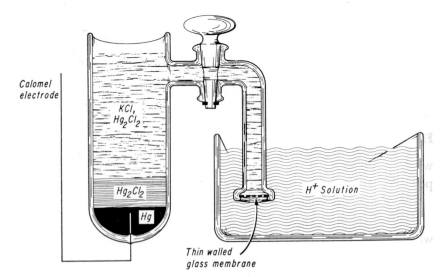

Fig. 17.18. *Glass electrode.*

walled bulb of specially selected glass. If the glass wall is thin enough and of suitable composition, very small but measurable currents can flow, and it is found that the potential difference between the electrode and external solutions depends directly on hydrogen ion concentration without being affected by oxidizing or reducing agents in the solution studied.

The experimental results for glass electrodes can be summarized by an equation for the electrode EMF in the form

$$\varepsilon = \varepsilon^0 - \frac{RT}{\mathfrak{F}} \ln [H^+]$$

where the standard potential ε^0 depends on the glass membrane and electrode system and is determined by measurements of a cell with known solutions and second reference electrode. Once ε^0 is known, the electrode can be used for measurements of solutions with unknown H^+ ion concentrations in a manner similar to that for the quinhydrone electrode.

The small currents obtainable with glass electrodes prevent use of potentiometric methods to measure EMF; instead, electronic vacuum tube voltmeters requiring very little current for a reading are employed. The precision is not as high as with the most sensitive galvanometers and accurate potentiometers usable with cells of low resistance, but potentials accurate to 10^{-3} v and 0.02 in *p*H can be obtained even with portable equipment. A glass electrode and voltmeter combination, often called a "*p*H meter," gives reliable results for *p*H over the concentration range 10^{-1} to 10^{-10} in aqueous solutions or systems containing water as a substantial component.

The underlying reasons why potentials set up at the boundary of glass and solution are sensitive only to hydrogen ion are complicated and not completely understood, but important factors are the presence of dissolved water and hydrogen ion (proton) conduction in the glass.

pH and Activity Coefficients

In the discussion of electrode potentials in this section the approximation of omitting activity coefficients has regularly been made. Because effects of ion interactions are thereby ignored, ion concentrations calculated by the resulting equations are not exact, especially at high concentrations. Thus a value $[H^+]$ calculated from an equation such as $\varepsilon = \varepsilon^0 - (RT/\mathfrak{F}) \ln [H^+]$ is somewhat in error, because the quantity $\gamma_{\pm} [H^+]$

should have been used in place of $[H^+]$. This causes an error of uncertain amount in the value of $[H^+]$ unless $\gamma_\pm$ for the solute is known or can be estimated with sufficient accuracy, which is often not the case.

The familiar quantity pH is similarly ambiguous in many cases. The term pH was originally defined by Sorensen by the equation

$$pH = -\log\,[H^+]$$

The definition gives a convenient scale of numbers, as a $1\,N$ solution of strong acid has a pH near 1.0 ($H^+ \cong 10^{-1}$); water has a pH near 7.0 ($H^+ \cong 10^{-7}$); and a $1\,N$ strong base has a pH near 14 ($H^+ \cong 10^{-14}$). Use of the logarithm of $[H^+]$ is also an advantage because EMF and equilibrium constant expressions involve logarithms of concentrations directly. The difficulty still remains that one calculates $\gamma_\pm[H^+]$ rather than $[H^+]$ from available equilibrium measurements. If pH is defined as $-\log\,[H^+]$, only an approximation to it is then known in most cases. The alternative is to redefine pH by the equation

$$pH = -\log\,\gamma_\pm[H^+]$$

which then makes pH a directly measured quantity, but one not exactly defined in relation to $[H^+]$ until $\gamma_\pm$ is known. All things considered, this latter definition is the best, as it defines a quantity derivable with reasonable accuracy from hydrogen ion equilibrium equations. In using it, however, one must remember that $\gamma_\pm$ depends on all the ions present and so is not a function of the concentration $[H^+]$ alone.

Although the discussion here has been concentrated on the quantities pH and $[H^+]$ because of the great importance of hydrogen ion equilibria, exactly similar questions arise in considering any other ion equilibrium. Thus EMF measurements with chloride ion electrodes involve $\gamma_\pm[Cl^-]$, where $\gamma_\pm$ is the mean activity coefficient of solute in the solution containing chloride ion.

17.12. Types of Cell Reactions

Complete cells may be classified as *chemical cells*, in which the free energy change and EMF result from ionic electrode reactions, or *concentration cells*, in which the cell process entails the transfer of matter from one electrode to the other in order to equalize concentrations.

Both types of cells are simplest when there is a single essentially homogeneous solution and so no difficulties from junction potentials, but it is often difficult or impossible to avoid use of two or more solutions if

a reaction of interest is to be studied. Under these circumstances, transference of ions across the boundary or boundaries between solutions is a
complicating factor which must be considered.

An example of a cell with solution boundary is the combination of
Zn–$ZnSO_4$ and Cu–$CuSO_4$ electrode reactions shown in Fig. 17.7. This
arrangement can be symbolized as

$$\text{Zn}: \text{ZnSO}_4(m_1); \text{CuSO}_4(m_2): \text{Cu}.$$

This is a chemical cell with the oxidation-reduction reaction
$\text{Zn} + \text{Cu}^{2+} = \text{Zn}^{2+} + \text{Cu}$, but transference of ions across the boundary
of the Zn and $CuSO_4$ solutions must be considered.

In writing EMF cells, the boundary between an electrode and the
electrolyte solution is indicated by a colon (:) and the boundary at a
liquid junction is indicated by a semicolon (;).

A simple form of concentration cell results from placing hydrogen
electrodes at different gas pressures in HCl solution:

$$\text{Pt}: \text{H}_2(P_1),\ \text{HCl}(m),\ \text{H}_2(P_2): \text{Pt}$$

If oxidation occurs at the left electrode, the reaction is $\text{H}_2(P_1) \longrightarrow \text{H}_2(P_2)$
and the cell EMF is given by

$$\mathscr{E} = -\frac{RT}{2\mathscr{F}} \ln \frac{P_2}{P_1}$$

The reader should satisfy himself that $\mathscr{E}^0$ for the cell is zero, and also
that $\mathscr{E}$ is positive for $P_2 < P_1$, as it should be. Since the process is one of
transfer of hydrogen gas from a higher pressure at one electrode to a
lower pressure at the other, this is a concentration cell, and there is no
significant boundary across which ions in solution must pass.

Two amalgam electrodes of different metal concentrations C_1 and C_2
in a solution of the metal ion also form a concentration cell without
transference. Thus the cell has the reactions

$$\text{Cd}(C_1 \text{ in Hg}): \text{CdSO}_4(m): \text{Cd}(C_2 \text{ in Hg})$$
$$\text{Cd}(C_1) \longrightarrow \text{Cd}^{2+}(m) + 2e^-$$
$$\underline{\text{Cd}(C_2) \longrightarrow \text{Cd}^{2+}(m) + 2e^-}$$

and the cell reaction is $\text{Cd}(C_1) = \text{Cd}(C_2).$

The cell reaction thus entails transfer of cadmium from one electrode
to the other by Cd^{2+} ion in solution. If the amalgams are dilute enough
that concentrations can be used with activity coefficients in both amalgams equal to unity, the EMF is

$$\mathcal{E} = -\frac{RT}{\mathcal{F}} \ln \frac{C_2}{C_1}$$

The value of $\mathcal{E}^0$ for the cell is zero because the electrode standard states and hence electrode $\mathcal{E}^0$ values are identical. The EMF is positive and reaction spontaneous for electrode C_1 as anode if $C_2 < C_1$; that is, the reaction proceeds in the direction which equalizes the amalgam concentrations.

Concentration cells with transference are formed when identical electrodes in solutions of different concentration are combined to form a cell with a boundary between the solutions. Such a cell with Ag–Ag$^+$ electrodes is

$$\text{Ag} : \text{AgNO}_3(C_1) \ ; \ \text{AgNO}_3(C_2) : \text{Ag}$$

Since each electrode reaction has the form Ag $\longrightarrow$ Ag$^+$ + e^-, the cell reaction is

$$\text{Ag}^+(C_2) \longrightarrow \text{Ag}^+(C_1)$$

which is spontaneous for anode oxidation at concentrations C_1 if $C_2 > C_1$. There is, however, the complication of transference because some silver ions must cross the boundary from solution C_1 to solution C_2, and nitrate ions in the opposite direction, as indicated in Fig. 17.19. The result is

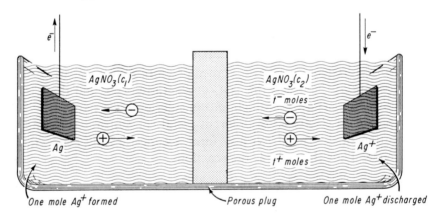

Fig. 17.19. *Concentration cell with transference.*

that silver ion concentration changes by the electrode reactions are thus partially compensated by the migration, or transference, of silver ion directly from one solution to the other. The relation of cell EMF to concentration is different than if there were no transference; moreover, there is the problem of potential differences between the solutions. The effect of transference is considered in Section 18.8; junction potential effects are taken up in the following section.

17.13. Junction Potentials and Transference

In most of the discussion of cell EMF's to this point, attention has been confined to cells involving only one electrolyte solution. When solutions with real and distinct differences in composition must be placed in contact to form a complete cell, the behavior of ions at or near the boundary during current flow and at equilibrium are real problems. The resulting effects to be discussed are interesting from the point of view of understanding properties of ions in solution, and a source of error if one wants measurements of electrode reactions only.

The nature of the problem can be illustrated by considering a typical simple junction of HCl and KCl solutions. If the current is driven spontaneously by electrode processes in which the oxidation electrode is in the HCl solution, hydrogen ions must migrate through the boundary layer from the HCl solution to the KCl solution, while chloride ions cross the boundary in the opposite direction and potassium ions in the KCl solution retreat from the boundary. All three kinds of ions thus change their environment and undergo changes in chemical potential. Unless by coincidence these effects compensate each other exactly, there will be a net change in free energy in the process.

The effect of the net junction free energy change on the EMF is commonly described as a junction potential difference between the solutions. This concept has been harshly criticized, because there is no direct way of measuring a potential difference between solutions. One can, however, proceed indirectly by comparing the measured EMF of a cell with liquid junctions with the EMF calculated from the electrode reactions alone. When this can be done, differences are obtained which are usually several millivolts and may be 50 mv (0.05 v) or more.

Values of order 10 mv or more are clearly too large to be ignored in measurements of any great accuracy, as they correspond to a free energy difference of 250 calories and a concentration change of 50% (if single electron oxidations occur at the electrodes). Much effort and ingenuity has therefore been devoted either in developing ways of calculating junction potentials for solution pairs of interest, or in minimizing the potential difference by modified methods of joining the solutions electrically.

A simple and often used experimental approach to minimize junction potential errors is by interposing a "salt bridge," as shown in Fig. 17.4 for a calomel electrode. In this device, the electrode solutions are separated by the salt solution with which both make contact. By suitable choice of solution, the potentials at the two junctions may often be reduced considerably, and moreover made of opposite sign to counteract each other.

The salt usually chosen is KCl in $1N$ or saturated ($\sim 4.2N$) solution, on the grounds that K^+ and Cl^- ions migrate with nearly the same speed and are otherwise very similar (except of course for the opposite sign of change and direction of migration). The concentration is made high so that most of the electrolyte in the boundary regions is composed of K^+ and Cl^- ions.

At either junction most of the current will be carried by K^+ and Cl^- ions, which move nearly equal amounts in opposite directions; hence it can be hoped that the net change in free energy will be small for each junction and in the opposite sense. There is fair evidence that salt bridges effect considerable improvements for simple, not too concentrated solutions.

A variation of the salt bridge attack on junction potentials is to add large and nearly equal quantities of the same salt to both solutions—the added salt containing ions not involved in the electrode reactions. If this is done, the total ion concentrations of the two solutions can be made nearly identical and almost entirely of ions of the added salt in each. The much closer similarity of the solutions reduces free energy changes by ion transport from one solution to the other and often virtually eliminates changes in EMF attributable to the junction. The price paid for the change is that the electrode reactions must then be studied for solutions with large total ion concentrations, and may be rather different than when there is no added salt.

17.14. Ionic Interactions and Debye-Hückel Theory

Ionic equilibria in solution show increasingly regular and characteristic properties as the ion concentrations are made very small. One is that deviations from ideal dilute behavior approach values proportional to the square root of the concentration. This is true for salts and strong acids generally, and it is particularly striking that the deviations become more nearly the same for all ionic solutes of any one valence type, and are larger for solutes of higher valence types. That is, all 1–1 solutes such as NaCl, KNO_3, and HCl have increasing similar deviations which become more nearly linear with square root of concentration at high dilutions. All 1–2 or 2–1 salts such as Na_2SO_4 and $CaCl_2$ have larger but similar deviations, and 2–2 salts such as $CuSO_4$ have still larger ones. A further important deduction from the evidence is that the equilibrium of any one ionic solute is affected by the concentration of *all* ionic solutes present.

These regularities point to an explanation of the common dilute behavior in terms of the charges on the ions in solution and the electrical forces between these charged species, with more specific chemical differences becoming apparent at higher concentrations.

The predominant effect of ion interactions at low concentrations began to be realized early in the twentieth century, but a real understanding of the effects was not forthcoming for some time. The mathematical and statistical problem of determining the consequences of Coulomb forces between charged particles in solution is difficult, because these forces fall off slowly with increasing distance between the charges, and so are important for ions considerable distances apart. Debye and Hückel in 1923 were able to devise an approximate treatment for sufficiently dilute solutions, which both accounts for the limiting square root behavior and also gives an illuminating and useful picture of the state of ions in such solutions.

The considerations on which the Debye-Hückel theory is based can be appreciated by a rough molecular picture of the motions of ions in solution. Any small region of an electrolyte contains equivalent numbers of positive and negative ions on the average, since they come from dissolving electrically neutral substances in the solvent. These ions and the solvent molecules are not fixed in position, however, but are in continuous irregular motion as they are agitated by thermal energy and forces exerted by other molecules and ions in their vicinity. Thus the picture of any fixed small region, as in Fig. 17.20, A, will shift continually in time, both ions and solvent moving into and from the region.

If one ion, say a positive ion, could be followed, a meandering path, as suggested by Fig. 17.20, B, would be observed. In the course of this wandering, it will come near other ions at intervals. If such an ion also has a positive charge, the two repel each other, but if it is negative there is an attractive force. The result is evidently that these additional forces will cause ions of unlike charge to approach each other more closely, while ions of like charge will keep greater distance in the absence of the coulomb forces, as suggested by the drawings in Fig. 17.20.

The magnitude of the force for two ions each of charge Ze at a distance

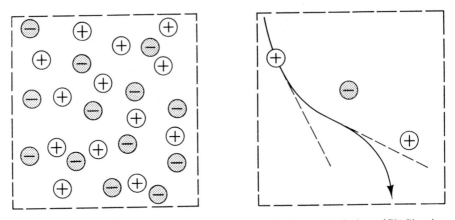

Fig. 17.20. (A) *Positive and negative ions in a small volume of solutions.* (B) *Showing how the motion of a positive ion is modified by the attraction of a negative ion and repulsion of another positive ion.*

r apart *in vacuum* is Z^2e^2/r^2, but for ions in solution this is diminished by the shielding effect of the solvent molecules surrounding them, as discussed in Sections 11.6 and 11.7. If the ions are far enough apart, the solvent polarization effect can be described by its dielectric constant ϵ, and the resultant average force is

$$F = \frac{Z^2e^2}{\epsilon r^2}$$

The corresponding potential energy V of interaction is then

$$V = -\frac{Z^2e^2}{\epsilon r}$$

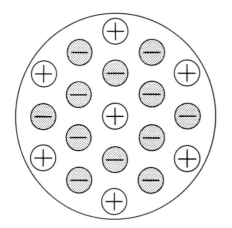

Fig. 17.21. *Excess, on the average, of negative ion charge in the immediate vicinity of a positive ion.*

The magnitude of this energy is of major importance in determining whether a particular solvent can permit ions to be stable in solution at all. For if the attractive force between unlike ions is too large, as in a solvent of low dielectric constant, the kinetic energy of ion motions will be insufficient to prevent recombination of ions of unlike charge. Only in strongly polar solvents such as water is the dielectric constant large enough for nearly com-

plete ionization at appreciable concentrations. If there is such ionization, positive ions on the average have negative ions closer to them, and
the other positive ions are at greater average distances. The average
excess of negative ions will be especially marked near the positive ion,
as suggested by the exaggerated sketch in Fig. 17.21 of what would
be seen in a snapshot focused on a particular positive ion.

The first objective of the Debye-Hückel theory is calculation of this
average distribution of charge around each ion, called the *ion atmosphere*,
and from it the decreased free energy of the ions in solution.

This is done by combining electrostatic theory for the relation between
charge density and electrical potential with a Boltzmann expression for
the greater probability of finding charge of opposite sign and lower
potential energy near the particular ion. The details of this approximate
calculation require more development of electrical and statistical theory
than is possible here. The result, however, can be used to calculate the
amount by which the ion has lower energy in solution because of the
net electrical attraction by ions of opposite sign. This decrease is just
the lowering of free energy of the ion—that is, is equal to the electrical
work necessary to remove the ion from the influence of ionic forces.

The calculated decrease in free energy of one mole of any one kind of
ion of charge $Z_x e$ in a solution of dielectric constant ϵ and density d is
given by

$$\Delta F_x = -N^2 \left(\frac{Z_x^2 e^2}{\epsilon}\right)\left(\frac{\pi e^2 d}{1000 \; \epsilon RT}\right)^{1/2}\left(\tfrac{1}{2}\sum_{\text{all ions}} Z_i^2 m_i\right)^{1/2} \qquad (17.20)$$

where the sum is over all kinds of ion i in solution, with charge $Z_i e$ and
molality m_i, and N is Avogadro's number.

Before putting the equation in a more convenient form for comparison
with experiment, the following features should be noticed.

1. The dielectric constant ϵ of solvent and charge and valence of the
ion appear (as $Z_x e$), because the effect of electrostatic forces is calculated.

2. The quantity RT appears because the Boltzmann factor with expo-
nent $Z_i^2 e^2/\epsilon KTr$ is used to express the average number of charges $Z_i e$ at
a distance r from the ion X.

3. The concentration dependence appears only in the factor
$(\tfrac{1}{2}\sum_{\text{all ions}} Z_i^2 m_i)^{1/2}$, and thus involves square root of a sum of *all* ion concentrations, multiplied by its valence Z_i.

The third factor is especially important, for it predicts *the square root
variation, the greater effect of higher valences Z_i, and the dependence on all ions*

present in the solution. These are precisely the points mentioned at the beginning as characteristic of electrolyte equilibrium at high dilution.

In order to put the prediction in form for comparison with experiment, it is necessary first to calculate the free energy change of the salt or acid of interest rather than the ions separately, because only the total change is measurable, and it is convenient to express this change in terms of the corresponding mean activity coefficient.

The expression of Eq. 17.20 refers to the free energy change per mole of one kind of ion x, and is equal to $RT \ln \gamma_x$, where γ_x is the ionic activity coefficient. For a binary solute yielding n^+ cations of charge Z_+e and n_- anions of charge (Z_-e), the mean ionic activity coefficient $\gamma_\pm$ of the solute can be introduced as discussed in Section 16.8, and the result is that

$$\ln \gamma_\pm = -(Z_+Z_-)\left(\frac{N^2e^2}{\epsilon RT}\right)\left(\frac{2\pi e^2\, d}{1000\ \epsilon RT}\right)^{1/2}\left(\tfrac{1}{2}\sum_{\text{ions}} Z_i^2 m_i\right)^{1/2} \quad (17.21)$$

The most frequent use of this equation is for solutes in water at 25°. If we insert the proper values of ϵ, R, and T, we obtain

$$\log \gamma_\pm = -0.509(Z_+Z_-)(\tfrac{1}{2}\sum Z_i^2 m_i)^{1/2} \quad (17.22)$$

The sum $\tfrac{1}{2}\sum Z_i^2 m_i$ is called the ionic strength (I) and was introduced by G. N. Lewis, who found empirically that it was useful and significant for electrolytes before the Debye-Hückel theory was developed.

17.15. Comparison of Debye-Hückel Theory with Experiment

The predictions of the Debye-Hückel theory embodied in Eq. 17.22 can be tested by a considerable number and variety of measurements at sufficiently low concentrations.

EMF and Concentration Dependence

One test can be based on the EMF measurements of the cell,

$$\text{Pt}:\text{H}_2(1\text{ atm}),\ \text{HCl}(m),\ \text{AgCl}:\text{Ag}$$

discussed in Section 17.3. As shown in Section 17.7, the EMF at 25°C including the mean activity coefficient of HCl is of the form

$$\mathscr{E} = \mathscr{E}^0 - 0.1183 \log m - 0.1183 \log \gamma_\pm$$

or

$$\mathscr{E} + 0.1183 \log m = \mathscr{E}^0 - 0.1183 \log \gamma_\pm$$

The Debye-Hückel theory predicts that $\log \gamma_{\pm}$ for this single electrolyte HCl should be given by

$$\log \gamma_{\pm} = -0.509[\tfrac{1}{2}(m_{H^+} + m_{Cl^-})]^{1/2} = -0.509m_{HCl}^{1/2}$$

and hence gives the equation

$$\varepsilon + 0.1183 \log m = \varepsilon^0 + 0.0604m_{HCl}^{1/2} \qquad (17.23)$$

This is evidently of the right form to account for the nearly linear plot of $\varepsilon + 0.1183 \log m$ against $m_{HCl}^{1/2}$ at low concentrations. The predicted slope 0.0604 should also agree with the limiting experimental behavior for concentrations at which Eq. 17.23 is accurate. That this behavior is approached is shown by agreement of the data with the dashed line in Fig. 17.13, which is drawn with the slope 0.0604.

An alternative and more sensitive test is to calculate values of the quantity

$$X = \varepsilon + 0.1183 \log m - 0.0604m_{HCl}^{1/2} \qquad (17.24)$$

which should be constant, and equal to the standard value ε^0, at concentrations for which the theory is adequate. These values, listed in Table 17.4, show that the theory gives quite constant values at the

TABLE 17.4.   *Test of the Debye-Hückel Prediction for Activity Coefficient of HCl in Water at 25°C.*

m_{HCl}	$\varepsilon_{25°}$	X (Eq. 17.24)
0.003215	0.52053	0.22246
0.004488	0.50384	0.22227
0.005619	0.49257	0.22205
0.007311	0.47948	0.22184
0.011195	0.45861	0.22162
0.01710	0.43783	0.22106
0.02563	0.41824	0.22050
0.1238	0.34199	0.21331

From H. S. Harned and R. W. Ehlers,
J. Am. Chem. Soc., **54**, 1350 (1932).

lowest concentrations. There is, however, a definite downward trend at higher molalities, and the actual behavior is then more complex than the predictions of the approximate theory.

Solubility and Activity Coefficients

The change in solubility of AgCl on adding KNO_3—the salt effect discussed in Section 16.9—can be used as another test of the theory. If C_s is the solubility of AgCl, then the truly constant solubility product including the activity coefficient $\gamma_\pm$ must be

$$K^0 = C_s^2 \gamma_\pm^2 = \text{constant}$$

For convenience in comparison with the theory, this can be written

$$\log C_s + \log \gamma_\pm = \tfrac{1}{2} \log K^0 = \text{constant}$$

The predicted value of $\gamma_\pm$ in this case is

$$\log \gamma_\pm = -0.509[\tfrac{1}{2}(C_{Ag^+} + C_{Cl^-} + C_{K^+} + C_{NO_3^-})]^{1/2}$$
$$= -0.509[C_s + C_{KNO_3}]^{1/2}$$

Hence a plot of $\log C_s$ against $(C_s + C_{KNO_3})^{1/2}$ should give a straight line of slope 0.509. The results shown in Fig. 17.22 are evidently of this form, and so confirm the approximate validity of the theory with definite deviations at the higher concentrations.

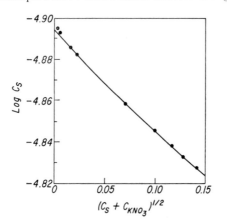

Fig. 17.22. *Plot of solubility C_s of silver chloride against square root of total salt concentration (of AgCl and KNO_3).*

Effect of Valence Type

A classic test of the effect of valence type, as expressed by the appearance of the valence product $Z_+ \times Z_-$ of the salt studied and the ionic strength I, was made by Brönsted and LaMer in 1924, shortly after the formulation of the Debye-Hückel theory. These workers chose to study the solubilities of sparingly soluble complex cobalt amine salts; these were chosen for low solubility in pure water, freedom from complications of hydrolysis, and convenience in making reliable analytical determination of solubilities on adding other electrolytes. For any such salt, the solubility S as a function of total ionic strength I must be of the form $S\gamma_\pm = \text{constant}$, which can be written

$$\log S = \text{constant} - \log \gamma_\pm$$

If the theory is valid,

$$\log S = \text{constant} + 0.509 Z_+ Z_- I^{1/2} \qquad (17.25)$$

where Z_+ and Z_- are the valencies of the ions of the salts. If the solubility for no added salt is S_0 and the ionic strength I_0, Eq. 17.25 can be written

$$\log S - \log S_0 = 0.5092 Z_+ Z_- (I^{1/2} - I_0^{1/2}) \qquad (17.26)$$

(since $\log S_0 = \text{constant} + 0.509 Z_+ Z_- I_0^{1/2}$). Plots of $\log S - \log S_0$ versus $I^{1/2} - I_0^{1/2}$ for 1–1, 1–2, and 3–1 salts are given in Fig. 17.23. In each case, the predicted linear variation with $I^{1/2} - I_0^{1/2}$ is found with the experimental error. Moreover, the slopes of the lines correspond to the value 0.509 for 1–1 salts, $2 \times 0.509 = 1.018$ for 1–2 salts, and $3 \times 0.509 = 1.527$ for 3–1 salts.

17.16. Activity Coefficients of Concentrated Electrolytes

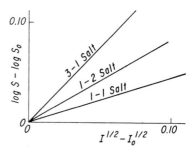

Fig. 17.23. (*log S — log S₀*) *versus* ($I^{1/2} - I_0^{1/2}$) *for* 1-1, 1-2, *and* 3-1 *salts.*

In the preceding section, the activity coefficients of strong electrolytes were considered primarily for low enough ion concentrations that the Debye-Hückel limiting variation is approached. The solutions for which this is true are sufficiently dilute that they are sometimes cynically described as slightly contaminated water. The comparative simplicity of such solutions is unfortunately lost at higher concentrations, and satisfactory theories are yet to be developed.

Experimental study of more concentrated solutions can be based on measurements of equilibrium properties in very much the same ways that they have been discussed already. The results are conveniently expressed in terms of either the mean activity coefficient or its logarithm (to which the free energy or chemical potential of the solution is proportional).

The results for activity coefficients of several salts in water at 25°C to concentrations of $0.1 N$ are shown in Fig. 17.24 by plots of $\log \gamma_\pm$ versus square root of concentration. This form is suggested by the prediction of the Debye-Hückel theory for dilute solutions, and the limiting slopes of the theory are used to draw the dashed straight lines of the plots.

The approach to the limiting slopes and pronounced change for higher valence as predicted are both impressive, but the increasing importance of effects specific to the solute at higher concentrations is also evident.

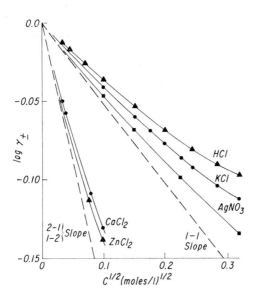

Fig. 17.24. *Mean activity coefficient as function of (concentration)*$^{1/2}$.

Various attempts have been made to predict the effects at higher concentration, but with only partial success. One factor neglected in the limiting equation is the effect of ion size in preventing too close approach of ions of unlike sign. Approximate allowance for this leads to an equation for $\log \gamma_{\pm}$ of the form (for water at 25°C)

$$\log \gamma_{\pm} = \frac{0.509 Z_+ Z_- I^{1/2}}{1 + aI^{1/2}}$$

$$(17.27)$$

where the quantity a is a sort of mean ion radius. The equation is of the right form to account for the less rapid change and upward curvature of the plots in Fig. 17.24. Moreover, plausible values of a in the range 2–5 Å give quite good fits of the data up to $0.1\,N$ for a number of salts. There are, however, sufficiently serious difficulties in justifying the reasoning which leads to Eq. 17.27 that it is probably best regarded as a semiempirical result. (Symptoms of these difficulties are the fact that unreasonably small or even negative values of a must sometimes be assumed to secure agreement.)

The values of $\gamma_{\pm}$ at concentrations above about $0.1\,N$ vary so markedly and individually that simple interpretation in terms of ion charge and size effects becomes impossible. Detailed accounts of available information and regularities discernible on comparing observations of many kinds are given in specialized monographs on electrochemistry; here it is only possible to give some examples of measured values of $\gamma_{\pm}$ and brief comments about the significance of ionic strength in concentrated solutions.

Table 17.5 lists activity coefficients for a number of simple electrolytes

TABLE 17.5. *Activity Coefficients of Electrolytes in Water at 25°C.*

Concentration (mols per 1000 g of H₂O, m)	NaCl	KCl	HCl	HBr	NaOH	CaCl₂	ZnCl₂	H₂SO₄	ZnSO₄	CdSO₄
0.005	0.928	0.927	0.930	0.930	—	0.789	0.767	0.643	0.477	0.476
.01	.903	.902	.906	.906	0.899	.732	.708	.545	.387	.383
.02	.872	.869	.878	.879	.860	.669	.642	.455	.298	—
.05	.821	.817	.833	.838	.805	.584	.556	.341	.202	.199
.10	.778	.770	.798	.805	.759	.524	.502	.266	.148	.137
.20	.732	.719	.768	.782	.719	.491	.448	.210	.104	—
.50	.680	.652	.769	.790	.681	.510	.376	.155	.063	.061
1.00	.656	.607	.811	.871	.667	.725	.325	.131	.044	.042
1.50	.655	.587	.898	—	.671	—	.290	—	.037	.039
2.00	.670	.578	1.011	—	.685	1.554	—	.125	.035	.030
3.00	.719	.574	1.31	—	—	3.384	—	.142	.041	.026
4.00	.791	—	1.74	—	—	—	—	.172	—	—

From D. A. MacInnes, *Principles of Electrochemistry* (Reinhold, New York, 1939, p. 167).

of several valence types in water at 25°C and up to concentrations of 4 molal. Some of these results are also plotted in Fig. 17.25, the plots being of $\gamma_\pm$ itself against molality m, rather than of log $\gamma_\pm$ versus $m^{1/2}$. The great diversity of behavior for all but the dilute end of the range is evident even from these few examples, and it is clear that individual study of ion and solvent interactions will be needed to account separately for the experimental observations.

As a practical matter of predicting and interpreting equilibrium behavior, one useful feature of the measured activities of concentrated elec-

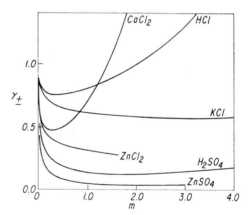

Fig. 17.25. *Activity coefficient for salt solutions at high concentrations.*

trolytes may often be used to advantage. This is that ranges of high concentration can be found in which $\gamma_\pm$, although far from the value 1.0 for ideal behavior, does not vary rapidly with concentration. Thus $\gamma_\pm$ for KCl is not far from 0.58 over a wide range, while minima for CaCl₂ and HCl occur for 0.25 and 0.5 molal solutions with smaller rates of change near these minima. By choosing concentrations in such ranges, equilibria of other ions can be studied with less complication from changes in ionic strength.

The reader should be cautioned about the rather special character of the systems discussed in this section, as the solutes considered have all been strong electrolytes in water. The effects are thus primarily from ion interactions for virtually complete ionization, as with salts and strong acids and bases. Weak acids and bases, such as acetic acid and ammonia in water, are only partially ionized in water at ordinary concentrations, and for such solutes the ionization equilibrium may be more important than interactions of the ions present. Equilibria of this kind are considered in Chapters 18 and 19, and are of even greater importance in solvents of low dielectric constant for which association and aggregations of ions also occur.

One must also keep in mind that water is a rather special solvent, so much so as to be virtually unique in many respects. Other strongly polar solvents, such as liquid HCN, ethylamine, methyl alcohol, and ammonia, can form strong electrolytes to a greater or lesser extent, and show characteristic effects at higher concentrations differing from those for the same solute in water. Our knowledge of these systems is much more meager than for aqueous solutions, and study of them has many possibilities for better understanding of ion and solvent behavior.

Finally, it may be mentioned that the prevalence of measurements at 25°C results primarily from experimental conveniences rather than any special importance or significance of this temperature. Studies of behavior at other temperatures are few in number and limited in scope, and more measurements can be expected to yield valuable information.

Problems

17.1. A current of 0.010 ampere flows 10 minutes through a cell with a copper anode. (a) What is the change in weight of this electrode as a result? (b) What is the change in weight of a silver electrode under the same conditions?

17.2. A galvanic cell is connected to an external circuit which can be adjusted to draw different currents, and the corresponding potential differences across the cell are measured with the following results:

I (amperes)	.00010	.00020	.00050	.0010
V (volts)	.6048	.6046	.6041	.6029

(a) What is the cell EMF, assuming that it is reversible? (b) From Ohm's law, what can be deduced about the cell from the variation of V with I?

(c) What further measurements would help you to decide whether the cell reaction was reversible?

17.3. Write electrode and cell reactions for each of the following cells:

$$Cd:CdCl_2(M_1); \; HCl(M_2), \; H_2(g): Pt$$
$$Zn:ZnCl_2; \; FeCl_2, \; FeCl_3: Pt$$
$$Pt:H_2(g), \; HBr, \; Hg_2Br_2(s): Hg$$

17.4. The familiar lead storage cell consists when charged of a lead anode, the lead dioxide coating on a lead-antimony electrode as cathode, and concentrated sulphuric acid electrolyte. (a) The initial oxidation and reduction steps are $Pb \longrightarrow Pb^{++} + 2e^-$ and $PbO_2 + 4H^+ + 2e^- \longrightarrow Pb^{++}$. Write the electrode and cell reactions. (Remember that $PbSO_4$ is virtually insoluble in water.) (b) From the reaction, explain why the state of charge of a storage battery is indicated by a reading of the electrolyte density and why discharged cells are referred to as "sulfated."

17.5. Write the electrode and cell reactions of the arrangement

$$Pt: \; H_2(g), \; NaOH, \; HgO(s): Hg$$

(The cathode reaction is reduction of mercuric oxide to mercury directly, not through mercurous oxide.)

17.6. A commercial process for producing metallic sodium is by electrolysis of molten $NaOH$ with inert metal electrodes (e.g., copper cathode and nickel anode). (a) Write the electrode reactions and cell reaction, and indicate where the products are evolved. (b) The reaction $Na + H_2O = NaOH + \frac{1}{2} H_2$ in practice modifies the primary electrode reactions. Explain why this is so and why the yield of sodium is half what one expects from the primary reactions.

17.7. The electrode potential for an oxidation of the form $M(s) = M^+ + e^-$ changes by approximately 59 mv (.059 v) at 25°C for a tenfold change in concentration of M^+, a handy figure to remember. (a) What is the corresponding figure for $Mg(s) = Mg^{2+} + 2e^-$? (b) What is the figure for $Sn^{2+} = Sn^{4+} + 2e^-$ if the concentration of Sn^{2+} ion is reduced by a factor 10?

17.8. What does the coefficient 0.059 in the EMF expression at 25°C become at 0°C and at 40°C?

17.9. Calculate the potentials at 25°C of the following electrodes, neglecting deviations from ideal dilute behavior:

$$Ag:AgCl(s), \; Cl^- \; (m = 0.001)$$
$$Pt:Br_2(l), \; Br^- \; (m = 0.50)$$
$$Pt:Fe^{2+} \; (m = 0.01), \; Fe^{3+} \; (m = 0.03)$$
$$Cr:Cr(OH)_3, \; OH^- \; (m = 10^{-5})$$
$$Pt:H_2 \; (600 \text{ mm Hg}), \; H^+ \; (m = 10^{-3})$$

17.10. Devise cells in which the following reactions could be studied at 25°C and calculate the approximate cell EMF for the indicated concentrations:

$$Cu(s) + 2Ag^+ (0.005) = Cu^{2+} (0.01) + 2Ag(s)$$
$$\tfrac{1}{2}H_2(g) \text{ (1 atm)} + AgI(s) = HI (0.0001) + Ag(s)$$
$$Pb(s) + SO_4^{2-} (0.001) + Zn^{2+} (0.01) = PbSO_4(s) + Zn(s)$$

17.11. The reaction $2Hg(l) + Cl_2(g) = Hg_2Cl_2(s)$ has been studied with the cell $Hg(l): Hg_2Cl_2(s)$, KCl (sat), $Cl_2(g)$: Pt. The EMF for various pressures $P(Cl_2)$ of chlorine at 25°C are:

$P(Cl_2)$ (mm Hg)	113.5	215.0	468.0
$\mathcal{E}(v)$	1.0662	1.0746	1.0838

(a) Show that the overall reaction follows from the electrode reactions. (b) Obtain the equation for the EMF as a function of $P(Cl_2)$ and calculate $\mathcal{E}^0$ for the reaction. (c) From the value of $\mathcal{E}^0$, calculate $\Delta \bar{F}^0_{298}$ for the formation of Hg_2Cl_2.

17.12. The standard potential of the silver-silver bromide electrode and the activities of aqueous HBr solutions of various molalities m have been studied in the cell

$$Pt: H_2(g) \text{ (1 atm)}, HBr(m), AgBr(s): Ag$$

Values obtained at 25°C are

m	.000312	.000404	.000844	.001355
$\mathcal{E}(v)$	.48469	.47381	.43636	.41243

(a) Use the method of Section 17.7 to determine $\mathcal{E}^0$ and the values of $\gamma_\pm$ for HBr at the different molalities. (b) Use the value of $\mathcal{E}^0$ to calculate the solubility product of AgBr in water at 25°C.

17.13. The hydrogen, HCl, silver-silver chloride cell has been studied with solutions of HCl in methanol. Some results at 25°C are as follows:

$m(HCl)$	.000390	.00130	.00211	.00427	.00775
$\mathcal{E}(v)$	.3861	.3274	.3041	.2712	.2445

(a) Plot $\mathcal{E}$ versus $\log m$ and compare with the corresponding plot for aqueous solutions of HCl. (b) Obtain a value for $\mathcal{E}^0$ by a suitable plot against $m^{1/2}$. Are the deviations from dilute behavior larger or smaller than for aqueous solutions of the same molality?

17.14. Two amalgam electrodes of thallium in mercury are placed in a solution of a mercury salt at 20°C. For mole fractions 0.01673 and 0.00325 of thallium in the electrodes the EMF is .04555 v, and for mole fractions 0.03721 and 0.01673 it is 0.02640 v. How well do these values satisfy the EMF equation based on ideal behavior of the amalgams?

17.15. A value of $\mathcal{E}^0$ for the half-cell reaction $Zn \longrightarrow Zn^{2+} + 2e^-$ is desired, as are values of activity coefficients for the 2–2 electrolyte $ZnSO_4$. Describe a suitable cell and the measurements you would make, and give the expression for the cell EMF you would use in analyzing the results.

17.16. The EMF of a cell is 0.07200 v at 25°C, 0.07552 v at 20°C, and 0.06847 v at 30°C. Calculate the values at 25°C of $\Delta \bar{F}$, $\Delta \bar{H}$, and $\Delta \bar{S}$, in calories per mole as energy units, for the cell reaction in passage of one faraday.

17.17. The EMF of the Clark cell

$$Zn: ZnSO_4(m), Hg_2SO_4(s): Hg$$

is given at 25°C by $\mathcal{E} = 1.378 - .0591 \log m\ ZnSO_4\ \gamma_\pm$. (a) Verify this equation if $\mathcal{E}^0$ for $2Hg(s) + SO_4^{2-} = Hg_2SO_4(s) + 2e^-$ is -0.615 v. (b) For the cell reaction with $n = 2$, $\Delta \bar{H}^0 = -76.00$ kcal. What is $\Delta \bar{S}^0$ for the reaction? (c) What is $\mathcal{E}^0$ for the cell at 40°C?

17.18. (a) The EMF of the cell

$$Pt: H_2(g)\ (1\ atm),\ NaOH(aq),\ Hg_2O(s):\ Hg(l)$$

does not depend significantly on concentration of base. Explain why this should be so by writing the electrode and cell reactions for basic solution. (b) The measured EMF of the cell at temperatures $t°C$ near 25°C is given by

$$\mathcal{E}\ (v) = 0.92565 - 0.0002948\ (t - 25)$$

Use this result to calculate $\Delta \bar{F}^0_{298}$ and $\Delta \bar{H}^0_{298}$ for the cell reaction. (c) Combine your answer to (b) with thermodynamic data for formation of liquid water to obtain $\Delta \bar{F}^0$ and $\Delta \bar{H}^0$ for the formation of $Hg_2O(s)$.

17.19. An antimony electrode, which is sometimes useful for pH measurements of moderate accuracy in the range $2 < pH < 7$, consists simply of a stick of antimony with an oxidized surface coating of Sb_2O_3, which is insoluble in water. The initial oxidation, $Sb(s) = Sb^{3+} + 3e^-$, is followed by reaction to form $Sb_2O_3(s)$. Write the overall electrode reaction and show that the electrode potential can be written in the form

$$\mathcal{E} = \mathcal{E}^0 - \frac{RT}{\mathfrak{F}} \ln \gamma_{H^+} M_{H^+}$$

$$\cong \mathcal{E}^0 + 0.059\ pH\ \text{at}\ 25°C$$

(At 25°C, $\mathcal{E}^0$ is approximately -0.145 v, but is not entirely reproducible and so should be calibrated.)

17.20. A quinhydrone electrode and 1 N calomel electrode are to be put into a solution to determine its pH from the cell EMF. Given the electrode potentials

$$\varepsilon\,(Q,\,QH_2) = -0.700 + 0.059\,pH,$$
$$\varepsilon\,(1\;N\;Hg_2Cl_2) = -0.280$$

(a) At what pH is the cell EMF zero? (b) Which is the negative electrode in more basic solutions? (c) A buffer solution measured in this way gives $\varepsilon = 0.105$ v with the calomel electrode negative. What is its pH?

17.21. A pH measurement is set up, using an Ag-AgCl and a glass electrode in the solution of interest. This is first calibrated by using a buffer solution of $pH = 4.20$, for which the EMF was 0.1200 V, with the Ag-AgCl electrode the anode. Measurement in the unknown solution gave $\varepsilon = 0.275$ v with the same polarity. What is the pH?

17.22. A hydrogen and a normal calomel electrode immersed in an unknown solution give an EMF of 0.572 v. What is the pH of the solution?

17.23. The EMF of the standard hydrogen electrode is by convention set at zero. If this value were on theoretical grounds to be made some other value, such as 0.100 v, what changes would be necessary in Table 17.3?

17.24. A solution is 0.1 molal in Fe^{2+} ions. (a) What must be the concentration of Cd^{2+} ions in the solution for both Fe^{2+} and Cd^{2+} to be plated out simultaneously? (b) What concentration of Ni^{2+} ions would be necessary to obtain solid iron and nickel?

17.25. Solid nickel dust is added to a 0.01 molal solution of Sn^{2+} ions. What are the concentrations of Sn^{2+} and Ni^{2+} ions at equilibrium?

17.26. The EMF of the cell $Pt(H_2): HCl(m): CuCl(s)$, Cu is 0.3774 v at 25°C for a 0.0076 molal solution and 700 mm pressure of hydrogen. (a) Calculate the oxidation potential of copper to CuCl, assuming $\gamma_\pm = 0.90$ at the molality of HCl. (b) The standard free energy of formation of Cl^- ion is $\Delta \bar{F}^0_{298} = -31.35$ kcal/mole. Calculate $\Delta \bar{F}^\circ$ for formation of $CuCl(s)$.

17.27. A galvanic cell has a measured EMF of 1.425 v, determined by a potentiometer drawing no current at balance. (a) When a current of 0.010 ampere is drawn, the terminal voltage drops to 1.415 v. Calculate the electrical work the cell can do by delivering this current for 1.00 hour and the change in free energy. (b) For a current of 1.00 ampere, the voltage is 0.425 v. Calculate the work when the same charge is transported as in part (a) and the change in free energy. Compare the answers with those to (a) and explain the differences and identities.

17.28. The reaction in discharge of a lead-acid storage cell is endothermic, with $\Delta H = +96.85$ kcal/mole. For no current drawn the EMF is 2.00 v, and the potential difference for 1.00 ampere is 1.90 v. (a) Calculate the heat developed in the cell from ohmic conduction when 1 faraday of charge is transported. (b) What is the total amount q of heat absorbed? (c) How much external electrical work is done? What are the values of ΔF and ΔH for the process? (d) Use your answers to show that the first law is satisfied, and from the second law of thermodynamics show that the discharge process is irreversible.

17.29. The cell of the preceding problem is charged at the rate of 1.00 ampere, a potential difference of 2.10 v being necessary. (a) Explain the difference of this number from the values 2.00 and 1.90 v for the conditions of the preceding problem. (b) Calculate the total heat, electrical work, ΔH, and ΔF when the cell is recharged by passage of 1 faraday. Compare your answers with those to the preceding problem and explain similarities and differences.

17.30. Much work has been done in attempting to develop practical "fuel cells" in which free energy change of chemical reaction is continuously converted into electrical work by galvanic cell action. In one version, oxygen fed to the cell reacts at the cathode with sodium ions of Na_2CO_3 electrolyte to form $Na_2O(s)$ and carbon is oxidized to C^{2+} at the anode followed by reaction to form $CO_2(g)$. The products then react to regenerate the electrolyte. (a) With four faradays of charge transported per mole of reaction, show that the overall cell reaction is $C(s) + O_2(g) = CO_2(g)$. (b) What is the reversible EMF of the reaction for gases at 1 atm pressure? (c) How much electrical energy in joules can then be obtained per mole of chemical reaction? (d) What is the maximum possible thermodynamic efficiency in converting chemical to electrical energy in this way? What is the maximum efficiency if the reaction were used in an engine operating between 1000°K and 300°K?

17.31. The vapor pressure of HCl above HCl solutions at moderate concentrations is too small to be measured accurately by ordinary methods, being only 3.66 mm above a 10 molal solution at 25°C. (a) Show how the vapor pressure above an m molal solution of HCl can be deduced from this figure and the EMF values of the cells

$$Pt(H_2): HCl(m): Hg_2Cl_2, Hg$$
$$Pt(H_2): HCl (10 \text{ molal}): Hg_2Cl_2, Hg$$

(b) For $m = 0.100$ molal, the two EMF values are 0.399 v and 0.030 v. Calculate the vapor pressure of HCl over the 0.100 molal solution. (c) How can the information from results of this kind be used to determine activity coefficients of aqueous HCl solutions?

17.32. The standard electrode potential for oxidation of $MnO_2(s)$ to MnO_4^- is -1.52 v in aqueous solution at 25°C, and for oxidation of MnO_4^- to Mn^{2+} is -1.67 v. Calculate the standard potential of the electrode reaction

$$Mn^{2+} + 2H_2O = MnO_2(s) + 4H^+ + 2e^-$$

17.33. The ionization constant of a weak acid HA can be determined from EMF measurements of cells containing the acid as one constituent of the electrolyte. Harned and Ehlers used the buffered cell

$$Pt, H_2 \text{ (1 atm)}: NaCl(m_1), NaA(m_2), HA(m): AgCl(s), Ag$$

(a) Show that if the thermodynamic ionization constant K_2^0, defined by

$$K_2^0 = \frac{m_{H^+}\gamma_{H^+}m_{A^-}\gamma_{A^-}}{m_{HA}\gamma_{HA}}$$

is introduced in the EMF expression, we obtain

$$\mathcal{E} = \mathcal{E}^0 - \frac{RT}{\mathcal{F}} \ln K_2^0 \frac{m_{HA}\gamma_{HA}m_{Cl^-}\gamma_{Cl^-}}{m_{A^-}\gamma_{A^-}}$$

What is the significance of $\mathcal{E}^0$? (b) Show, for large salt concentrations m_1 and m_2 and small K_2^0 (weak acid), that this can be approximated as

$$\mathcal{E} = \mathcal{E}^0 - \frac{RT}{\mathcal{F}} \ln K_2^0 - \frac{RT}{\mathcal{F}} \ln \left(\frac{m_1 m}{m_2}\right) - \frac{RT}{\mathcal{F}} \ln \frac{\gamma_{Cl^-}\gamma_{HA}}{\gamma_{A^-}}$$

(c) Suggest a procedure for evaluating K_2^0 from EMF data for various concentrations.

17.34. Devise a concentration cell with mercury electrodes which could be used to test whether mercury exists as Hg^+ or as Hg^{2+} ions in aqueous solution, describe the measurements you would make with the cell, and explain how the data should be analyzed.

Suggested Readings

Comprehensive discussions of electrochemistry are given in *Electrochemistry* by E. C. Potter (Macmillan, New York, 1956) and *Modern Aspects of Electrochemistry* by J. O'M. Brockris (Academic Press, New York, 1954). An advanced collection of review articles is contained in *The Structure of Electrolyte Solutions*, edited by W. J. Homer (Wiley, New York, 1959).

An extensive compilation of electrode potentials is *Oxidation Potentials* by W. M. Latimer (2nd ed., Prentice-Hall, Englewood Cliffs, N.J., 1952). Another valuable source is *Electrochemical Data* by B. E. Conway (Elsevier, New York, 1952).

Chapter 18

Ionic Conductance in Solution

IN THE PRECEDING chapter, the relations between EMF of galvanic cells and the equilibrium of electrolyte solutions, which combine with electrodes to form such cells, have been considered in detail. Because the cell EMF is an equilibrium property directly related to thermodynamic free energy changes, much can be learned from EMF measurements about reaction equilibria in solution and at electrode surfaces. This method of investigation has serious limitations, however, because of the necessity that the reactions involved be reversible if methods of equilibrium thermodynamics are to be applied. This requirement is stringent enough that many interesting systems have been impossible to study by EMF measurements, simply because suitable reversible electrodes have not been found.

In this chapter, a different approach toward the understanding of electrolyte solutions is considered—that of studying their ability to conduct electric currents under the influence of an externally applied potential difference. In contrast to EMF studies, conduction of electric current is an inherently irreversible process, since when a steady electric current flows, electrical energy supplied from the external battery or generator is dissipated, either by an increase in temperature of the electrolyte, or by a flow of heat to the external surroundings if the solution is kept at constant temperature.

The ability of a substance to conduct electricity must therefore be analyzed in terms of the motion of electric charge carriers, rather than in terms of states of equilibrium for no current flow. On the other hand, conductance measurements are possible, and useful conclusions can be drawn, for many ionic systems which no one has so far been able to incorporate into reversible galvanic cells. The study of conductance is in any case a useful method often capable of high precision, which gives insight into the kinetic aspects of ion behavior in solution.

18.1. The Nature of Conductance

Before turning attention to the principal subject of ionic conduction in solution, a brief survey of the principal types of conductors and conduction processes is helpful because of the comparisons and contrasts. The most frequently encountered types are metallic, gaseous, and ionic.

Of the classes of substances which can carry appreciable currents, pure metals such as copper, silver, and platinum have by far the lowest electrical resistance, and the potential difference necessary to pass a given current through a metal sample of specified size and shape is very small in comparison with other substances. As discussed in Section 7.5, the current carriers in metals are known from a variety of evidence to be "free" electrons. These are highly mobile because of the availability of unfilled orbitals of low energy in the atoms of the crystal, which combine in such a way that the conducting electrons can move quite freely from one atom to another. That there is as much resistance as there is to electron flow or current, results principally from the fact that the atoms are not in perfectly fixed positions, but oscillate randomly about their average lattice points and interfere with orderly flow of electrons through the structure.

In contrast, in ionic and covalent crystals there are atoms and ions with completely filled electron shells, and as a result no opportunity for electron transport through the structure by the agency of unfilled states of low energy. Thus, although salts such as the alkali halides (NaCl, KCl, and others) exist in wholly ionic form in the solid crystals (Section 7.4), the positive and negative ions are immobilized by the binding forces in the solid structures and are unable to carry current. Small currents can be observed in ionic crystals, especially at high temperatures, but these are attributed to impurities or failure of the crystal structure to be perfect, rather than to any intrinsic properties of the ideal structure.

The conduction of electricity in gases was described briefly in Section 3.1. If very little gas is present in a space between two electrodes at different potentials, the current carriers are primarily electrons liberated from the cathode by such processes as thermionic emission, photoelectric action of light, or the force of high electric fields. When gas is introduced, electrons may be captured by or ionize the gas molecules, and the current is then carried largely by gaseous ions. The currents depend in a complex way on gas pressure, electrode geometry, and other factors, and very little matter is transported from one electrode to the other.

Electrolyte conductance is significantly different from the other types in that substantial quantities of material are inevitably transferred between anode and cathode on passage of an electric current. This indicates very directly that the current carriers in molten salts and electrolyte solutions are not electrons of little mass and identical regardless of electrode or electrolyte composition, but are much more massive ions which are chemically distinct, their identity being fixed according to the composition of the electrolyte and often related to that of the electrode.

The ions already existing in electrolytes are thus set in motion by an applied potential difference between metal electrodes, with positive ions (cations) being attracted to the cathode, and negative ions (anions) to the anode. If electrolysis occurs and a steady current continues to flow, it is because electrons are given up at the anode and received from the cathode, thus neutralizing the ions and producing continuous electron flow in the external metal circuit. Such neutralizations clearly result in the appearance of chemical substances at the electrodes. The converse process of ion formation by electron gain or loss is also possible, as discussed in Chapter 17.

Electrode processes of the kind just indicated need not occur reversibly or at all, in which case excess ions of one sign accumulate near the electrodes and impede further flow of current. The problems which result for conductance measurements are taken up in Section 18.4. Regardless of these specific questions, however, the significance of material transport (because the current carriers are ions rather than electrons) and the need of considering the electrode boundaries beyond which metallic electrons carry the current, should both be evident.

18.2. Ionic Conduction and Electrical Equivalents

An elementary type of ionic conduction is that taking place through molten (fused) salts, such as sodium chloride (Fig. 18.1). The binding forces that prevent displacements of ions in the solid are no longer effective in the liquid state, and both kinds of ions are able to migrate. As a result, molten sodium chloride will conduct electricity when a potential difference is applied to electrodes in the liquid, the sodium ions moving toward the negatively charged cathode, and the chloride ions toward the positive anode.

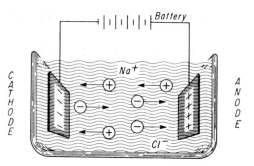

Fig. 18.1. *Ion migrations in fused salt electro-lyte.*

At the anode, each chloride ion gives up an electron to the positive electrode, and chlorine gas is evolved, according to the oxidation formula

$$Cl^- \longrightarrow \tfrac{1}{2}Cl_2(g) + e^-$$

At the cathode each sodium ion is neutralized by an electron from the electrode to the form sodium metal, corresponding to the reduction formula

$$Na^+ + e^- \longrightarrow Na(s)$$

It is obvious from the above that for the circuit and the electrode reactions given, an electron traverses the electrolytic cell when one is given up by the cathode and taken out at the anode. For each such electron one singly charged ion (or univalent atom) is involved at *each* electrode; for 6.02×10^{23} electrons, 6.02×10^{23} singly charged ions will be involved, or one-half that number of doubly charged ions, one-third that number of triply charged ions or trivalent atoms, and so on; in other words, one gram equivalent weight for the particular chemical species. The number of 6.02×10^{23} electrons ("one equivalent") is equal to 96,494 coulombs, or one faraday. This is recognized as Faraday's law, stated in Section 1.1 as important evidence for the atomic theory. In the example, passage of one faraday through the electrolytic cell releases one gram equivalent weight of chlorine at the anode and one gram equivalent weight of sodium at the cathode as a result of electrode processes. Through the migration of the ions in the

cell, there will be a corresponding reduction in the concentration of sodium ions in the vicinity of the anode and of chloride ions in the vicinity of the cathode.

18.3. Electrolytic Conductance by Ions in Solution

Just as the ions of a salt in its liquid state can conduct an electric current under the influence of a potential field, so can they also in solution, where they are also free of the restrictive forces of the solid state and free to migrate in a potential field. From this point of view, the only difference between the ions of a salt in its liquid state and the ions of a salt in solution is that in the latter case the ions are on the average further from one another, and are separated by a medium whose electrical properties may modify the behavior of ions dissolved in it and whose chemical properties may alter the electrode reactions.

The conductivity of such solutions of electrolytes will depend upon the number of ions in a given volume of solution and their rate of motion through the solution. In the model assumed here, salts, as examples of strong electrolytes, are considered completely ionized. As will be discussed in Section 18.12, interactions with ions of opposite charge and with solvent molecules prevent a single ion from behaving as a completely independent particle. The degree of association with other ions is reduced as the concentration of the salt in the solution is reduced, as discussed in Section 16.5, and forces between ions become smaller as their average distances apart increase.

By far the most common solvent is water, and aqueous solutions of electrolytes will be given principal consideration in the remainder of this discussion. The high dielectric constant of water reduces the Coulomb interaction forces between ions, and the strongly directional orbitals of oxygen in the water molecules account for the high degree of *solvation* (association of solvent molecules with dissolved ions), which is observed in aqueous solutions.

An important consideration in determining the reactions which take place at the electrodes in aqueous solutions is that there is always at least a small concentration of hydrogen ions and hydroxyl ions present, and, from the equilibrium reaction indicated by Eq. 18.1, a large source of those ions to replace any which might be consumed in the electrode reaction:

$$H_2O \rightleftharpoons H^+ + OH^- \tag{18.1}$$

(In aqueous solutions the hydrogen ion is solvated by at least one water molecule. This is often indicated by writing the oxonium ion or hydronium ion—H_3O^+, rather than H^+—to show explicitly that there is solvation, rather than the simple hydrogen ion. However, since this is usually merely a reminder that the hydrogen ion is solvated and does not purport to specify the degree of solvation, we shall in general refer to the hydrogen ion H^+, recognizing that it is always associated with one or more water molecules when it is in aqueous solution.)

At the anode, the oxidation of hydroxyl ions is possible,

$$4OH^- \rightleftharpoons 2H_2O + O_2 + 4e^- \tag{18.2}$$

and this reaction is the one which will take place whenever it is easier than that involving the cation of the solute. This may be determined by the relative values of the half-cell oxidation potentials (Section 17.9).

At the cathode, the reduction of hydrogen ions is always a possible reaction,

$$2H^+ + 2e^- \rightleftharpoons H_2 \tag{18.3}$$

and will be the reaction which takes place whenever it is easier. Again, the determination of the oxidation potentials for it and the reaction involving the other ion will indicate which reaction is taking place. For example, in the case of the electrolysis of an aqueous solution of sodium chloride in which the activity of the sodium ion is unity, the competing electrode reaction would be

$$Na^+ + e^- \longrightarrow Na \tag{18.4}$$

For this, the potential calculated according to the method described in Section 17.8, using the standard oxidation potential ε^0 from Table 17.3, B at 25° is

$$\varepsilon_{Na} = -\left[\varepsilon^0 - \frac{RT}{\mathfrak{F}} \ln a_{Na^+}\right] = -2.714 + 0 \tag{18.5}$$

$$= -2.714 \text{ v}$$

(The meaning of the negative sign is obvious from the study of the preceding chapter.)

For the reduction of the hydrogen ion, assuming its activity to be approximately 10^{-7}, the potential at 25°C is

$$\varepsilon_{H_2} = -[0 - 0.059 \log 10^{-7}]$$
$$= -0.413 \text{ v}$$

Since the potential for the reduction of the hydrogen ion is much less negative than that for the reduction of the sodium ion (in spite of the much greater activity of the sodium ion), the cathode reaction of reduction of hydrogen ion to hydrogen is thermodynamically the easier one. Whether it takes place, however, involves further questions of sufficient applied potential and reversibility of the electrode.

18.4. Determination of Electrolytic Conductance

The ease with which a sample of a substance conducts electricity is expressed by the potential difference necessary to cause a specified current flow. Under ordinary conditions the two quantities are directly proportional to one another, and Ohm's law, stating this fact, is usually written in the form

$$V = RI$$

where R is the resistance of the sample, with units of *ohms* if the potential difference V is in volts and the current I in amperes.

Although this form of Ohm's law is the most common one, and the one first learned in elementary physics, an alternative, equally valid form is simpler and more useful for discussion of electrolytes and a number of other problems. This formulation is written

$$I = GV \qquad (18.6)$$

where the quantity G is called the conductance. It is obviously related to resistance R, by the expression $G = 1/R$. For I in amperes, V in volts, G has units of reciprocal ohms (ohm^{-1}), often called the *mho* (ohm spelled backward).

The reason for using the concept of conductance is that the current through an electrolyte increases directly with its concentration, whereas

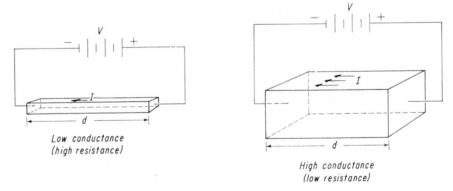

Low conductance
(high resistance)

High conductance
(low resistance)

Fig. 18.2. *Dependence of conductance on sample dimensions.*

resistance varies inversely with concentration. The conductance G, however, depends both on the nature of the substance and on the dimensions of the sample measured, a long column of small cross section having a smaller conductance than a shorter one of larger area, as suggested in Fig. 18.2.

The dependence on dimensions can be eliminated, and a quantity defined which is characteristic only of the substance, by considering the current density (current per unit area), I/A, and the potential gradient in the substance, which determines the force acting on a charged particle within the substance. The potential gradient is the rate of potential change along the direction of current flow and for samples of uniform area (either of those in Fig. 18.2) it is the ratio of potential difference to length d of the sample, or V/d. The *specific conductance* κ is defined as the ratio of current density to potential gradient:

$$\kappa = \frac{\text{current density}}{\text{potential gradient}} = \frac{I/A}{V/d} = \frac{d}{A}\frac{I}{V}$$

From Eq. 18.6, κ is related to the measured conductance $G = I/V$ by the formula

$$\kappa = G\frac{d}{A} \qquad (18.7)$$

From this equation κ is in units of ohm^{-1} cm^{-1}, or mho/cm, if G is in mhos, d in cm, and A in cm^2.

The reason for defining κ in this form is that, unlike G, it does not depend on the quantity and shape of the conducting medium. Thus a sample of four times the cross section obviously carries four times as much current for the same V, but the value $\kappa = Gd/A$ is constant. Similarly, while doubling the length d results in half the current, κ is unchanged. The significance of κ as a specific property should be apparent; its value is sometimes defined as being that of a one-centimeter cube with electrodes of 1 cm^2 area, but the true significance is not so restricted.

The determination of conductances of electrolytes is unfortunately not simply a matter of measuring between electrodes dipping in the solution the potential difference corresponding to a measured current. The difficulty is that without special precautions potential differences— called "electrode potentials"—develop in the vicinity of the electrodes, which add to the potential drop across the solution itself; the resulting potential difference in the metallic circuit is the sum of these effects. Thus in the cell of Fig. 18.1, passage of current begins to liberate sodium at the cathode surface and chlorine at the anode. At both electrodes are thus created potential differences that reduce the potential drop across the solution itself to a lower value, which depends on electrode conditions and the applied potential. Even if no electrode reaction occurs, accumulation of excess positive ions at the cathode and negative ions at the anode causes unwanted potential differences near the electrodes.

The effect just described is termed *electrode polarization*, and arises whatever the electrode material and solution may be, as the consequence of the simultaneous presence of two types of conduction in the same circuit, electrolytic conduction by ions and metallic conduction by electrons.

To avoid error, the potential differences set up near the electrodes as a result of polarization effects must be eliminated by special arrangements. The most common is use of alternating currents which are reversed in direction with sufficient frequency to prevent appreciable accumulation of reaction products or excess ions at the electrodes. Frequencies of 1000 cycles/sec or more are usually high enough to prevent electrode potential differences arising from polarization and are ordinarily employed in precision conductance measurements. Unfortunately, a resulting complication is that the conductance cell acts also as a capacitance cell, and the alternating currents are capacitance charging and discharging currents of the kind considered in Chapter 11. This must be taken into account, for example, by balancing capacitance as well as conductance in a bridge circuit.

Other methods of avoiding electrode potentials have been employed in recent work. In one, direct current is used, and the potential difference measured between probes which are reversible for one of the ions in solution, thus giving definite compensating electrode potentials. In another, electrodes in contact with solution are eliminated in favor of ones outside the solution container. Still another method has been to utilize magnetic fields to produce currents in the solution, the currents so produced being in turn determined from their magnetic effects.

18.5. Specific and Equivalent Conductance

The specific conductances of several representative electrolytes in water at 25°C are plotted in Fig. 18.3 as a function of the concentration of electrolyte. It will be seen that the magnitude of the conductance varies widely with the nature of cation and anion. Thus hydrogen chloride, as a representative strong acid, is a much better conductor than are simple monovalent (1:1) salts such as sodium and potassium chloride; sodium hydroxide also has a conductance considerably higher than the salts. Acetic acid, on the other hand, is a very much poorer conductor at the concentrations for which Fig. 18.3 permits comparison.

From Fig. 18.3 it is apparent that the specific conductance increases at least approximately in proportion to the concentration, as would be expected from the increasing numbers of conducting ions. The plots for the poorer conducting electrolytes, however, show definite curvature, and all electrolytes show some curvature. Evidently factors other than the increase in the number of ions are involved.

For an understanding of these factors it is convenient to examine not the conducting ability of a given volume of solution, but rather that of a given *total number* of possible ions in relation to the concentration of the solution. In principle, this could be done directly by comparing the

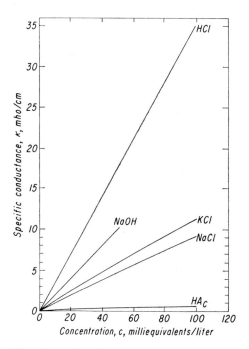

Fig. 18.3. *Specific conductance as function of concentration for several electrolytes at 18°C.*

conductances across volumes of solutions taken to contain the same amount of ionizable solute at various concentrations, between electrodes separated by constant distance in order to keep the potential gradient (and hence the force acting on the ions) the same for all solutions. For example, we could determine the conductances of solutions of differing concentrations and of volumes sufficient to contain one gram equivalent weight of solute electrolyte capable of providing cations with 0.602×10^{24} positive charges and anions with 0.602×10^{24} negative charges (in units of electronic charge), whether there be singly, doubly, or triply charged ions. Such a procedure, however, would require impractically large electrodes for dilute solutions; thus, two electrodes of one centimeter separation encompassing one gram equivalent weight of solute in a solution of $0.001 N$ concentration, would each have an area 10^6 cm², equal to a square 10 meters on each edge.

Values for the conducting ability of solutions containing one gram equivalent of ionizable solute can be far more easily obtained by defining a quantity, the *equivalent conductance* Λ, as the ratio of the specific conductance (κ) to the concentration in equivalents per unit volume. The unit volume implicit in the definition of the specific conductance is 1 cm³; hence if c is the concentration in equivalents per liter, Λ is obtained as

$$\Lambda = \frac{\kappa}{c/1000} = \frac{1000\kappa}{c} \tag{18.8}$$

EXAMPLES

The measured resistance of a $3 \times 10^{-3} N$ solution measured between two electrodes 1 cm² in area and 0.30 cm apart is 1250 ohms. Calculate the measured conductance, and the specific and equivalent conductances. By definition,

$$G = \frac{1}{R} = \frac{1}{1250} = 800 \times 10^{-6} \, \text{mho}$$

$$\kappa = \frac{Gd}{A} = \frac{800 \times 10^{-6}}{1} \times \frac{0.30}{1.00} = 240 \times 10^{-6} \, \text{mho/cm}$$

$$\Lambda = \frac{1000 \, \kappa}{c} = \frac{10^3 \times 240 \times 10^{-6}}{3 \times 10^{-3}} = 80 \, \text{mho cm}^2 \text{ per g equiv}$$

18.6. Variation of Equivalent Conductance with Concentration. Strong and Weak Electrolytes

Consideration of the equivalent conductance of various electrolytes indicates different types of behavior for solutions of what are termed strong electrolytes and weak electrolytes. Strong electrolytes form solutions which are good conductors, and weak electrolytes solutions which are but poor conductors in ordinary concentrations. Comparison in Fig. 18.4 of the equivalent conductances of the strong electrolyte, hydrochloric acid, and the weak, acetic acid, shows 50 to 100 fold greater equivalent conductance for hydrochloric acid at concentrations of $0.2 N$. To be noted, however, is the increase in equivalent conductance with decreasing concentration, which is extremely marked for acetic acid. In contrast with the case of strong electrolytes, there is much greater curvature in the acetic acid plot.

Although the graph of equivalent conductance of hydrochloric acid against concentration appears to be almost linear in Fig. 18.4, some curvature is noted. This can be seen more clearly in the inset graph at the right of the figure, in which the scale for the abscissa is foreshortened. The behavior is made even more apparent in Fig. 18.5, in which equivalent conductances of hydrochloric acid (upper graph) and sodium chloride (lower graph) are plotted against concentration and against the square root of concentration with the scales for both abscissa and ordinate expanded. Even though a salt such as sodium chloride may be completely ionized in the crystalline form, its ions are not completely independent of one another in solution, although far more so than they are in the crystal. If they were mutually independent, the equivalent conductivity would be independent of concentration, and the plots in Fig. 18.5 would be horizontal straight lines.

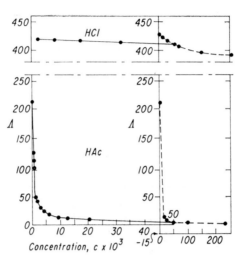

Fig. 18.4. *Equivalent conductance of hydrochloric acid and acetic acid as function of concentration at 25°C.*

Neither is the equivalent conductivity, and hence the dissociation, a simple function of the concentration. However, when the equivalent conductivity of a strong electrolyte is plotted against the square root of the concentration, the data are quite well fitted by a straight line at low concentrations. Following the initial empirical observation of this relation by Kohlrausch in 1897, a satisfactory theory in agreement with this feature of the experimental data was developed, which is described in Section 18.12.

Of the various conductance data, the equivalent conductivity of an infinitely dilute solution, defined by

$$\Lambda_0 = \lim_{c \to 0} \Lambda \qquad (18.9)$$

is of great importance, because it is a measure of the ability of ions to carry an electric current in a particular solvent medium, when the ions are sufficiently far apart so that there is no interaction between them.

The value of the linearity of the $\sqrt{c}$ plot in extrapolating to the equivalent conductivity (Λ_0) at zero concentration is obvious compared with the first-power concentration graphs, in which the curvature increases as the concentration approaches zero. For weak electrolytes, ion association can further change conductivity so drastically at low concentrations that neither plot will give reliable values of Λ_0. Such abrupt changes for acetic acid are shown by the plots of Λ versus c in Fig. 18.4.

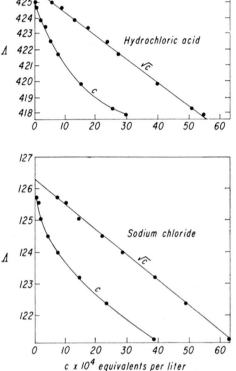

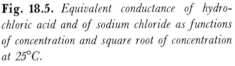

$c \times 10^4$ equivalents per liter

$\sqrt{c} \times 10^3$ [equivalents per liter]$^{1/2}$

Fig. 18.5. *Equivalent conductance of hydrochloric acid and of sodium chloride as functions of concentration and square root of concentration at 25°C.*

18.7. Ionic Conductivities

For a series of pairs of strong electrolytes with the same two ions present throughout, and the ion of opposite sign common within each pair, it is observed that there is a constant difference between the equivalent conductivities at infinite dilution of each pair. For example, the equivalent conductivities at infinite dilution of five compounds of sodium and potassium (K compound and Na compound) are compared in Table 18.1, and the corresponding differences within each pair is noted. The difference between conductivities of the two potassium and sodium compounds containing the same anion is constant. (The lesser precision of the determination for the hydroxides and acetates is indicated by the smaller number of significant figures given.)

This phenomenon was first noted by Kohlrausch in 1875, who pointed out that these constant differences could mean that the conductivity of

TABLE 18.1. *Equivalent Conductivity at Infinite Dilution Λ_0 at 18°C, of Electron Pairs with Common Ions (Sodium and Potassium Compounds), and Equivalent Conductivity Differences within Each Pair (in mho cm^{-2}/g. equiv.).*

CATION OF GIVEN PAIR	ANION OF GIVEN PAIR				
	Cl^-	NO_3^-	SO_4^{2-}	OH^-	$CH_3CO_2^-$
K^+	130.0	126.3	133.0	238	99
Na^+	108.9	105.2	111.9	216.5	77
Λ_0(K compound) $-$ Λ_0(Na compound) $=$	21.1	21.1	21.1	21.5	22

each ion was independent of the other ions present in solution. If this is true, it follows that ionic conductivities must be additive, and that the total conductivity (Λ_0) of a solution will be the sum of the individual ionic conductivities, λ_0^+, λ_0^-, and so on. This is expressed as Kohlrausch's law:

$$\Lambda_0 = \lambda_0^+ + \lambda_0^- + \cdots \qquad (18.10)$$

The calculation of Λ_0 for weak electrolytes (not experimentally determinable with any accuracy) is made possible by the independent migration of separate ions. To obtain the value of Λ_0 for acetic acid, for example, we need know only the values for hydrochloric acid, sodium chloride, and sodium acetate. (The values in the calculation following are for 18°C. Note difference from the values given in the figures.) Thus by adding

$$\Lambda_{0,HCl} = \lambda_{0,H^+} + \lambda_{0,Cl^-} = 379.4 \text{ mho cm}^{-2} \text{ (g. equiv.)}^{-1}$$

and

$$\Lambda_{0,NaC_2H_3O_2} = \lambda_{0,Na^+} + \lambda_{0,C_2H_3O_2^-} = 87.4 \text{ mho cm}^{-2} \text{ (g. equiv.)}^{-1}$$

and subtracting

$$\Lambda_{0,NaCl} = \lambda_{0,Na^+} + \lambda_{0,Cl^-} = 109.0 \text{ mho cm}^{-2} \text{ (g. equiv.)}^{-1}$$

we obtain

$$\lambda_{0,H^+} + \lambda_{0,C_2H_3O_2^-} = 357.8 \text{ mho cm}^{-2} \text{ (g. equiv.)}^{-1}$$

This sum is evidently the limiting equivalent conductance (Λ_0) of acetic acid.

18.8. Determination of Transport Numbers

Conductance measurements determine the sum of the conductances of all ions present in an electrolyte solution. Since both the anions and cations contribute separately to the total current flow by their own transfer through the electrolytic cell, experiments of a different kind have to be devised from which these separate contributions can be quantitatively determined. Obviously, knowledge of the current carrying abilities of the ionic species will yield a greater understanding of the nature of electrolytic conductance and of solute phenomena of ions. A number of methods have been developed for determining the fraction of the total current passing through an electrolysis cell which is carried by a given ion species. The values so determined are called *transport* or *transference numbers*.

For infinitely dilute solutions, the transport number of a given ion species is equal to the ratio of the conductivity of the ion to that of the salt. Thus the limiting transport numbers for the position or negative ions, t_0^+ and t_0^-, can be expressed as

$$t_0^+ = \frac{\lambda_0^+}{\Lambda_0}, \qquad t_0^- = \frac{\lambda_0^-}{\Lambda_0} \qquad (18.11)$$

By definition, the sum $t_0^+ + t_0^-$ must be unity; hence the measurement of t_0^+ and Λ_0 suffices to determine both the relative current-carrying abilities and the conductances of the two ionic species in solution.

Transport numbers are usually determined by one of the following methods.

Hittorf Method

Conventional techniques of analytical chemistry are employed to measure concentration changes occurring during electrolysis, and from these, transport numbers are calculated.

An electrolytic cell is used which can, as shown in Fig. 18.6, be divided at will into three compartments—anode, cathode, and an intervening one. A solution of the salt under investigation is placed in the cell, and the number of equivalents of cation and anion in each of the three compartments is determined. A carefully measured quantity of electricity is then passed through the cell. For each equivalent of electricity flowing through the cell (an equivalent of electricity = one faraday = 96,494 coulombs = 6.02×10^{23} electrons), one equivalent of chemical change will occur at both the anode and the cathode according to the respective anode and cathode reactions; a total of one equivalent of the solute ions will be transferred through the solution, as the sum of anions moving from left to right and cations in the opposite

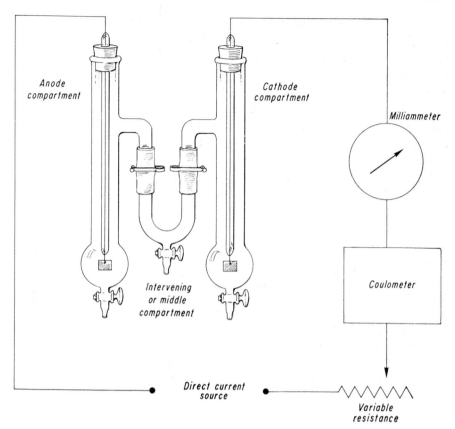

Fig. 18.6. *Hittorf apparatus for determination of transport number.*

direction. Note particularly that the *sum* of equivalents of cations and anions transferred is equal to the equivalents of electricity which flow; the individual quantities of each must be smaller.

The actual changes in quantity of ionic solute in the electrode compartments of the cell are governed by both the transport of ions and the formation or removal of ions from the solution by electrode reactions. For a total current flow corresponding to one equivalent, t^+ equivalents of cations leave the anode region and t^- equivalents of anions enter it. These processes alone would produce a net negative charge in the region of the anode, but in addition the electrode reaction either supplies one equivalent of cations or removes one equivalent of anions. If the former, there is an increase of t^- ($= 1 - t^+$) equivalents of the ionic solute in the anode compartment; if the latter, a loss of t^+ ($= 1 - t^-$) equivalents in the cathode compartment.

In either case, the solution remains electrically neutral—a necessary condition for any steady process, as the net charge creates strong electrical forces acting to restore neutrality. For a known electrode reaction, measurements of the change in number of equivalents in the anode or cathode compartments per equivalent of charge transported determines the transport numbers. (If measurements of quantity of solute in the central compartment show no change, it is presumed that diffusion has not caused transport of solute to or from the electrode compartments.)

To illustrate, consider the electrolysis of a solution of silver nitrate between silver electrodes. At the anode, silver is oxidized to silver ion,

$$Ag \longrightarrow Ag^+ + e^-$$

and at the cathode, silver ion is reduced to metallic silver,

$$Ag^+ + e^- \longrightarrow Ag$$

Thus if q faradays of electricity pass through the cell, q equivalents of silver will be dissolved and deposited at the anode and cathode respectively. (There is no change in the total quantity of silver ion in the cell.) In spite of the fact that exactly the same number of equivalents, q, are involved at each of the two electrodes, it is obvious that a smaller quantity of silver ion is transferred through the solution, for if q equivalents were transferred by silver ion alone there would be no opportunity for the nitrate ion to carry current. The quantity of current transferred by the silver ion must instead be a smaller quantity, $t_0^+ q$ faradays, and that by the nitrate ion, $t_0^- q$ faradays. (The sum $t_0^+ q + t_0^- q$ is q faradays, as it must be, because $t_0^+ + t_0^- = 1$.)

In the anode compartment, the quantity of silver ion present will increase by the difference between the quantity gained from oxidation and that lost by migration, $q - t_0^+ q$ $[= q(1 - t_0^+) = t_0^- q]$ equivalents, and correspondingly the quantity of nitrate ion will increase by migration by $t_0^- q$ equivalents. Hence the result is a net gain of $t_0^- q$ equivalents of silver nitrate in the anode compartment, and electrical neutrality is preserved.

In the cathode compartment, the quantity of silver ion present will decrease by the difference between the amount lost by reduction at the electrode and the amount gained by migration, or $q - t_0^+ q$ $[= q(1 - t_0^+) = t_0^- q]$ equivalents, and the quantity of nitrate ion decreases through migration by $t_0^- q$ equivalents—a net loss of t_0^- of equivalents of silver nitrate from the anode compartment.

By means of careful quantitative measurements of the amount of silver nitrate in the anode and cathode compartments before and after electrolysis, and of the quantity of electricity passing through the solution, the transference numbers of the two ions of any binary salt may be determined following the above reasoning. An illustration of the Hittorf method follows.

ILLUSTRATION

An 0.01 N silver nitrate solution is electrolyzed by passage of 0.1000 amp for 579 seconds. The anode compartment solution weighing 20.09 g is found to contain 58.2 mg of silver. Calculate the transport number of Ag^+ ion.

The number of equivalents in the electrolysis is

$$q = \frac{0.1000 \times 579}{96500} = 0.000600 \text{ equivalents}$$

After electrolysis the anode compartment contains $58.2 \times 10^{-3}/107.9 = 0.000539$ equivalents (g equiv wt of silver is 107.9). The original silver content was 10^{-2} equiv/liter $\times 20.09/1000$ liter $= 0.000201$ equivalents, and the gain in the anode compartment is therefore $0.000539 - 0.000201 = 0.000338$ equivalents. The ratio of this gain to the quantity electrolyzed is t_0^-, hence

$$t_0^- = \frac{0.000338}{0.000600} = 0.563$$

Thus a fraction 0.563 (56.3%) of the current is carried by the nitrate ion, and a fraction $1 - 0.563 = 0.437$ or 43.7% by the silver ion.

Moving Boundary Method

The method just described, devised by Hittorf in 1853, was used for many years to study transport numbers, and is valuable for an introduction to the subject. In more recent years, methods of greater accuracy have largely superseded it for precise work, and the moving boundary technique in particular has been highly developed.

In this method, two solutions with one ion in common, say the cation X^-, are brought together in a vertical tube to form a sharp boundary above which one solution remains stable and separate from the other, which is below the boundary. This is shown in Fig. 18.7. Electrolysis is produced by the potential difference across the electrodes as shown, so that the cations M^+ of the upper solution move upward. (The cations N^+ of the lower solution also move upward, but if they are of a species which migrates more slowly than the species M^+, the boundary will remain sharp. The velocity of migration, called the mobility, is discussed in Section 18.10.)

After q equivalents have passed, the boundary separating the solutions of cations M^+ and N^+ will be at a higher position, indicated by the dashed line in Fig. 18.7. Hence during the electrolysis all the ions M^+ originally in the volume between the initial and the new boundary positions have passed through the surface indicated at the new position. The ratio of the number of equivalents of cations so migrating to the total number of equivalents q of charge carried by both cations and anions through the boundary surface is obviously the transference number t^+ of the M^+ ions from the salt M^+X^-. If the tube is of cross-sectional area A (cm²) and the boundary displacement is d (cm) during the passage of q equivalents, for an initial concentration of M^+ of C equivalents/liter we then have the number of equivalents of M^+ migrating, $n_+ = (C/1000)Ad$, and

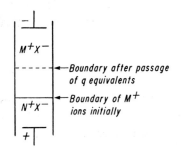

Fig. 18.7. *Moving boundary determination.*

$$t^+ = \frac{n_+}{q} = \frac{CAd}{1000q} \qquad (18.12)$$

To be useful, the method obviously requires some means of making the boundary sharp. Suitable choice of upper and lower solutions with special techniques for forming the boundary initially have been developed, and its position is made evident by the different refractive indices of the solutions. In precise work, consideration must also be given to the changes of solution densities resulting from the ion displacements.

EXAMPLE

A 0.020 molar solution of LiCl above BaCl₂ solution in a moving boundary experiment was electrolyzed in a tube of cross section 0.180 cm², and the boundary moved 8.00 cm in 2,300 seconds. The average current was 0.00369 amp. Calculate t^+ for the Li$^+$ ion. The number of equivalents of Li$^+$ passing the final boundary position is

$$n_+ = \frac{0.020 \times 0.18 \times 8.0}{1000} = 0.00029$$

and the total equivalents passing during electrolysis are

$$q = \frac{It}{\mathcal{F}} = \frac{0.00369 \times 2,300}{96,500} = 0.00088$$

Hence $t^+ = 0.00029/0.00088 = 0.33$.

(Note that the Li^+ ion carries only one-third of the current and the Cl^- ion two-thirds, despite the small size of the *gaseous* Li^+ ion. This indicates possible hydration of Li^+ in solution.)

Concentration Cells with Transference

Section 17.13 referred to the complications arising in electrochemical cells with two solutions in contact, and means of reducing this junction potential effect were discussed. This section will consider the effect on the cell EMF of ion transport across the boundary, and the use of such cells to determine transport numbers will be described.

The effect can be illustrated by means of the cell cited as an example in Section 17.9:

$$Ag:AgNO_3(C_1); AgNO_3(C_2):Ag$$

For one mole of electron flow, 1 equivalent of silver ions is reduced at the cathode and 1 equivalent of silver ions evolved at the anode. At the same time, as indicated sche-
matically in Fig. 18.8, silver ions pass from solution 1 to solution 2 and nitrate ions enter 1 from 2. If the transport number of Ag^+ ions is t^+, then t^+ equivalents of Ag^+ enter solution 2 while simultaneously 1 equivalent is removed by electrolytic reduction at the cathode. The net result is therefore a *loss* of $1 - t^+ = t^-$ equivalents of Ag^+ from solution 2 for each mole of electrode reaction.

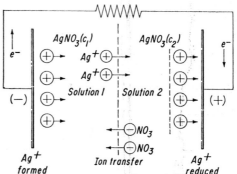

Fig. 18.8. *Concentration cell.*

The same number (t^- equivalents) of nitrate ion is lost from solution 2 by migration into solution 1, and so the cell process is the net transfer of t^- moles of $AgNO_3$ from solution 2 to solution 1 for each mole of electrons:

$$t^-AgNO_3(C_2) \longrightarrow t^-AgNO_3(C_1) \qquad (18.13)$$

for electron flow as shown in Fig. 18.8.

If concentrations are written in place of activities and junction potentials are neglected, the EMF is

$$\mathcal{E} = - \frac{RT}{\mathcal{F}} \ln \frac{(C_1^2)^{t^-}}{(C_2^2)^{t^-}}$$

the concentration products being raised to the t^- power because only t^- equivalents are transferred per Faraday. This can be written

$$\mathcal{E} = - 2t^- \frac{RT}{\mathcal{F}} \ln \left(\frac{C_1}{C_2}\right)$$

and the EMF is only a fraction t^- of the value if there were no transference. Thus measured values can be compared with calculated values, and transport numbers obtained for the ion which does not take part in the electrode reaction (in this case NO_3^-).

Values of t^- ranging from 0.535 to 0.532 (depending on concentration) are found for NO_3^- in aqueous $AgNO_3$ solutions, and reasonably consistent results have been obtained for a number of other electrolytes.

18.9. Transport Numbers of Ions

The preceding discussions have shown the importance of transport numbers in defining the relative current-carrying abilities of ions, and it is now of interest to examine results obtained for a number of 1:1 electrolytes in water at 25°C. Values of the transport number of the cation in solutions of chloride and acetate salts at several concentrations are listed in Table 18.2. The values in parentheses for zero concentration (infinite dilution) were obtained by extrapolation.

TABLE 18.2.   *Transport Numbers of Cations of 1:1 Electrolytes in Water at 25°C.*

c (moles/liter)	HCl	LiCl	NaCl	KCl	NaAc	KAc
0	(0.8209)	(0.3363)	(0.3962)	(0.4905)	(0.5506)	(0.6425)
0.01	0.8251	0.3289	0.3918	0.4902	0.5537	(0.6498)
0.05	0.8292	0.3211	0.3876	0.4899	0.5573	(0.6569)
0.20	0.8337	0.3112	0.3821	0.4894	0.5610	—
0.50	0.838*	0.303†	—	0.4888	—	—
1.00	0.841*	0.297†	—	0.4882	—	—

* From EMF measurements.
† From Hittorf method. All others by moving boundary method.
Abridged from Robinson and Stokes, *Electrolyte Solutions*, (Butterworth, London, 1955).

A considerable number of conclusions can be drawn from these data, which the reader can easily verify: (a) The transport numbers change by small but measurable amounts with concentration. Hence we can speak strictly of independent ion mobilities only at zero concentration. (b) The hydrogen ion is remarkable in carrying more than 82% of the current in HCl solutions. This suggests a special and distinct process by which hydrogen ions contribute to the conductance. (This may be compared also with the high conductance of HCl and other strong proton acids in water.) (c) The sequence of alkali metal ions Li^+, Na^+, K^+ carry progressively larger fractions of the current, even though the sizes of the gaseous ions increase, which would of itself produce the opposite effect. The inversion is usually explained by greater hydration of the smaller ions—that is, attachment of water molecules which make the ions larger. (d) The effect in (c) occurs also in acetate solutions, and comparison indicates that acetate ion is a less effective carrier of current than chloride ion—which would be expected on the basis of simple ion sizes without hydration effects.

The differences revealed by comparison of transport numbers become even clearer if these numbers are combined with limiting equivalent conductance values of the salts to obtain limiting ion conductances. From Eq. 18.11 of the preceding section, the relation is $t_0^+ = \lambda_0^+/\Lambda_0$, from which λ_0^+ may be calculated. (Also λ_0^-, from $\lambda_0^+ + \lambda_0^- = \Lambda_0$.) Thus, for HCl, $\Lambda_0 = 426.2$ and $t_0^+ = 0.8209$; hence $\lambda_0^+(H^+) = 0.8209 \times 426.2 = 349.8$, and $\lambda_0^-(Cl^-) = 426.2 - 349.8 = 76.4$. By such combinations, the ion conductances listed in Table 18.3 have been obtained.

TABLE 18.3. *Ion Conductances in Water at 25°C.*

Cation	H^+	Li^+	Na^+	K^+	Ag^+	Tl^+
λ_0^+	349.8	38.7	50.10	73.50	61.9	74.7
Cation	H_4N^+	$(CH_3)_4N^+$	Mg^{2+}	Ba^{2+}	Cu^{2+}	La^{3+}
λ_0^+	73.6	44.9	53.1	63.6	56.6	69.7
Anion	OH^-	F^-	Cl^-	Br^-	I^-	NO_3^-
λ_0^-	198.6	55.4	76.35	78.14	76.8	71.46
Anion	HCO_3^-	CH_3COO^-	SO_4^{2-}	CO_3^{2-}	$Fe(CN)_6^{3-}$	$Fe(CN)_6^{4-}$
λ_0^-	44.5	40.9	80.0	69.3	100.9	110.5

Of the many inferences possible from the table, only a few can be discussed here. Reasonably simple ions, not too highly charged, have λ_0

values in the range 60–80, with bulkier complex ions having lower conductance values. Of the exceptions, H^+ and OH^- ions are conspicuous for their extraordinarily large values. The sequence of values of both alkali metal cations and halogen anions are inverse from the expectation based upon sizes of the gaseous ions (Compare with Ion Speeds and Viscosity, p. 593.) To approach an understanding of these effects, it is worthwhile to calculate the actual average speeds of migration of ions, and then to compare them with what would be expected from a simple model of ion motion in a fluid such as water.

18.10. Ion Mobility and Viscosity

Ion Mobility

The speed of an ion moving through a solvent such as water increases with the electrical force acting on it, and is proportional to the electric field strength in the solution, usually expressed in volts per centimeter. The *mobility* ω of an ion is defined as the ratio of its average speed v to the field; the units of mobility are thus $cm^2 \, volt^{-1} \, sec^{-1}$. The value of ω for a particular ion in a particular solvent is readily deduced from the ion conductance, as illustrated below.

Consider a uniform column of solution of area A cm^2 and length d cm,

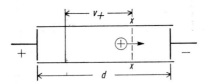

Fig. 18.9. *Determination of ion mobility.*

with a potential difference V between the electrodes, as in Fig. 18.9. The electric field V/d then produces a speed v_+ of the cations moving from left to right, and all the ions in a column v_+ cm long will pass through any surface, such as X, in 1 second. The current I_+ of positive ions through this surface is the corresponding quantity of charge in this column v_+ cm in length, which for a concentration m_+ moles/liter of cations with valence Z_+ is

$$ I_+ = (v_+ A) \frac{m_+}{1000} Z_+ \mathfrak{F} $$

where $\mathfrak{F}$ is the faraday ($= 96,494$ coulombs or one equivalent of electrons).

From the definition of the mobility—$\omega_+ = v_+/(V/d)$—substitution from the above equation permits the mobility of a cation to be given as

$$\omega_+ = \frac{1000}{\mathfrak{F}m_+Z_+} \frac{I_+/A}{V/d} \tag{18.14}$$

This can be expressed in terms of the equivalent cations conductance (λ^+) if the definitions of equivalent and specific conductance in Sections 18.4 and 18.5 are recalled. For $\lambda^+ = (1000/c)\kappa_+$, if c is the concentration in equivalents/liter, and κ_+ is the specific conductance corresponding to the positive ion current I_+.

Since $c = m_+Z_+$ and $\kappa_+ = (I_+/A)/(V/d)$ one has

$$\lambda^+ = \frac{1000}{m_+Z_+} \frac{I_+/A}{V/d}$$

Comparison with Eq. 18.14 shows immediately that

$$\omega_+ = \frac{\lambda^+}{\mathfrak{F}} \tag{18.15}$$

The equivalent ion conductance then differs from the ion mobility by the faraday $(\mathfrak{F})$ as a universal conversion factor.

EXAMPLE

From the ion conductances, calculate the speeds of H^+ and Cl^- ions in dilute solution at 25°C if a field strength $V/d = 1.00$ v/cm is applied. We have

$$v_+ = \omega_+ \frac{V}{d} = \frac{\lambda_0^-}{\mathfrak{F}} \frac{V}{d} = \frac{350}{96,500} \times 1.00 = 0.0036 \text{ cm/sec}$$

the speed of the hydrogen ions. Similarly,

$$v_- = \frac{\lambda_0^-}{\mathfrak{F}} \frac{V}{d} = \frac{76.4}{96,500} \times 1.00 = 0.00080 \text{ cm/sec}$$

the speed of the chloride ions.

These speeds are obviously very small by ordinary standards at the field strengths usually employed, and the distances traveled during electrolysis in conductance cells are only a minute fraction of the electrode separations. Thus one has to think of the whole volume of ions being displaced slightly, rather than of the ions singly traveling any such distance as the length of the cell.

Ion Speeds and Viscosity

The slow average speeds acquired by ions in solution must result from the opposition they meet in moving between the solvent molecules. The phenomena can be represented as resembling the motion of a sphere through a viscous fluid, the accelerating force on the charged ion being due to the electric field, and the resistance from the viscosity representing in a crude way the hindering effect of the solvent molecules. (See Fig. 18.10.)

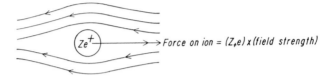

Fig. 18.10. *Solvent flow.*

Stoke's law, mentioned in Section 3.3 in connection with falling oil drops in a viscous gas, states that for spheres of radius r the retarding viscous force will be

$$F_{\text{vis}} = 6\pi\eta rv$$

where v is the speed of the sphere and η the coefficient of viscosity of the fluid. If we write v_+ for the speed of a cation, and use the electrical force Z_+eV/d (since V/d equals the force per *unit* charge), we have

$$(Z_+e)\frac{V}{d} = 6\pi\eta rv_+$$

or

$$v_+ = \frac{(Z_+e)}{6\pi\eta r}\frac{V}{d} \qquad (18.16)$$

This interpretation of ion speeds in terms of viscosity can be tested by calculating the speed (or mobility, if the field $V/d = 1$ v/cm) of an ion of representative size in water, and comparing this result with actual ion speeds. Let an ion radius $r = 1.5 \times 10^{-8}$ cm, a monovalent ion $Z_+ = 1$, $V/d = 1$ v/cm $= (1/300)(\text{esu/cm})$, and $\eta = 0.0089$ poise for water at 25°C ($e = 4.8 \times 10^{-10}$ esu); then we have

$$v_+ = \frac{1 \times 4.8 \times 10^{-10}}{6\pi \times 0.0089 \times 1.5 \times 10^{-8}}\frac{1}{300} = 0.00064 \text{ cm/sec}$$

While this calculated speed does not closely approximate that obtained from conductance measurements of chloride ion in the preceding example, it is at least comparable with it. Very good agreement could hardly be expected, for an ion moving through solvent molecules similar to it in size does not correspond with the assumption of Stoke's law, a sphere moving through a uniform viscous fluid. Even so, the reasonable agreement in magnitude calculated suggests that there is some connection between ion speeds and molecular processes giving rise to solvent viscosity. Other lines of evidence lead to a similar conclusion; for example, ion conductances usually increase with temperature at about the same rate that solvent viscosity decreases (Walden's rule).

The most conspicuous deviations from the usual behavior and values of ion conductances in water are shown by hydrogen and hydroxyl ions, which have abnormally high mobilities; the hydrogen ion in water has the form H_3O^+ and is even further hydrated. The greater mobility of H_3O^+ is usually attributed to a proton transfer process, by which the proton "jumps" from a given H_3O^+ ion to an adjacent water molecule:

$$\overset{+}{\underset{H}{HOH}} + \overset{}{\underset{H}{OH}} \longrightarrow \overset{}{\underset{H}{HO}} + \overset{+}{\underset{H}{HOH}}$$

By this transfer, the ion and molecule have in effect exchanged places without actually bodily displacing one another. The process is limited instead by the rate of finding receptive neutral water molecules to accept protons from neighboring hydronium ions.

A similar process can be written for hydroxyl ions:

$$\overset{-}{\underset{H}{O}} + \underset{H}{HO} \longrightarrow \underset{H}{OH} + \overset{-}{\underset{H}{O}}$$

18.11. Conductance and Dissociation of Weak Electrolytes

The striking differences in equivalent conductances of strong and weak electrolytes have already been shown in Section 18.6. The large decrease of the equivalent conductance with increasing concentrations, observed for a weak electrolyte such as acetic acid in water, is principally the result of the increasing association between ions of opposite charge at higher concentration. For example, by the reaction

$$H^+ + Ac^- \longrightarrow HAc$$

where the symbol Ac^- represents the atoms composing the acetate ion (CH_3COO^-), two ions are replaced by a neutral molecule. Accordingly only a fraction of the acetic acid is ionized and able to carry current. The fraction of ionized acid at a particular concentration is, to a quite good approximation, the ratio of the equivalent conductance Λ at that concentration to the equivalent conductance Λ_0 for infinite dilution (complete ionization). The degree of dissociation (α) of molecules into ions can be calculated by

$$\alpha = \frac{\Lambda}{\Lambda_0} \qquad (18.17)$$

For a binary weak electrolyte (uniunivalent, didivalent, and so on), the ionization equilibrium is $AB \rightleftharpoons A^+ + B^-$ or $AB \rightleftharpoons A^{2+} + B^{2-}$.

The equilibrium concentrations of the species present in a solution of gross concentration C are $(1 - \alpha)C$ for AB, αC for A^+, and αC for B^-. The ionization constant K_i is thus

$$K_i = \frac{[A^+][B^-]}{[AB]} \qquad \frac{C\alpha \cdot c\alpha}{C(1 - \alpha)} = \frac{C\alpha^2}{1 - \alpha}$$

a result known as the Ostwald dilution law. Expressing α in terms of Λ and Λ_0 gives

$$K_i = \frac{c\Lambda^2}{\Lambda_0(\Lambda_0 - \Lambda)} \qquad (18.18)$$

If this explanation of weak electrolyte behavior is correct, constant values of K_i should be obtained from measured values c and of Λ, together with the value of Λ_0 obtained as described in Section 18.7. At 25°C, $\Lambda_0 = 390.71$ for acetic acid, and the use of very precise conductance data in the range 0.00003 to 0.2 molar gives the value of K_i listed in Table 18.4.

TABLE 18.4.   *Ionization Constant of Acetic Acid at 25°C from Conductance Measurements.*

C (moles/liter)	0.00002801	0.0002184	0.002414	0.0200	0.200
Λ	210.38	96.493	32.217	11.566	3.651
Λ/Λ_0	0.5384	0.2470	0.0825	0.0296	0.00930
K_1 ($\times 10^5$)	1.758	1.769	1.790	1.806	1.755

(Values of MacInnes and Shedlovsky, as quoted in Robinson and Stokes, *Electrolyte Solutions*.)

The constancy of the calculated K_i to within two percent is strong evidence for the explanation of incomplete dissociation. At the same time, the differences are far greater than the experimental error of the extremely careful work, and show small residual effects attributable to small ion interaction even at the small ion concentrations existing. (For $C = 0.2$, the ion concentration $\alpha C = 0.0019$ moles/liter.) For less weak electrolytes, the ion product is less constant from one concentration to another because of the higher ion concentrations and the correspondingly greater strong electrolyte effects, to be discussed in the next section.

18.12. Ion Interactions in Strong Electrolytes

The failure of such electrolytes as KCl and HCl to have precisely constant values for equivalent conductance even at high dilution cannot be explained by association of ions as for weak electrolytes, because the variation of equivalent conductance values with concentration has a completely different form, as described in Section 18.6. The characteristic variation for strong electrolytes, linearity with the square root of concentration, was attributed by a number of workers before 1923 to the mutual electrical forces between ions. In that year Debye and Hückel developed their classic quantitative theory of the effect of interionic attractions, as discussed in Section 17.11.

The formation of an average ion atmosphere of opposite charge about any ion, as it moves randomly through a solution, leads to resulting modified equilibrium properties. When an electric field is applied, there is added to this random motion of the ion and its associated atmosphere, a net drift in the direction of the field at a rate permitted by the resistive force of the surrounding solvent on the associated ion atmosphere. The ion atmosphere, however, does not react instantaneously to changes in position of the central ion, and as a result the atmosphere lags slightly behind the central ion with its net drift velocity, as indicated in Fig. 18.11. The attractive forces between

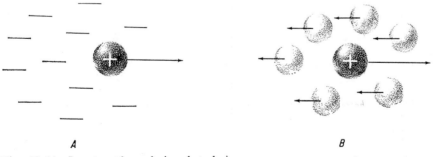

A   *B*

Fig. 18.11. *Ion atmospheres during electrolysis.*

the cation and the lagging negative ion atmosphere is a retarding force, which slows the cation's motion and so decreases its effective conductance.

The second factor reducing ion speeds at higher ion concentrations results from interactions of the atmosphere ions with the solvent. Since these "ions" have an excess of opposite charge, there is a net motion in the direction opposite to the motion of the central ion, which through ion-dipole interaction carries solvent molecules slightly in the atmosphere's direction of motion. The result is that any central ion must move "upstream" against an opposing flow of solvent molecules.

The successful calculation of these effects for dilute solutions was made by Onsager in 1927, generalizing earlier work of Debye and Hückel. The expression for equivalent conductance obtained from the theory is of the form

$$\Lambda = \Lambda_0 - A\Lambda_0 I^{1/2} - \frac{B}{\eta} I^{1/2}$$

where I is the ionic strength defined in Section 17.11, and the constants A and B involve the valence type, electron charge, thermal energy kT, and the dielectric constant. Both correction terms vary as the square root of concentration (corresponding to the dependence of the ionic strength I, on concentration), the first (involving Λ_0) representing the ion atmosphere lag, and the second (with solvent viscosity η) giving the effect of solvent drag.

Comparison of this prediction with experimental measurements is made in Fig. 18.12 for sodium chloride as a uniunivalent salt and

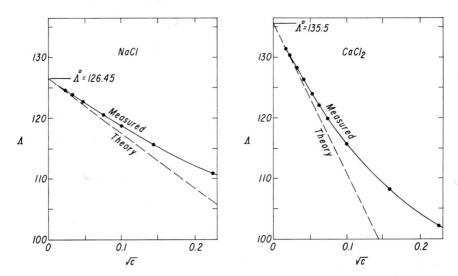

Fig. 18.12. *Theoretical and measured variation of equivalent conductance with concentration for aqueous solutions at 25°C.*

calcium chloride as a diunivalent salt. The experimental data approach the limiting slope of the theory at low concentrations, but deviate considerably from the theory at higher concentrations. Even though the theory considers the effect of cation charge and predicts larger effects with greater charge, the deviations are larger for $CaCl_2$ than for NaCl. The differences shown result from the approximate character of the theory, in which a number of approximations, such as the neglect of the finite size of the ions, were made to reduce otherwise great mathematical difficulties. Many efforts have been made to develop improved theories usable at much higher concentrations, but none so far advanced have been generally accepted for concentrations greater than 0.1 normal.

18.13. Ion Association in Electrolytes

The singular role of water as a solvent for salts has been mentioned on several occasions. While the obvious importance of aqueous solutions of electrolytes justifies their having received principal attention both in experimental measurements and in the discussion heretofore, properties in water are not typical of many other solvents.

Water, with a dielectric constant 78.5 at 25°C, is one of very few liquids having a dielectric constant greater than 50 under ordinary conditions. (The discussion of dielectric constants in Chapter 11 brought this out.) The only liquids of higher dielectric constant which have received much attention as solvents are formamide (109), sulfuric acid (110), and hydrogen cyanide (118). There are even fewer pure solvents with constants in the range 35–78. This classification of solvents according to dielectric constant ϵ emphasizes the exceptional character of aqueous solutions. It is meaningful because a high dielectric constant reduces the Coulomb force of attraction $F = q_1 q_2 / \epsilon r^2$ between charges q_1 and q_2, at distance r, and permits a high degree of dissociation even at reasonable concentrations of the ions in solution.

The effects observed in aqueous solution for such solutes as HCl, NaCl, and other species giving monovalent ions, are not found in solvents of lower dielectric constant or even in water for ions of higher charge. The reason is that the larger attractive forces present in either case result, even at low concentrations, in association of oppositely charged ions. The consequences are striking in conductance determinations because either the number or the mobility of conducting ions is sharply reduced. When the solvent dielectric constant is less than about 10, measurements at concentrations low enough that complete ionization is approached are extremely difficult, and to make estimates of limiting equivalent conductances or other properties of single ions is much more complicated.

Despite such difficulties, there has been considerable success in understanding the first form of ion association as concentration increases. This equilibrium requires only that ions of opposite sign which approach closely enough act as a unit of zero net charge (called an ion pair); see Fig. 18.13. This was assumed by Bjerrum to take place when the

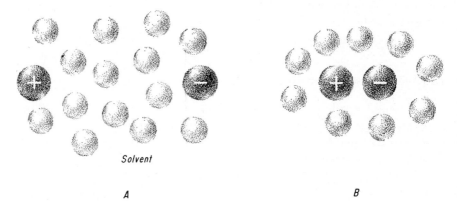

Solvent

A   B

Fig. 18.13. *Ion association:* (A) *free ions;* (B) *ion pair.*

energy of attraction from Coulomb forces exceeded thermal energy of random motion. Fuoss and Kraus were able to show that this hypothesis accounted very well for the initial decrease of equivalent conductance with increasing concentration in solvents of low dielectric constant, and that different ionization constants in several solvents could be explained if the dielectric constants of the solvents were considered.

Ion pair effects can be significant even in water for ions of high charge type, such as the divalent ions from $MgSO_4$, and the trivalent ions from lanthanum ferricyanide, $LaFe(CN)_6$. The interpretation of conductance data for such cases in terms of ion pair formation is a promising approach, but entails the complication of having to estimate somehow what conductance is to be expected for complete dissociation.

The formation of ion pairs is only the first step in further associations forming increasingly complex groups of ions with increasing concentrations. The assumption of ion triplets, $\oplus\ominus\oplus$ and $\ominus\oplus\ominus$, explains some effects in a range of concentrations above that for which ion pairs are predominantly present, but the situation in general is far more complicated, especially when solvent dielectric constants are low. Much work remains to be done in the study of electrolytes at high concentrations and in nonaqueous solvents before either the experimental evidence or the theory can be even moderately adequate.

Problems

18.1. A 0.01 molal solution of $SnCl_2$ in water is electrolyzed. What are the anode and cathode reactions at reversible electrodes? What are the reactions for a 0.0001 molal solution?

18.2. A 1.0 normal solution of $CuSO_4$ in water is electrolyzed between platinum electrodes. (a) What are the electrode reactions? (b) For 0.1 ampere current, the necessary potential difference across the cell is 1.59 v and for 0.5 amperes it is 1.99 v. Estimate the minimum potential difference for steady current flow (the decomposition potential).

18.3. Electrolysis of a 1.0 molal solution of HCl with $a = 0.81$ evolves hydrogen and chlorine at the electrodes. (a) Calculate the minimum potential difference necessary for steady current to flow with evolution of gas if the gases are at 1.0 atm pressure and the electrodes are reversible. (b) The observed decomposition potential is 1.42 v. Explain the difference.

18.4. If the products of electrolysis in aqueous solution are hydrogen and oxygen at 1.0 atm, what is the reversible decomposition potential?

18.5. A sulphuric acid solution is electrolyzed by an average current of 0.50 amperes flowing for 2.00 hours. Calculate the volumes of gases liberated at the electrodes if the temperature is 25°C and the gas pressures are equalized to the barometric pressure of 740 mm.

18.6. Currents are sometimes calibrated by an iodine coulometer, in which $I_2(g)$ set free by electrolysis at one coulometer electrode is determined by titration with $Na_2S_2O_3$. If 17.5 cm^3 of 0.12 molar $Na_2S_2O_3$ are required to react with the I_2 set free in electrolysis for 3.0 hours, what was the total charge transport in faradays and the average current in amperes?

18.7. A conductivity cell is calibrated by measuring its resistance when filled with a 0.10 molal solution of KCl (7.479 g per kg H_2O), which has been found by accurate standardizing measurements to have a specific conductance of 0.012856 ohm^{-1} cm^{-1} at 25°C. (a) Calculate the cell constant (ratio of measured to specific conductance) if the measured resistance is 1190 ohms. (b) For parallel plate electrodes, what must be the electrode area if the plates are 1.00 cm apart? (c) What will be the measured resistance for a solution of specific conductance 0.00532 ohm^{-1} cm^{-1}?

18.8. A cell suitable for measuring strong electrolytes in the concentration range 0.0002 to 0.01 normal can conveniently have a cell constant of about 1.50 cm. A possible method of calibrating such a cell would be to fill it with mercury which has a specific resistance 0.96×10^{-4} ohm cm at 25°C. What resistance would have to be measured?

18.9. The measured resistances of a series of NaCl solutions at 25°C in a suitable conductivity cell were found to be:

C (moles/liter)	0.0005	0.0010	0.0020	0.0050
R (ohms)	7637	3846	1940	790.2

In a separate calibration experiment, the resistance of a standard KCl solution with specific conductance of 0.01409 ohm^{-1} cm^{-1} was found to be 338.9 ohms. (a) Calculate the equivalent conductances of the NaCl solutions. (b) Test Kohlrausch's law by plotting Λ against $C^{1/2}$. (c) By extrapolation to $C=0$ obtain a value for Λ_0.

18.10. Measured resistances of solutions of cyanoacetic acid in water at 25°C are as follows:

C (mole/liter)	.0004566	.001856	.007335
R (ohm)	631.5	190.8	70.35

The cell used had a resistance of 71.05 ohms when filled with a 0.01 demal KCl solutions (0.7462 g KCl per kg of H_2O) of specific conductance 0.001409 ohm^{-1} cm^{-1}. (a) Calculate the equivalent conductances Λ and plot against $C^{1/2}$. Also, examine by numerical analysis whether an equation of the form $\Lambda = \Lambda_0 - \text{constant} \times C^{1/2}$ can fit the data within their precision. (b) What conclusions can be drawn about this acid in water? (Compare with Figs. 18.4 and 18.5.) Discuss the feasibility of extrapolating to $C = 0$ to obtain Λ_0.

18.11. At 25°C, the limiting equivalent conductance Λ_0 of $Ba(OH)_2$ is 262.2, that of $BaCl_2$ is 140.0, and that of NH_4Cl is 149.9. Calculate Λ_0 for NH_4OH.

18.12. In a Hittorf experiment, an electrolyzing current of 0.105 amperes flows for 32 minutes through an HCl solution. The cathode and anode compartments each contained 0.005 moles of HCl initially, and hydrogen and chlorine are evolved at the electrodes. (a) If the transport number of H^+ in the solution is 0.84, how many moles of HCl are present in the anode and cathode compartments after electrolysis? (b) How much hydrogen and chlorine are given off? (c) If each compartment has a volume 30 cm^3, what are the concentrations in each before and after electrolysis?

18.13. A 1.00 molal $FeCl_3$ solution is electrolyzed in a Hittorf cell and a sample from the cathode compartment is found on analysis to be 0.795 molal in $FeCl_3$ and 0.250 molal in $FeCl_2$. (a) Calculate the transport number of Fe^{3+} ions, remembering that 1 mole of Fe^{3+} transports three equivalents. (b) If the cathode compartment contains 50 g of solution initially, how many coulombs are required to effect the given amount of electrolysis?

18.14. A 0.05 molal solution of KCl is electrolyzed at 25°C in a Hittorf experiment and the number of equivalents transported determined by the amount of silver deposited in a silver coulometer connected in series with the transference cell. This weight of Ag is found to be 0.4068 g. The anode solution, weighing 132.9 g, is found to contain 0.3560 g of KCl. What is the transference number of potassium ion in the solution?

18.15. In a moving boundary transference experiment, a 1.00 normal KCl solution is used with a lower solution of $BaCl_2$. With a current of 0.200 ampere, the boundary moved 5.08 cm in 1500 sec in the tube used. The volume per unit length of the tube was obtained from the increase in weight on filling a known length with mercury; this increase was 40.74 g for 10.0 cm length. (a) Calculate the transference number of K^+ and Cl^- ion. (b) If the current in KCl solution were carried exclusively by K^+ ion, what boundary displacement would have been observed?

18.16. A moving boundary experiment is used to measure hydrogen ion mobilities directly. With a potential difference of 25.0 v between two electrodes 10.0 cm apart, the boundary moves at a rate of 0.540 cm per minute. Calculate the mobility and equivalent conductance of hydrogen ions in the solution.

18.17. Consider the galvanic cell

$$\text{Ag, AgCl}(s): \text{HCl}(m_1); \text{HCl}(m_2): \text{AgCl}(s), \text{Ag}$$

(a) Show that the cell reaction for one faraday is $t^+ \text{HCl}(m_1) = t^+ \text{HCl}(m_2)$, and that the cell EMF, if the junction potential is neglected and activity coefficients are set equal to one, is

$$\varepsilon = -2t^+ \frac{RT}{\mathfrak{F}} \ln \frac{m_2}{m_1}$$

(b) Verify from this equation and from qualitative reasoning which solution must be more concentrated if the EMF is positive for the cell as written.

18.18. For the cell in Problem *18.17*, the following EMF values have been measured at 25°C:

m_1 (moles/kg)	m_2 (moles/kg)	ε (volts)
0.10050	0.07844	0.00995
0.10050	0.005260	0.1188
0.005260	0.003457	0.01745

Calculate average values of t^+ for the three experiments.

18.19. Write the reaction and EMF expression for the cell

$$\text{Pt, H}_2 \text{ (1 atm)}: \text{H}_2\text{SO}_4(m_1); \text{H}_2\text{SO}_4(m_2): \text{H}_2 \text{ (1 atm), Pt}$$

(a) Calculate the EMF for $m_2 = 0.0050$, $m_1 = 1.00$, if the transference number t^+ of hydrogen ion is 0.82, assuming activity coefficients equal to one in both solutions. (b) Actually $\gamma_\pm = 0.643$ for the dilute solution and 0.131 for the more concentrated one. What is the correct EMF (except for junction potential errors)?

18.20. The viscosity of water is 0.0089 poise at 25°C, 0.0152 at 5°C, and 0.0055 at 50°C. Estimate the equivalent conductance of KCl solutions at 5°C and 50°C from the value at 25°C.

18.21. Walden measured the equivalent conductance of tetraethylammonium picrate at several temperatures in a number of solvents to obtain data for testing his rule that the conductance Λ_0 varies inversely with viscosity η. Use the data below to make such tests by calculating $\Lambda_0\eta$:

Solvent	$t°C$	Λ_0 (ohm^{-1} cm^2/equiv)	η (poise)
H_2O	0	31.2	.00180
	18	53.3	.00106
	100	197.0	.00028
CH_3OH	0	72.5	.000792
	25	102.9	.000546
	50	153.4	.000371
C_2H_5OH	0	32.0	.00177
	25	51.5	.00110
	50	88.7	.00064

18.22. For which of the following ion solutes would you expect Walden's rule to work best and least well: tetramethylammonium bromate, potassium chloride, hydrochloric acid?

18.23. Equivalent conductances Λ_0 in methanol at 25°C are 204 for HCl, 104 for NaCl, and 101 for sodium picrate. (a) What is Λ_0 for picric acid in methanol? (b) The value of Λ for a 0.1 molar solution of picric acid is 9.3 ohm^{-1} cm^2/equiv. Estimate the degree of ionization in this solution and obtain an approximate ionization constant of picric acid in methanol. (c) What additional measurement would you have to make to be able to calculate ion conductances from the equivalent conductances above?

18.24. The electrical forces on di- and trivalent ions in solution are two and three times those on singly charged ions, yet their equivalent ion conductances are not very different (see Table 18.3). Explain.

18.25. The ionization of monochloracetic acid in water has been studied by conductance measurements. At 25°C, the specific conductance of a 0.00181 molar solution is 4.09×10^{-4} ohm^{-1} cm^{-1}. The specific conductance of a 0.00100 molar sodium monochloracetate solution, assumed to be wholly ionized, is 0.875×10^{-4} ohm^{-1} cm^{-1}. Combine these data with values from the text to obtain Λ_0 for monochloracetic acid, the degree of ionization of the acid solution, and the ionization constant.

18.26. The ion-product $K_w = [H^+][OH^-]$ is 1.0×10^{-14} for water at 25°C. Calculate the specific conductance of pure water from ion conductances.

18.27. The specific conductance of even so-called conductivity water is usually of the order 1×10^{-6} ohm^{-1} cm^{-1}, and one reason for the larger value is dissolved CO_2, which ionizes weakly. Estimate the concentrations of H^+ and HCO_3^- which would account for the value 1×10^{-6}, assuming the ion conductance of HCO_3^- to be about 45.

18.28. A conductivity cell filled with distilled water has a resistance of 175,000 ohms, and when the water is saturated with calcium oxalate the resistance falls to 16,400 ohms. From separate experiments the cell constant is known to be 0.325 cm^{-1}, and the ion conductances to be 60 and 71. Calculate the solubility of calcium oxalate.

18.29. (a) Assuming that the degree of ionization α is equal to Λ/Λ_0 for a weak 1–1 electrolyte, show that Ostwald's dilution law can be written

$$C\Lambda = -K_i\Lambda_0 + K_i\Lambda_0^2 \frac{1}{\Lambda}$$

(b) From this equation, explain a graphical method for determining K_i and Λ_0 from measurements of Λ at different solute concentrations C. (c) Trimethyl tin chloride is partly ionized in ethanol. Conductivity measurements at 25°C gave the following values:

C (moles/l)	0.000089	0.000260	0.000318	0.00104
Λ (ohm^{-1} cm^2/equiv)	14.1	9.29	8.68	5.12

Determine K_i and Λ_0 by the method you described in (b).

18.30. Equivalent conductances of NH_4OH at 25°C in water are as follows:

C (moles/l)	0.0001	0.0005	0.001	0.005	0.01
Λ (ohm^{-1} cm^2/equiv)	93	47	34	16	11.3

(a) Use the method of the preceding problems to test Ostwald's dilution law and obtain values of K_i and Λ_0. (b) Use a value of Λ_0 deduced from Table 18.3 to obtain a value of K_i. Explain why it is better.

18.31. Activity coefficients can be deduced from EMF measurements on transference cells with two solutions of different concentrations if the transference number of one ion and the activity coefficient of one solution is known. The EMF of the cell

$$\text{Ag, AgCl: NaCl (0.1 molar); NaCl (0.01 molar): AgCl, Ag}$$

is 0.04303 V at 25°C. Using ion conductances to calculate t^+ for the sodium ion, calculate $\gamma_\pm$ in the 0.1 molar solution if $\gamma_\pm = 0.9034$ for the 0.01 molar solution.

18.32. The following table gives equivalent conductances in ohm^{-1} cm^2/equiv of 1–1, 2–1, and 3–1 chloride salts in water at 25°C. Make suitable plots of the values of Λ against $C^{1/2}$ and from the results answer the following questions. (a) How does the range in which Λ versus $C^{1/2}$ is approximately a straight line depend on the valence type? (b) How does the slope, attributed to ion interactions, depend on the valences?

C (equiv/liter)	Λ_{KCl}	Λ_{LaCl_3}	Λ_{BaCl_2}
.0005	147.81	135.96	139.6
.001	146.95	134.34	137.0
.005	143.55	128.02	127.5
.01	141.27	123.94	121.8
.05	133.37	111.48	106.2
.10	128.96	105.91	99.1

18.33. Conductance measurements can often be used to advantage in determining equilibrium ion concentrations in solution. (a) Show how the equilibrium constant of the reaction $Cl_2 + H_2O = HCl + HOCl$ can be determined if the amount of chlorine initially introduced and Λ_0 of HCl are known, ionization of HOCl being negligible.

18.34. Calculate the radii which Li$^+$, Na$^+$, K$^+$ ions would have to have in water if their motions were determined by viscous flow of uniform solvent as expressed by Stokes' law. Compare the answers with crystallographic radii listed in Chapter 7.

18.35. In conductance, ions of opposite sign move in opposite directions under electric forces due to the applied potential. In diffusion of electrolytes, ions of both signs move in the same direction of lower concentrations. (a) Discuss the nature of the driving force and potential difference in ion diffusion. (b) What is the opposing force which limits the rate of diffusion? (c) In diffusion of HCl in water, one would expect hydrogen ion to be more mobile, as it is for conductance. Explain how it comes about that H$^+$ and Cl$^-$ move at the same average rate and preserve electrical neutrality of the solution at all points.

Suggested Readings

Much of the material of this chapter is discussed in the references for Chapters 17 and 19. The book *Electrolyte Solutions* by R. A. Robinson and R. H. Stokes (Butterworth's, London, 1955) discusses measurements and analysis of conductance and diffusion. The most exhaustive advanced discussion of theory is in *The Physical Chemistry of Electrolyte Solutions* by H. S. Harned and B. B. Owen (3rd ed., Reinhold, New York, 1958).

Chapter 19

Ionic Reactions
in Solution

MANY CHEMICAL REACTIONS involve interaction between separate ionic species or ions, in contrast with the reactions involving the breaking and reforming of covalent bonds which are so prevalent for compounds of organic chemistry. Ionic reactions can occur whenever the reacting ions can approach one another closely enough to permit their electrostatic fields to interact. Such situations can be realized in mixtures of molten salts, but are much more often observed when the ions are in solution, and the most common ionic reactions take place in aqueous solution, although ionic processes are important in a number of nonaqueous solvents. The chemistry of such systems is receiving increasing attention. The present discussion will include such ionic reactions as the dissociation of weak electrolytes (acids or bases), hydrolysis, precipitation, and the formation of complex ions, together with other related topics. Many oxidation-reduction reactions involve ions; some important ones are discussed, for example, in L. B. Clapp's *Chemistry of the Covalent Bond*.

While reactions with covalent compounds proceed at rates sufficiently slow to be readily observed, reactions between ions are ordinarily completed during elapsed times of thousandths or millionths of a second, and can for many purposes be considered instantaneous. The precipitation of silver chloride, which occurs upon the mixing of a solution containing chloride ion with one containing silver ion, is such an example. The detailed study of the kinetics of such reactions has only recently been productive, and most of our information about ionic reactions in solution has come from the study of equilibrium properties.

19.1. Equilibria in Ionic Solutions

Ionic equilibria in solution are subject to the same thermodynamic factors as any other equilibria, and may be set up in terms of the difference in free energy between the products and reactants of the equilibrium reaction, as discussed in detail in Section 16.5 and those following. The approximations inherent in employing ionic concentrations rather than employing ionic activities in making calculations have been pointed out, as has the effect of the total ion concentration upon individual ion activities. In the discussions which follow, calculations will use ion concentrations without activity coefficient corrections. The reader should remember that this simplification is a rather drastic one for even moderately concentrated solutions, and prevents the results from being precise even if the solutions are dilute. The expressions employed will become thermodynamically exact by substituting the activity $a = \gamma m$ for the concentration, with the appropriate adjustment of the equilibrium constants. The much more complicated calculations then involved are necessary for the greater accuracy obtained.

The solute dissociation considered in Section 16.5 might well have been that of the weak electrolyte, acetic acid, in aqueous solution. The chemical equation for this dissociation can be written

$$HAc \rightleftharpoons H^+ + Ac^-$$

The equilibrium constant for this reaction is called the ionization (or dissociation) constant K_i, and its dependence on the ion concentration is

$$K_i = \frac{[H^+][Ac^-]}{[HAc]} \tag{19.1}$$

For C moles of acetic acid dissolved to form 1 liter of solution, producing C_i moles each of H^+ and Ac^-, the ionization expression becomes

$$K_i = \frac{C_i^2}{C - C_i} \tag{19.2}$$

(In writing $[H^+] = [Ac^-] = C_i$ we have neglected any contribution to

[H$^+$] by ionization of water; the justification of this will be given in Section 19.9.)

If the degree of ionization is α (percentage ionization = 100α), the equation is reduced to

$$K_i = \frac{\alpha^2 C}{1 - \alpha} \qquad (19.3)$$

When the degree of ionization (α) is small, $(1 - \alpha)$ is approximately equal to unity, and the dilution law becomes

$$K_i \cong \alpha^2 C \qquad (19.4)$$

and $\alpha \cong \sqrt{K_i/C}$. The fraction ionized is thus proportional to the square root of the ionization constant, and inversely proportional to the square root of the concentration of the dissociating weak electrolyte.

ILLUSTRATION

The value of K_i at 25°C for acetic acid is 1.8×15^{-5} moles liter^{-1}. For a 0.01 molar solution of acetic acid, what is the degree of dissociation and what is the concentration of hydrogen ion in solution?

$$K_i = \frac{\alpha^2 C}{1 - \alpha} \cong \alpha^2 C$$

$$\alpha = \sqrt{K_i/C} = \sqrt{\frac{1.8 \times 10^{-5} \text{ moles liter}^{-1}}{10^{-2} \text{ moles liter}^{-1}}}$$

$$= 0.043$$

or 4.3%. [H$^+$] $= C_i = \alpha C = 4.3 \times 10^{-2} \times 10^{-2} = 4.3 \times 10^{-4}$ moles liter^{-1}. (The approximate value $\alpha = 0.043$ is small enough that replacing $1 - \alpha$ by 1 is justified for $C = 0.01$ moles liter^{-1}. At much lower concentrations, α becomes too large for this approximation to be acceptable; its value can then be obtained by solving Eq. 19.3 as a quadratic equation in α.)

All ionic equilibria to be discussed herein are subject to the same governing thermodynamic factors as other equilibria. For example, the variation of K_i with temperature is given by $(d \ln K_i/dT) = \Delta H_i/RT^2$, where ΔH_i is the heat of ionization.

19.2. Common Ion Effect

The *common ion effect*, already discussed in Section 16.6 for the case of slightly soluble salts, has a very similar counterpart in ionization phenomena. As an example, consider the effect of adding ion from some external source to acetic acid solution by dissolving in the acid solution a salt such as sodium acetate. The common ion is acetate ion, and the total acetate concentration is then the sum of that resulting from the ionization of the acid plus that added in the form of the salt.

If sodium acetate is added in the amount of C_s moles per liter of the final solution, the concentration of acetate ion resulting from this source, $[Ac^-]_s$, will be C_s moles liter^{-1}. (Practically all salts are strong electrolytes, and may be assumed completely ionized in aqueous solution.) Since the concentration of acetate ion resulting from the ionization of the acid present in amount C_a moles liter^{-1} is $[Ac^-]_i = C_i = \alpha C_a$, the total acetate ion concentration is

$$[AC^-]_{total} = [AC^-]_i + [AC^-]_s$$
$$= C_i + C_s$$

The final concentration of H$^+$ ion resulting from the ionization of the acid will be C_i moles liter^{-1}. (Another source of H$^+$ is by the slight ionization of the water, but the amount is very small, as shown in Section 19.9.) By using $[H^+] = C_i$ in Eq. 19.1 with the above value for $[Ac^-]$, we obtain

$$K_i = \frac{C_i(C_i + C_s)}{C - C_i}$$

or

$$K_i = \frac{\alpha^2 C_a + \alpha C_s}{1 - \alpha} \qquad (19.5)$$

When α is small and C_a is not too large, this reduces to $K_i = \alpha C_s$, or

$$\alpha = \frac{K_i}{C_s} \qquad (19.6)$$

ILLUSTRATION

To a solution of acetic acid there is added sodium acetate, with resulting final concentrations of acid and salt 0.01 molar and 0.1 molar, respectively. Calculate (a) the degree of dissociation of the acid and (b) the hydrogen ion concentration of the solution.

$$\alpha = \frac{K_i}{C_s} = \frac{1.8 \times 10^{-5} \text{ moles liter}^{-1}}{10^{-1} \text{ moles liter}^{-1}}$$

$$= 1.8 \times 10^{-4}$$

or 0.00018%.

$$[H^+] = \alpha C = 1.8 \times 10^{-4} \times 10^{-2} = 1.8 \times 10^{-6} \text{ moles liter}^{-1}.$$

(Had α been found large compared with 1, it would have been necessary to solve the quadratic, Eq. 19.5.)

Comparison with the illustration of Section 19.1 indicates the effectiveness of a common ion in reducing the ionization of a weak electrolyte; α is smaller by a factor $4.3 \times 10^{-2}/1.8 \times 10^{-4}) = 2400$, and $[H^+]$ is similarly 2400 times smaller, when 0.1 molar Ac^- is added to the solution. It is evident that the acidity of a solution of weak acid can be controlled in this manner, and this will be discussed in greater detail in Section 19.9.

19.3. Acids and Bases

Acids and bases have been variously defined (see Clapp, Chapter 9), but perhaps the most useful systematic definition is that given by Brönsted of an acid as a proton donor, and a base as a proton acceptor. The importance of proton transfer in a very large number of characteristic acid-base reactions results from the unique property of the proton as a bare positive nucleus with no electrons attached. It is thus distinguished from other ions by having a size approximating 10^{-13} cm, compared with a radius of order 10^{-8} cm characteristic of the electron charge distributions. This makes possible enormously larger attraction by electrons of other molecules, with the result that protons in any solution are invariably combined with the species for which they have the greatest affinity, which may be other ions, solvent molecules, or both.

A conjugate acid-base pair by the Brönsted definition is composed of two species which differ by one proton according to the scheme expressed by

$$\text{acid} = \text{proton} + \text{base}$$

A series of important examples is listed in Table 19.1, together with acid ionization constants for water solutions, which will be discussed further in subsequent sections.

In each case, the acid form (which may be a positive ion, neutral molecule, or negative ion) is written to correspond to a proton plus the conjugate base. This convention *does not* mean that bare protons necessarily exist in solution as products of acid dissociation. On the contrary, many observations indicate that such protons combine with solvent molecules to form more stable ions. In water this process is represented by

$$H^+ + H_2O \longrightarrow H_3O^+$$

and in ethanol and ammonia solvated protons result from the reactions

$$H^+ + C_2H_5OH \rightleftharpoons C_2H_5OH_2^+$$
$$H^+ + NH_3 \rightleftharpoons NH_4^+$$

TABLE 19.1. *Conjugate Acid-Base Pairs, with Acid Ionization Constants* K_i *in Water at* $25°C$.

Acid	$\rightleftharpoons$ Proton +	Base	K_i
HCl	$\rightleftharpoons$ H^+ +	Cl^-	large
H_2SO_4	$\rightleftharpoons$ H^+ +	HSO_4^-	large
$H_2C_2O_4$	$\rightleftharpoons$ H^+ +	$HC_2O_4^-$	3.8×10^{-2}
HSO_4^-	$\rightleftharpoons$ H^+ +	SO_4^{2-}	1.2×10^{-2}
H_3PO_4	$\rightleftharpoons$ H^+ +	$H_2PO_4^{2-}$	7.5×10^{-3}
HCOOH	$\rightleftharpoons$ H^+ +	$HCOO^-$	1.8×10^{-4}
CH_3COOH	$\rightleftharpoons$ H^+ +	CH_3COO^-	1.8×10^{-5}
$HC_2O_4^-$	$\rightleftharpoons$ H^+ +	$C_2O_4^{2-}$	4.9×10^{-5}
H_2CO_3	$\rightleftharpoons$ H^+ +	HCO_3^-	4.5×10^{-7}
H_2S	$\rightleftharpoons$ H^+ +	HS^{2-}	9.1×10^{-8}
H_2PO_4	$\rightleftharpoons$ H^+ +	HPO_4^{2-}	6.2×10^{-8}
NH_4^+	$\rightleftharpoons$ H^+ +	NH_3	6.0×10^{-10}
HCO_3^-	$\rightleftharpoons$ H^+ +	CO_3^{2-}	5.6×10^{-11}
HPO_4^{2-}	$\rightleftharpoons$ H^+ +	PO_4^{3-}	10^{-12}
H_2O	$\rightleftharpoons$ H^+ +	OH^-	1.8×10^{-16}
NH_3	$\rightleftharpoons$ H^+ +	NH_2^-	small

These solvated protons—which can be termed the "hydrogen ions" of the solution—have evidently lost the reactivity expected of the bare proton. Further interaction of these solvated protons with solvent is possible to produce more or less well-defined species such as $H_5O_2^+$ and $H_9O_4^+$. However, the first step in solvation is obviously unique.

The extent to which the initial solvation of a proton occurs in water can be estimated from the enthalpy decrease for the union of a proton and a water molecule; this is of the order 200,000 to 300,000 calories per mole. (A value of 288,000 calories has been found from experimental data.) The fraction of uncombined protons in aqueous solution is given roughly by $e^{\Delta H/RT}$, and over the range of enthalpy change above will vary from 10^{-145} to 10^{-217}, a fraction so small as to be meaningless. (Compare with the 10^{24} molecules per gram molecular weight!)

The hydrated proton, H_3O^+, is called the *oxonium ion*, or sometimes the *hydronium ion* or the *hydroxonium ion*. In this textbook we shall *for convenience* write H^+ for the proton when it is in aqueous solution, but we must always remember that in aqueous solution the proton is hydrated, and is properly called the oxonium ion (or hydronium or hydroxonium).

One notes with interest that the oxonium ion is an acid by the Brönsted definition, with water as the conjugate base:

$$H_3O^+ \rightleftharpoons H^+ + H_2O$$

As with all conjugate acid-base pairs, this represents merely the acid-base relation of oxonium ion and water. The role which this pair plays in actual reactions can be considered clearly in terms of the neutralization reaction written in the Brönsted terms of a proton transfer from the acid of the first conjugate pair to the base of the second:

$$\text{acid 1} + \text{base 2} \rightleftharpoons \text{base 1} + \text{acid 2}$$

For the familiar neutralization of a strong acid by a strong base, the corresponding proton transfer equation is $HCl + OH^- \rightleftharpoons Cl^- + HOH$, the proton transferring to the stronger base. In the same way, the use of oxonium ion-water as one conjugate acid-base pair, gives for the reaction of acids going into aqueous solution

$$HCl + H_2O \rightleftharpoons Cl^- + H_3O^+$$

or

$$HAc + H_2O \rightleftharpoons Ac^- + H_3O^+$$

Here water acts as a fairly strong base relative to the solute acids. Thus while oxonium ion is itself but insignificantly dissociated, it is the characteristic component of all aqueous acid solutions.

The ionization of the weak base, ammonia, in aqueous solution may be similarly considered as a proton transfer phenomena,

$$H_2O + NH_3 \rightleftharpoons OH^- + NH_4^+$$

The reaction is more often written $NH_4OH \rightleftharpoons NH_4^+ + OH^-$, but the extent to which ammonia exists as the hydrate in water is a matter of some uncertainty. A proton is transferred from association with base 1, OH^-, to the stronger base 2, NH_3. It will be noticed that ammonium ion is an acid in aqueous solution, and is also the acid component in acid ammonia solution, NH_3 being the base.

19.4. Ionization of Weak Acids and Bases

The ionization of a weak acid was illustrated in Section 19.1, and in Table 19.1 the ionization constants, K_i, of several weak acids were listed. Typical weak acid ionization constants range from 10^{-2} to 10^{-8}.

The ionization constants given are for the ionization of a single hydrogen ion, which may be a primary, secondary, or higher degree ionization. Generally the secondary ionization constant of a polybasic (or polyprotic) oxy-acid is 10^{-5} smaller than the primary, and the tertiary smaller by a like factor than the secondary (namely, the constants for H_3PO_4, $H_2PO_4^-$, and HPO_4^{2-}). Similar factors for polybasic acids other than oxy-acids range from 10^{-3} to 10^{-8}. Thus only the primary ionization need be considered in calculating the hydrogen ion concentration in an aqueous solution of a polybasic acid, as the secondary ionization is negligibly small relative to the primary.

The properties of aqueous solutions involving substances commonly recognized as bases used to be considered separately from acids, but in terms of conjugate acid-base pairs there is no need for such a distinction. For all bases, their strength is indicated by the conjugate acid strength defined by acid ionization constants. Thus a weak base corresponds to a strong conjugate acid, and a strong base to a weak acid in an inverse relationship.

Strengths of bases in aqueous solution are often characterized by the hydroxyl ion concentrations of their solutions, corresponding to the limited concept of bases as agents for producing hydroxyl ions in water. In many cases hydroxyl ions are a direct result of dissociation if the solute contains hydroxyl groups, as for the alkali metal hydroxides KOH and NaOH:

$$NaOH \longrightarrow Na^+ + OH^-$$

The alkali metal ions are neutral with respect to accepting or donating protons in aqueous solution, and their concentrations are therefore equal to the quantity of solid added per liter of solution. The hydroxyl ion, however, by the reaction $OH^- + H^+ \longrightarrow H_2O$, has strong proton affinity and is a strong base in the Brönsted sense. The ultimate concentration of hydroxyl ion will therefore be affected by presence of other sources of and competitors for protons.

A second characteristic source of hydroxyl ion in aqueous solution is from the solvent, as indicated by the reaction

$$B + H_2O \longrightarrow BH^+ + OH^-$$

where B represents such species as NH_3, CH_3NH_2, $C_6H_5NH_2$. The strengths of such bases have often been characterized by the values of basic dissociation constants, K_b, defined by

$$K_b = \frac{[BH^+][OH^-]}{[B]} \tag{19.7}$$

Values of K_b such as those listed in Table 19.2 are convenient for calculating concentrations of hydroxyl ion, but it can readily be seen that there is nothing new or independent of acid ionization constants added by this further definition of basic constants. This results from the species BH^+ and B being a conjugate acid-base pair with the acidity constant K_a given by

$$K_a = \frac{[B][H^+]}{[BH^+]} \qquad (19.8)$$

On comparing the expressions for K_a and K_b, one sees that

$$K_a K_b = [H^+][OH^-] \qquad (19.9)$$

The product $[H^+][OH^-]$ is essentially a constant characteristic of solvent water at the particular temperature (to be discussed in the next section). If this constant product is denoted by $K_w = [H^+][OH^-]$, K_b can be calculated from K_a by the relation

$$K_b = \frac{K_w}{K_a} \qquad (19.10)$$

which shows the inverse relationship between the acid and base dissociation constants of a conjugate pair.

TABLE 19.2.   *Ionization Constants of Bases in Aqueous Solution at 25°C.*

Base	K_b
CH_3NH_2	4.0×10^{-4}
$C_2H_5NH_2$	5.6×10^{-4}
$(CH_3)_2NH$	7.4×10^{-4}
NH_3	1.8×10^{-5} *
$(CH_3)_3N$	7.4×10^{-5}
NH_2NH_2	3×10^{-6}
$Pb(OH)_2$	3×10^{-8} †
$Zn(OH)_2$	1.5×10^{-9} †
$C_6H_5NH_2$	4.6×10^{-10}
$Be(OH)_2$	5×10^{-11} †

* NH_3 value from Yost and Russell, *Systematic Inorganic Chemistry*, p. 135, quoting Everett and Wynne-Jones, *Proc. Roy. Soc.*, London, *A* **169**: 190 (1938). This value for ammonia is based on the total concentration of nonionized ammonia in solution, whether or not any is actually hydrated in aqueous solution by the reaction $NH_3 + HOH \rightleftharpoons NH_4OH$. There is no certain evidence that NH_4OH exists in aqueous solution; from our knowledge of bond strengths, a complex of the form NH_3—H_2O cannot be expected to be very stable.

† Constant for the ionization of one hydroxyl ion (for example, $Pb(OH)_2 \rightleftharpoons PbOH^+ + OH^-$).

19.5. The Ion Product Constant of Water, K_w

The equation for the dissociation of water as a Brönsted acid to yield a proton and the hydroxyl ion was given in Table 19.1, together with the value for the dissociation constant at 25°C:

$$K_a = \frac{[H^+][OH^-]}{[H_2O]} = 1.8 \times 10^{-16} \qquad (19.11)$$

Obviously, the amount of water dissociating relative to the amount present is very small. The concentration of undissociated water, [HOH], is therefore essentially constant for a given temperature, and may be combined with the dissociation constant to give a new constant, called the *ion product constant* for water, K_w:

$$K_w = K_a[H_2O] = [H^+][OH^-] \qquad (19.12)$$

The variation of the ion product constant for water over a range of temperatures may be seen by study of Table 19.3.

TABLE 19.3. *Values for the Ion Product Constant of Water for Various Temperatures.*

Temperature (°C)	K_w
0	1.14×10^{-15}
5	2.92×10^{-15}
15	4.51×10^{-15}
20	6.81×10^{-15}
25	1.01×10^{-14}
40	2.92×10^{-14}
60	9.61×10^{-14}
100	5.50×10^{-13}

The dissociation of water increases rapidly with increasing temperature; at the boiling point, the constant is almost 500 fold the value at the freezing point. For most calculations for room temperature, it is satisfactory to take the value of $K_w = 10^{-14}$.

In pure water the dissociation

$$H_2O \rightleftharpoons H^+ + OH^-$$

produces equal quantities of hydrogen and hydroxyl ions; hence $[H^+] = [OH^-]$, and from Eq. 19.12 one has $[H^+]^2 = 10^{-14}$ (at room temperature), from which

$$[\text{H}^+] = 10^{-7} \text{ moles/liter}$$
$$[\text{OH}^-] = 10^{-7} \text{ moles/liter}$$

At the boiling point the concentration of hydrogen ion would be

$$[\text{H}^+] = \sqrt{K_w} = \sqrt{5.5 \times 10^{-13}} = 7.4 \times 10^{-7} \text{ moles/liter}$$

To satisfy the thermodynamic requirements for the equilibrium, Eq. 19.12 must be valid for water in all dilute aqueous solutions. (In concentrated solutions adjustment must be made for the differing dependence of the free energy of the ions and molecules upon the ionic environment.) Thus the hydrogen and hydroxyl ion concentrations are not independent of one another even when there are other sources of either one than from the ionization of water, but are related by Eq. 19.12:

$$[\text{H}^+] = \frac{K_w}{[\text{OH}^-]}; \qquad [\text{OH}^-] = \frac{K_w}{[\text{H}^+]} \qquad (19.13)$$

At room temperature in an acid solution where $[\text{H}^+] = 10^{-2}$, the concentration of hydroxyl ion is therefore

$$[\text{OH}^-] = \frac{10^{-14}}{10^{-2}} = 10^{-12} \text{ moles/liter}$$

Alkaline solutions (with hydrogen ion concentration less than that of water; $[\text{H}^+] < 10^{-7}$) can be specified in terms of their hydrogen ion concentrations. For example, a solution containing $[\text{OH}^-] = 10^{-4}$ will at room temperature have hydrogen ion concentration,

$$[\text{H}^+] = \frac{10^{-14}}{10^{-4}} = 10^{-10}$$

These examples make evident an important consideration in aqueous solution equilibria in that $[\text{H}^+]$ and $[\text{OH}^-]$ may not both be greater than 10^{-7}, and—except near the neutral point, where $[\text{H}^+] = [\text{OH}^-] = 10^{-7}$—that one is small compared to the other.

19.6. The Expression of Acid Strength as *p*H

The usefulness of expressing acid or alkaline strength in aqueous solutions by hydrogen ion concentrations is increased by the introduction of the concept of *p*H, defined by

$$p\text{H} = -\log [\text{H}^+] \qquad (19.14)$$

The use of a *p*H scale to specify $[\text{H}^+]$ has the advantage that the wide range of concentrations encountered are expressed within a convenient range of units, through the logarithmic relation. This relation also makes equal *ratios* of concentrations correspond to the same change of pH, as an increase of pH by one unit represents a decrease in $[H^+]$ by a factor ten; and pH is the negative power of ten which expresses $[H^+]$.

ILLUSTRATION

(a) The pH of a solution is 6.231. Calculate $[H^+]$.

$$\log [H^+] = -pH = -6.231$$
$$= -7 + 0.769$$
$$[H^+] = 5.86 \times 10^{-7}$$

(b) Calculate $[H^+]$ and pH for a solution at 25°C with $[OH^-] = 6.45 \times 10^{-9}$ moles/liter.

$$[H^+] = \frac{10^{-14}}{6.45 \times 10^{-9}} = 1.55 \times 10^{-6} \text{ moles/liter}$$

$$pH = -\log 1.55 \times 10^{-6} = 6 - \log 1.55$$
$$= 5.809$$

An important method of determining pH is by use of EMF measurements of cells in which hydrogen ions in solution take part in one of the electrode reactions, or one half-cell. As shown in Chapter 17, $\log [H^+]$ varies linearly with the EMF in such cases. Thus for the quinhydrone electrode in the approximation in which activities are replaced by concentration,

$$pH = -\log [H^+] = -\frac{\varepsilon + 0.458}{0.0592}$$

where ε is the electrode potential.

Other concentrations than that of hydrogen ion can also be expressed in powers of ten and by corresponding "p" values, with the same conveniences of a small range of numbers and equal changes of "p" values corresponding to equal changes in the ratio of concentrations. Equilibrium constants—as, for example, ionization constants, K_i—also vary over many powers of ten and are often expressed in terms of pK, defined by

$$pK = -\log K$$

ILLUSTRATION

The acidity constant of acetic acid in water at 25°C is 1.75×10^{-5}. Calculate pK.

$$pK = -\log 1.75 \times 10^{-5} = 5 - \log 1.75$$
$$= 4.76$$

19.7. Hydrolysis

The salt of a weak acid or a weak base when dissolved in water establishes a chemical equilibrium with the water itself. Such reactions are called *hydrolysis reactions*, and may be considered in terms of proton transfer and conjugate acid-base pairs, in which one of the pairs will always involve water, acting either as an acid or as a base.

For example, a salt such as sodium acetate dissolves in water as sodium and acetate ions. Sodium ion undergoes no reaction other than hydration with adjacent water molecules, but acetate ion is a base in the Brönsted sense, and can accept a proton from a water molecule:

$$\text{acid 1} + \text{base 2} \rightleftharpoons \text{base 1} + \text{acid 2}$$

$$\text{HOH} + \text{Ac}^- \rightleftharpoons \text{OH}^- + \text{HAc}$$

The equilibrium constant for the reaction is

$$K = \frac{[\text{OH}^-][\text{HAc}]}{[\text{H}_2\text{O}][\text{Ac}^-]} \tag{19.15}$$

Since the concentration of water is essentially constant, it is combined with the equilibrium constant, the product being the hydrolysis constant

$$K_H = K[\text{H}_2\text{O}] = \frac{[\text{OH}^-][\text{HAc}]}{[\text{Ac}^-]} \tag{19.16}$$

This hydrolysis constant is readily calculated from the ionization constant of acetic acid. From Eq. 19.1,

$$\frac{[\text{HAc}]}{[\text{Ac}^-]} = \frac{[\text{H}^+]}{K_i}$$

whence

$$K_H = \frac{[\text{H}^+][\text{OH}^-]}{K_i}$$

Since $[\text{H}^+][\text{OH}^-] = K_w$ (Eq. 19.12) in any aqueous solution,

$$K_H = \frac{K_w}{K_i} \tag{19.17}$$

Substituting values for K_w and K_i, the hydrolysis constant for sodium acetate at 25°C is

$$K_H = \frac{10^{-14}}{1.8 \times 10^{-5}} = 5.5 \times 10^{-10}$$

From the magnitude of the constant it is evident that only a small fraction of the acetate ions present are hydrolyzed. (A contrary impression is frequently held erroneously by many students.)

If the concentration of the sodium acetate is C moles/liter and the fraction hydrolyzed is α, then

$$[OH^-] = \alpha C$$
$$[HAc] = \alpha C$$
$$[Ac^-] = (1 - \alpha)C$$

Substitution in Eq. 19.16 gives

$$K_H = \frac{\alpha^2 C}{1 - \alpha}$$

and if $\alpha \ll 1$,

$$K_H = \alpha^2 C \qquad \alpha = \sqrt{\frac{K_H}{C}} = \sqrt{\frac{K_w}{K_i C}} \qquad (19.18)$$

For 0.01 molar sodium acetate, the degree of hydrolysis is

$$\alpha = \sqrt{\frac{10^{-14}}{1.8 \times 10^{-5} \times 10^{-2}}} = 2.3 \times 10^{-4}$$

or 0.023% and the concentration of hydroxyl is

$$[OH^-] = \alpha C = 2.3 \times 10^{-4} \times 10^{-2} = 2.3 \times 10^{-6}$$

From this the concentration of hydrogen ion is

$$[H^+] = \frac{10^{-14}}{2.3 \times 10^{-6}} = 4.3 \times 10^{-9}$$

or

$$pH \doteq -\log 4.3 \times 10^{-9} = 9 - 0.37 = 8.63$$

While the degree of hydrolysis is indeed small, the solution is at the same time definitely alkaline. The alkalinity is expressed by the pH value 8.63 as compared with $pH = 7.0$ for neutral solutions. The concentration of OH^- is correspondingly larger by a factor $(2.3 \times 10^{-6})/10^{-7} = 23$.

The hydrolysis of the salt of a weak base and strong acid is similar, as illustrated by the hydrolysis of ammonium chloride. In this case the reaction of chloride ion with solvent molecules need not be considered, but for ammonium ion there is the reaction

$$NH_4^+ + H_2O \rightleftharpoons NH_3 + H_3O^+$$

involving the transfer of a proton from the acid NH_4^+ to the base H_2O. The equilibrium constant is

$$K = \frac{[NH_3][H_3O^+]}{[NH_4^+][H_2O]}$$

This is commonly expressed as a hydrolysis constant by writing H^+ for H_3O^+, and combining $[H_2O]$ with the constant K, with the result

$$K_H = \frac{[NH_3][H^+]}{[NH_4^+]} \qquad (19.19)$$

By substituting for the ratio $[NH_3]/[NH_4^+]$ from the expression for the ionization constant for ammonium hydroxide, an equation analogous to Eq. 19.18 is obtained:

$$K_H = \frac{K_w}{K_i} = \frac{[NH_3][H^+]}{[NH_4^+]} \qquad (19.20)$$

It is obvious that the hydrolysis constant again will be small, and that calculations similar to previous calculations are possible using this expression. Two acid-base equilibria must be considered for the hydrolysis of a salt of a weak acid and a weak base, because both ions react with the solvent. If the salt is symbolized by the ions BH^+ and A^-, where BH^+ could represent ammonium ion and A^- acetate ion, for example, the acid-base equilibria are

$$BH^+ + H_2O \rightleftharpoons B + H_3O^+$$
$$H_2O + A^- \rightleftharpoons OH^- + HA$$

The relative extent to which these two reactions take place determines the acidity and amount of neutral nonionized products HA and B. These are of course governed by the acid ionization constants

$$K_{BH^+} = \frac{[H^+][B]}{[BH^+]}$$

$$K_{HA} = \frac{[H^+][A^-]}{[HA]}$$

The ratio of these acidity constants is often called the hydrolysis constant K_H and is given by

$$K_H = \frac{[HA][B]}{[A^-][BH^+]} = \frac{K_{BH^+}}{K_{HA}} \qquad (19.21)$$

Evidently K_H can be large and the nonionized products HA and B present in high concentration if K_{HA} is small and K_{BH^+} large. The first condition is met if HA is a weak acid; the second if B is a weak base, and consequently BH^+ a strong acid. Rather than using Eq. 19.21, involving the ionization constant of the strong acid K_{BH^+}, the small basic ionization constant

$$K_B = \frac{[BH^+][OH^-]}{[B]} = \frac{K_w}{K_{BH^+}} \qquad (19.22)$$

is customarily used in the hydrolysis expression (compare with Eq. 19.10), and hence

$$K_\mathrm{H} = \frac{K_w}{K_\mathrm{B}K_\mathrm{HA}} \qquad (19.23)$$

The overall equilibrium for the hydrolysis for this weak acid–weak base salt may be written

$$\mathrm{BH^+ + A^- + H_2O \rightleftharpoons B(HOH) + HA}$$

or

$$\mathrm{BH^+ + A^- + H_2O \rightleftharpoons B + HA + H^+ + OH^-}$$

If K_B and K_HA are of the same order of magnitude, $[\mathrm{H^+}] \cong [\mathrm{OH^-}] \cong \sqrt{K_w}$ (since the equilibrium $\mathrm{H^+ + OH^- \rightleftharpoons H_2O}$ still governs). The hydrolysis is now seen to be essentially a proton transfer from the strong acid, $\mathrm{BH^+}$, to the strong base, $\mathrm{A^-}$. Write the degree of hydrolysis as α, and represent the original salt concentration by C; then $[\mathrm{B}] = [\mathrm{HA}] = \alpha C$, and $[\mathrm{BH^+}] = [\mathrm{A^-}] = C(1 - \alpha)$. Substitution of these values in Eq. 19.21 gives

$$K_\mathrm{H} = \frac{\alpha^2}{(1-\alpha)^2} = \frac{K_\mathrm{BH^+}}{K_\mathrm{HA}}$$

$$\alpha = \frac{\sqrt{K_\mathrm{BH^+}/K_\mathrm{HA}}}{1 + \sqrt{K_\mathrm{BH^+}/K_\mathrm{HA}}} \qquad (19.24)$$

If we also use the relation of Eq. 19.23, $K_\mathrm{H} = K_w/K_\mathrm{B}K_\mathrm{HA}$, then

$$\alpha = \frac{\sqrt{K_w/K_\mathrm{HA}K_\mathrm{B}}}{1 + \sqrt{K_w/K_\mathrm{HA}K_\mathrm{B}}} \qquad (19.25)$$

Thus the degree of hydrolysis for weak acid–weak base salts is independent of concentration and depends only upon the acidic and basic ionization constants. When these are of the order of 10^{-4} (as with methyl ammonium formate—Tables 19.1 and 19.2), $\alpha \cong 10^{-3}$; if of order 10^{-5} (ammonium acetate), $\alpha \cong 10^{-2}$; of order 10^{-7} (hydrazine bicarbonate), $\alpha \cong 0.5$; of order 10^{-10} $[(\mathrm{C_6H_5NH_3})_2\mathrm{CO_3}]$, $\alpha \cong 0.999$.

19.8. Solution of Ionic Equilibrium Problems

Situations are often met in which two or more ionic equilibria must be considered; examples are found in acid-base titrations, hydrolysis or solvolysis, or in buffer solutions. Although the principles used in determining the concentrations of the various species in solution are straightforward, the presence of a number of different ions and molecules results in mathematics involving several variables. If the equations expressing the principles are not developed logically and systematically, considerable confusion results. This is avoided by first writing down all the equations which must be satisfied and then simplifying them by suitable approximations.

The first consideration is to list all the chemical equilibria involved, for each of which there is a corresponding equilibrium constant expression.

Thus acid-base ionizations involve such equations as

$$HA \rightleftharpoons H^+ + A^- \qquad BH^+ \rightleftharpoons B + H^+$$

with corresponding equilibrium constants

$$K_{HA} = \frac{[H^+][A^-]}{[HA]} \qquad K_{BH^+} = \frac{[B][H^+]}{[BH^+]}$$

Solvent ionization is also to be considered—in water, for example:

$$HOH \rightleftharpoons H^+ + OH^- \qquad K_w = [H^+][OH^-]$$

The second consideration is to list conditions imposed by known concentrations and the stoichiometry of the particular situation

Thus it may be specified that a weak acid HA is added to solvent in amount C_A moles per liter. Both the neutral acid HA and anion A^- result, but if there is no other source of A^-, it must be true that

$$[HA] + [A^-] = C_A$$

If a salt MA added in amount C_s moles/liter ionizes completely, there is a further supply of A^- and the condition becomes

$$[HA] + [A^-] = C_A + C_s$$

The concentration $[M^+]$, by complete ionization $MA \longrightarrow M^+ + A^-$, is obviously $[M^+] = C_s$.

The third consideration, which is closely related to the second but is usefully given special emphasis, is the *principle of electrical neutrality*. This simply states that in ionic solutions the total quantities of positive and negative charge must be equal, as must obviously be true when all the substances from which the solution is constituted are balanced with respect to electrical charge initially.

Thus for an acid HA in water, there are ions H^+, A^-, and OH^-, the concentrations of which must satisfy

$$[H^+] = [A^-] + [OH^-]$$

Dissolving a salt MA produces M^+ ions as well, and the solution is electrically neutral only if

$$[M^+] + [H^+] = [A^-] + [OH^-]$$

The principle of electrical neutrality is not only a convenient way of deducing one of the necessary conditions; it is also frequently a useful starting point in solving particular problems, as examples to follow will show.

When all conditions have been written, there should be as many equations as there are unknown quantities. If the equations are too few, either some necessary equation has been overlooked or there is insufficient information to solve the problem; if there are more equations than there are unknowns, either too much information has been required or specified, or else not all of the equations set down are independent. (This last situation is most likely to occur because stoichiometric conditions include electrical neutrality.) Effective procedures for solving the problems are best illustrated by example.

Acid and Solvent Ionization

In discussing ionization of acetic acid, $HAc \rightleftharpoons H^+ + Ac^-$, as an example of a weak acid, the ionization of water was neglected and the concentrations of H^+ and Ac^- set equal: $[H^+] = [Ac^-]$. This cannot be exactly true because of the presence of hydroxyl ion from the ionization of water, most easily noted by considering the requirement of electrical neutrality:

$$[H^+] = [Ac^-] + [OH^-] \qquad \text{(electrical neutrality)}$$

The other equations are

$$\left. \begin{aligned} \frac{[H^+][Ac^-]}{[HAc]} &= K_A = 1.8 \times 10^{-5} \\ [H^+][OH^-] &= K_w = 1 \quad \times 10^{-14} \end{aligned} \right\} \qquad \text{(equilibria)}$$

and for C_A moles/liter of acetic acid added:

$$[HAc] + [Ac^-] = C_A \qquad \text{(stoichiometry)}$$

Any of the four unknown variables—$[H^+]$, $[HAc]$, $[Ac^-]$, or $[OH^-]$—may be determined from the solution of these four simultaneous equations.

Thus one can solve for $[H^+]$ and pH (within the approximation of setting activity coefficients equal to unity):

$$[Ac^-] = [H^+] + \frac{K_w}{[H^+]}$$

from electrical neutrality and K_w, and

$$[HAc] = C_A - [Ac^-] = C_A - [H^+] - \frac{K_w}{[H^+]}$$

Substitution in K_A gives

$$[H^+] \cdot \frac{[H^+] + \dfrac{K_w}{[H^+]}}{C_A - [H^+] - \dfrac{K_w}{[H^+]}} = K_A$$

This can be rearranged as a cubic equation in $[H^+]$, which can be solved with sufficient effort. Usually such difficult solutions can be avoided by considering the relative magnitudes of the quantities involved. In this and many cases, the key to justifiable approximation is that $K_w = 10^{-14}$ and $[H^+]$ and $[OH^-]$ cannot both be larger than 10^{-7}. For acid solutions, $[OH^-]\,(= K_w/[H^+])$ will in fact be much less than $[H^+]$ in most cases, and to a sufficient approximation

$$\frac{[H^+]^2}{C_A - [H^+]} = K_A$$

This is the equation used in Section 19.1 and is obviously adequate if $[H^+]$ is greater than 10^{-6}, as then $[OH^-]$ is less than 10^{-8} (less than 1% of $[H^+]$). The further approximation of neglecting $[H^+]$ in comparison with C_A is often justified and gives the still simpler equation: $[H^+]^2 = K_A C_A$.

Neutralization of HCl by Ammonia

A solution, C_A molar in HCl, is titrated by adding ammonia. The titration curve giving the pH of the solution for increasing amounts (x) of ammonia is to be calculated, neglecting changes in C_A because of increased volume of solution. There are five species present: $[H^+]$, $[Cl^-]$, $[NH_4^+]$, $[NH_3]$, and $[OH^-]$. The five equations are

$$\left.\begin{aligned} \frac{[H^+][NH_3]}{[NH_4^+]} &= K = 6 \times 10^{-10} \\[4pt] [H^+][OH^-] &= K_w = 10^{-14} \end{aligned}\right\} \qquad \text{(equilibria)}$$

$$\left.\begin{aligned} [Cl^-] &= C_A \\ [NH_4^+] + [NH_3] &= x \end{aligned}\right\} \qquad \text{(stoichiometry)}$$

$$[H^+] + [NH_4^+] = [Cl^-] + [OH^-] \qquad \text{(electrical neutrality)}$$

By solving the last four equations for $[NH_4^+]$ and $[NH_3]$ in terms of $[H^+]$ and known quantities, we obtain

$$[NH_4^+] = C_A + \frac{K_w}{[H^+]} - [H^+]$$

$$[NH_3] = x - \left(C_A + \frac{K_w}{[H^+]} - [H^+]\right)$$

These may be substituted in the first equation for the ammonia ionization to give

$$[H^+] \cdot \frac{x - \left(C_A + \frac{K_w}{[H^+]} - [H^+]\right)}{C_A + \frac{K_w}{[H^+]} - [H^+]} = K$$

This equation can be solved for $[H^+]$ as a cubic in x, but a simpler approach is to solve for x in terms of $[H^+]$:

$$x = \left(C_A + \frac{K_w}{[H^+]} - [H^+]\right)\left(1 + \frac{K}{[H^+]}\right)$$

Solutions give x for any pH, but simpler approximations are adequate whenever the pH is not near 7. Thus for acid solutions with pH less than 6, $K_w/[H^+]$ is less than 1% of $[H^+]$ and $K/[H^+]$ is usually much less than 1, giving

$$x \cong C_A - [H^+]$$

for acid solutions. For alkaline solutions with pH greater than 8, $[H^+]$ is negligible in comparison with $K_w/[H^+]$; hence

$$x \cong \left(C_A + \frac{K_w}{[H^+]}\right)\left(1 + \frac{K}{[H^+]}\right)$$

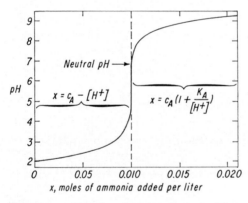

Fig. 19.1. *Titration of 0.01 molar hydrochloric acid with ammonia; pH versus moles of ammonia added per liter.*

for alkaline solutions. Often C_A is large enough that $K_w/[H^+]$ is much less than C_A for any pH of interest, in which case $x \cong C_A[1 - (K/H^-)]$ is an adequate approximation.

The two approximations both fail near $pH = 7$ but the range $pH = 6$ to $pH = 8$ is usually covered in a very small range of x, this being near the end point. For neutralization, $[H^+] = [OH^-] = 10^{-7}$, whence $x = C_A[1 + (K/[H^+])]$; and for ammonia, $K/[H^+]$ then equals $6 \times 10^{-10}/10^{-7} = 0.006$, so $x \cong C_A$ within less than 1%.

With approximation of this kind, titration curves of pH for added base x can easily be constructed. Figure 19.1 gives the titration curve for a $0.01M$ HCl solution. The curves for the titration of weak acid with base can be similarly deduced, and the results for 0.01M acetic acid titrated with NaOH and with ammonia are shown in Fig. 19.2.

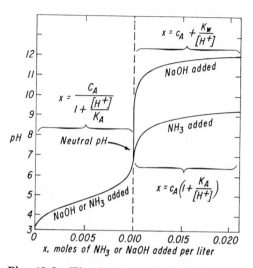

Fig. 19.2. *Titration of acetic acid with NH_3 or NaOH and with ammonia; pH versus moles of base added per liter. (Acid concentration 0.01 molar.)*

19.9. Buffer Solutions

A buffer solution is one in which *both* the acid and base members of a conjugate acid-base pair are present in such high concentration that they control the hydrogen ion concentration, and consequently the hydroxyl ion concentration. This control is evident through consideration of the pair acetic acid–acetate ion:

$$\text{HAc} \rightleftharpoons \text{H}^+ + \text{Ac}^-$$

When [HAc] and [Ac$^-$] are both large relative to [H$^+$], adding H$^+$ shifts the equilibrium to the left in accordance with the thermodynamic requirements for equilibrium, increasing the concentration of HAc and decreasing that of Ac$^-$ and H$^+$. Similarly, if hydrogen ion is removed from the solution, for example by the addition of hydroxyl ion (H$^+$ + OH$^- \rightleftharpoons$ H$_2$O), the equilibrium will shift to the right, decreasing the concentration of HAc and increasing that of Ac$^-$ and H$^+$.

The buffer action is effective only if both HAc and Ac$^-$ are present in considerable amount. Simply adding acetic acid to water does not make both concentrations appreciable, for in that case [Ac$^-$] $\cong$ [H$^+$], which is controlled by the ionization constant for acetic acid. The concentration of acetate ion can be increased by the addition of sodium acetate to the solution, and the buffering action against H$^+$ greatly improved. Alternatively, the buffer could be prepared by partially neutralizing a solution of acetic acid with sodium hydroxide.

At equilibrium the ion concentrations in the buffered solution must satisfy the equilibrium constant expression of Eq. 19.1,

$$K_i = \frac{[\text{H}^+][\text{Ac}^-]}{[\text{HAc}]}$$

By rearrangement,

$$[\text{H}^+] = K_i \frac{[\text{HAc}]}{[\text{Ac}^-]} = K_i R \qquad (19.26)$$

whence it is seen that if sufficient sodium acetate is added to an acetic acid solution to make the ratio $R = 1$, $[\text{H}^+] = K_i = 1.8 \times 10^{-5}$ moles/liter, regardless of the actual concentration of acetic acid. (Compare with $[\text{H}^+] = 4.3 \times 10^{-4}$ moles/liter for $0.01M$ acetic acid solution calculated in Section 19.1, and $[\text{H}^+] = 1.8 \times 10^{-6}$ moles/liter for a solution of $0.01M$ acetic acid–0.1 molar sodium acetate.)

The buffering action can be demonstrated by considering a solution containing C_A moles/liter of acetic acid and C_s moles/liter of sodium acetate. From the stoichiometry

$$[\text{HAc}] + [\text{Ac}^-] = C_A + C_s$$
$$[\text{Na}^+] = C_s$$

and electrical neutrality requires that

$$[\text{Na}^+] + [\text{H}^+] = [\text{Ac}^-] + [\text{OH}^-]$$

Since the solution is acid, $[\text{OH}^-]$ can be neglected with the result that $[\text{Ac}^-] = C_s + [\text{H}^+]$ and

$$[\text{HAc}] = C_A + C_s - [\text{Ac}^-] = C_A - [\text{H}^+]$$

Hence, substituting in Eq. 19.26, the hydrogen ion concentration is initially

$$[\text{H}^+] = K_i \frac{C_A - [\text{H}^+]}{C_s + [\text{H}^+]} \cong K_i \frac{C_A}{C_s}$$

if $[\text{H}^+] \ll C_A$ and C_s.

Now consider adding a small amount (x moles/liter) of a strong base such as NaOH. The new condition is

$$[\text{Na}^+] = C_s + x$$

and this gives

$$[\text{H}^+] = K_i \frac{C_A - [\text{H}^+] - x}{C_s + [\text{H}^+] + x} \cong K_i \frac{C_A - x}{C_s + x}$$

If x is small compared with C_A and C_s, the value of $[H^+]$ will be little changed. Thus if $C_A = C_s = 1.0$ moles/liter and $x = 0.018$ (corresponding to 1000 times as much hydroxyl ion as the initial hydrogen ion concentration), the new value of $[H^+]$ is

$$[H^+] = K_i \frac{1 - 0.018}{1 + 0.018} = 0.96 K_i$$

The decrease in hydrogen ion concentration is less than 4% and the change in pH only 0.02 units, even though 1000 times the initial concentration of hydrogen ion has been neutralized by the added hydroxyl ion. Essentially, the buffer provides that the added amount x of hydroxyl has been neutralized by acetic acid, $[HAc]$ changing from C_A to $C_A - x$, and consequently $[Ac^-]$ increasing from C_s to $C_s + x$.

If x moles of a strong acid such as HCl are added, one has

$$[H^+] + [Na^+] = [Ac^-] + [OH^-] + [Cl^-]$$

Since $[Cl^-] = x$ and $[OH^-]$ can be neglected,

$$[Ac^-] = C_s + [H^+] - x$$

and hence

$$[HAc] = C_A - [H^+] + x$$

The hydrogen ion concentration is then

$$[H^+] = K_i \frac{C_A - [H^+] + x}{C_s + [H^+] - x} \cong K_i \frac{C_A + x}{C_s - x}$$

For $C_A = C_s = 1.0$ moles/liter and $x = 0.18$ moles/liter, $[H^+] = 1.04 K_i$. The value of $[H^+]$ thus increases by less than 4% on adding 1000 times the original amount of $[H^+]$, because the added quantity of hydrogen ion reacts with acetate ion to form acetic acid, both of which are present in quantities much larger than that of the acid added.

The value of buffer solutions in chemistry is thus obvious. Nature also uses them extensively. For example, human blood is heavily buffered by the pairs H_2CO_3–HCO_3^-, and $H_2PO_4^-$–HPO_4^{2-}, which maintain the pH at approximately 7.35 in normally healthy persons. In fact, medical diagnosis makes use of blood pH measurements. (In diabetic coma, for example, blood pH may fall as low as 6.82.) Other body fluids have their pH similarly under control by buffers.

19.10. Indicators

The use of acid-base indicators to sense the point of neutralization of an acid by a base, or the contrary, is familiar; phenolphthalein and litmus are common examples. (Indicators may also be used in oxidation-reduction titrations, but such oxidemetric indicators will not be discussed here.) Essentially, an indicator is an acid-base pair added in such low concentration to a solution that it has no effect on the solution, but which undergoes a change in color in the transition between its acidic and basic forms. For a particular indicator, this change will occur at a character-istic pH. Different useful indicators have been found which show significant changes at sufficiently different values of pH to cover a wide range of solution acidities. The color change is generally not perfectly sharp, but gradual over a range of pH values. Color in a solution contain-ing indicator molecules is due to absorption of visible light in parts of the spectrum by electronic energy changes. The change in the electronic structure of the indicator molecule or ion associated with the gain or loss of a proton, sufficiently alters the energy absorption to produce the color change observed. The hydrogen ion concentration at which an acid-base indicator undergoes a color change can be determined by measuring the EMF of a hydrogen electrode. (Similarly the oxidation potential at which an oxidation-reduction indicator undergoes a color change can be measured by an inert platinum electrode in the solution.)

Representing the indicator pair by HIn-In$^-$, its equilibrium reaction is

$$\underset{\text{(color A)}}{HIn} \;\rightleftharpoons\; H^+ + \underset{\text{(color B)}}{In^-}$$

The ionization constant is

$$K_{Ind} = \frac{[H^+][In^-]}{[HIn]} \tag{19.27}$$

whence

$$[H^+] = K_{Ind} \frac{[HIn]}{[In^-]} \tag{19.28}$$

(The similarity of indicators to buffers is obvious; the difference is that buffers are present in such large concentrations that they control the solution, while indicators are present in such small concentration that they have no effect on the solution. Good indicators absorb sufficiently to give detectable color and color changes for concentrations of order 10^{-5} moles/liter.) The ratio $[HIn]/[In^-]$ must be reasonable; hence neither $[HIn]$ or $[In^-]$ can be too small, and the range of $[H^+]$ which can be measured by a given indicator is necessarily limited. When the ratio is unity ($[HIn] = [In^-]$), the hydrogen ion concentration $[H^+] = K_{Ind}$. The indicator constant thus provides a means for determining the hydrogen ion concentration at which the indicator color change occurs.

A series of indicators, so well chosen to cover the entire range of pH that it is almost "standard," is given in Table 19.4.

TABLE 19.4.   *Acid-Base Indicators.*

Indicator	K_{Ind} at 25°C	pH of Color Transition Range at 25°C	Color Acidic	Color Basic
Picric acid	1.6×10^{-1}	0.0– 1.3	Clear	Yellow
o-Cresol red		0.2– 1.8	Red	Yellow
Thymol blue	3.2×10^{-2}	1.2– 2.8	Red	Yellow
Bromphenol blue	1.05×10^{-4}	3.0– 4.6	Yellow	Blue
Methyl orange	2.0×10^{-4}	3.1– 4.4	Red	Yellow-orange
Methyl red	1×10^{-5}	4.4– 6.3	Red	Yellow
Bromcresol green	2.14×10^{-5}	3.8– 5.4	Yellow	Blue
Litmus		5.0– 8.0	Red	Blue
Bromcresol purple	6×10^{-7}	5.4– 7.0	Yellow	Purple
Bromthymol blue	1.0×10^{-7}	6.0– 7.6	Yellow	Blue
Phenol red	2×10^{-8}	7.2– 8.8		
o-Cresol red	5.0×10^{-9}	7.2– 8.8	Yellow	Red
Phenolphthalein	2.0×10^{-10}	8.3–10.0	Colorless	Red
Alizarine yellow R		10.1–12.1	Yellow	Red
Nitramine		11.0–13.0	Yellow	Orange-brown
Indigo disulfonate		11.6–14.0	Blue	Yellow

As with all matters, there are complicating factors in the choice of good indicators. In addition to the necessary marked color change within a desired pH range, one must consider "salt error" and "protein error," which, for example, make litmus unsatisfactory as an indicator for colorimetric determination of pH. References listed at the end of the chapter discuss these factors in detail.

19.11. Solubility Product Constant

When a sparingly soluble salt is in saturated aqueous solution there will be equilibrium between the solid salt and its ions in solution. For example, with silver chloride,

$$AgCl(s) \rightleftharpoons Ag^+ + Cl^-$$

Applying the usual conditions for equilibrium yields the equilibrium constant

$$K'_{eq} = \frac{a_{Ag} \times a_{Cl^-}}{a_{AgCl}}$$

which, since the activity of the crystalline solid is constant, can be replaced by

$$K_{eq} = a_{Ag^+} \times a_{Cl^-} \qquad (19.29)$$

In dilute solutions, which is the case with sparingly soluble salts, the activity approaches the concentration, and Eq. 19.29 is approximated by

$$K_{SP} = [Ag^+][Cl^-] \qquad (19.30)$$

The constant is the *solubility product constant;* the solubility product principle is the generalization of the above expression,

$$K_{SP} = [A^{n+}]^m[B^{m-}]^n \qquad (19.31)$$

TABLE 19.5.   *Values of the Solubility Product Constant at 25°C for Several Substances.*

Substance	K_{SP}	
AgBr	7.7×10^{-13}	
AgCl	1.6×10^{-10}	
Ag_2CrO_4	$9 \ \times 10^{-12}$	
$BaCO_3$	8.1×10^{-9}	
$BaSO_4$	1.1×10^{-10}	
$CaCO_3$	8.7×10^{-9}	
CoS	$3 \ \times 10^{-26}$	(18°C)
CuS	8.5×10^{-45}	(18°C)
FeS	3.7×10^{-19}	(18°C)
$Fe(OH)_3$	1.1×10^{-36}	(18°C)
Hg_2Cl_2	$[Hg_2^{2+}][Cl^-]^2 = 2.0 \times 10^{-18}$	
HgS	about 10^{-53}	
$PbCl_2$	1.7×10^{-5}	
$PbSO_4$	2.3×10^{-8}	
PbS	4.2×10^{-28}	
$SrCO_3$	1.6×10^{-9}	
TlCl	2.2×10^{-4}	
ZnS	1.2×10^{-23}	(18°C)

for the sparingly soluble compound A_mB_n, which follows from the thermodynamic considerations of the equilibrium

$$A_mB_n \rightleftharpoons mA^{n+} + nB^{m-}$$

Values for the solubility product constant of several substances are given in Table 19.5.

19.12. Calculation of Solubility from the Solubility Product Constant

If s is the solubility of a sparingly soluble salt AB in moles/liter, then $[A^+] = [B^-] = S$ and $K_{SP} = S \cdot S$, or $S = \sqrt{K_{SP}}$ for a uniunivalent salt. For polyionic salts represented by A_mB_n, which ionize by the reaction $A_mB_n \longrightarrow mA^{n+} + nB^{m-}$, $[A^{n+}] = mS$ and $[B^{m-}] = nS$, if S is the solubility. Then

$$K_{SP} = [A^{n+}]^m[B^{m-}]^n = (mS)^m(nS)^n = m^mn^nS^{m+n}$$

which may be solved to determine S from a known value for K_{SP}. [For Ag_2CrO_4, this becomes $K_{SP} = (2S)^2(S) = 4S^3$, and $S = (K_{SP}/4)^{1/3}$ moles/liter.]

In the presence of a common ion the solubility equilibrium will be altered, the effect of which may be calculated from the solubility product expression. This is discussed in detail in Section 16.6. This effect is of practical importance both in accomplishing the quantitative separation of one ion from a solution by precipitation, and also to a limited extent in industrial processes.

Counter to the common ion effect, which lowers the solubility of a given salt, is the *salt effect*, by which the value of the solubility product constant is increased as the ionic concentration of the solution increases; this in turn results in increased solubility of the salt. This effect, due to the lowering of the ionic activity coefficients of the slightly soluble salt, also has been thoroughly discussed in Section 16.6. It is significant in analytical work, particularly in schemes of qualitative analysis, where the addition of successive reagents may build up to a fairly highly concentrated ionic environment. In such procedures, provision is frequently made to separate the ions of interest from the extraneous ionic atmosphere resulting from reagent additions.

Precipitates of slightly soluble salts can be dissolved if the solubility product of the ions can be reduced to less than the solubility product constant. Sufficient reduction of the concentration of any one of the ions can effect this, and such reduction can be accomplished in any of several ways. In the case of a precipitate involving the hydroxyl ion or the anion of a weak acid, the addition of hydrogen ion will reduce this ion concentration. For example, the solution of precipitated FeS by reduction of $[S^{2-}]$ will take place upon the addition of H^+.

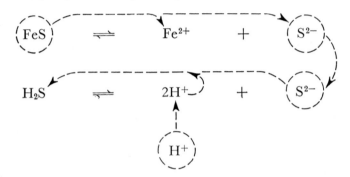

By taking up S^{2-} as the unionized weak acid H_2S (or HS^-), $[S^{2-}]$ is reduced sufficiently that the solution is unsaturated, $[Fe^{2+}][S^{2-}] < K_{SP}$, and FeS precipitate will dissolve.

The ion concentration of one of the precipitating ions can be reduced in other ways: formation of complex ions, such as $Ag(NH_3)_2^+$, will decrease $[Ag^+]$ and effect the solution of silver salt precipitates (see Section 19.13); oxidation or reduction of one of the precipitating ions will remove its control over the second, as in the solution of precipitated copper sulfide by oxidizing the sulfide ion to free sulfur ($S^{2-} \rightleftharpoons S - 2e^-$) with nitric acid.

19.13. Ion Complexes

A complex ion results from the association of a simple ion with other ions or neutral molecules, and such ions can form whenever the free energy of the complex is less than the sum of the free energies of the separate ions or molecules. Examples are extremely numerous, and complex ion structure determination and theory are well advanced, but only limited consideration can be undertaken here.

The argentous silver ion, Ag^+, forms several complex ions in solution:

$$Ag^+ + 2CN^- \rightleftharpoons Ag(CN)_2^-$$
$$Ag^+ + 2NH_3 \rightleftharpoons Ag(NH_3)_2^+$$
$$Ag^+ + 2Cl^- \rightleftharpoons AgCl_2^-$$
$$Ag^+ + 2S_2O_3^{2-} \rightleftharpoons Ag(S_2O_3)_2^{3-}$$

The equilibria are subject to the law of mass action, and the equilibrium constant for each is usually given for the reverse reaction (the dissociation of the complex ion): this constant is called *the instability constant* or *the dissociation constant.*

TABLE 19.6. *Instability Constants at 25°C for Several Complex Ions.*

Ion	K_{instab}
$Ag(CN)_2^-$	3.8×10^{-19}
$Ag(NH_3)_2^+$	7×10^{-8}
$Ag(S_2O_3)_2^{3-}$	4.8×10^{-14}
$Cd(NH_3)_4^{2+}$	2.5×10^{-7}
$Cd(CN)_4^{2-}$	1.4×10^{-17}
$Co(NH_3)_6^{3+}$	1.25×10^{-5}
$Cu(NH_3)_4^{2+}$	4.6×10^{-14}
$Fe(CNS)_6^{3-}$	3.1×10^{-4}
$Fe(CN)_6^{3-}$	about 10^{-44}
$Hg(CN)_4^{2-}$	4×10^{-42}
$HgCl_4^{2-}$	1.1×10^{-16}
NH_4^+	5.6×10^{-10}
$Ni(NH_3)_6^{2+}$	2.1×10^{-8}
$Ni(CN)_4^{2-}$	about 10^{-22}
$Zn(CN)_4^{2-}$	2×10^{-17}
$Zn(NH_3)_4^{2+}$	9.8×10^{-10}
$Zn(OH)_4^{2-}$	5.0×10^{-31}

For the cyanide complex, this is

$$K_{instab} = \frac{[Ag^+][CN^-]^2}{[Ag(CN)_2^-]} \qquad (19.32)$$

Values for several instability constants are given in Table 19.6, which also serves to list the formulas of the more commonly encountered complex ions. Note that the number of ions involved in complexing of a given central ion is generally the same regardless of the complexing ion (for example, $Zn(CN)_4^{2-}$, $Zn(NH_3)_4^{2+}$, $Zn(OH)_4^{2-}$); this number is called the *coordination* number. Note also that NH_4^+ can be regarded as a proton complexed by a single ammonia molecule.

ILLUSTRATION

What would be the final concentration of silver ion when 0.1 mole of KCN is added to one liter of 0.03 molar $AgNO_3$ solution?

Since the salts are completely ionized, the initial amount of Ag^+ present is 0.03 moles, and the amount of cyanide ion added is 0.1 mole. The silver cyanide complex ion equilibrium is represented by

$$Ag(CN)_2^- \rightleftharpoons Ag^+ + 2CN^-$$

and

$$K_{instab} = \frac{[Ag^+][CN^-]^2}{[Ag(CN)_2^-]} = 3.8 \times 10^{-19}$$

Set

$x = [Ag^+]$ = the final concentration of silver ion not associated

and

$$[Ag(CN)_2^-] = 0.03 - x$$

There will be two cyanide ions associated with each silver ion forming a complex, so the cyanide ion remaining per liter is

$$[CN^-] = 0.1 - 2(0.03 - x) = 0.04 + 2x$$

Substitution of these values in the instability constant expression yields

$$\frac{x(0.04 - 2x)^2}{0.03 - x} = 3.8 \times 10^{-19}$$

From this equation, x must be *less* than $[0.03/(0.04)^2] \times 3.8 \times 10^{-19} = 7.12 \times 10^{-18}$. This is clearly so much less than 0.03 and 0.04 that this upper limit is the true value to very high accuracy; hence $[Ag^+] = 7.12 \times 10^{-18}$ moles/liter.

Instability constants generally are so small that it may almost always be assumed that the concentration of complex ion will be approximately equal to that of the cation originally present (following the necessary stoichiometric considerations). The amount of the complexing ion or compound remaining will be the difference between the *amount* added to the solution and the *amount* necessary to react with all of the cations originally present. (Some anions act as the central ions of complexes, but these are not considered here.)

19.14. Ionic Reactions in Nonaqueous Systems

An important effect governing ionization and ionic reactions in nonaqueous systems is that dependent on the dielectric constant of the solvent. In Section 17.14, it was pointed out that the force between two ions each of charge Ze at distance r in a medium of dielectric constant ϵ is

$$F = \frac{Z^2 e^2}{\epsilon r^2} \tag{19.33}$$

When the dielectric constant is large, as for water ($\epsilon = 78.5$ at 25°C), the forces of interionic attraction are sufficiently reduced to permit the ions to be relatively independent of one another. For solvents of lower dielectric constant such as, methanol ($\epsilon_{20°} = 31.2$) or ethanol ($\epsilon_{20°} = 25.8$), the effect of the interionic forces is greater. Many dissociation constants are 10^4 or 10^5 smaller in ethanol than in water, and this factor can be understood from electrostatic considerations.

[The difference in the electrical free energy of a pair of ions of charges e^+ and e^- separated by distance r in two media of different dielectric constants, ϵ_1 and ϵ_2 is given by the Born equation

$$\Delta F = \frac{e^2}{r}\left(\frac{1}{\epsilon_1} - \frac{1}{\epsilon_2}\right) \qquad (19.34)$$

which represents the difference of electrical work in separating the charges completely. For water and ethanol, using dielectric constants 78 and 25, and the distance between the ions as 2 Å, $\Delta F = -6200$ cals mole^{-1}. The ratio of equilibrium constants corresponding to the electrical free energy difference will be $e^{-\Delta F/RT} = 3 \times 10^4$.]

The dielectric constant is not the only factor, but many of the differences in the behavior of otherwise similar solvents must be ascribed to differences in dielectric constant.

The extent of acidic or basic ionization will depend largely upon the acidic or basic strength of the solvent. Water has strong basic properties and a strong attraction for protons; consequently many acids appear approximately equally strong in aqueous solution—for example, $HClO_4$, H_2SO_4, HNO_3, and HCl. For all these acids, the equilibrium

$$HA + H_2O \rightleftharpoons H_3O^+ + A^-$$

is almost completely to the right. However, in a solvent which is a weak base, such as glacial acetic acid, differences in acid strength of these same acids will be readily apparent. For acetic acid, having much less affinity for protons, the equilibrium

$$HA + CH_3COOH \rightleftharpoons CH_3COOH_2^+ + A^-$$

lies much less far to the right, and difference in acidity can become apparent. For example, the conductivity of $HClO_4$ in glacial acetic acid is fifty times that of HNO_3.

Water, by its basic properties, has a "leveling effect" upon strong acid, while a more acidic solvent will have a "spreading effect" upon them. Similarly, a more basic solvent than water, such as liquid ammonia, will have a leveling effect upon the acidic properties of a series of compounds which are quite different one from another in water. Thus the equilibrium

$$HA + NH_3 \rightleftharpoons NH_4^+ + A^-$$

lies quite far to the right even for acids which are weak in water, because ammonia is a stronger base. For example, acids as different as hydrochloric, nitric, acetic, and formic in water (see the dissociation constants in Table 19.1), all have approximately the same power as acid catalysts when in solution in liquid ammonia. All acids have almost complete dissociation in strongly basic solvents, and very little dissociation in strongly acidic solvents.

For solvents which do not interact with protons, such as benzene and other hydrocarbons, the solvent will be a neutral medium and only if a second conjugate acid-base system is present can a reaction take place. The same will be true with respect to other types of ionic reactions.

Problems

19.1. Formic acid, HCOOH, is a weak acid in water, with an ionization constant $K_a = 1.77 \times 10^{-4}$. Calculate the degree of ionization and the pH of (a) a 0.001 M solution, (b) a 0.1 M solution.

19.2. The ionization constant of boric acid in water is 5.80×10^{-10} at 25°C. Calculate the ionization and pH of a 0.01 M solution.

19.3. Calculate the degree of ionization of 10^{-4} molar acetic acid by the approximate Eq. 19.4 and by the more accurate Eq. 19.3. What is the fractional error using Eq. 19.4 in this case?

19.4. Sulfurous acid, H_2SO_3, ionizes in water according to the equilibria $H_2SO_3 = H^+ + HSO_3^-$, and $HSO_3^- = H^+ + SO_3^{2-}$. For the first $K_1 = 1.7 \times 10^{-2}$, and for the second $K_2 = 6.2 \times 10^{-8}$. (a) For C moles of sulfurous acid added to water to form one liter of solution, write the equations expressing the two conditions of equilibrium, the forms in which the acid exists in solution, and electroneutrality. (b) Discuss which concentrations of ions may be safely neglected in the equations if $C = 10^{-5}$ and if $C = 10^{-1}$ moles/liter. (c) Using justifiable approximations, calculate the ion concentrations of H^+, HSO_3^-, and SO_3^{2-} at these total concentrations.

19.5. The solubility of AgCl in water is 0.87×10^{-5} at 15°C and 1.35×10^{-5} moles/kg at 25°C. Calculate $\Delta \bar{H}$ for solution of AgCl in water.

19.6. The solubility product of PbI_2 in water is 0.75×10^{-8} at 15°C and 1.4×10^{-8} at 25°C. (a) Calculate an average $\Delta \bar{H}$ of solution of PbI_2. (b) Estimate the solubility of PbI_2 at 40°C.

19.7. (a) What is the pH of a 0.01 M solution of benzoic acid ($K_a = 6.3 \times 10^{-5}$)? (b) What is the pH when sodium benzoate is added to make the solution 0.02 molar in the salt?

19.8. It is desired to adjust the pH of a 0.1 M solution of acetic acid to a value 4.7 by adding sodium acetate. What concentration will be needed?

19.9. (a) Calculate the ionization and pH of a 0.05 M formic acid solution. (b) HCl is added until the solution is 0.10 M in HCl. Will the ionization be greater or less? What is the resulting pH?

19.10. What are the bases conjugate to methanol and phenol? What are the acids conjugate to methanol, aniline, pyridine, and dimethyl ether?

19.11. For the following weak bases in water give the conjugate acid and its acidity constant K_a:

Base	AgOH	CH_3NH_2	$C_6H_5NH_2$	$(NH_2)_2CO$
K_b	1.1×10^{-4}	4.0×10^{-4}	4.6×10^{-10}	1.5×10^{-14}

19.12. The concentration of hydroxyl ion in solution can in some cases be inferred indirectly from rates of reaction which are found in other solutions to be proportional to $[OH^-]$. In this way, the concentration of OH^- in 0.10 molar sodium acetate was calculated to be 8×10^{-6} molar. Use this value and K_a for ionization of acetic acid to calculate the ion product $K_w = [H^+][OH^-]$ for water.

19.13. From kinetic measurements, $[OH^-] = 9 \times 10^{-4}$ molar in a 0.051 molar solution of KCN in water at 25°C. Calculate K_a for HCN.

19.14. The ion product K_w for water can be obtained from EMF measurements by using the cell

$$\text{Pt, } H_2 \text{ (1 atm): } KOH(m_1); KCl(m_2): AgCl(s), Ag$$

(a) Show that the EMF of this cell can be written if m is sufficiently large as

$$\mathcal{E} = \mathcal{E}^0 - \frac{RT}{\mathfrak{F}} \ln \frac{m_2}{m_1} - \frac{RT}{\mathfrak{F}} \ln K_w - \frac{RT}{\mathfrak{F}} \ln \frac{\gamma_{Cl^-}}{\gamma_{OH^-}}$$

where $\mathcal{E}^0$ is the standard EMF of the cell with HCl as electrolyte. (b) Show how this equation may be used to obtain K_w from measured EMFs. (Remember that activity coefficients approach unity by definition as ionic strength goes to zero.)

19.15. Show that for an acid HA, the acidity constant K_a and pH are related by

$$pK_a = pH - \log \frac{[HA]}{[A^-]}$$

in the approximation of dilute solutions.

19.16. Calculate the degree of hydrolysis and pH of a 0.1 molar sodium acetate solution.

19.17. (a) From the appropriate acid or base ionization constants, calculate the hydrolysis constants K_H of urea hydrochloride, sodium bicarbonate, ammonium carbonate. (b) Show that $pK_H = -\log K_H$ satisfies $pK_H = pK_w - pK_a$.

19.18. Calculate the percent hydrolysis of a 0.1 molar solution of KCN in water, given that $pK_a = 9.14$ for HCN in water at 25°C.

19.19. What is the extent of hydrolysis in a 0.005 molar Na_2CO_3 solution?

19.20. (a) Write the reactions occurring when aniline acetate is dissolved in water. (b) If 0.001 moles are dissolved to form 50 cm³ of solution, calculate the pH and concentrations of all other species present.

19.21. Calculate the pH of the following solutions in water at 25°C, making any justifiable approximations: (a) 0.1 M ethyl amine. (b) 0.01 M in benzoic acid and 0.02 M in sodium benzoate. (c) A solution 0.01 M in acetic acid and equivalent of aniline. (d) A solution 0.01 M in acetic acid and equivalent of ammonia. (e) A solution 0.05 M in Na_2CO_3 and in HCl. (f) 0.01 M $NaHCO_3$.

19.22. Phosphoric acid, H_3PO_4, is a tribasic acid in water, and the acidity constants for loss of the first, second, and third protons are $K_1 = 7.5 \times 10^{-3}$, $K_2 = 6.2 \times 10^{-8}$, $K_3 = 5 \times 10^{-13}$. (a) Write the equations expressing the conditions of equilibrium, the content of dissolved phosphoric acid, and electrical neutrality. (b) For a 0.001 M solution, calculate the pH and all ion concentrations, making suitable approximations to simplify the computations.

19.23. (a) Calculate the pH of a solution 0.02 molar in formic acid and 0.01 M in sodium formate. (b) Calculate the pH after addition of 0.001 moles of HCl.

19.24. Repeat Problem *19.23* for a solution which is initially 0.015 M in both the acid and its sodium salt.

19.25. Calculate the pH of a solution which is 0.01 M in sodium carbonate and in sodium bicarbonate.

19.26. A 0.05 M HCl solution is titrated with ammonia. Calculate the amounts of ammonia to yield solutions of pH from 2 to 10, choosing the values to define a curve like the one in Fig. 19.1.

19.27. Make a calculation similar to Problem *19.26* for a 0.05 M acetic acid solution titrated with NaOH.

19.28. An aqueous solution which is 0.007 M in H_2S and 0.003 M in NaOH has a pH of 6.9 at 25°C. Calculate K_a for H_2S.

19.29. A useful rule in choosing an acid-base pair for controlling pH is that pK_a ($= -\log K_a$) for the acid should not differ by more than one unit from the desired pH. Derive the relation between pK_a and pH if C_a moles of acid and C_b moles of the conjugate base are introduced to make up a solution; from this give reasons for a rule of the kind stated.

19.30. Consider the counterpart for indicators of the rule for buffers given in the preceding problem; that is, what sort of relation between pH to be detected and indicator K_a should be satisfied and why?

19.31. (a) What thermodynamic function can be obtained from the temperature dependence of the values of K_w listed in Table 19.3. (b) By a suitable plot of quantities derived from values of K_w and T in Table 19.3, obtain an average value of this function and compare with directly measured values discussed in an earlier chapter.

19.32. (a) What information can be obtained by thermodynamic reasoning from measurements of the dependence of ionization constants on pressure at constant temperature? (b) If K_i were found to decrease with increased pressure on a solution, what can you infer about the changes on ionization?

19.33. By extreme precautions against impurities, Kohlrausch and Heydweiller were able to obtain water of specific conductivity 0.062×10^{-6} ohm^{-1} cm^{-1} at 25°C, rather than values of order 1–2×10^{-6} ordinarily obtained for "conductivity water." Assuming their value is due entirely to solvent ionization, calculate the corresponding value of K_w.

19.34. (a) Calculate the concentrations $[H^+]$ and $[Ac^-]$ in a $0.1\ M$ acetic acid solution, assuming activity coefficients γ equal to one. (b) Use the Debye-Hückel theory to estimate ionic activity coefficients for the concentrations found in (a) and calculate more accurate values of concentrations. (Assume $\gamma_{HAc} = 1$.) By how much does the calculated pH differ from the value obtained by setting all γ equal to one?

19.35. (a) Calculate without activity coefficient corrections the concentration of sodium acetate necessary in a $0.05\ M$ acetic acid solution to give $pH = 4.5$. (b) Estimating activity coefficients from the equation $\log \gamma_\pm = -0.51 I^{1/2}$, where I is the ionic strength, obtain a more accurate answer.

19.36. The solubility of $CaCO_3$ in water in equilibrium with gaseous CO_2 is found to be proportional to the cube root of the partial pressure of CO_2. Show from equilibrium considerations that this should be approximately true.

19.37. For solutions of an acid HA, which are not so dilute that the significance of pH is simple and exact, Hammett introduced as a measure of acidity a function H_0, defined by

$$H_0 = pK_a - \log \frac{[HA]}{[A^-]}$$

where all quantities on the right are measurable in a number of cases. (a) What is the relation between H_0 and pH in dilute solution? (b) By obtaining an expression for H_0 in terms of $[H^+]$, give reasons for changes in the relation between H_0 and pH.

19.38. Consider an acid base pair, HA and A^- with acidity constant K_a, in which the total concentration $C = [HA] + [A^-]$ in solution is constant. (a) Show that for acid solutions with $pH < pK_a - 1$, the following relations are approximately true:

$$\log [HA] \cong \log C \qquad \log [A^-] \cong \log C - pK_a + pH$$

(b) Show on the other hand that for $pH > pK_a + 1$, it is approximately true that

$$\log [HA] \cong \log C + pK_a - pH \qquad \log [A^-] \cong \log C$$

(c) When $pH \cong K_a$, the approximations to obtain these relations are not accurate. However, show that for $pH = pK_a$, $\log [HA] = \log [A^-] = \log (C/2)$. (d) Make plots of $\log [HA]$ and $\log [A^-]$ on the same graph against pH in the range 0 to 14, taking $C = 0.1\ M$, $pK_a = 4.5$. Also plot $\log [H^+]$ and $\log [OH^-]$ against the pH. (Plots of this kind are useful for visualizing relative concentrations.)

19.39. The examples and problems on acid-base equilibria so far have neglected the changes in concentration of a solute initially present by addition of a second solution in appreciable volume. Consider titration of 50 cm³ of 0.1 M ammonia solution with 0.05 M HCl solution. What volume V of HCl solution must be added to make the $pH = 8.5$? (Hint: The equilibrium expressions and conditions of electroneutrality are unchanged, but the equations for quantity must be expressed in terms of the original volume and volume V added. Volume changes of mixing are small and may be neglected.)

19.40. A solution of 100 cm³ volume is 0.1 M in ammonia and 0.1 M in trimethylamine. What volume of 0.05 M HCl must be added to make the $pH = 9.0$?

19.41. Consider a buffer solution containing C_A moles of acid A and C_B moles of conjugate base, as from a salt with the acid anion, per liter of solution. Show for fixed C_B that

$$\left(\frac{\partial pH}{\partial C_A}\right)_{C_B} = -\frac{1}{C_A}$$

19.42. The buffer capacity B of a solution is defined for a constant total quantity $C_A + C_B$ of acid and conjugate base as the derivative

$$B = \left(\frac{\partial C_A}{\partial pH}\right)_{C_A + C_B}$$

Thus the less the pH changes for a given change in C_A, the larger the buffer capacity. (a) Show that $B = -2.303\ C_A C_B/(C_A + C_B)$. (b) Show that the buffer capacity is a maximum if $C_A = C_B$ and $pH = pK_a$.

19.43. A number of substances, notably amino acids, exist in aqueous solution mainly as dipolar ions (zwitterions) which can act either as acids or bases.

Thus glycine in water can be written $^+NH_3CH_2COO^-$ with the reactions in water at 25°C:

$$^+NH_3CH_2COO^- = NH_2CH_2COO^- + H^+ \qquad K_1 = 1.7 \times 10^{-10}$$
$$^+NH_3CH_2COOH = {}^+NH_3CH_2COO^- + H^+ \qquad K_2 = 4.5 \times 10^{-3}$$

(a) Calculate the pH of a 0.01 M glycine solution. (b) Show that the pH of an "isoelectric" solution (one with $[^+NH_3CH_2COOH] = [NH_2CH_2COO^-]$) is given by $pH = \frac{1}{2}(pK_1 + pK_2)$.

19.44. (a) The acids $HClO_4$, HNO_3, and HCl are equally strong in water, but very different in glacial acetic acid as the solvent; perchloric, for example, is many times stronger than nitric acid. Explain the difference in the two solvents. (b) Suggest two solvents, in one of which a series of bases would appear equally strong, while in the other significant differences would be apparent. Explain the reasons for your choice.

Suggested Readings

An elementary discussion of ionic solutions first published in 1936 has recently been issued in a paperback edition: *Ions in Solution* by R. W. Gurney (Dover, New York, 1963). An original and provocative discussion by the same author is given in the book *Ionic Processes in Solution* (McGraw-Hill, New York, 1953).

A modern well-balanced examination of acid-base reactions and related behavior will be found in *The Proton in Chemistry* by R. P. Bell (Cornell University Press, Ithaca, 1959); an earlier book by the same writer, which contains valuable material, is *Acid-Base Catalysis* (Oxford, 1941). Indicators are discussed in *Acid-Base Indicators* by I. M. Kolthoff (Macmillan, New York, 1937).

Chapter 20

The Phase Rule and Some Applications

EQUILIBRIUM STATES and the attainment of equilibrium have been previously discussed in some detail and from various viewpoints. The thermodynamic requirements for equilibrium in terms of the enthalpy, the free energy, and the entropy have been considered in Chapters 12 and 14; both homogeneous equilibria (for example, chemical equilibria in solution, Chapters 14 and 19) and heterogeneous equilibria (Chapters 11, 14, and 19) are now familiar to the student. The study of equilibria in gas reactions constituted Chapter 15, and solution equilibria Chapter 16. Heterogeneous equilibria have been considered in detail in Section 15.5 and Chapter 16. All the important thermodynamic relations developed have been for equilibrium conditions.

The thermodynamic conditions applying to *any* equilibrium of substances present in more than one phase were first properly established and expressed by the American theoretical physicist J. Willard Gibbs in several papers appearing from 1876 to 1878. His work was definitive and complete, leaving nothing to be added to his general statements of conditions which are necessarily satisfied by systems in equilibrium, whatever their differences in chemical constitution. Prior to Gibbs' time, the circumstances under which different phases could coexist were not at all understood, and it was more than twenty years before the full implications of this work began to be appreciated and put to use in the study of equilibria. Since then, many systems have been studied, and much accomplished in appreciating the molecular aspects of their behavior, but the thermodynamic reasoning concerning possible states of equilibrium is based entirely on the work of Gibbs. One of the important consequences he deduced, called the *phase rule*, is a statement concerning the possible conditions of coexistence of phases in equilibrium. This rule is a primary consideration in discussing phase equilibria and phase changes, the concern of the study of heterogeneous systems.

20.1. The Phase Rule

A system containing several chemical species can exist in many possible states: a gaseous phase, one or more (or no) liquid phases, and one or more (or no) solid phases; the separate phases may have various compositions. Any one of these may be the state of the entire system, but the total quantity may also be divided among two, three, or more phases which are simultaneously present, with varying amounts of the different species in each one.

For any conceivable situation to be an actual stable state, the thermodynamic requirements for equilibrium must be satisfied. In considering phase equilibria of a single substance in Sections 14.11 and 14.12, the severe limitations imposed by these requirements on the possible conditions under which two or more phases can coexist were pointed out.

When more than one species is present, new possibilities of variation are presented, because the compositions of the different phases may change. At the same time, however, more restrictions enter if for each species there is to be equilibrium among two or more phases. The phase rule is a deduction from thermodynamic principles, which expresses the amount of freedom possible in varying the state of equilibrium of several phases without inducing phase transitions which would result in a change in the number of phases present.

To derive the phase rule, the number of parameters necessary to define a system of several species in a number of phases must be considered. If there are S species, the composition of any one phase is specified by the values of $S - 1$ mole fractions (or other composition variables), the composition of the remaining species being fixed. (Thus for three solutes in aqueous solution with mole fractions N_2, N_3, N_4, the mole fraction of water is necessarily $N_1 = 1 - N_2 - N_3 - N_4$.) For P phases, the total number of composition variables which must be independently assigned is

$$\text{number of composition variables} = P(S - 1). \qquad (20.1)$$

In addition to the required composition variables, the two remaining parameters which change the thermodynamic state if varied are temperature and pressure. If the values for one or both of these are different in several phases in contact with one another, spontaneous changes will act to reduce the differences, and complete equilibrium can exist only if the pressure and temperature are everywhere the same. This common value for the pressure and that for the temperature are two more variables to be specified for any state of equilibrium. The total number of thermodynamic variables is then temperature plus pressure plus composition variables, and is therefore

$$\text{total number of variables} = P(S - 1) + 2 \qquad (20.2)$$

Even though these are necessary to define a system, not all of these variables are independent. For the case of one species only, as was shown in Section 14.11, equilibrium among two or more phases is possible only if the species A has the same chemical potential $\overline{F}_A$ in every coexisting phase. Thus for three phases $(P = 3)$:

$$\overline{F}_A(\text{phase } 1) = \overline{F}_A(\text{phase } 2) = \overline{F}_A(\text{phase } 3)$$

and there are two equations which must be satisfied. These will be called "restrictions." When more than one species is present, exactly the same conditions must be satisfied by all other species present as well; this requirement can be demonstrated rigorously by an elaboration of the methods used for one species. Thus for species B, C, $\cdots$, the following equalities must hold at equilibrium:

$$\overline{F}_B(\text{phase } 1) = \overline{F}_B(\text{phase } 2) = \overline{F}_B(\text{phase } 3)$$
$$\overline{F}_C(\text{phase } 1) = \overline{F}_C(\text{phase } 2) = \overline{F}_C(\text{phase } 3)$$

The number of equations is thus $P - 1$ for each component species; each equation is a relation between the variables temperature, pressure, and composition. (In the existence of the relationship between these quantities, one less than the total number are independently variable.) The total number of restrictions for S species required by the above equalities is therefore

$$\text{number of restrictions} = S(P - 1) \qquad (20.3)$$

The number of quantities which can be independently varied is called the *number of degrees of freedom*, F, or the *variance* of the system. This must be the total number of variables less the number of restrictions, since each restriction expresses one of the total number of variables in terms of the other variables. The number F remaining is thus $F = P(S - 1) + 2 - S(P - 1)$, which gives

$$\text{degrees of freedom} = F = S + 2 - P \qquad (20.4)$$

If there are no other restrictions on the system, this equation can be applied without further analysis of such restrictions. Immediately the previous results for one species can be checked: for $S = 1$, $F = 3 - P$. With one phase present, $F = 2$ and the two independent variables are T and P. For two phases, $F = 1$ and P and T are not independent; the value for one will be fixed as the value for the other is chosen. For three, $F = 0$ and both T and P are fixed (at the triple point values). Four phases cannot coexist with only one species present in the system, $F = -1$ having no physical meaning.

With the presence of a second species, the number of degrees of freedom is increased by one for a given number of phases in equilibrium: $F = 4 - P$. For one phase, $F = 3$, the three independent variables being temperature, pressure, and the mole fraction of one species. For two phases, $F = 2$ and only two variables are independent; an example is the equilibrium between solution phase of, say, benzene in toluene, and the vapor phase. For any particular choice of temperature and composition, the pressure has a fixed value (equal to the vapor pressure of the solution), which cannot be changed without the disappearance of one phase, and hence the disappearance of the equilibrium. Similar limitations exist for other phase equilibria, and a number of examples are discussed in later sections.

The number of independent variables is further restricted if any other conditions must be met by the system. The most important of these result when chemical reactions can take place between two or more of the various species present. Thus if SO_3, SO_2, and O_2 are the three species of the system, their relative amounts can change by the reaction $2SO_3 = 2SO_2 + O_2$, and only concentrations so chosen to satisfy the requirement that $\Delta \bar{F} = 0$ represent equilibrium. Two values arbitrarily chosen fix the third. For example, from the application of the requirement $\Delta \bar{F} = 0$, assuming ideal gas behavior for the three species, $K_P = P_{SO_2}^2 P_{O_2} / P_{SO_3}^2$.

Other restrictions are also possible. In the preceding example, one could consider the special case that only the species SO_3 is initially introduced into the system. As before, $\Delta \bar{F} = 0$ is a necessary condition, but also necessary is the requirement that the concentrations of SO_2 and O_2 be equal. There are then two restrictions rather than one when all three species are derived from the introduction of but one.

A similar situation occurs for an ionizable solute in water—acetic acid, for example. The reaction $HAc = H^+ + Ac^-$ results in three solute species, HAc, H^+, Ac^-, and there are two restrictions: $\Delta \bar{F} = 0$ and $[H^+] = [Ac^-]$.

If we denote the total number of additional restrictions of this kind by R, the resulting number of degrees of freedom is

$$F = S - R + 2 - P \qquad (20.5)$$

The quantity $S - R$, total number of species less number of restrictive conditions on them, is usually expressed as $C = S - R$, where C is called the number of *components*. The phase rule is then written

$$F = C + 2 - P \qquad (20.6)$$

The number of components (C) is often defined as the smallest number of quantities necessary to describe the chemical composition of the system, or as the smallest number of species from which the system can be constructed. The number to be used in setting the value for C can usually be decided without difficulty on this basis, especially after some experience, but the proper value can always be found by counting *all* species and subtracting the number of independent restrictions on the compositions arising from chemical reactions, chemical equilibria, and special conditions.

EXAMPLES

(a) The system $NH_4HS(s)$, $NH_3(g)$, $H_2S(g)$ has three species. The equilibrium $NH_4HS(s) = NH_3(g) + H_2S(g)$ forms one restriction, making $C = 2$ for arbitrary initial amounts of the three; if only $NH_4HS(s)$ is initially present, $C_{NH_3} = C_{H_2S}$ is a second restriction and $C = 1$. There are two phases, solid NH_4HS and gas with NH_3 and H_2S (plus a negligible amount of gaseous NH_4HS always in equilibrium with the solid). Hence $F = C + 2 - P = 2 + 2 - 2 = 2$ for arbitrary initial amounts, and $F = 1 + 2 - 2 = 1$ if NH_4HS only is initially present. The one variable in the latter case is either the temperature, which fixes the dissociation pressure, or the pressure, which when specified then fixes the temperature.

(b) For the equilibrium $CaCO_3(s) = CaO(s) + CO_2(g)$, there are three phases, two solid and one gaseous. There are two components, hence F is one.

(Requiring the amounts of CaO(*s*) and $CO_2(g)$ to be equal does not further restrict the system because the compositions of CaO as a solid and CO_2 as the sole gas present are already fixed.)

(c) Sulfuric acid in water is a two-component system regardless of the number of possible ionization equilibria. If only the equilibrium $H_2SO_4 + H_2O = H_3O^+ + HSO_4^-$ is considered, there are four species. For the equilibrium, $\Delta \bar{F} = 0$, and a second condition is that $[H_3O^+] = [HSO_4^-]$; hence $C = S - R = 4 - 2 = 2$. If self-ionization of water, $2H_2O = H_3O^+ + OH^-$, is included, there is one more species, OH^-, or five in all; but then there are two equilibria, and two equilibrium constants representing $\Delta \bar{F} = 0$. The restrictions that $[H_3O^+] = [HSO_4^-]$ or $[H_3O^+] = [OH^-]$ are no longer valid, but overall electroneutrality, expressed by $[H_3O^+] = [HSO_4^-] + [OH^-]$, provides a restriction which, added to those of the two equilibria, makes three in all, and $C = S - R = 5 - 3 = 2$, just as when the self-ionization of water was ignored. The reader can verify for himself that $C = 2$ also even when the further ionization $H_2SO_4 + H_2SO_4 = H_3SO_4^+ + HSO_4^-$ and $HSO_4^- + H_2O = H_3O^+ + SO_4^{2-}$ are considered.

20.2. One-component Systems

The phase diagram of a typical one-component system, CO_2, has been presented in Section 11.1 and Fig. 11.1. The application of the phase rule is unambiguous:

$$F = C - P + 2 = 3 - P \qquad (20.7)$$

In any of the areas of Fig. 11.1 labeled solid, liquid, or vapor, but a single phase is present, and hence there are two degrees of freedom $(F = 3 - 1 = 2)$. Within these areas, it is clear that both the temperature and the pressure may be varied independently. The system has a *variance* of 2.

Along any of the three lines—the sublimation pressure curve, the melting curve, or the vapor pressure curve—there are two phases present in equilibrium: solid-vapor, solid-liquid, or liquid-vapor, respectively. Thus there is one degree of freedom $(F = 3 - 2 = 1)$, for along any line, if either the temperature or the pressure is arbitrarily chosen, the value of the other is accordingly fixed. The variance of the system is 1.

At the triple point, where three phases are in equilibrium, there are no degrees of freedom $(F = 3 - 3 = 0)$, and the system is *invariant;* the values for both the pressure and temperature are fixed by the system itself.

The critical point illustrates interestingly a basic concept of the phase rule, although initially it may appear a deviation from the rule. For a given substance, both the critical temperature and critical pressure have definite and fixed values; the system is invariant. Yet a single-component system with two phases (liquid and gas) present should, according to the simple application of the phase rule, have one degree of freedom. The explanation lies in the presence of an additional restriction of the system itself, for at the critical point it is required that all properties of the liquid become identical with all properties of the gas. This restriction of the system reduces by one the number of degrees of freedom otherwise available.

Water comprises another single-component system which has been extensively studied, and the phase diagram of water is given in Fig. 20.1, A and B. The latter has a more limited temperature range but has

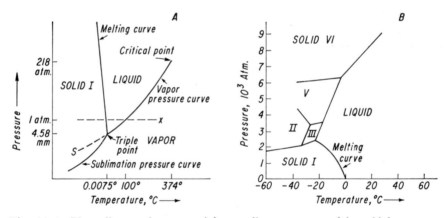

Fig. 20.1. *Phase diagram for water:* (A) *at ordinary pressures;* (B) *at high pressures.*

a pressure range fiftyfold greater, so the boundaries of the area of the vapor phase are merged with the abscissa. Bridgman and others have demonstrated the presence of several different solid phases of water, shown here as I, II, III, V, and VI. (The existence of Ice IV has not been corroborated.) Note that the melting point of Ice I falls with increasing pressure, until at 2040 atmospheres, where the melting point is 22.0°C, Ice III becomes the solid phase in equilibrium with the liquid. For Ice III, as well as for V and VI, the melting point increases with increasing pressure. Ice VII, forming at about 20,000 atmospheres, is not shown.

In Fig. 20.1, A, the vapor pressure curve for the metastable super-cooled water is represented by the dashed line labeled *S*. It is obvious, since this curve is entirely within the area of the solid phase, that equilibrium with solid does not obtain. Although there is *metastable equilibrium* between supercooled liquid and vapor, the supercooled liquid vapor pressure (and hence its corollary chemical potential) is greater than the equilibrium vapor pressure of ice below 0°C, so that if any solid phase is introduced into the metastable system (even but a minute crystal), true equilibrium will be established between the solid and vapor, and the metastable phase will disappear.

A third interesting single-component system is that of sulfur, which is illustrated in Fig. 20.2. The phase diagram shows two crystalline solid forms (rhombic and monoclinic), a liquid phase, and vapor. Actually, seven crystalline solid forms have been identified, in addition to amorphous solids, and the liquid is believed to be an equilibrium mixture of three molecular species, S_λ, S_μ, and S_π, corresponding to the atomicities S_8, S_6, and S_4. The system is further complicated by the slowness of the equilibrium processes and the prevalence of *unstable equilibrium*. For example, when liquid sulfur cools slowly, crystals of monoclinic sulfur are formed in the neighborhood of 100°C, and upon further cooling into the area where rhombic

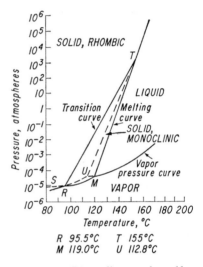

R 95.5°C   T 155°C
M 119.0°C   U 112.8°C

Fig. 20.2. *Phase diagram for sulfur.*

sulfur is the stable form, these monoclinic crystals persist. However, after some time at these lower temperatures, the rhombic crystals do form. (The vapor pressure curve for monoclinic sulfur in its unstable range is indicated by line S in Fig. 20.2.)

The evidence for the unstable equilibrium comes from the determination of the melting point of sulfur. If rhombic sulfur (stable at room temperature) is heated rapidly, a melting point of 112.8°C (point U in Fig. 20.2) can be determined. However, when the monoclinic form is heated, a melting point of 119.0°C is found (point M in Fig. 20.2), and the temperature of the triple point, R, for the equilibrium transition between the rhombic and monoclinic solids in equilibrium with sulfur vapor is known to be 95.5°C. Thus U represents an unstable melting point. Further, these two melting points were determined for the unstable and stable equilibria, respectively, with the single liquid form designated S_λ:

$$S_{\text{rhombic}} \overset{112.8°C}{\rightleftharpoons} S_\lambda$$

and

$$S_{\text{monoclinic}} \overset{119.0°C}{\rightleftharpoons} S_\lambda.$$

Liquid sulfur consists of the equilibrium mixture:

$$S_\lambda \rightleftharpoons S_\mu \rightleftharpoons S_\pi.$$

The temperatures of unstable and stable equilibria between rhombic and monoclinic sulfur with the equilibrium mixtures of the liquid (at the corresponding temperatures) have been reported as 110.4°C and 114.6°C, respectively.

The sulfur system is thus greatly complicated by the slowness of the equilibrium processes and the resulting unstable equilibria. Within the limitations inherent to these difficulties, however, the phase rule is applicable, the points S, T, and M being invariant triple points; along the lines separating various phase areas there is one degree of freedom, while within the areas themselves there are two.

20.3. Thermal Analysis; Cooling Curves

In phase rule studies, consideration of the rate of cooling of a system is unusually revealing in indicating the type of system at hand, and in bringing greater understanding of the processes a system undergoes on cooling (or on warming). Although such consideration may be little more than trivial for one-component systems in themselves, it is preliminary to later consideration of the cooling curves of more complex systems.

Follow the cooling of the single-component system, water, at one atmosphere pressure, from a temperature of 300°C (point x in Fig. 20.1, A), where the vapor is the stable phase. If heat is removed from the system at a constant rate, the temperature drops at a rate depending on the relation between the amount of water present in the system, the heat capacity of water vapor, and the rate at which heat is being removed. Assuming an equilibrium reversible process, this fall in temperature continues until, at 100°C, liquid begins to condense from the vapor. With liquid and vapor coexisting in equilibrium, the temperature remains constant, and the continued removal of heat results in further condensation of vapor to liquid, until the vapor phase disappears. The

single-phase system of water liquid then experiences further decrease of temperature, the rate controlled as before, until, at 0°C, water solid begins to form. The temperature again remains constant as long as the system is in two-phase equilibrium, but the fall begins again when all the liquid has become solid, the rate depending on the three factors enumerated above.

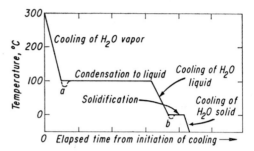

These relations are shown in Fig. 20.3, in which the tempera-ture of a given one-component water system is plotted against the time elapsed from the ini-tiation of cooling. While no units are indicated for elapsed time, the slopes of the three cooling lines and lengths of the lines of the two phase transi-tions are drawn in the proper relative scale. Cooling curves for more complex systems are discussed later in this chapter. The study of phase relations and the determina-tions of phase diagrams by means of cooling curves is sometimes called *thermal analysis*.

Fig. 20.3. *A cooling curve for the single com-ponent system, water. (The dotted portions* a *and* b *represent momentary nonequilibrium super-cooling phenomena occurring in the practical measurement of cooling rates. Example worked out for* 1 g H_2O *with heat loss at rate of* 200 *calories per index mark on abscissa.)*

20.4. Two-component Systems

Two-component systems have already been considered—in Sections 11.11 and 11.12, for relations between liquid solutions and vapor, and in Section 16.2, for relations between liquid solutions and the solid phase.

For such systems, the phase rule reduces to

$$F = C - P + 2 = 4 - P \qquad (20.8)$$

Liquid-Vapor Equilibrium

In a system such as cyclohexane-carbon tetrachloride solution in equilibrium with vapor, there are two phases (solution and vapor), and $F = 4 - 2 = 2$. In the vapor pressure diagram shown in Fig. 11.19, the temperature is fixed, leaving one degree of freedom for the system. That will be either the pressure *or* the composition, the value for the one being determined by the value chosen for the other. Such systems are often presented by boiling point-composition diagrams, the vapor pressure having by definition the constant value of one atmosphere, with either the temperature or the composition being the independent variable.

Similarly, two-component phase diagrams may be drawn for solid-liquid equilibria, most effectively in terms of composition-melting point (or freezing point) curves at constant atmospheric pressure. The forms of such phase diagrams will vary according to the properties of the two components involved; examples of several common types of diagrams are given below.

Solid-Liquid Equilibria. Completely Miscible Solid and Liquid Phases

When the two components of the system are totally miscible in the solid phase over the entire range of composition, and are also totally miscible in the liquid phase for all compositions, the composition-temperature diagram takes the form shown in Fig. 20.4. From phase rule considerations, solid-liquid systems and liquid-vapor systems will have similar phase diagrams. Diagrams for totally miscible solid-liquid systems are similar to those for totally miscible liquid-vapor systems; diagrams for partially miscible solids, to those for partially miscible liquids. The two components, naphthalene and 2-naphthol, are expected to be mutually soluble from their molecular similarity.

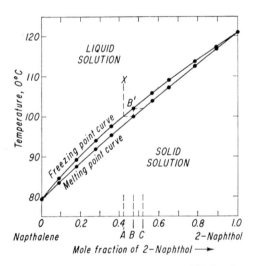

Fig. 20.4. *Solid-liquid phase equilibria for two-component system naphthalene–2-naphthol as function of temperature.*

Above the freezing point curve is a region of one phase, the liquid solution. The number of degrees of freedom

$$F = C - P + 2 = 2 - 1 + 2 = 3$$

Usually, the pressure is fixed (atmospheric), the remaining two degrees of freedom are the temperature and composition, both of which can be independently varied within the area representing the liquid phase. The same is true in the area below the melting point curve, in which the solid phase will be found.

In the region bounded by freezing and melting point curves, liquid and solid solutions will exist in equilibrium with one another. With two phases present, the number of degrees of freedom is

$$F = 2 - 2 + 2 = 2$$

Since one of them is the pressure on the system, there is but one further independent variable. This can be either the composition of either phase (the composition of the other in equilibrium therefore being determined) or the temperature of the solid-liquid system. Given a particular temperature, say 100°C, the composition of the liquid and solid phases are both fixed (at the values A and B, respectively). The overall composition of the system may be any value between A and B, the relative amounts of liquid and solid varying accordingly. Conversely, if the composition of liquid is specified, so long as any solid phase is present in equilibrium, the temperature can have but one value.

Thermal analysis gives cooling curves for system forming solid solutions which differ significantly from those of other type systems, such as those of the single component system discussed in Section 20.3. For example, from initial conditions of temperature (108°C) and composition (A) at point x, heat is withdrawn from the system at a constant rate. The rate of temperature decrease, along line KL in the temperature-time

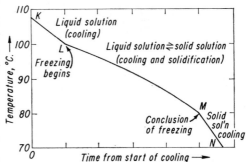

Fig. 20.5. *Cooling curve for naphthalene–2-naphthol two-component system. Totally miscible liquid and solid solutions.*

plot (Fig. 20.5), is dependent upon the quantity of liquid, its specific heat, and the rate of heat withdrawal. At 100°C, the freezing point of liquid solution of composition A (Fig. 20.4, and point L in Fig. 20.5), the solid solution of composition B in equilibrium with liquid of composition A separates, forming a two-phase system. Further removal of heat does not cause the temperature to continue to fall *at its former rate*, the difference being that increasing amounts of solid are freezing out. However, since the solid solution of composition B is richer in 2-naphthol than the liquid from which it is separating, the liquid solution remaining will become less rich in 2-naphthol, and more rich in naphthalene. The liquid solution composition will then have less 2-naphthol than indicated by A, and the temperature will drop correspondingly. The solid solution in equilibrium with the naphthalene-enriched liquid itself will be poorer in 2-naphthol than solid B, but still richer than the equilibrium liquid. Thus, as heat leaves the system, the liquid will "slide down" the freezing point curve from the point at 100°C where solid first began to separate, and the solid separating in equilibrium with liquid will "slide down" the melting point curve, until the last remaining liquid is almost pure naphthalene.

The decrease in slope at point L of the cooling curve results from the separation of the first solid solution. From this point on, the heat that must be removed comes from the solidification of the liquid, in addition to the amounts represented by the heat capacity of the liquid and solid present. Thus, since part of the heat removed is heat of solidification, cooling takes place more slowly when liquid and solid are both present. The proportion of solid increases and that of liquid decreases as heat continues to be lost, and because of the difference in heat capacities between solid and liquid, the total heat capacity of the system is not constant, and hence the slope of the cooling curve changes.

When the last of the liquid solution solidifies (point M in Fig. 20.5), the slope of the cooling curve will increase, the heat lost resulting from the heat capacity of the solid itself; the heat capacity being essentially invariant over the temperature range involved, this slope will be essentially invariant. (The slope of the section MN is greater than that of KL, since the heat capacity of the solid solution is less than that of the liquid solution.)

The cooling curves for systems where the solid phase is a solution have no "halt" (range of temperature constancy) for solidification, which is observed when a pure substance is separating from a liquid. The absence of a "halt," and the changing slope during solidification is characteristic of a solid solution, just as the constancy of temperature during solidification is characteristic of the separation of a pure substance.

20.5. Fractional Distillation and Crystallization

For the system naphthalene–2-naphthol discussed in the preceding section, upon cooling a liquid solution of a given composition, A, the solid first separating is richer in 2-naphthol than the liquid. If this solid formed upon the initial crystallization is separated and remelted, the resulting liquid will have a composition represented by *B*. When this is cooled to point *B'*, the resulting crystals initially found will be still richer in 2-naphthol (composition represented by *C* in Fig. 20.4), and if this process is repeated, pure 2-naphthol can ultimately be separated. This is known as *fractional crystallization*.

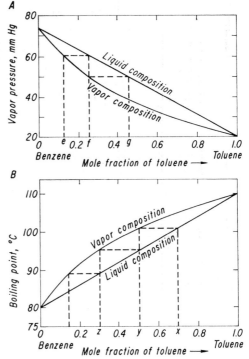

Similarly for systems of two miscible liquids and vapor. In Fig. 20.6, A and B, are vapor pressure and boiling point diagrams for the system benzene-toluene. (The vapor pressure diagram for this system in terms of vapor composition alone was shown in Fig. 11.19.) The vapor pressure (Fig. 20.6, A) is given in terms of the composition of the liquid and also that of the vapor in equilibrium with it, shown by the line labeled "Liquid composition" and "Vapor composition," respectively. The intersection of a given vapor pressure ordinate

Fig. 20.6. *Two-component system benzene-toluene. Miscible solution-vapor equilibrium:* (A) *vapor pressure at 20°C versus composition;* (B) *boiling point versus composition.*

with these two lines gives the compositions of the vapor and liquid in equilibrium at that pressure. For a liquid of composition *g*, the vapor in equilibrium will have the composition *f*. If this vapor is separated from the liquid, and then condensed by increasing the pressure of the system, the resulting liquid will be richer in benzene than the original, and by sufficient repetition of this process, pure benzene could eventually be separated.

Instead of considering this liquid-vapor equilibrium at constant temperature, the temperatures of equilibrium for a fixed total pressure can be measured. If the fixed pressure is one atmosphere, a boiling point-composition phase diagram is obtained (Fig. 20.6, B). Again, the compositions of the liquid and of the equilibrium vapor are represented by the lines appropriately labeled. The means of separation of the two liquids just discussed is presented in this diagram by considering a liquid of composition x, boiling at 101°C to form vapor of composition y. Upon condensing this vapor, liquid of composition y is formed, which upon boiling at 95°C forms vapor of composition z. Repetition of this process yields vapors richer and richer in benzene, until finally pure benzene may be obtained. The process is called *fractional distillation*, and is especially familiar in organic chemistry. The analogy to fractional crystallization may be seen without difficulty.

20.6. Solutions with Maximum or Minimum Boiling Point. Azeotropic Mixtures

Boiling point diagrams of the type discussed in the preceding section describe but the simplest type solutions in which there is little solvent-solute interaction. Equally important are solutions whose behavior is not ideal, but where the two components may interact, with thermal or other changes accompanying the process of solution. The two types, having maximum or minimum points for intermediate compositions, represent solutions with negative or positive deviations from ideal solution laws.

Minimum Boiling Solutions

An example of an azeotropic mixture with minimum boiling point is the solution of 1-propanol and water. The vapor pressure-composition diagram for this system is shown in Fig. 11.22. The solution vapor pressures are the sums of the two component vapor pressures, and the corresponding curve is similar in appearance to that shown in Fig. 20.7, A, although the latter is not drawn to scale.

Since the higher the vapor pressure the lower the boiling point, the maximum in the vapor pressure-composition curve has a corresponding minimum in the boiling point-composition curve (Fig. 20.7, B). Pressure and boiling point values are given for equilibrium compositions of both the liquid and vapor phases, and it is clear that their values coincide only for the two pure substances and for the mixture of composition corresponding to the maximum vapor pressure and the minimum boiling point.

The separation of the two pure compounds A and B by fractional distillation from a solution of intermediate composition is impossible under these circumstances. For example, assume that a liquid solution of composition p (Fig. 20.7, B) is heated to its boiling point, t_p, at which temperature it is in equilibrium with vapor of composition q, richer in component B than the liquid. The residual liquid is hence richer in component A and, as evaporation proceeds, the boiling temperature of the solution will increase until but pure A remains, when it reaches t_A.

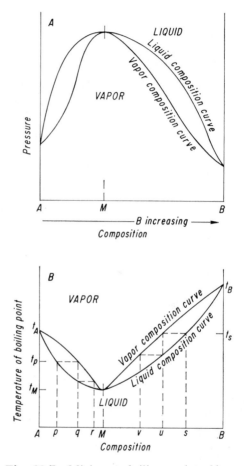

If the vapor of composition q is condensed and then re-distilled at temperature t_r, as in a fractional distillation, vapor of composition r results, again richer in B than the equilibrium liquid. This process continues until the equilibrium boiling temperature has fallen to t_M, where the composition of the liquid and vapor are identical. As further distillation of liquid M takes place there is no change in boiling point or composition, the liquid phase being finally fully transformed to vapor of the same composition, M. This is called the *constant boiling mixture*.

Fig. 20.7. *Minimum boiling point binary liquid solution phase diagrams:* (A) *vapor pressure-composition at constant temperature;* (B) *boiling point-composition diagram.*

Similarly, if the starting liquid were of composition s, richer in B than liquid M, the equilibrium vapor at the boiling point t_s would have composition u, richer in A than liquid s. Analogously to the other case, the residual liquid would increase in boiling temperature until there remained pure B at temperature t_b, and the fractionally distilled vapor would attain the composition M of the minimum boiling point, identical with that of its equilibrium liquid. Thus the fractional distillation of a solution of a liquid pair with minimum boiling point will separate the solution of composition of minimum boiling point as distillate, from the one pure component which was present in the original solution in concentration greater than that of the minimum boiling mixture.

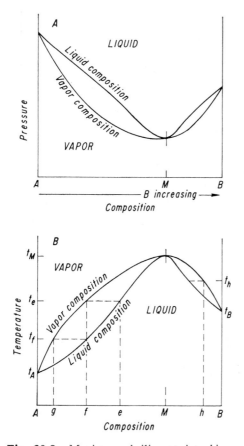

Countless binary liquid systems follow this behavior. Ethanol and water are also such a pair, and the "grain alcohol" of commerce is the distillate of the minimum boiling mixture, 95.57% ethanol by weight, boiling point temperature 78.15°C.

Maximum Boiling Mixtures

Azeotropic mixtures with negative deviations of vapor pressure compared with ideal solutions will exhibit maxima in their boiling point-composition phase diagram. Again there are many examples of such binary solutions, some of which are of great practical importance: hydrochloric or any of the other hydrogen halide acids and water, nitric acid and water, formic acid and water, and chloroform and acetone (see Fig. 11.21).

Fig. 20.8. *Maximum boiling point binary liquid solution phase diagrams:* (A) *vapor pressure-composition at constant temperature;* (B) *boiling point-composition.*

The form of the vapor pressure and boiling point curves in terms of both the composition of the liquid and of the vapor is shown by Fig. 20.8, A and B. Considering the boiling point diagram (b), assume a liquid solution of composition e, which when at its boiling point t_e will be in equilibrium with vapor of composition f, more concentrated in component A than the liquid e. As vapor is formed, the residual liquid therefore becomes richer in B, and its boiling increases until it reaches t_M, where the liquid and vapor have the same composition M. Further evaporation of the solution is at constant temperature t_M, and the liquid of composition M is called the constant boiling solution.

From the fractionating process, upon repeated condensation and distillation of the vapor f, ultimately the vapor will be pure A, distilling over at temperature t_A. Starting with an original solution of composition such as h, more concentrated in B than the maximum boiling mixture, fractional distillation will similarly result in the separation of pure B coming off at temperature t_B, with the constant boiling solution as the final distillate at temperature t_M. Again, the two pure components cannot be separated from the same initial solution.

By considering the variation in the boiling point and composition of the constant boiling mixture with change in atmospheric pressure, solutions of precisely known composition may be easily prepared by fractional distillation. For example, aqueous hydrochloric acid solution compositions for the constant boiling mixture have the following values at the pressures listed in Table 20.1.

TABLE 20.1.   *Azeotropic Mixture Composition with Pressure HCl-H_2O Solutions.*

Pressure (mm Hg)	Percent by Weight of HCl	Temperature of Boiling Point (°C)
730	20.314	107.4°C
740	20.290	107.8
750	20.266	108.1
760	20.242	108.5
770	20.218	108.9

In ordinary practice, a solution less than 20% by weight HCl is used, water fractionating over at 100°C, followed by the constant boiling mixture of 20.242% HCl at 108.5°C.

Although an azeotropic mixture in boiling at constant temperature acts as though it were a single substance, there is no compound formation. The slight variation in composition of the mixture with atmospheric pressure is clear indication that a definite compound is not formed.

20.7. Binary Liquid Mixtures of Limited Miscibility

The mutual repulsive forces resulting in positive deviations from the vapor pressure expected for ideal solutions are in some cases so large that two liquids have but limited miscibility. The totally miscible range is delineated in terms of either temperature or composition, or both. Carbon tetrachloride-water and benzene-water are such partially miscible pairs and have been discussed in Section 16.4 in connection with extraction. Neither provides a suitable example for illustrative purposes, since the solubility of either member of a pair in the other member is much too small in the range of ordinary temperatures for meaningful diagrams to be drawn.

In the comprehensive sense, a binary system of limited miscibility may be represented in the pressure-temperature-composition volume of a three-dimensional phase diagram as a spheroidal region (sometimes called a "miscibility gap"), within which the system is stable as two equilibrium solutions rather than as a single phase. (This discussion would be equally valid if the condensed phases were solids rather than liquids although, practically, equilibrium is achieved more slowly.) Typical isothermic and isobaric planes are shown in Fig. 20.9, A and B, respectively, for the system of Fig. 20.7. Note that Fig. 20.9 is merely an extension of Fig. 20.7, and itself could be further extended to show the solid-liquid equilibria existing at higher pressures and lower temperatures.

For a given temperature there are an upper and a lower critical solution pressure, P'_c and P_c, and for a given pressure an upper and lower critical solution temperature, T'_c and T_c, which mark the limits of the two-phase liquid equilibrium. Outside the ranges demarcated by these *consolute points* the second liquid phase does not exist.

If, in the temperature-composition diagram (Fig. 20.9, B), the composition of the system is varied by adding to component B component A, at a temperature $t_1 > T_c$ and $< T'_c$, initially a solution of A in B will result. The addition of more A will increase its concentration in the solution until the solution reaches composition d. At this point, the further addition of A does not result in further increase in the concentration of A in the solution first formed, but rather in the formation of a second liquid phase, a solution of composition c. As more A is added, the compositions of the two solutions remain fixed at d and c, respectively, with the quantity of solution c increasing at the expense of solution d. Finally, when the overall composition of the system corresponds to c,

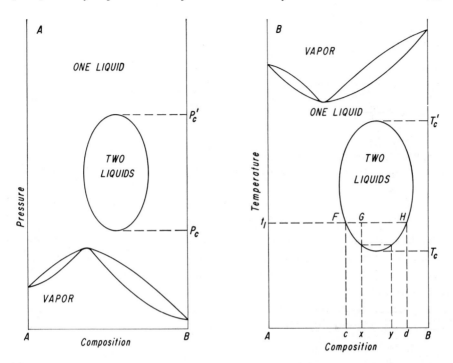

Fig. 20.9. *Binary liquid system with limited miscibility:* (A) *isothermic phase diagram;* (B) *isobaric phase diagram.*

the liquid phase of solution *d* disappears and the single solution phase of composition *c* remains. Further addition of *A* merely increases its concentration in this solution.

Alternatively, if an isopleth of composition *x* is followed from some temperature below T_c to one above T'_c, a single solution obtains until the temperature corresponds to that of the intersection of the isopleth with the boundary of the two-phase region. Thereupon a second liquid solution of composition *y* appears. Further increase in temperature results in the formation of more of the second solution (richer in *B*), and at temperature t_1 the two solutions in equilibrium have compositions *c* and *d*. Continual heating results in the system again reverting to a single phase, when the isopleth intersects the upper part of the two-phase boundary curve.

In many cases, either because of incomplete laboratory data or for reasons involving the nature of the system, even more restricted phase diagrams for these systems than those shown are presented. Ethylmethyl ketone-water and trimethyl amine-water provide two examples, as shown

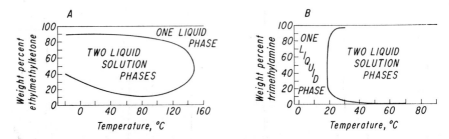

Fig. 20.10. *Partially miscible binary liquid systems:* (A) *ethylmethylketone-water* (*EMK-H₂O*); (B) *trimethylamine-water* (*TMA-H₂O*).

in Fig. 20.10. The former has only a single stable liquid phase at temperatures above 150°C; the latter, only at remperatures below 18.5°C. Overlapping of "miscibility gaps" (as discussed above) with phase transitions between the liquid and solid and liquid and vapor states also occurs, as shown in the two-component diagrams of Fig. 20.11. The meaning of these will become clear to the student with study. Obviously, many other variations are possible, and it is impractical to attempt to discuss all of them in detail. Rather, by a fundamental understanding

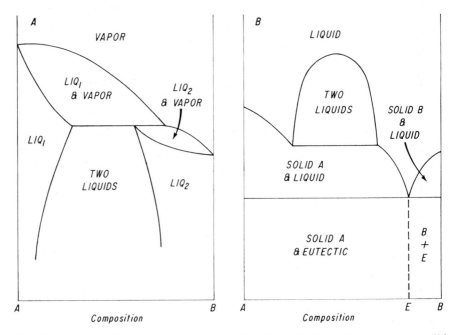

Fig. 20.11. *Phase diagrams for partially miscible binary liquids with vapor state or solid state present:* (A) *boiling point diagram;* (B) *freezing point diagram.*

of the phase rule each can be interpreted in its own way when it is encountered.

20.8. Determination of Relative Quantities of Two Phases in Equilibrium

Whenever two phases are in equilibrium, the equilibrium compositions on the phase diagram can be connected by a *tie line*, and the relative quantities present for the intermediate overall composition can be easily determined. In the two-component systems, illustrated by the isobaric of Fig. 20.9, B, the tie lines all coincide with isothermals. The two-phase equilibrium regions of binary solid-liquid and liquid-vapor systems provide other examples.

The ratio of the quantities of each of the two equilibrium liquids (or other phases, in the general case) will be the inverse of the ratio of the differences between the overall gross system composition and the composition of each of the two solutions. In Fig. 20.9, B, for overall composition G this ratio is

$$\frac{\text{quantity of solution } c}{\text{quantity of solution } d} = \frac{d - x}{x - c}$$

(This can be stated equivalently as the ratio of the lengths of the two segments of the tie line, *GH/GF.*) Consideration of the mole fractions of the two liquids making up the whole system provides a simple proof of the equation above.

Similar considerations apply validly to two-phase areas in three-component systems. Fig. 20.19, A to F, provides illustrations of tie lines connecting equilibrium solid-liquid solution phases of the system Pb-Bi-Sn.

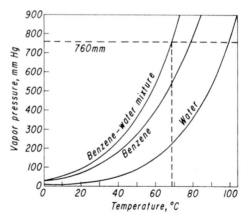

Fig. 20.12. *Vapor pressures of benzene, water, and benzene-water mixtures at various temperatures.*

20.9. Immiscible Liquids. Steam Distillation

The special case of systems of two immiscible liquids is of interest because of its practical importance in organic chemistry and in industry. For the immiscible components *A* and *B*, the total vapor pres-

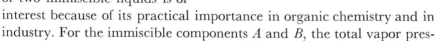

sure of the solution will be $P = P_A + P_B$, according to the given temperature. The variation with temperature is indicated in Fig. 20.12, where the vapor pressures of the benzene-water system are plotted. The sum of the vapor pressures of benzene and water is equal to normal atmospheric pressure at 69.3°C, so the mixture will distill over at this temperature. (The boiling point of pure benzene is 80.1°C.) Similarly, the boiling point of the mixture at any reduced pressure may be ascertained to be below that of either of the pure liquids.

When one of the two liquids is water, the phenomena permits a *steam distillation* to be carried out. This is useful where the higher temperature of ordinary distillation would cause decomposition of the organic substance. Other refinements are possible, such as the purification of a heat-labile solute preferentially soluble in one liquid or the other. These are discussed in laboratory manuals for organic chemistry.

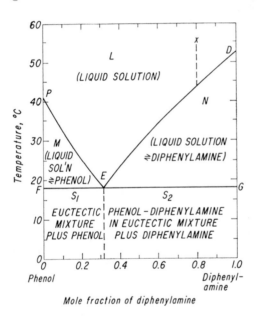

Fig. 20.13. *Temperature-composition: phase diagram for two-component system with pure components only as solid phases (phenol-diphenylamine).*

20.10. Two-component Systems. Solid-liquid Equilibria. Completely Miscible Liquids. Pure Components as Only Solids

A commonly found two-component system is one where the components form a continuous series of solutions in the liquid state, but which exist in the solid state only as the pure components. An example of such a paired system is phenol-diphenylamine, and its solid liquid phase equilibria are shown in Fig. 20.13.

In Section 16.2, the depression of the freezing point of a liquid upon the addition of a solute was described and explained on the basis of the free energy changes. It is evident from Fig. 20.13 that the melting point of diphenylamine (53°C) is lowered upon the addition of phenol, and that of phenol (41°C) is lowered upon the addition of diphenylamine.

The point where the two freezing point curves intersect is the minimum freezing point of the mixture, and is called the *eutectic point*. For this example, the eutectic corresponds to the composition 0.32 mole fraction diphenylamine and the eutectic temperature is 18.1°C.

A solution of this composition is thus one for which the two components freeze out simultaneously; this usually results in a fine-grained mixture of the two solid phases. The application of the phase rule may be made as in Section 20.3. In the area *L*, with one phase (solution liquid) present, there will be two degrees of freedom (aside from pressure, which is constant): the temperature and the composition.

Throughout all of area *M* there are two phases present in equilibrium: phenol solid and solution liquid, of compositions represented by the line *PE* for the different possible temperatures. In addition to the pressure there is one degree of freedom, either the composition or the temperature. (Although it may seem that for a given temperature the composition is variable within the range limited by pure phenol and line *PE*, actually the compositions of the two phases are fixed, only the relative amounts of each being varied.) Similarly, throughout area *N* there is a two-phase equilibrium system composed of diphenylamine solid and liquid solution of a composition to be found on the line *DE* at a point determined by the temperature of the system.

Below the line *FEG* two solid phases exist—phenol and diphenylamine. In area S_1, they

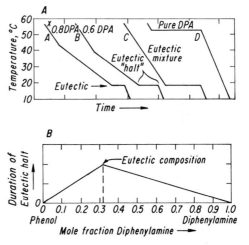

Fig. 20.14. (A) *Typical cooling curves for binary system with eutectic. Phenol-diphenylamine (DPA). (See Fig. 20.7.)* (B) *Duration of eutectic halt as means of determining eutectic composition.*

are present in the proportion of the eutectic mixture plus excess phenol; in area S_2, in the proportion of eutectic mixture plus excess diphenylamine. Since there is no chemical equilibrium between the two solids of distinct chemical species, the phase rule imposes no restriction on their composition.

Consideration of typical cooling curves for the systems represented by

Fig. 20.13 illustrate further the phase relations of the systems. If a mixture containing 0.8 mole fraction of diphenylamine at 55°C (point x in Fig. 20.14, A) loses heat at a constant rate, the change in temperature with time is represented by curve A of Fig. 20.14, A. The temperature decreases at a constant rate until it reaches the point at which diphenylamine begins to separate (intersection of composition line with line DE of Fig. 20.13.) The latent heat of fusion, which must be removed upon solidification, results in a slower rate of temperature decrease, noted by the first break in curve A of Fig. 20.14, A. With the removal of diphenylamine by solidification, the resulting solution contains less diphenylamine, and the temperature at which equilibrium exists between the solution and diphenylamine will be lower. As heat continues to be removed from the system, and diphenylamine continues to separate as solid, the system "slides down" the line DE to the left, with the resulting middle section of the cooling curve A, until the eutectic temperature is reached. At this point the solution is of the eutectic composition, and is in equilibrium with both solid phenol and solid diphenylamine. The solid phases separating upon further removal of heat are pure phenol and pure diphenylamine, in the proportions of the eutectic composition. (Thus the composition of the liquid solution is unchanged as eutectic solid separates.) The temperature remains constant at the eutectic value (flat portion of cooling curve) until the last of the liquid separates. This is called the eutectic "halt." Cooling continues with the solid, consisting of phenol and diphenylamine, in eutectic mixture with additional diphenylamine, as indicated in the final portion of the cooling curve.

For an original solution equal in amount but of composition nearer that of the eutectic mixture, curve B of Fig. 20.14, A for 0.6 mole fraction diphenylamine is representative. The initiation of crystallization occurs at a lower temperature, and the duration of the equilibrium crystallization and cooling is less before the eutectic temperature and composition is reached. Consequently more of the liquid solution will crystallize as eutectic mixture than in the previous case, and the eutectic halt will be longer.

If the liquid solution is initially of eutectic composition, the liquid cools without crystallization until the eutectic temperature is reached, whereupon solid eutectic mixture separates (curve C of Fig. 20.14, A). The temperature remains constant as solidification takes place, whereupon the temperature falls again at a constant rate.

To determine the exact eutectic composition, it is advantageous to plot the duration of the eutectic halt for different initial compositions.

As shown in Fig. 20.14, A, the duration of the halt will have a maximum value for the eutectic composition, will be zero for the two pure substances, and will decrease linearly with composition from the maximum. Thus determination of the duration of the halt for but two compositions, selected to be on either side of the eutectic composition, suffices in principle to permit extrapolation to the point of intersection at the maximum, although better practice is to determine several points on either side.

From thermodynamic considerations, the cooling curves of a system, as defined with the quantity of the system constant and the removal of heat at a steady rate, are nothing more than temperature-enthalpy graphs for the system. The graphs given here, with the abscissa increasing toward the right with time would be replaced by the enthalpy of the system decreasing toward the right. This conversion to enthalpy-time plots is unnecessary for many purposes, and cooling curves are usually drawn because they are obtained directly from temperature-time measurements.

20.11. Melting Points as an Index of Purity, and in Identification

Frequently in organic chemistry use is made of melting point determinations as an index of purity (in fractional crystallizations, for example), or in determining the identity of unknown substances. The circumstances of these uses are best understood in terms of binary phase diagrams and cooling curves.

For pure diphenylamine (or phenol, similarly), the cooling curve (*D* in Fig. 20.14, A) is significantly different from those of all mixtures except that of the eutectic, from which it differs in the temperature at which solidification takes place. (The eutectic halt is replaced by the melting point halt.) The essential feature is the constant temperature during the entire crystallization (or conversely, melting). This is of practical importance in the identification of compounds by their melting points. The student's previous experience has probably made him familiar with the technique of the "mixed melting point," in which the identity of a substance is finally checked by adding to it a small sample of a known substance believed to have the same identity. If the melting point (or crystallization point) is different for the mixture of the unknown and known than for either separately, they are not samples of the same compound. For substances which are completely miscible as liquids and with only pure substances as solids, the melting point will always be lowered on the addition of the second substance (the "impurity"). If solid solutions are formed, the melting point will be either lowered or raised (as in the naphthalene–2-naphthol system of Fig. 20.4). In either case, there will be exhibited a melting point "range," and the extent of this range will be varied as the composition is varied by addition of more of the second substance or, in purification processes, as repeated crystallizations take place. The possibility exists that a given particular composition may have the same melting point for particular systems—in cases of compound formation, discussed in Section 20.12, or for solid solutions in cases where there is a maximum or minimum in the melting point. Determination of the melting points for a series of compositions eliminates these possibilities for all systems save the rare exceptions consisting of pairs of optical isomers with constant melting point, such as camphoroxime.

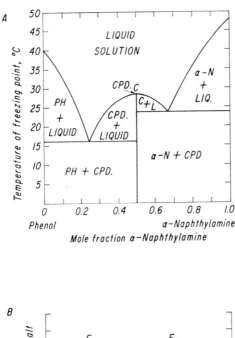

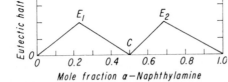

Fig. 20.15. (A) *Freezing point-composition diagram for two-component system with binary compound formation (phenol-α-naphthylamine).* (B) *Duration of eutectic halt.*

20.12. Two-component Systems with Compound Formation

Only the simplest types of phase diagrams for two-component systems have been considered in the preceding sections. The complications and ramifications are almost infinite, and the interested student may refer to treatises on the phase rule, such as those listed at the close of the chapter, which treat the subject extensively. An important class of two component systems exists in which intermediate binary compounds are formed; examples of this behavior are sufficiently frequent and important to be worth consideration here.

In contrast with vapor pressure or boiling point diagrams, freezing point diagrams can provide an indication of the formation of a compound between the two original components. This is shown in Fig. 20.15 for the binary system phenol–α-naphthylamine, in which the intermediate compound $C_6H_5OH \cdot C_{10}H_7NH_2$ is formed. Two eutectics occur, E_1 for phenol and compound, and E_2 for α-naphthylamine and compound. Between these eutectics, there occurs a maximum C in the melting point curve corresponding to the composition of mole fraction 0.5 (equimolar ratio of the two constituents), at which the compound alone is present in both the liquid and solid phases. The areas below the curve on either side of this maximum encompass equilibria between the binary compound and liquid solution. Below the respective eutectic temperatures are found the solid phases, phenol and compound, and the phases α-naphthylamine and compound. The remainder of the diagram may be analyzed in the same manner as for the simpler case of Section 20.10. In this connection, note that if the phase diagram of Fig. 20.15 is bisected along the line of mole fraction 0.5, either resulting half corresponds to the simple eutectic diagram of Fig. 20.13.

Thermal analysis is useful here, in much the same fashion as elsewhere. For liquid of the composition of the compound, the cooling curve is analogous to that of any pure substance, with the characteristic melting point halt. Similarly, for this composition the eutectic halt is zero, as shown in Fig. 20.15. There are two maximum durations of the eutectic halt, corresponding to the two eutectic compositions.

20.13. Two-component Systems with Formation of Compound with Incongruent Melting Point (Peritectic)

In systems of the type discussed in the preceding section, the binary compound formed could be separated and then melted to be in equilibrium with liquid of the same composition. A variation occurs in systems where the solid compound can be separated from the liquid solution, but because it decomposes at temperatures below its own melting point, the solid compound is never in equilibrium with liquid solution of identical composition. Such a compound is said to have an *incongruent* melting point, distinguishing it from the preceding type with congruent melting point.

An example is the silica-alumina system, for which the phase diagram is shown in Fig. 20.16. Silica exists in two crystalline forms (as shown) within the range of temperatures of the diagram—tridymite and crystobalite, the latter melting at 1710°C. Alumina exists as the crystal corundum, with the melting point 2050°C. The composition of the binary compound, aluminum silicate (known as mullite), corresponds to the formula $3Al_2O_3 \cdot 2SiO_2$ (70 weight per cent Al_2O_3). This compound decomposes at 1810°C into solid alumina and a liquid solution of about 54% by weight of alumina.

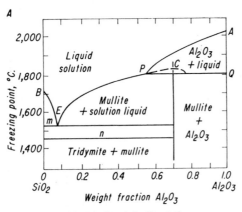

Area m: Crystobalite + liquid solution
Area n: Crystobalite + mullite

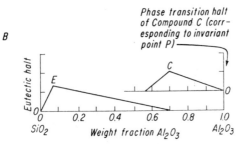

Fig. 20.16. (A) *Freezing point-composition diagram for binary compound with incongruent melting point; SiO_2-Al_2O_3 system: area m, crystobalite + liquid solution; area n, crystobalite + mullite.* (B) *Duration of eutectic halt for SiO_2-Al_2O_3 system.*

The single eutectic, E, is between crystobalite and mullite, with the areas beneath the freezing point curves indicating equilibria between the phases shown. Below the curve EP, at temperatures above the eutectic, liquid solution is in equilibrium with mullite, while at temperatures above P under curve PA it is in equilibrium with solid Al_2O_3. A phase transition occurs at P, and this transition point is called the *peritectic*. Whenever the system corresponds to a point along the line PQ, there will be three phases in equilibrium: liquid of composition P, compound mullite, and Al_2O_3.

The dotted curve PC represents a continuation of EP to indicate the maximum in the freezing point curve, which would occur if the compound did not decompose at lower temperatures. It would correspond to the demarcation of a pseudo-equilibrium between mullite and liquid solution at superperitectic temperatures, could one be achieved.

Thermal analysis of this system is interesting, and is distinguished by two arrests in temperature for isopleths between P and C. The first halt in the cooling curve occurring at the temperature of the peritectic corresponds to the separation of mullite, and is called a transition halt. (The transition is the disappearance of solid Al_2O_3 and the formation of mullite. In practice, the complete transition is difficult to achieve, because the particles of alumina, usually small corundum crystals, become coated with mullite, and thus are effectively "sequestered" from the equilibrium system. Intense agitation during cooling helps to prevent this.)

The second halt occurs at the eutectic temperature, and corresponds to the separation of the solid eutectic mixture. The duration of these two halts for different isopleths is shown in Fig. 20.16, and these curves prove useful in identifying the system, and fixing the composition of the compound form.

This example is the first discussed in this text for an inorganic system, and illustrates also a different indication of composition than by mole fractions. The possible binary systems—exhibiting interesting phase equilibria, both inorganic and organic—are infinite, both in number and complexity. Many common systems, often of tremendous practical importance, will involve equilibria of many phases, solid or liquid, possibly as many as a dozen or more. Examples are iron-carbon (useful in steel manufacture), water-soap (a nebulous and difficult system, but valuable for its applications in the soap industry), sulfur trioxide-water, copper-zinc, and many others.

20.14. Three-component Systems

In preceding sections the phase relations in two component systems have been illustrated by means of two dimensional phase diagrams on the printed page. These were necessarily partial representation of the different possible thermodynamic states, which require three variables—temperature, pressure, and one composition variable—for their complete description. In order to use composition as one of the two coordinates in a plane diagram, either pressure or temperature had to be kept fixed. The phase diagrams are thus isothermal or isobaric planes cut through the three-dimensional solid necessary to show all three variables of the system. (This was in contrast with one-component systems where all variables can be represented in a two-dimensional diagram.)

For three-component systems there are four possible variables, and it is not possible even in a three-dimensional diagram to show two variables of composition, in addition to both temperature and pressure.

The inadequacy of three dimensional geometry is not too serious for systems existing as condensed phases, because moderate changes of pressure seldom change the phase transitions of such phases very much, and these transitions are usually studied at the single fixed pressure of one atmosphere. The results are conveniently represented by three dimensional triangular prisms, with temperature as vertical coordinate, as shown in Fig. 20.17. Compositions at any one temperature are then

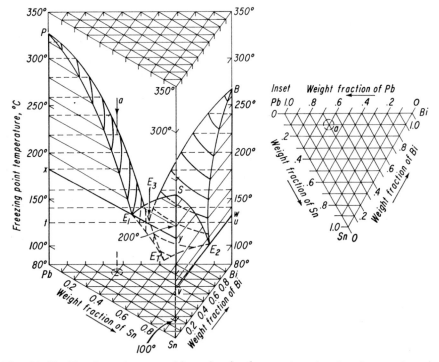

Fig. 20.17. *Freezing point-composition prism for three-component system, pure components as the only solids (Pb-Bi-Sn).*

plotted in the triangular area on a plane cutting the prism at right angles to the temperature axis.

In describing three-component systems it is customary to indicate composition in terms of mole fractions or weight fractions on a triangular coordinate graph, illustrated in the inset of Fig. 20.17. The three corners are labeled to correspond to the three pure components. For any one, the vertex corresponds to a weight fraction equal to unity, the opposite base to a weight fraction of zero, and the ordinates parallel to the base are equal to intermediate values of the weight fraction. Since the sum of the three weight fractions must have its value equal to unity

$(W_{Pb} + W_{Bi} + W_{Sn} = 1)$, when the values of any two are determined, the third is fixed. Any mixture of the three components may thus be represented. Other coordinate systems could be used which would equally well give the composition of three-component systems. By using the equilateral triangle, however, advantage can be taken of geometric proportions which correspond directly to relative quantities of the components present. Books on phase rule discuss this in greater detail.

These composition coordinates are drawn in perspective in Fig. 20.17, with the vertical coordinate shown representing the temperature. The three surfaces shown $(PE_1E_TE_3, SE_1E_TE_2,$ and $BE_2E_TE_3)$ indicate the freezing points of the system, at which the first crystallization of liquid solution initially occurs when the liquid is cooled.

The example illustrated is the condensed phase system of lead-bismuth-tin, for which only pure components occur as solid phases. Various fixed composition-temperature points are given in Table 20.2.

TABLE 20.2.   *Temperature Composition Values for Fixed Melting Points of the Pb-Bi-Sn System.*

Point	Composition (Weight Fraction)			Temperature (°C)
	Pb	Bi	Sn	
Pure metal				
Lead, P	1.0	—	—	327
Bismuth, B	—	1.0	—	271
Tin, S	—	—	1.0	232
Binary eutectic				
Pb-Sn (E_1)	0.37	—	0.63	182
Sn-Bi (E_2)	—	0.58	0.42	133
Bi-Pb (E_3)	0.45	0.55	—	127
Ternary eutectic				
Pb-Bi-Sn (E_T)	0.32	0.53	0.15	96

For three-component systems, the phase rule indicates

$$F = C - P + 2 = 5 - P \qquad (20.9)$$

With but one phase present and the pressure fixed, there are three degrees of freedom remaining. Two are required to fix the composition of the system (the concentrations of two components automatically fixing that of the third), the remaining parameter to be fixed being the temperature. This is the case in the space above the three feeezing-point surfaces, representing liquid solution of variable composition and temperature.

On the surface $PE_1E_TE_3$, and in the space between it and the line for the pure component lead, two phases are present in equilibrium: lead solid and liquid solution. From the phase rule, $F = S - 2 = 3$. Thus at fixed pressure two other variables must be specified, either the concentration of two components in the equilibrium solution, or the concentration of one component and the temperature. The same is similarly true on the other two three-component solution-solid surfaces and the space between them and their two respective pure solid lines.

The binary phase diagram for the two component condensed system lead-tin is apparent in Fig. 20.17 on the surface of zero concentration of bismuth. (This is the flat plane surface in the left front of the prism containing the points P, E_1, S, x, and y.) The line PE_1 is the freezing point curve for solutions of tin in lead, and the line SE_1 that for solutions of lead in tin. The point E_1 is the binary Pb-Sn eutectic. The area PE_1x corresponds to the two-phase equilibrium of lead and liquid solution, and the area SE_1y to that for tin and liquid solution. The interpretation is exactly the same as for the two-phase systems discussed in Section 20.10. Similarly the binary system tin-bismuth is represented by the surface at the right of the prism as drawn, the freezing point curves being SE_2 and BE_2, and the lead-bismuth system by the surface at the rear, curves PE_3 and BE_3, the respective binary eutectics occurring at E_2 and E_3. From this it is clear that the prismatic solid for three components includes three two-component phase diagrams as special cases.

A fourth eutectic point for the ternary mixture occurs at the point represented by E_T, in both Fig. 20.17 and 20.18. (The latter consists of three polythermal projections of the prism along its vertical (temperature) axis on a plane perpendicular to this axis.) This is connected with the three binary eutectics by the curves indicated, and shown uniquely in Fig. 20.18, A. These follow the intersections of the three freezing point surfaces, and for any plane, through the prism, will be minima intersection points. On these lines, equilibrium exists between three phases (two pure solids and ternary liquid solution), and $F = 5 - 3 = 2$. Pressure being constant, one may vary either the concentration of one component or the temperature independently, but not both.

At the ternary eutectic, E_T, the ternary liquid solution is in equilibrium with the three pure solids—lead, bismuth, and tin. Hence $F = 5 - 4 = 1$, and at fixed pressure the system is invariant, there being a unique liquid composition which can be in equilibrium with the three solids simultaneously.

To understand the system more clearly, consider the cooling of a liquid solution initially fixed at a in Fig. 20.17, of composition by weight fractions of 0.6 Pb, 0.3 Bi, and 0.1 Sn. Cooling takes place along the isopleth until it intersects the surface $PE_1E_TE_3$, at approximately 230°C, where lead solid begins to crystallize. The concentration of lead in the solution is accordingly decreased, and since the concentrations of bismuth and tin are not changed relative to one another, the composition will move directly away from the point representing pure lead, along a plane containing the line for pure lead and point a. A set of such "crystallization paths" are shown in Fig. 20.18, C, and that for the ex-

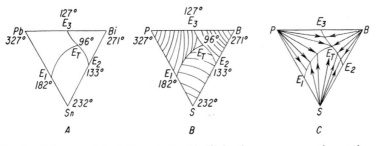

Fig. 20.18. *Polythermal projections of the Pb-Bi-Sn three-component phase prism.*

ample chosen corresponds to the uppermost of the lines radiating from P. Crystallization continues along this line until the eutectic valley (Curve E_3E_T) is reached, where a second solid phase, bismuth, begins to crystallize from the solution. The concentration of tin in the remaining solution increases as lead and bismuth separate, and the crystallization path corresponds to the curve E_3E_T until the tertiary eutectic E_T is reached. At this point solid tin also begins to crystallize, and the three solid phases crystallize together in the proportions of the eutectic mixture until no more liquid remains. (Since at E_T the solution liquid also has the composition of the eutectic mixture, no further change in liquid composition takes place during this solidification.)

Thermal analysis is a useful technique in studying three-component systems, and in examples such as the one considered where the opaqueness of the liquid precludes visual observation of the initiation of crystallization, it is essential. The cooling curve for the process just described is roughly shown in Fig. 20.19. The different segments of the cooling curve correspond to the processes indicated.

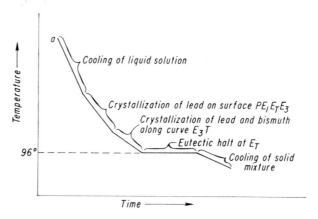

Fig. 20.19. *Cooling curve for a three-component solution of lead-bismuth-tin system.*

The polythermal projections of Fig. 20.18 present a number of important characteristics of the system in a single plot, and are often used. Another useful form of representation is illustrated by the isothermal projections of Fig. 20.20, here chosen to fall between various significant temperatures of the system.

In Fig. 20.20, A, the isothermal projection for a temperature below the melting point of lead, but above that of bismuth, two areas are delineated. These are divided by a curved line corresponding to the intersection of the isothermal plane with the surface $PE_1E_TE_3$ of the prism shown in Fig. 20.17. The larger area corresponds to the liquid solution of lead, bismuth, and tin. The smaller segment with the lines radiating from the vertex Pb represents the portion of the isothermal on and under the surface, where liquid solution is in equilibrium with solid lead. The radial lines are called *tie-lines*.

For any given system of overall composition represented by a point on a tie line, the two phases in equilibrium are of composition corresponding to the extremes of the line (in this case, lead metal), and ternary solution of the composition found at the intersection of the tie line and the curve. Since in the simple instance illustrated the solid equilibrium phase is always a pure component, the composition of liquid solution in equilibrium may be ascertained by drawing a straight line from the vertex of the triangle representing the solid through the

point representing the overall composition of the solution, to the point
of intersection with the curve. The coordinates of this point correspond
to the composition of the liquid solution phase. The quantities of pure

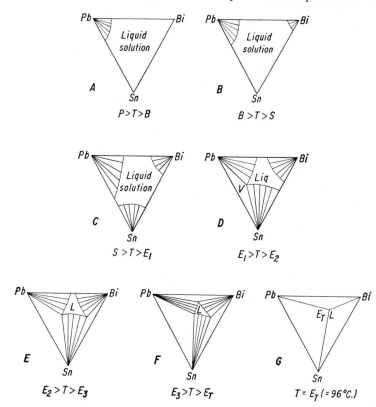

Fig. 20.20. *Isothermal phase projections of the Pb-Bi-Sn three-component phase prism;
T represents the temperature of the isothermal.*

solid and this solution will be present in such relative amounts as to
correspond with the overall composition of the system. These will be
inversely proportional to the distances along the tie line from the point
representing the overall composition of the system to the points corresponding to the two equilibrium phases.

In the successive graphs A, B, and C of Fig. 20.20 the solid phases
Pb, Bi, and Sn appear. Thus at the temperature for the isothermal
shown in (C), within a certain range of compositions of the system
solid tin will be present, the isothermal diagrams (A) and (B) show
that at those temperatures any tin present will always be in liquid
solution, regardless of composition

In the isothermal below the lead-tin binary eutectic, Fig. 20.20, D, point V corresponds to the intersection of the two freezing point surfaces, $PE_1E_TE_3$ and $SE_2E_TE_1$. Accordingly equilibrium exists between lead solid, tin solid, and liquid of composition V. This is the case throughout the triangular area Pb-Sn-V, the relative amounts of the three phases being set according to the point of the overall composition within the area. Similarly for the other analogous areas appearing successively in E and F. For the isothermal taken through the tertiary eutectic, E_T (in G), the three pure solids are shown to be in equilibrium only with liquid of the eutectic composition.

Other tertiary systems of infinite variety could be discussed. For example, if a binary compound is formed between two of the three components, a fourth freezing point surface will be found on the prism, and there will be two tertiary eutectics.

Similarly, there are countless other examples of binary systems and, in addition, quarternary systems and others of greater complexity, many of considerable importance. All can be analyzed in the fashion of the simple illustrations discussed here and, while more complex, their analyses are inherently no more difficult. The interested student can find thorough discussions in the references at the close of this chapter.

Problems

20.1. (a) Nitrogen and hydrogen are introduced in arbitrary amounts in a closed system. How many components are there at equilibrium? (b) Ammonia is introduced in a closed system. How many components are there? In each case, also calculate the variance.

20.2. Solid NaH decomposes at high temperatures into liquid sodium and hydrogen. List the species and restrictions and find the variance.

20.3. Mercuric oxide decomposes to gaseous mercury atoms and oxygen to a significant extent in the range 350°C to 600°C. List the species and restrictions and calculate the variance of a system initially containing only HgO and of one initially containing Hg and an arbitrary pressure of oxygen.

20.4. NaCl and KNO_3 are dissolved in arbitrary amounts in water. (a) How many independent composition variables are there? Which ones would you use to specify the compositions? (b) Determine the variance and show that it is the same whether or not partial or complete ionization of the salts is assumed.

20.5. How many components are there in aqueous solution of arbitrary amounts of KCl and $BaCl_2$?

20.6. Water is heated to $1500°K$, at which temperature dissociation to molecular and atomic hydrogen and oxygen must be considered. List the species and restrictions and find the variance.

20.7. In the two-component system KCNS-NH$_4$CNS, thermal analysis by cooling the melt shows two temperatures at which breaks or halts in the temperature-time curve occur. These temperatures (t_1 and t_2) for various compositions (mole fraction of NH$_4$CNS) are as follows:

N(NH$_4$CNS)	0.0	0.20	0.40	0.60	0.80	1.00
t_1 (°C)	179	170	164	161	155	147
t_2 (°C)	—	163	155	151	148	—

(a) From these data, construct the phase diagram, label the state of the system in each region, and identify the transition at each transition curve. (b) Sketch the general shape of a representative cooling curve, as at 0.60 mole fraction NH$_4$CNS.

20.8. Thermal analysis of benzene-naphthalene mixtures show two temperatures (t_1 and t_2) of breaks or halts in the cooling curve of the initial melt. The data for several mole fractions of benzene are as follows:

N(C$_6$H$_6$)	0.0	0.20	0.40	0.60	0.80	0.90	1.00
t_1 (°C)	80	69	54	38	11	0	-4
t_2 (°C)	—	-5	-4	-3	-4	-5	—

(a) Construct the phase diagram, labeling all regions and transition curves. (b) Sketch the shapes of the cooling curves for 0.6 and 0.9 mole fraction benzene, explaining the reasons for the changes in slope.

20.9. A series of aqueous acetic acid solutions of mole fraction N have the following boiling points at 760 mm Hg and vapor compositions Y:

N (liq)	0	.200	.400	.600	.700	.800	.900	1.000
t (°C)	100.0	101.2	103.2	105.8	107.9	110.5	113.8	118.1
Y (vapor)	0	.122	.260	.430	.545	.670	.820	1.000

(a) Using these data, construct a boiling point composition diagram. (b) An equimolar solution is distilled. From your diagram, what is the composition of the first vapor? If this vapor is condensed and the liquid then brought to its boiling point, what is the boiling point and the composition of the first vapor? (c) If the equimolar solution is heated until the boiling point rises by 2.0°C, what are the compositions of liquid and vapor in equilibrium at the higher temperature?

20.10. Solutions of water and isobutyl alcohol exhibit limited miscibility of two solution phases. The minimum boiling point is 89°C, and below this temperature the water-rich phase has a composition of approximately 8% alcohol by weight, while the other phase has approximately 75% alcohol by weight. Boiling points and weight percentages of alcohol at higher temperatures are as follows:

Liquid (weight %)	0	2	5	10	40
Vapor (weight %)	0	40	57	63	63
t (°C)	100	96	93	89	89
Liquid (weight %)	70	80	90	95	100
Vapor (weight %)	63	65	73	82	100
t (°C)	89	89.5	91.5	94.5	107

(a) Plot the phase diagram, labeling the different areas and transition lines.
(b) Describe what happens when vapor which is 40% alcohol is cooled from 100°C to 80°C.

20.11. (a) For ideal solutions, the vapor pressure-liquid composition curve is a straight line, but the boiling point-liquid composition curve is not. Explain the difference. (b) A solution shows negative deviations from the ideal vapor pressure curve. Show by suitable plot how the boiling point curve will differ from that for an ideal solution.

20.12. (a) An 80 mole percent phenol-diphenylamine solution is cooled to 35°C. Using the tie-line rule, estimate the fraction of the original amount of diphenylamine which has crystallized as pure solid. (b) What is the fraction of the original amount present as pure solid just above the eutectic temperature (18°C)?

20.13. Boiling points at 750 mm Hg and vapor compositions Y of ethanol-benzene solutions are as follows for different mole fractions N of benzene in solution:

N (C₆H₆)	0	10	20	50	75	90	100
N (C_6H_6)	0	10	20	50	75	90	100
Y (C_6H_6)	0	24.5	40	53	61	69	100
t (°C)	77.5	72.5	70.5	68	68.5	71	79.5

(a) Draw the phase diagram, labeling the various areas and boundaries. (b) What are the temperature and compositions of the minimum boiling mixture? (c) Liquid which has 10 mole percent benzene is heated. What is the composition of the first vapor to escape? If this vapor is condensed and again distilled, what is the second vapor composition? What is the final result after a number of repetitions?

20.14. Water and benzene are an immiscible liquid pair. Look up vapor pressure data for the two liquids at different temperatures, and from a plot of the sum against temperature, find the boiling point at 700 mm of the mixture. What is the composition by weight of the escaping vapor at 700 mm when steam is passed through the mixture?

20.15. A mixture of water and n-decane, which have negligible miscibility, boils at 96.5°C under 755 mm pressure. (a) Find the mole percent and weight percent of n-decane in the escaping vapor, if the vapor pressure of water is 670 mm at this temperature. (b) How many grams of steam are required to carry over 100 g of n-decane?

20.16. An unknown organic liquid is immiscible in water, and a mixture of the two boils at 90°C under 750 mm pressure. The vapor on analysis is found to contain 70% of the unknown liquid by weight. What is its molecular weight?

20.17. In the temperature range 60°C to 210°C, nicotine and water are only partially miscible and two solutions can coexist for sufficient percentages of both components. At 70°C, one solution has 11 weight percent nicotine and the other 69 weight percent. Calculate the amounts of nicotine present in each solution if 10 g of nicotine and 20 g of water are mixed.

20.18. Thermal analysis of solutions of formic acid and formamide gave the following temperatures (t_1 and t_2) of breaks or halts in the cooling curves for different mole percents N of formamide:

N	0	10	20	30	40	50
t_1 (°C)	7.9	0.5	−10.5	−13	−1.5	1.0
t_2 (°C)	—	−16.5	−16.5	−16.6	−16.4	—

N	60	70	80	90	100
t_1 (°C)	−1	−9	−14.5	−5.0	2.5
t_2 (°C)	−18.0	−18.0	−18.0	−17.9	—

(a) Draw the phase diagram and label the various areas. (b) What do you conclude about the solid states of the system? Why is only one temperature given for the 50 mole percent solution? (Note: More extensive study shows more solid phases than the data given indicate.)

20.19. The figure below shows the temperatures at which sulfuric acid-water solutions of various compositions first begin to freeze.

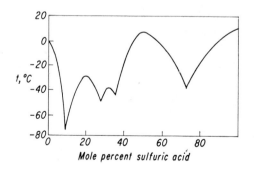

(a) Complete the phase diagram and identify the solid phases and their compositions. (b) H_2SO_4 may be regarded as an addition compound of the system H_2O-SO_3. What other compounds are suggested by your phase diagram?

20.20. Lead-bismuth alloys have a freezing point diagram as shown in the figure.

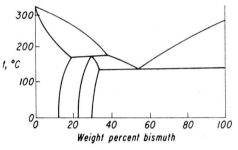

Label the phases present in the different areas.

20.21. The freezing point curve of solutions of $FeCl_3$ in water shows a series of maxima at 60.0, 72.0, 78.3, and 81.8 weight percent $FeCl_3$. Calculate the compositions of the corresponding salt hydrates.

20.22. For zinc-magnesium alloys, eutectic halts are found at 345°C for melts with less than 84.3 weight percent zinc, and at 368°C for melts richer in zinc. (a) What is the formula of the intermediate compound? (b) The durations (t) of the eutectic halts under similar thermal conditions for various compositions are as follows:

Weight percent zinc	20	30	40	50	60	70	80	90	95	97.5
t (min)		45	75	100	140	115	70	20	85	145	145

Plot these data against composition and find the eutectic compositions.

20.23. Naphthalene and dibenzyl solutions on freezing give solid phases containing only the pure components. (a) Use the following values to construct the phase diagram:

$C_{10}H_8$ melts at 80.2°C with a heat of fusion 4550 cal/mole
$C_{14}H_{14}$ melts at 52.5°C with a heat of fusion 5650 cal/mole

(b) How much naphthalene can be obtained pure by fractional crystallization from an 80 weight percent naphthalene solution?

20.24. Using the phase diagram of phenol-α-naphthylamine in Fig. 20.15a, answer the following. (a) What are the changes as α-naphthylamine is successively added to pure phenol at 20°C? (b) Give the phases present and estimate the relative amounts in each for the following temperatures and gross mole fractions N of α-naphthylamine:

t (°C)	30	10	25	30	10
N	0.1	0.1	0.6	0.8	0.8

20.25. Mixtures of water, phenol, and acetone have ranges of limited miscibility at 30°C, much as phenol and water are only partially miscible. A triangle diagram for the system is shown below, the compositions being in weight percent.

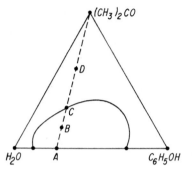

(a) What is the state of the system at the points A, B, C, and D? Estimate the relative amounts of phases present at D and at B. (b) Acetone is added to a phenol-water system of composition A. Describe in detail what happens to the system with increasing amounts.

20.26. The three binary mixtures of lead, tin, and bismuth show simple eutectic behavior. The triangle diagrams for the ternary mixture at 200°C and at 150°C appear as follows.

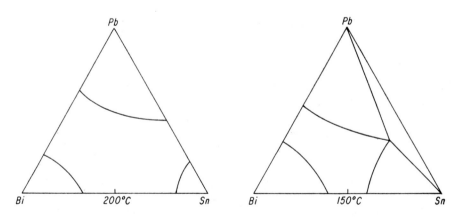

(a) Label the different regions in the diagrams. (b) Which of the elements would you expect to have the highest melting point on the basis of the diagrams? which the lowest? (c) At constant pressure, what is the variance of the system containing liquid and the three solid elements all in equilibrium? If this state is found at 97°C, what is the state of the system at lower temperatures?

20.27. The salts NaCl and NaNO₃ have limited solubility in water. In the triangle diagram shown below, points *A* and *B* represent the solubilities of NaCl and NaNO₃ respectively.

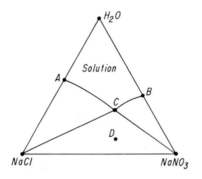

(a) What do the curves *AC*, *BC*, and the point *C* represent? (b) Label the areas and state the nature of the system with gross composition *D* with estimates of the relative amounts of the different phases.

20.28. Aluminum chloride reacts with water to form Al(OH)₃, which precipitates out as a solid. List the species which are then present on adding AlCl₃ to water, and determine the number of components and the variance.

20.29. Liquid N₂O₄ is in equilibrium with a vapor containing the various oxides of nitrogen: NO, NO₂, N₂O₄, and N₂O₃. Find the number of components and the variance.

20.30. (a) The various solid phases of ice were found by measuring the volume of a fixed amount of ice as a function of pressure at constant temperature. Sketch the *P-V* curve you would expect with increasing pressure as a solid phase transition is approached and passed. (b) In representing the solid and liquid phases of water, a phase diagram is convenient in which log *P* is plotted against $1/T°K$, rather than *P* against *T*, because a large range of pressure can be shown. Explain why the transition lines are nearly straight and what the slopes represent. Make such a plot, using information from Fig. 20.1 and other sources as a guide.

20.31. From the following information about the phases of acetic acid sketch the phase diagram. The liquid boils at 118°C; there are two solid phases *A* and *B*; the vapor pressure of *A* is 9.1 mm when it melts at 166°C, and *A* is denser than the liquid; the higher pressure phase *B* is denser than *A*, and there is a triple point for liquids *A* and *B* at 55°C and 2000 atm pressure.

20.32. The freezing point diagram of the system Sn-SnO₂ is shown below.

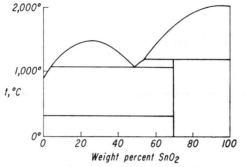

Label the various areas and identify the various solid phases.

20.33. Lithium sulfate and ammonium sulfate have limited solubility in water; Li_2SO_4 forms the hydrate $Li_2SO_4 \cdot H_2O$, and Li_2SO_4 and $(NH_4)_2SO_4$ form the double salt $LiNH_4SO_4$. The triangle diagram for the three component system is shown below.

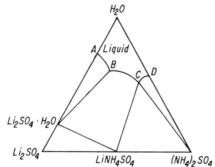

Identify the transition lines *AB*, *BC*, *CD* and the coexistence points *B* and *C*. Label the different areas according to the phases present.

Suggested Readings

A careful derivation and excellent discussion of the phase rule will be found in *Heat and Thermodynamics* (4th ed.) by M. W. Zemansky (McGraw-Hill, New York, 1957). Another good reference is *Principles of Chemical Thermodynamics* by C. E. Reid (Reinhold, New York, 1960). A classic treatise on the subject with a wealth of illustrative examples is A. Findlay's *The Phase Rule and Its Applications* (9th ed.) by A. N. Cambell and N. O. Smith, which is available as a paperback (Dover, New York, 1951). Other examples and problems in analysis of phase diagrams are given in *Problems in Physical Chemistry* by L. G. Sillén, P. W. Lange, and C. O. Gabrielson (Prentice-Hall, Englewood Cliffs, N.J., 1952),

Chapter 21

Surface Chemistry

WITH THE EXCEPTION of the considera-
tion of heterogeneous equilibria and the phase rule (Chapter 20),
phenomena at surfaces have had little explicit discussion in this text.
Even the attention given has been more concerned with physical
than with chemical properties and processes.

For electrode reactions and processes with electrochemical cells
(Chapter 17), reactions taking place at surfaces have been mentioned,
and some special surface effects considered. Likewise, ionic reactions
resulting in precipitation or solution necessarily involve surfaces (Chapter 18). However, the peculiar properties, physical and chemical, of
surfaces in themselves have not been discussed; an introduction to some
of the considerations involved will constitute this chapter. This will be
no more than an introductory treatment, and it will become quite
obvious that we still have relatively little knowledge of surface chemistry.

21.1. The Nature of Surfaces

Every object that can be seen involves some kind of a surface or
interface. Phase discontinuities, of which surfaces are composed, can
exist between two or more solids, two or more liquids, liquids and solids,
liquids and gases, and solids and gases; it is only between two gases
that a surface or phase boundary cannot exist.

The very fact that a surface does exist demonstrates that the interatomic or intermolecular forces on the surface must differ from those in the interior of the liquid or solid, where there is a uniform field of force. A molecule on the surface is necessarily subjected to a field of force which has a net attraction toward the bulk of the liquid or solid. The free energy, entropy, and other thermodynamic properties of the molecules on the surface will have different values than those in the interior of the substance. By consideration of the energy required to create a new surface of measurable area, as, for example, in breaking a steel bar, one could compute from force-distance measurements the energy associated with a unit area of surface, or the surface energy. Surface energies of liquids can also be determined, although obviously not in the same way; the methods used and their interpretation are given below.

The interaction of matter in the gaseous or liquid phase with surface often has the appearance of solution in the surface itself. This process is called *adsorption*, and several theories for it will be discussed. It is to to be distinguished from the process of *absorption*, which involves the taking up of some second phase throughout the whole mass of the absorbing body, rather than at just the surface. When it is difficult to distinguish between the two, the ambiguous term *sorption* may be used.

For a given mass of material, any effect of the surface will depend upon the extent of the surface which is present; this in turn will depend upon the state of subdivision. A finely powdered solid or liquid suspended as a fog will have a large surface area per unit mass compared with a single crystal of a solid or a single drop of a liquid of the same mass. In fact, it is only for high states of subdivision that the surface free energy becomes sufficiently large relative to the gross free energy that it can no longer be neglected, as it is in most practical thermodynamic treatments involving gross matter.

21.2. The Surface of Solids

The particles making up the surface of solids are essentially fixed in position, and only limited local movements are produced by polishing, grinding, or surface working. Solid surfaces cannot spontaneously contract to lower the total surface free energy. Without polishing, a solid surface locally will be very uneven, with peaks, pits, and hollows of small radii. This will result in marked variation of properties from one part of the surface to another. "Active centers" of solid catalysts (Chapter 22) are sometimes explained in these terms.

Under sufficiently high pressures, some "flow" will take place on the surface of most metals; this explains the phenomenon of polishing. Polished surfaces have measurable differences in properties from unpolished or natural surfaces. Thus when plane faces of two unpolished metals are adjoined, intimate contact is impossible in any region where either surface is irregular; the extent of these regions can be inferred from precise measurement of electrical resistance across the boundary regions.

The remarkable increase in area when a solid mass is subdivided may be easily demonstrated in terms of area per unit mass. Assume that the density (d) of the substance is constant regardless of the state of subsidivision, and that all particles are uniform cubes with side of length l. The mass of such a cube will be dl^3, and its surface area $6l^2$. Hence the surface area per unit mass will be

$$a = \frac{6l^2}{dl^3} = \frac{6}{dl} \tag{21.1}$$

For any given substance, the surface area per unit mass relative to that for a cube of unit edge length will be

Edge length of cube	1	10^{-2}	10^{-4}	10^{-6}
Area per unit mass relative to cube of unit edge length	1	10^2	10^4	10^6

Thus, if the length is in centimeters, a unit mass of cubes with edges of 100 Å would have a total area one million times greater than if it were but a single cube 1 cm on each edge. Surface effects, and surface properties such as surface energy, thus become of tremendous importance for finely divided substances.

21.3. The Surface of Liquids

A minute solid particle usually maintains the shape produced by subdivision or agglomeration, but a small volume of liquid will assume the shape of most stable equilibrium. If gravity and adhesional effects of other surfaces are negligible, small droplets become spherical, as is almost the case for small drops of water and mercury in air or on surfaces they do not wet. A sphere is the form requiring the least surface area for a given volume, or quantity of matter, and hence minimizes any free energy which is characteristic of the surface and dependent proportionally on its area.

In its visible properties, a liquid's surface may appear to be a skin or membrane stretched tightly under tension to surround the interior of the liquid. Corresponding to such appearance, a characteristic property of the surface called the surface tension (γ) is defined as the force acting across a line of unit length in the surface, the usual dimensions being dynes/cm.

If undisturbed by mechanical agitation or rapid thermal changes, liquid surfaces appear placid to the eye, but they must on a molecular scale be in a state of relatively violent agitation. For a liquid in equilibrium with its vapor, the mass w of vapor striking a unit area of surface in unit time may be calculated from kinetic theory. If the vapor density d is small enough for ideal gas behavior, the result is

$$w = d\sqrt{\frac{RT}{2\pi M}} \qquad (21.2)$$

where M is the molecular weight. For water at 25°C, about 10^{20} molecules will strike 1 cm² of surface in 1 second; since there is equilibrium across the surface between the liquid and vapor, an equal number of molecules must leave the surface each second. This figure is about 10^5 times greater than the approximately 10^{15} molecules/cm² which can be contained in the surface as calculated from the dimensions of the water molecule. In other words, if all molecules striking the surface condense at least temporarily, the surface is replaced 100,000 times each second by molecules from the interior of the liquid and from the vapor, which is a turbulent situation, indeed.

21.4. Surface Tensions and Surface Energy

Consider the surface tension γ (as defined above) acting on a thin film of liquid stretched across a platinum wire frame $ABCD$ as shown in Fig. 21.1, the end AD being movable. The force (f) resulting from the two surfaces (front and back) of the film which acts on the wire AD (of length b) will be

$$f = 2\gamma b \qquad (21.3)$$

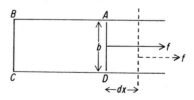

Fig. 21.1. *Work to increase surface area of liquid film.*

A displacement of AD a distance dx by the applied force f will require work done on the system of amount

$$w = f\,dx = 2\gamma b\,dx = \gamma\,dA \qquad\qquad (21.4)$$

where dA is the increase in the area of the surface ($dA = 2b\,dx$). The surface tension may therefore be expressed by

$$\gamma = \frac{w}{dA} \qquad\qquad (21.5)$$

or as the work required per unit increase in surface area. The usual units are ergs/cm², which correspond dimensionally with the units dynes/cm for γ expressed as a tension.

From the definition (and Eq. 21.4), the surface tension γ can be measured as a ratio of applied force to the linear extension it produces when equilibrium is reached, and can equally well be represented as the ratio of work done on the film to the equilibrium increase in area. Because the change is between equilibrium states, the surface work must satisfy the laws of thermodynamics; this fact leads to a useful thermodynamic significance of the surface tension now considered.

Ordinarily, surface effects are most conveniently examined at fixed temperature and pressure. When this is the case, the free energy change $dF_{T,P}$ of the system must satisfy $dF_{T,P} \leqq -w_{\mathrm{ext}}$ (see Section 17.6), where w_{ext} is external work done *by* the system. The equality sign applies at equilibrium, and w_{ext} is then $-\gamma\,dA$ from Eq. 21.4. Hence we have

$$dF_{T,P} = \gamma\,dA \qquad\qquad (21.6)$$

and on writing $dF_{T,P} = (\partial F/\partial A)_{T,P}\,dA$, we see that $\gamma = (\partial F/\partial A)_{T,P}$. Thus the surface tension γ is equal to the partial change of free energy with respect to surface area; for this reason, it is often called a *surface free energy*. The value of γ at any particular temperature and pressure is a useful and significant molecular property of the surface, but as always the full molecular significance cannot be deduced from thermodynamic arguments alone. Before considering the values for different surfaces or interfaces in Section 21.7, we examine first some experimental consequences of surface tension.

21.5. Surface Free Energy and Capillary Rise

Consider two fluids L and V in contact with each other and with a solid wall S, as shown in Fig. 21.2. From experiment, there is a definite angle θ for which the system is in equilibrium, and the relation between the angle and the tensions, or free energies, of the interfaces can be deduced.

For equilibrium and no external forces acting on the surfaces, $dF_{T,P} = 0$, where $dF_{T,P}$ is the sum of all changes of surface free energy from any small displacement of the surfaces. Assume now that the boundary between fluids L and V is displaced a distance dx along the wall, as shown in the figure.

For a width b of surface perpendicular to the plane of the drawing, the area of surface SL between S and L will decrease by an amount $b\, dx$, while the surface SV will increase by

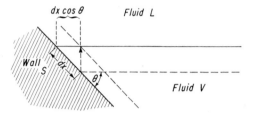

Fig. 21.2. *Surface equilibrium at a solid wall.*

$b\, dx$ and the surface LV by $b\, dx \cos \theta$. If the interfacial (surface) tensions are denoted by γ_{SL}, γ_{SV}, and γ_{LV}, the total change in free energy is

$$dF_{T,P} = -\gamma_{SL}b\, dx + \gamma_{SV}b\, dx + \gamma_{LV}b\, dx \cos \theta$$
$$= (-\gamma_{SL} + \gamma_{SV} + \gamma_{LV} \cos \theta)b\, dx$$

For the change dx this will be zero as required for equilibrium if

$$\gamma_{SL} = \gamma_{SV} + \gamma_{LV} \cos \theta \qquad\qquad (21.7)$$

The value of the observed contact angle θ is thus determined by the relative values of the three interfacial tensions.

The considerations leading to Eq. 21.7 may also be applied to the familiar phenomenon of changes of fluid level in a capillary tube. When a capillary tube is placed vertically in a liquid, the equilibrium level of the liquid within the tube is usually above that of the large plane surface of the liquid outside, as shown in Fig. 21.3. The solid (S) is in this case the wall of the capillary, and the two fluids are the liquid (L) and its equilibrium vapor (V).

Evidently a rise in capillary level is accompanied by a lowering of the outside level, which in this case is in the large chamber. The lowering is negligibly small if the area of outside surface is sufficiently large. However, a rise within the capillary requires that amounts of liquid appear at the capillary surface level which are equal to those lost at the large outside surface level; the opposite is true of the vapor. There is thus a net amount of work w_{ext} done against gravity for any change in level, and the equilibrium condition $dF_{T,P} = -w_{ext}$ must be used. If changes in chemical potential of liquid and vapor with height are neglected, $dF_{T,P}$ is due only to surface area changes. For a rise dh in a capillary of radius r, the surface area SL increases by $2\pi r\, dh$, the area SV decreases by $2\pi r\, dh$, and the area LV changes negligibly. Hence

$$dF_{T,P} = (\gamma_{SL} - \gamma_{SV})2\pi r\, dh$$
$$= -w_{\text{ext}} \qquad (21.8)$$

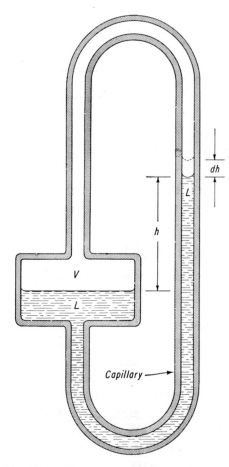

Next, the net work w_{ext} must be found for the two processes of raising the liquid a height h into a volume $\pi r^2\, dh$ and of lowering the same volume of vapor the same distance. For liquid and vapor densities d_L and d_V the masses transferred are $m_L = d_L \pi r^2\, dh$ and $m_V = d_V \pi^2\, dh$, hence

$$w_{\text{ext}} = m_L gh - m_V gh$$
$$= (d_L - d_V)\pi r^2 h\, dh \quad (21.9)$$

Inserting this in Eq. 21.8 gives the equilibrium condition

$$(\gamma_{SL} - \gamma_{SV})$$
$$= \tfrac{1}{2}(d_L - d_V)rhg \quad (21.10)$$

and using Eq. 21.7 gives the final relation for the interfacial tension between liquid and vapor in terms of the capillary rise and capillary radius, and liquid and vapor densities:

Fig. 21.3. *Liquid rise in capillary tube.*

$$\gamma_{LV} = \frac{(d_L - d_V)rhg}{2\cos\theta} \quad (21.11)$$

This relation is the familiar equation for the determination of the surface tension of a liquid by the capillary rise. No assumptions of adhesion (or "sky hooks"), often introduced to obtain this equation, have been made in deriving this from equilibrium free energy considerations. For most common liquids the angle θ is less than $10°$, and the assumption that $\cos\theta = 1$ introduces an error of no more than 1 or 2%. The density of the vapor may usually be assumed negligibly small relative to that of the liquid, so $d_L - d_V \cong d_L$. However, as the system approaches the critical point, the liquid and vapor densities approach the same value, and $\gamma_{LV} \longrightarrow 0$. This corresponds with the observed vanishing of the liquid-vapor interface at the critical point.

In cases where the angle of contact between liquid and solid is greater than $90°$, $\cos\theta$ will be negative, and instead of a capillary rise there will be a capillary depression. Examples of this are mercury on glass, and water on a paraffined surface.

An interesting demonstration of the role played by surface energy to bring the total free energy of a system to a minimum at equilibrium involves placing aniline in warm water. An approximately spherical shape will be assumed by the aniline. By minimizing the water-aniline interfacial area, the surface free energy is minimized.

Other thermodynamic properties of the surface such as the surface enthalpy, may also be evaluated. Thus from Eq. 15.27 we have

$$H = F - T\left(\frac{\partial F}{\partial T}\right)_P \qquad (21.12)$$

If only surface effects are involved, H may be replaced by $dH_{\text{surface}} = (\partial H/\partial A)_{T,P}\, dA$ and F by $(\partial F/\partial A)_{T,P}\, dA = \gamma\, dA$, giving

$$H_{\text{surface}} = \gamma - T\left(\frac{\partial\gamma}{\partial T}\right)_P \qquad (21.13)$$

and may be evaluated by determining γ at several temperatures. Extensions to thermodynamic quantities such as S, E, C_P, C_V, and others, may be made in similar ways, using the appropriate thermodynamic equations.

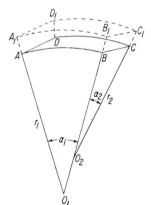

Fig. 21.4. *Displacement of a curved surface*

21.6. Surface Tension and the Vapor Pressure of Curved Surfaces

The vapor pressure of a curved liquid surface will be greater if that surface is concave than if it is convex, all other factors being equal. This difference depends upon the degree of curvature, and also upon the surface tension of the liquid. This is apparent if one considers the displacement of a curved surface, as shown in Fig. 21.4, and the corresponding energy changes.

Surface $ABCD$ is a section cut from a larger surface by pairs of planes with the bounding sides meeting at right angles. The two radii of curvature from centers of curvature O_1 and O_2 are r_1 and r_2, and the surface subtends the two angles α_1 and α_2. Permit this surface to be displaced away from the centers of curvature to boundaries $A_1B_1C_1D_1$ by distance dx, with the boundary normals coincident with those of the original position. In radians, angle $\alpha_1 = AB/r_1$ and angle $\alpha_2 = BC/r_2$. The length of the boundary $A_1B_1 = AB + (AB/r_1)\,dx$, and $B_1C_1 = BC + (BC/r_2)\,dx$; hence the area of the displaced surface is $[AB + (AB/r_1)\,dx][BC + (BC/r_2)\,dx]$, which, if dx is small, is approximately $ABCD[1 + (dx/r_1) + (dx/r_2)]$; the increase dA of the surface area $ABCD$ is then $ABCD\,dx\,[(1/r_1) + (1/r_2)]$. The corresponding energy required to create this new area is

$$\gamma ABCD\,dx\,[(1/r_1) + (1/r_2)]$$

Consider now the difference in the pressure on the concave side, P_z, and that on the convex side, P_y. The work done against this pressure difference for the displacement dx is $w_{\text{ext}} = -ABCD(P_z - P_y)\,dx$, and $-w_{\text{ext}}$ must equal the net addition in surface energy:

$$-w_{\text{ext}} = ABCD(P_z - P_y)\,dx = \gamma ABCD\,dx \left(\frac{1}{r_1} + \frac{1}{r_2} \right)$$

and

$$(P_z - P_y) = \left(\frac{1}{r_1} + \frac{1}{r_2} \right) \qquad (21.14)$$

For a spherical surface, $r_1 = r_2 = r$, and

$$(P_z - P_y) = \frac{2\gamma}{r} \qquad (21.15)$$

Thus the pressure against the concave side is the larger one at equilibrium, and the difference increases for larger surface tension or smaller radii of curvature.

This result suggests that the vapor pressure over a curved liquid surface, such as that of a small drop of liquid, is larger than the usual equilibrium vapor pressure over a flat surface. This is indeed the case, and an equation relating vapor pressure to radius of a spherical drop can be derived by considering the free energy changes when vapor condenses on the drop surface. An increase of dn_L moles in quantity of liquid increases the free energy by $\bar{F}_L\,dn_L$, while the decrease $dn_V = -dn_L$ in moles of vapor reduces the free energy by $-\bar{F}_V\,dn_L$. Adding to this the contribution $\gamma\, dA$, by the increase dA in area of the drop, gives at equilibrium

$$dF_{TP} = (\overline{F}_L - \overline{F}_V)\, dn_L + \gamma\, dA = 0. \tag{21.16}$$

If the vapor pressure P_r is low, when the drop is in equilibrium with vapor, the ideal gas expression may be used for the chemical potential of the vapor; that is, $\overline{F}_V = \overline{F}^0 + RT \ln P_r$. The chemical potential of the liquid depends only slightly on pressure (see Section 15.5), and so is practically the same as for a flat surface. Hence we can write $\overline{F}_L = \overline{F}_V(P_0) = \overline{F}^0 + RT \ln P_0$, where P_0 is the ordinary vapor pressure over a flat surface. Equation 21.16 then becomes

$$(RT \ln P_0 - RT \ln P_r)\, dn_L = -\gamma\, dA. \tag{21.17}$$

In order to determine the dependence of P_r on drop radius r, dn_L and dA must be expressed in terms of this radius. Evidently $A = 4\pi r^2$, hence $dA = 8\pi r\, dr$, while $\overline{V}_L n_L = 4\pi r^3/3$, where $\overline{V}_L$ is the volume per mole of liquid, which changes very little with r; this gives $dn_L = 4\pi r^2\, dr/\overline{V}_L$. Inserting these values in Eq. 21.17 gives

$$RT \ln P_0 - RT \ln P_r = \frac{-2\gamma \overline{V}_L}{r},$$

which can be written in the equivalent forms

$$\ln \frac{P_r}{P_0} = \left(\frac{2\gamma \overline{V}_L}{RT}\right)\frac{1}{r} \qquad P = P_0 \exp\left[\frac{2\gamma \overline{V}_L}{RT}\frac{1}{r}\right] \tag{21.18}$$

This result, known as the Kelvin equation, shows that the vapor pressure P_r of a drop becomes equal to the ordinary vapor pressure P_0 for an infinite radius r (as of course it must), but may be considerably larger than P_0 if the drop is sufficiently small. For water at 25°C, $\gamma = 71.97$ dynes cm^{-1}, and $v_L = 18.07$ cm^3 mole^{-1}. For a sphere of radius 10^{-6} cm, $P/P_0 = 1.111$.

Thus the equilibrium vapor pressure for a very small droplet is significantly greater than for the same liquid with a flat surface, and the difference will be larger the greater the surface tension of the liquid, the lower the density, or the smaller the size of the droplet.

This phenomenon has practical effects which are far reaching. A vapor may exist at pressures greater than the gross equilibrium vapor pressure in the absence of a liquid surface, and only condense as a fog if condensation nuclei are introduced. Fine spray droplets blown by high wind from the tops of breaking ocean waves far out at sea will evaporate quickly, since their vapor pressure will be greater than that in the surrounding atmosphere. Since larger droplets will have a lower equilibrium vapor pressure than smaller ones, the former will grow and enlarge still further at the expense of the latter, which are unstable relative to the larger drops.

A variety of quantitative experimental verifications of the Kelvin equation have been made, and it can be extended to solubility equilibria of finely ground solid solutions, in turn leading to precipitation phenomena such as "aging" of precipitates in gravimetric analysis, and so forth.

From these considerations it seems obvious that when a second (liquid) phase is formed from a previously single vapor phase, it will not occur by the coincidence of several molecules upon which other vapor molecules would condense. The equilibrium vapor pressure of this "pure liquid" nucleus would be so high relative to pressure of the gas that such a nucleus would immediately re-evaporate. The water droplet of radius 10^{-6} cm that has its vapor pressure enhanced 11% contains 140,000 molecules. The mechanism for condensation to a new second phase must almost necessarily assume the presence of impurities or other particles with flat surface of sufficient extent for initial condensation to take place.

21.7. Measurement of Surface Tension

The measurement of surface tension by capillary rise has been considered in the previous section. Other useful methods are those of (a) the maximum bubble pressure, (b) the falling drop, and (c) the du Noüy tensiometer.

(a) The maximum bubble method is perhaps the most useful in measuring the surface tension of liquids. A capillary tube of internal radius R is immersed vertically in a liquid to a depth h, as shown in Fig. 21.5.

To form a bubble, the pressure on the vapor within the capillary is increased somewhat above that in the exterior liquid at depth h. The bubble forms and grows in size as long as the excess gas pressure is greater than the equilibrium pressure necessary to maintain the bubble at the particular size. This latter pressure, P_{equil}, relative to the free surface, is the sum of two terms: the hydrostatic head at the bubble surface and the equilibrium pressure difference to maintain the curved bubble surface against the force resulting from the surface tension. If variations in depth of different parts of this bubble surface are neglected, the hydrostatic head is $hd_L g$, and if the surface is assumed to be spherical, the further pressure difference required for equilibrium, is $2\gamma/r$ (Eq. 21.15), giving

$$P_{\text{equil}} = hd_{Lg} + \frac{2\gamma}{r}. \tag{21.19}$$

When the bubble first begins to form (Fig. 21.5, *A*), the radius r is large ($r_1 > R$, where R is the radius of the tube), and decreases as the bubble shape approaches a hemisphere, when $r_2 = R$ (Fig. 21.5, *B*). Up

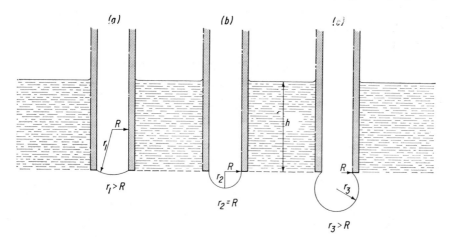

Fig. 21.5. *Maximum bubble tube.*

to this point of growth an increasing gas pressure must be applied as r decreases, to make the bubble continue to grow. But beyond it, $r_3 > R$, and the radius r starts to increase (compare *B* and *C* in Fig. 21.5), and P_{equil} *decreases*. Hence any increase of applied pressure over the equilibrium pressure for the minimum radius when $r = R$ causes instability and the bubble quickly detaches itself from the tube or bursts.

The maximum stable pressure P_{max}, for $r = R$, is evidently

$$P_{\text{max}} = P_{\text{equil}} = hd_{Lg} + \frac{2\gamma}{R} \tag{21.20}$$

from which γ can be calculated. For accurate values, a correction must be made to account for the pressure variation over the bubble surface, which makes it slightly aspherical.

(b) The falling drop method by use of a "stalagmometer" depends upon the measurement of the weight of drops falling slowly from the tip of a vertical tube. This method requires careful experimental techniques, and the theory is imperfectly understood. The surface tension can, however, be measured with considerable accuracy by the formula

$$\gamma = \frac{mg}{r} f\left(\frac{v}{r^3}\right), \qquad (21.21)$$

where m is the mass of the drop, r its radius, v its volume, g the gravitational constant, and f a function evaluated by available tables for given values of v/r^3.

(c) The Du Noüy tensiometer consists of a ring of platinum wire of radius R attached to a torsion balance, by means of which the force required to pull the ring from the surface of a liquid is determined. The length of the film lifted by the ring is equal to its circumference, and since it has two surfaces (inside and outside of the ring) the force required is

$$f = 4\pi R\gamma. \qquad (21.22)$$

Representative values for the surface tension of a number of substances of different types are given in Tables 21.1 and 21.2. The surface tension in contact with vapor at the saturation pressures for most liquids will usually be slightly but measurably larger than when the liquid is in contact with air.

Changing the vapor or gas in contact with a liquid does not affect the interfacial tension very much, as might be expected from free energy considerations. Dissolved solutes will significantly increase or decrease the surface tension of a liquid, and the magnitude of the change increases with increasing concentration. Surface effects in solution are complicated, however, by the tendency of a solute to concentrate in the surface or away from it, as will be discussed later.

21.8. Effect of Temperature upon Surface Energy

The relation of surface free energy to other surface thermodynamic properties can be deduced from the thermodynamic relations $(\partial F/\partial T)_P = (F - H)/T = -S$. In considering surface effects, F may be replaced in this equation by the surface free energy $F^\sigma = (\partial F/\partial A)_{T,P} = \gamma$, the surface tension, if H and S are similarly replaced by surface enthalpy $H^\sigma = (\partial H/\partial A)_{T,P}$ and $S^\sigma = (\partial S/\partial A)_{T,P}$. Subtraction and rearrangement gives

$$H^\sigma = \gamma - T\left(\frac{\partial \gamma}{\partial T}\right)_P, \qquad S^\sigma = -\left(\frac{\partial \gamma}{\partial T}\right)_P \qquad (21.23)$$

TABLE 21.1. *Typical Values for Surface Tension.*

Pure Liquid at 20°C	In Contact With	γ (dynes cm^{-1})
Acetic acid	Vapor	27.8
Acetone	Air or Vapor	23.70
Aniline	Vapor	42.9
Benzene	Air	28.85
Bromine	Air or Vapor	41.5
Chlorine	Vapor	18.4
Chloroform	Air	27.14
Ethyl acetate	Air	23.9
Ethyl alcohol	Vapor	22.75
Ethyl ether	Vapor	17.01
Isopentane	Air	13.72
Glycerol	Air	63.4
Mercury	Vapor	484.
Methyl alcohol	Air	22.61
Methyl ethyl ketone	Air	24.6
Nickel carbonyl	Air	14.6
Nitrous oxide	Vapor	1.75
n-Octane	Vapor	21.80
Propionic acid	Vapor	26.7
n-Propyl alcohol	Vapor	23.78
Toluene	Vapor	28.5
Water (at 18°C)	Air	72.75

Pure Metal Liquid	Temperature °C	In Contact With	γ (dynes cm^{-1})
Al	700	Air	840
Sb	750	H$_2$	368
Cd	320	H$_2$	630
Pb	350	H$_2$	453
Pb	750	H$_2$	423
Hg	15	Air	487
Hg	19	H$_2$	470
Pt	2000	Air	1819
K	62	CO$_2$	411
Na	90	CO$_2$	294
Na	100	Vacuum	206.4
Sn	253	H$_2$	526
Zn	477	H$_2$	753

TABLE   21.1.   (Continued)

Fused Salt Liquid	Temperature °C	In Contact With	γ (dynes cm^{-1})
$BaCl_2$	962	Air	171.
$CuCl_2$	772	Air	152.
LiCl	614	N_2	137.8
KCl	909	N_2	88.0
NaCl	803	N_2	113.8
NaCl	1172	N_2	88.0
NaF	1010	N_2	199.5
NaI	861	N_2	77.6
$NaNO_3$	322	N_2	119.7
Na_2SO_4	900	N_2	194.8

TABLE   21.2.   *Interfacial tension at 20°C of Water in Contact with Various Liquids.*

Contact Liquid	γ (dynes cm^{-1})
Benzene	35.00
Carbon tetrachloride	45.
Ethyl ether	10.7
n-Hexane	51.1
Mercury	375.
n-Octane	50.8
n-Octyl alcohol	8.5

from which surface enthalpy and entropy may be evaluated. Recall that A here denotes "surface area," not "work content."

As defined and used so far, all surface quantities have been in terms of a unit area of surface, and hence presumably involve different numbers of surface molecules for different substances. As for bulk properties, we might expect that simpler and more illuminating relations would be found if the quantities could be compared on a molar basis—that is, for equal numbers of surface molecules. Without some molecular theory, no unique definitions of "molar surface" properties are possible, because there is no a priori way of determining how many molecules are to be counted as belonging to unit surface (how thick the surface is or how deep to go with the surface in counting). An arbitrary, but simple and useful, conversion is to multiply the specific quantities by a "molar area" defined as the two-thirds power of the molar volume $\overline{V}_L$, which is readily calculated from the liquid density d_L by the relation $\overline{V}_L = M/d_L$, where M is the molecular weight. Thus the "molar surface free energy" is taken to be $F^\sigma \overline{V}_L^{2/3} = \gamma \overline{V}_L^{2/3}$, with similar relations for H^σ and S^σ.

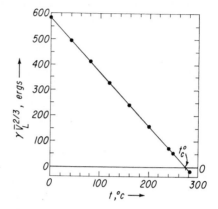

The molar surface energy, $\gamma \overline{V}_L^{2/3}$, for many liquids is found experimentally to vary in a simple way with temperature. Values for liquid CCl_4 in equilibrium with its vapor are given in Table 21.3 and plotted in Fig. 21.6. The data fall closely on a straight line, which however does not quite extrapolate to $\gamma \overline{V}_L^{2/3} = 0$ at the critical temperature T_c.

Fig. 21.6. *Molar surface energy* $(\gamma V_L^{2/3})$ *as a function of temperature for liquid carbon tetrachloride in equilibrium with its vapor.*

For this and a variety of liquids the results can be represented by

$$\gamma \overline{V}_L^{2/3} = k(T_c - T - 6) \qquad (21.24)$$

Eötvös first put forward an equation similar to this, on the basis that surface parameters should be compared in terms of "molar surfaces," but without the provision for vanishing at $T_c - 6$. The equation is

TABLE 21.3.   *Values of* $\gamma \overline{V}^{-/3}$ *for Liquid* CCl_4 *in Equilibrium with its Vapor at Several Temperatures.*

t (°C)	γ (ergs cm^{-2})	$\overline{V}_L$ (cm^3)	$\gamma \overline{V}_L^{2/3}$ ergs
0	27.99	94.1	581
40	23.27	98.7	499
80	18.69	104.1	413
120	14.33	110.0	330
160	10.21	117.3	246
200	6.35	125.4	160
240	2.79	135.2	73.9
250	1.94	137.9	51.8
283.15	−0.70	148.2	−19.6

usually called the Ramsay-Shields equation, named for the men who added this correction. For nonassociated ordinary liquids, $k \cong 2$; for associated liquids, $k < 2$; and for liquids of high molecular weight, $k > 2$. Since $(\partial F / \partial T)_P = -S$, it is seen that the Eötvös "constant" k is the molar surface entropy.

The molar surface enthalpy may be determined from Eq. 21.23; neglecting variation of $\overline{V}_L$ with temperature, it is approximately

$$H = k(T_c - 6) \qquad (21.25)$$

Several other empirical relations relating surface tension to temperature are useful. Since surface tension decreases approximately linearly with temperature and vanishes at the critical temperature, we may write

$$\gamma = \gamma_0 \left(1 - \frac{T}{T_c} \right) \qquad (21.26)$$

where the constant γ_0 is evaluated experimentally at some temperature T_0. Van der Waals proposed

$$\gamma = \gamma_0 \left(1 - \frac{T}{T_c} \right)^\mu \qquad (21.27)$$

where μ is slightly greater than 1. The Katayama modification of the Ramsay-Shields equation,

$$\gamma \left(\frac{M}{d_L - d_V} \right)^{2/3} = k' T_c \left(1 - \frac{T}{T_c} \right) \qquad (21.28)$$

takes into account the difference in densities between the liquid and the vapor.

21.9. The McLeod Equation and the Parachor

Another empirical equation which has been useful is that deduced by McLeod:

$$\frac{\gamma}{(d_L - d_V)^4} = K \qquad (21.29)$$

where K is independent of temperature and pressure, but not of the liquid studied. The McLeod equation is in agreement with those of van der Waals and Katayama if $\mu = 1.2$. There seems to be no simple theoretical explanation of this constancy, except possibly in the neighborhood of the critical point. However, from the McLeod equation Sugden obtained a quantity he called the *parachor*,

$$p = \frac{M}{d_L - d_V} \gamma^{1/4} \qquad (21.30)$$

which is fairly constant over a wide temperature range and has the important property of being nearly additive in terms of submolecular structural units. In Table 21.4, values of the parachor are given for several constitutive species. The measured parachor of a compound of unknown structure can be compared with the parachors calculated from the constitutive species in different isomeric possibilities, thus determining the structure which best fits the data. The fair success of these procedures indicates some relation of the parachor to atomic and molecular structure, but no real and simple molecular significance has yet been established. Much use has been made of the parachor in the past, but development of other measurements more readily interpreted by theory have decreased its importance.

TABLE 21.4.   *Values of Parachor Contributions.*

Element	Value	Structural Constituent	Value
Hydrogen	17.1	Semipolar bond	−1.6
Carbon	4.8	Nonpolar double bond	23.2
Nitrogen	12.5	Triple bond	46.6
Oxygen	20.0	3-membered ring	16.7
Fluorine	25.7	4-membered ring	11.6
Aluminum	38.6	6-membered ring	6.1
Silicon	25.0	Naphthalene ring	12.2
Phosphorus	37.7	Ester	−3.2
Sulfur	48.2		
Chlorine	54.3		
Bromine	68.0		
Iodine	91.0		
Mercury	69.		
Lead	76.2		
Bismuth	80.		

21.10. Effect of Composition on Surface Tension

The addition of a solute to a liquid alters the surface tension in a variety of ways, depending on both the solute and the solvent. Consideration of free energies make it apparent that a solute which lowers the surface tension will concentrate in the surface, since in that manner the total free energy of the system will be minimized. In aqueous solutions of organic compounds, for example, the solute concentrates in the surface to the extent that practically the entire surface is occupied by solute, as evidenced by a resulting value for the surface tension of about 25, as compared with $\gamma > 70$ for the pure solvent, water.

Conversely, solutes which would cause the surface tension of the solution to be greater than that of the solvent will concentrate away from the surface layer, in the interior of the solution, in order that the free energy be minimized. It is obvious that the surface tension of the solution will then be increased only slightly above that of the pure solvent. In general, inorganic salts behave in this manner in aqueous solution.

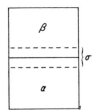

Any consideration of the effect of composition upon the surface tension must evidently take into consideration the surface region rather than the bulk solution, and an adsorption phenomenon is thus involved.

Fig. 21.7. *Surface concentration between two phases, α and β; solid line represents actual phase separation; Region σ, enclosed by broken lines, represents hypothetical surface region.*

Consider a system of two phases, α and β, separated by a phase boundary nominally represented by the solid line across the center of Fig. 21.7. The broken lines indicate a surface region, σ, within which the properties differ significantly from those in either of the bulk volumes of phases α and β. Without some further criterion, the extent of the region is obviously not well defined, but a thickness of a few molecular diameters would be expected for any reasonable criterion. Let N_i^α be the total number of moles of component i in phase α, N_i^β in phase β and N_i the total number of moles present in the system.

If there were no molecules in the surface region, the equality $N_i = N_i^\alpha + N_i^\beta$ would be satisfied; the number N_i^σ in this region must therefore satisfy $N_i^\sigma = N_i - N_i^\alpha - N_i^\beta$.

A surface concentration of component i is defined by

$$\Gamma_i = \frac{N_i^\sigma}{A} = \frac{N_i - N_i^\alpha - N_i^\beta}{A} \qquad (21.31)$$

where N_i^σ represents the number of moles in the virtual region σ and A is the area of the surface layer.

If N_i^α and N_i^β were to be determined from the actual numbers of molecules in these phases outside the surface region, Γ_i would necessarily be positive. Without a knowledge of the thickness to be assigned the surface layer, these values cannot be determined. If instead one uses values computed by assuming that bulk conditions continue to the solid boundary in each phase, the sum $N_i^\alpha - N_i^\beta$ can be either greater or less than the total number N_i, depending on whether the total numbers in the boundary regions are fewer or more than in the bulk phases of the same total volume. Using these calculable values, N_i^σ and Γ_i can be negative as well as positive, depending on the properties of the solute i relative to those of the solvent. Similarly one can define the usual thermodynamic quantities for each component in terms of surface quantities.

If the position of the solid line is properly set relative to the broken lines delineating the surface areas, the excess surface concentration of one component, which may be called number 1, will be zero ($\Gamma_1 = 0$). If this is the solvent, then for $\Gamma_i > 0$ component i is said to be adsorbed on the surface, and for $\Gamma_j < 0$ component j is said to be negatively adsorbed.

21.11. The Gibbs Adsorption Isotherm

As indicated previously, for the excess surface free energy we may write

$$F^\sigma = F - F^\alpha - F^\beta \qquad (21.32)$$

and, if equilibrium is to be maintained,

$$dF^\sigma = dF - dF^\alpha - dF^\beta \qquad (21.33)$$

The value for the chemical potential, $\overline{F}_i$, of a given component i will be the same in all phases, and hence from Eq. 21.16

$$dF^\sigma = \Sigma \overline{F}_i (dN_i - dN_i^\alpha - dN_i^\beta) + \gamma \, dA \qquad (21.34)$$

where Σ denotes a sum over all components. Since, for each species (from Eq. 21.31)

$$dN_i^\sigma = dN_i - dN_i^\alpha - dN_i^\beta \qquad (21.35)$$

we have

$$dF^\sigma = \Sigma \overline{F}_i dN_i^\sigma + \gamma \, dA \qquad (21.36)$$

A more useful form of this equation may be obtained from mathematical manipulation. First, consider the change in F^σ as the surface is increased from zero extent to its final area, while keeping composition, temperature, and pressure fixed. Under these conditions, all the $\overline{F}_i^\gamma$ and γ remain constant as the N_i^σ and the area A increases from zero to their final values, and the surface free energy is

$$F^\sigma = \Sigma \overline{F}_i N_i^\sigma + \gamma A$$

The total differential dF^σ of this expression when composition and hence the $\overline{F}_i$ vary is

$$dF^\sigma = \Sigma \overline{F}_i \, dN_i^\sigma + \Sigma N_i^\sigma \, d\overline{F}_i + \gamma \, dA + A \, d\gamma$$

If the equilibrium condition (Eq. 21.36) is subtracted, there results

$$\Sigma N_i^\sigma \, d\overline{F}_i = -A \, d\gamma$$

which can be written, using Eq. 21.31,

$$d\gamma = -\Sigma \frac{N_i^\sigma}{A} d\overline{F}_i$$

$$= -\Sigma \Gamma_i \, d\overline{F}_i$$

This is the general form of the Gibbs adsorption isotherm relating changes in surface tension to the surface composition and chemical potentials of the components.

For a two-component system, with the phase boundary so defined that $\Gamma_1 = 0$ for the solvent, this reduces to

$$d\gamma = -\Gamma_2 \, d\overline{F}_2 \qquad (21.37)$$

The consequences of this equation depend on the liquid solution forming the interface. For an ideal solution (see Eq. 16.2),

$$d\overline{F}_2 = RT \, d \ln X_2 \qquad (21.38)$$

(X_2 is written for the mole fraction in this equation to avoid confusion with other usage in this chapter.) If the solution is sufficiently dilute, the molar concentration C_2 is proportional to X_2. Substitution in Eq. 21.36 gives

$$\Gamma_2 = -\frac{1}{RT} \frac{d\gamma}{d \ln C_2} = -\frac{C_2}{RT} \frac{d\gamma}{dC_2} \qquad (21.39)$$

This is the form of the Gibbs adsorption isotherm as usually given, and it has been verified experimentally for dilute solutions by several investigators, using a number of ingenious techniques to measure $d\gamma/dC_2$. By determination of the surface tension over a range of concentrations, the area of surface per molecule can be obtained; this is one of the important uses of the equation.

Many modern detergents are "surface active" agents: compounds which lower the surface tension of water and aqueous solutions, and in solution become more concentrated in the surface. Soap is surface active, but some soaps have anomalous behavior in that the surface tension of the solution passes through a minimum as the concentration increases. According to the theory this should not happen, and the current suggested explanation for this is that it is due to impurities.

21.12. Monolayer Films

Perhaps the extreme case of adsorption on a liquid surface may be found in monolayer (or unimolecular) films. On water surfaces, these are generally formed by compounds such as long chain fatty acids, with a water-soluble polar group at one end of the molecule and a water-insoluble hydrocarbon group at the opposite end. In a sense, these are "insoluble" films, since the compounds will not dissolve in the bulk of the liquid to any great extent, and only the polar group has an affinity for the solvent.

For dilute aqueous solutions, the lowering of the surface tension is proportional to the concentration of the solute. The difference is a sort of two-dimensional surface pressure, π, with units of force per unit length, and may be written

$$\pi = \gamma_0 - \gamma = HC_2 \tag{21.40}$$

where γ_0 is the surface tension of pure solvent, γ is the surface tension of a solution of concentration C_2, and H is a constant. For positively adsorbed substances $H > 0$, while for those negatively adsorbed, $H < 0$. From Eq. 21.40, $\dfrac{d\gamma}{dC_2} = -H = -\dfrac{\pi}{C_2}$, which when substituted in Eq. 21.39 yields

$$\Gamma_2 = \frac{\pi}{RT} \tag{21.41}$$

$$\pi = \Gamma_2 RT$$

Recalling that the dimensions of Γ_2 are moles per unit area of surface, Eq. 21.41 is essentially the equation of state of the ideal gas as applied to a surface film in two dimensions with solute concentration Γ_2.

The physical significance of π will be better understood in terms of Langmuir's surface balance, shown schematically in Fig. 21.8. The surface of the liquid (water) is cleaned by moving the sweep, which rests uniformly on the surface, out away from the fixed barrier, carrying dirt and debris ahead of it. The movable barrier is then placed in con-

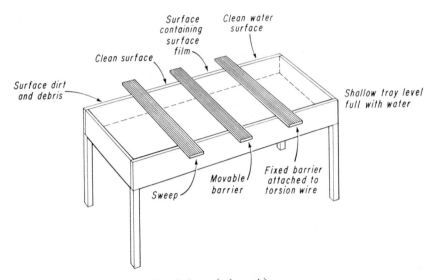

Fig. 21.8. *The Langmuir surface balance (schematic).*

tact with the surface, thus confining the area of the surface between it and the fixed barrier. A known small amount of a surface solute, such as stearic acid, is then placed on the surface. (A solution of the solute in a volatile organic solvent is convenient for this; the organic solvent quickly evaporates, leaving the surface solute dispersed on the surface.) The barrier is then moved along the surface toward the fixed barrier, pushing the surface solute ahead of it. On the opposite side of the fixed barrier is a clean water surface, so any resultant force on the barrier will be a measure of the surface pressure difference π. The magnitude of this force is determined by means of the counteracting force which must be applied by means of a torsion wire in order to maintain the barrier in its original rest position.

Much can be learned from surface area-pressure measurements, supplemented by localized surface tension and surface potential measurements (see Section 21.13). Analogies to be drawn with the condensed and gaseous states of matter in three dimensions lead to the classifications of *coherent* films, which include *condensed* and *expanded* films, and *noncoherent* films, often called "*gaseous.*"

Noncoherent surface films in which π (surface pressure)-A (area) data approximate gaseous behavior are rare. Two of the best examples for which data are available are the ethyl esters of the dibasic acids $(CH_2)_{10}(COOH)_2$ and $(CH_2)_{11}(COOH)_2$.

In Chapter 8, properties of imperfect gases were conveniently shown by plots of the product PV/n against pressure P, as in Figs. 8.7 and 8.8. The analogue for surface films results in plots of values of $\pi A/n_\sigma$ against the surface pressure π; results for the two esters mentioned are shown in Fig. 21.9.

These curves have intercepts at $\pi = 0$ which are close to the ideal value $10^{16} kT = 396$ for $k = 1.37 \times 10^{-16}$ ergs deg^{-1} and an average $T = 289°$K. (The factor 10^{16} is included because the data are for areas expressed in Å^2 rather than cm^2.)

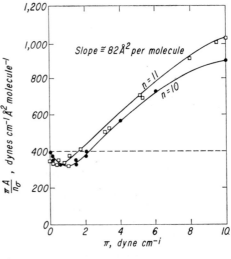

Fig. 21.9. *Surface film π versus πA data for dibasic esters $C_2H_5COC(CH_2)_nCOOC_2H_5$ (gaseous type film). [From Adam & Jessop, Proc. Roy. Acad.* **A112:** 376 (1926).]

For increasing pressures, initial decreases of $\pi A/n_\sigma$ are followed by a considerable range of approximately linear increase. This is like the effects in gases attributed to predominantly repulsive forces, and represented approximately by the excluded volume b in van der Waals' equation. If we similarly write a surface equation $\pi(A - n_\sigma b') = n_\sigma kT$, or $\pi A/n_\sigma = kT + b'\pi$, the quantity b' can plausibly represent an excluded area per molecule. The value corresponding to the positive slopes in Fig. 21.9 is $b' = 82$ Å^2 per molecule. To see whether this is reasonable, we consider a simplified argument, like that for gases in Section 8.7. Each pair of molecules excludes an area $\pi(2a)^2$ or $4\pi a^2$—four times the area occupied by a single molecule. Assuming that the total number of molecules (N) excludes the same area as one half this number of pairs ($N/2$) leads to the value of $2\pi a^2$, corresponding to the excluded area per molecule of 82 Å^2. The corresponding molecular area would then be about 41 Å^2. A gaseous surface molecule would be assumed to be lying on its side, occupying an area equal to a horizontal cross section of 50 Å^2, estimated from bond lengths and angles, and understandably larger than the vertical cross section for fatty acids, dibasic esters, and others of 20.5 Å^2, calculated from measurements of condensed films (to be shown below).

In Fig. 21.10, corresponding πA versus π curves are shown for fatty

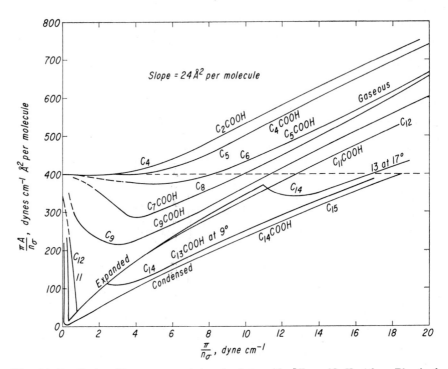

Fig. 21.10. *Surface film π versus πA data for fatty acids.* [*From N. K. Adam,* Physical Chemistry, *Fig.* XVII.2, *p.* 543, *Oxford University Press,* 1956.]

acids, the data for those with less than 12 carbons coming from surface tension measurements, and the remainder from surface film measurements. For the smaller molecules exhibiting "gaseous" behavior, the slope is about 24 Å^2 per molecule, and the corresponding area of 12 Å^2 would be the horizontal cross section, in general accordance with the preceding. It would be expected that molecules with soluble groups on both ends might lie flat on the surface, and be of the gaseous type at low surface pressures.

While the compressibility factor curves most easily demonstrate the analogy of surface films as two-dimensional gases, other similarities between film behavior and gas behavior are helpful in further understanding surface films in more complex situations. For example, if surface pressure-area measurements at constant temperature for a series of fatty acids are plotted, as in Fig. 21.11, one sees immediately a similarity with pressure-volume isotherms such as those for carbon dioxide shown in Fig. 8.9 and discussed in Section 8.6. The broken curve corresponds to "perfect gas" behavior ($\pi A = 396$); the lauric acid (C_{12})

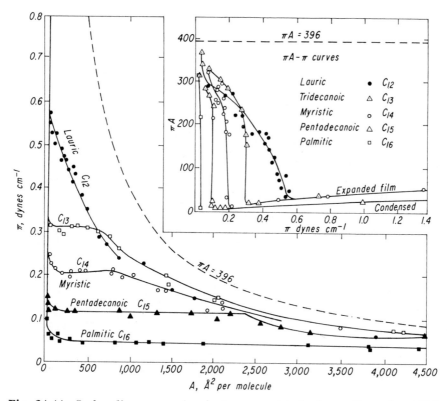

Fig. 21.11. *Surface film π versus A and πA versus π data for fatty acids at about* 15°C.
[*From Adam and Jessop*, Proc. Roy. Soc. **A110**: 423 (1926).]

curve is representative of gaseous behavior, and the negative deviation
from the "perfect" case increases with increasing chain length. This is
presumed due to the greater associative forces within the film itself,
with increasingly longer hydrocarbon molecules undissolved above the
carboxy group dissolved in the surface. There are undoubtedly associative forces acting within the carboxy groups dissolved in the water
surface, resulting from hydrogen bonding involving the water itself.
This is to be compared with the increase in the attractive forces between
carbon dioxide molecules as the temperature is decreased. The flat
portion of each curve would indicate the presence of two phases: a
coherent phase (expanded) and a noncoherent or gaseous phase. The
expanded phase can be thought of as little islands of condensed film,
separated by free solvent surface upon which the individual surface
insoluble molecules are moving about as in Brownian motion (the in-
coherent phase). This model is supported by two independent experi-

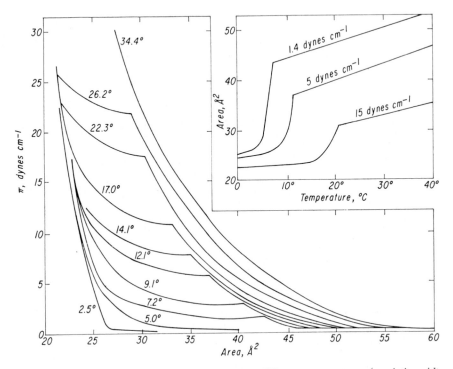

Fig. 21.12. *Expanded film π versus A curves at different temperatures (myristic acid).* [*From N. K. Adam,* Physical Chemistry, *Fig.* XVII.8, *p. 552, Oxford University Press,* 1956.]

ments: one, showing that the electric surface potential (see Section 21.13 below) measured across different small areas of the film varies markedly from point to point, with a range from the fully covered (condensed) surface and the gaseous surface; two, by means of optical studies of the surface illuminated by plane polarized and elliptically polarized light. The value of π for the flat portion corresponds to an equilibrium "surface vapor pressure."

For a higher fatty acid, isotherms obtained from surface film pressure measurements, as shown for myristic acid in Fig. 21.12, also indicate a strong lateral attraction between molecules. The 34.4° isotherm is typical of a gaseous film throughout the pressure range shown. For the lower temperatures plotted, there is a sharp transition on any given isotherm from the gaseous film to the expanded film as higher pressures are approached, and then a gradual transition from the expanded to the condensed film. The range for the expanded film extends further and further into that for the gaseous film as the temperature is lowered, until at 2.5°C there is almost a sharp transition, indicating the presence of only the condensed film. Note that at high surface pressures a limiting area of about 20.5 Å² per molecule is approached.

21.13. Electrical Effects at Interfaces

If we consider a fatty acid forming a monolayer surface on water, with all of the negatively charged carboxy groups oriented toward the water, and the hydrocarbon groups oriented away from it, it is obvious that there exists at such an interface a uniform separation of electrical charges. This situation could be likened to the charge separation on the two parallel flat plates of a condenser of large surface area. This is called an electrical double layer, and was first treated by Helmholtz in 1879. The potential difference across the layer is

$$V_\sigma = \frac{4\pi\sigma m}{\epsilon}, \tag{21.42}$$

where σ is the charge density per unit area of the surface, m is the distance across the layer, and ϵ is the dielectric constant. This can also be written

$$V_\sigma = \frac{4\pi N_\sigma \mu}{A\epsilon}, \tag{21.43}$$

$$V_\sigma = 4\pi\Gamma_2 \frac{\mu}{\epsilon},$$

where N_σ is the total number of dipoles in area A, and μ is the dipole moment of each. (Note similarities with equations of Section 11.6.)

Potential differences across an interface have been measured under many conditions. For a fatty acid, usually enough dilute hydrochloric acid is added to repress the ionization

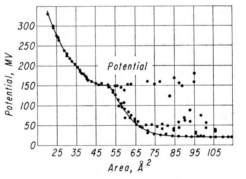

Fig. 21.13. *Potential area of myristic acid monolayers. At areas greater than 52 Å² molecule^{-1} the film is heterogeneous (gaseous and liquid-expanded).* [*Taken from W. D. Harkins,* The Physical Chemistry of Surfaces and Films, *Rheinhold, New York, 1952, Fig. 24, p. 131.*]

of the weak fatty acid. For surface pressures below that indicating a condensed surface layer, the surface potential is not uniform over the entire surface. For example, the increase in the potential difference across a clean water surface when it is covered by a condensed layer of stearic acid is approximately 400 mV. This is called the surface potential. To avoid local effects, the entire surface must be mapped. The variation of surface potential with surface area is shown in Fig. 21.13, taken from Harkins.

The double layer has been described and discussed as though it were a sharply defined layer. Orientation of the permanent dipoles of the water molecules immediately below the surface film undoubtedly takes place to a considerable extent, and the disturbance may be effective through several molecular layers in the water. Even though this uncertainty exists, making it impossible to obtain both μ and ϵ from surface potential measurements, the surface potential as defined can be determined, and provides data helpful for a better understanding of surface phenomena.

21.14. Dispersed Phases

Whenever one phase of a multiphase system is highly subdivided and the resulting small particles distributed relatively uniformly through the continuous second phase, it may be referred to as a dispersed phase. It is also called a dispersion, or a colloid; sometimes these two terms are applied to the complete multiphase system of dispersed phase in the dispersion medium. Such is a colloidal system.

The distinguishing characteristic of colloidal systems is that the

TABLE 21.5. *Types of Dispersed Systems.*

Dispersed Phase	Dispersion Medium	Example
(Gas)	(Gas)	(These are true solutions)
Liquid	Gas	Fogs
Solid	Gas	Smokes
Gas	Liquid	Foams
Liquid	Liquid	Emulsions
Solid	Liquid	Colloidal solutions such as a gold solution
Gas	Solid	Pumice stone (a solidified foam)
Liquid	Solid	Jellies
Solid	Solid	Ruby glass (gold solution dispersed in glass)

diameters of the particles of the dispersed phase range from perhaps 10–200 Å, and their interactions with the dispersing medium are such that the earth's gravitational field does not produce settling. (The reader will recall that atomic dimensions and lengths of interatomic bonds in molecules are of the order of a few angstroms. The greatest dimension of the tobacco mosaic virus is 2500 Å, which is about the limit of resolution of a microscope using visible light.) Examples of colloidal systems are abundant in nature. With some poetic license, different types of colloidal dispersions are listed in Table 21.5.

21.15. The Chemistry of Colloids

Almost all early knowledge of colloids was solely chemical. Thomas Graham in 1861 was so systematic in his organization and studies of colloids that he is called the "father of colloid chemistry," even though colloidal solutions were known centuries previously. Glass made ruby-colored by colloidal gold dates to the sixteenth century; colloidal silicic acid in aqueous solution and gold dispersed as a colloidal aqueous solution had been described prior to Graham's paper. Almost all substances can be colloidally dispersed in some way, the most common methods being mechanical or chemical. Silver sols or hydrosols (colloidal aqueous solutions), prepared by reduction of the silver ion, by oxidation, or by precipitation, will range in color throughout the visible spectrum, depending upon the particular conditions of formation. Sulfur and iodine form sols. Whole ranges of oxide hydrosols (compounds of metal, metal oxide, and water in varying proportions) can be formed from iron, aluminum, chromium, vanadium, and tin. Sulfide sols of many of these same metals can also be formed. Their properties are highly dependent upon the particular mode of formation.

Sols such as these are subject to precipitation by the addition of electrolytes to the colloidal solutions. There are no overall general rules governing this behavior, but the efficiency of a given salt as a coagulating agent will depend upon:

1. The electrical charge on the water surface of the Helmholtz double layer surrounding the micelle (the individual colloidal particle). Positive micelles are precipitated by negative ions, and so on.

2. The nature of the precipitating ion. For various metallic sulfide and oxide hydrosols the precipitation orders of effectiveness are $Ca^+ > Rb^+ > K^+ > Na^+ > Li^+$ and $Cl^- > Br^- > I^-$. In other cases these orders will be reversed.

Organic polymers, both natural and synthetic, form colloidal solutions, and much of the chemistry of physiology has to do with colloids. Hofmeister, in studying the "salting-out" of proteins (precipitation from solution by addition of electrolytes), found the effectiveness of different ions to be similar for different colloids.

Hofmeister's series for egg albumin were

$$SO_4^{2-} > PO_4^{3-} > CH_3COO^- > \text{citrate} > HCO_3^- >$$
$$CrO_4^{2-} > Cl^- > NO_3^-$$

and

$$Li^+ > Na^+ > K^+ > NH_4^+ > Mg^{2+}$$

(This is also called a lyotropic series.)

Some sols are highly hydrated. These are known as lyophilic sols ("water loving"), and examples of these may be found in sols of proteins, carbohydrates, and some colloidal hydroxides. They are generally characterized by a markedly higher viscosity than that of the pure solvent, and are salted out only with fairly high concentrations of added electrolyte.

In contrast, lyophobic ("water hating") sols indicate they are but little solvated, and have no large increase in viscosity over the solvent viscosity. They are usually sols of pure metal or metal oxide, although colloidal dispersions of other elements (for example, sulfur or inorganic compounds) may be found among them. Their micelles are highly charged, and but small concentrations of added electrolyte are sufficient to cause salting out.

21.16. Physical Properties of Colloids

Colloidal solutions have unusual physical properties, and extensive investigations have led to a fairly good understanding of the structure of colloidal systems.

Optical Properties

Colloidal micelles are too small to be observed optically with a microscope; although an electron microscope is useful for particles within their range of sizes, present techniques do not permit observation of these micelles while in suspension. However, by means of the Tyndall effect, their number, position, and motion within a colloidal solution may be observed. For this observation, a high-powered microscope is trained on the solution, behind which a black absorbing screen is placed, and the solution is illuminated from the side. Under these conditions, no direct light enters the microscope, but the micelles appear as points of light on the dark field. (Note that this effect was used in Millikan's oil drop experiment.) These points are observed to dart about with sudden changes in the direction of motion, which result from collisions with other micelles. The phenomenon is called *Brownian motion*. Debye has worked out a practical theory for the determination of molecular weights by the measurement of scattered light from colloidal solutions.

Molecular weights, which are taken to be the micellar weights, may also be obtained from osmotic pressure measurements, from viscosity measurements, from measurements of diffusion, and by means of sedimentation-velocity or sedimentation-equilibrium values, as determined by use of the ultracentrifuge. The values for the molecular weight as determined by these different and independent methods are usually in agreement within experimental error when the different types of averaging processes inherent to different methods (such as weight averaging or number averaging) are taken into account.

Further useful information on colloidal systems can be obtained by measuring the motion of the colloid particles through the solution under the influence of an electric field. This process is called *electrophoresis;* electrophoretic measurements have been of particular value in studies of blood plasma and in the separation of the several globulins present in plasma. *Electroosmosis* involves colloidal phenomena at membranes under the influence of electric fields.

The quantitative and theoretical considerations of the above phenomena and data derived from them are sufficiently extensive and specialized that a proper treatment is beyond the scope of this book.

21.17. Adsorption on Solids; Adsorption Isotherms

Solid surfaces adsorb molecules of all types from any gaseous or liquid phases in contact with them. The amounts adsorbed and the rate at which adsorption or disorption take place depend strongly and in a variety of ways on such factors as the chemical identities of the adsorbent and the solid, the solid structure and the nature of the surface exposed, the temperature, and pressure or concentration of the phase in contact.

The amount of gas which small masses of such natural adsorbents as charcoal, kieselguhr, and silica gel take up can be prodigious. Thus one gram of charcoal at 0°C has been found to adsorb 10^{-3} moles (of the order of one-tenth gram) of krypton at equilibrium with the gas at a pressure of only 16 mm Hg. Metal surfaces also frequently adsorb and hold small quantities of gas very tenaciously; prolonged evacuation accompanied by heating to high temperatures, electron bombardment, or other drastic treatment is necessary to remove the last traces of adsorbed gas from the metal surface. Thus solid surfaces are ordinarily quite dirty on a molecular scale, and great pains must be taken if reliable studies of their true properties are to be made.

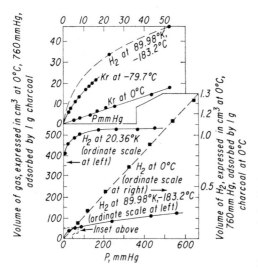

Fig. 21.14. *Adsorption isotherms for H_2 and Kr on charcoal.*

These observations clearly indicate stable surface attachment of adsorbed molecules, particularly when these molecules are attached to the bare clean surface. The large amounts of gas adsorbed by porous or finely divided solids are generally attributable to the large surface area per gram of solid. (From the analysis to follow, one can estimate that one gram of powdered charcoal has a surface area of several million square centimeters.)

The attractive forces responsible for adsorption are naturally to be compared with the kinds of forces between molecules invoked to explain molecular attraction and condensation of gases, and cohesion of solids. All atoms and molecules exhibit the van der Waals (or better, London) attraction by mutual polarization; one therefore expects a general, although variable behavior which is sometimes called *physical adsorption*. Many other more chemically specific effects are also observed, as when particular molecules are very highly adsorbed, or when contact with the surface promotes chemical reaction. In such cases, one suspects more specific interactions, and the term chemisorption is used.

The first notable progress in molecular theory of adsorption was made by Langmuir in 1916, when he presented a kinetic theory of the so-called *adsorption isotherm*. This term refers to the relation at constant temperature between quantity of gas adsorbed on a surface and the concentration, or pressure, in the gas phase; the relation is thus a sort of surface equation of state.

Figures 21.14 and 21.15 show some simple isotherms for adsorption of gases on charcoal. The ordinate in each case is the quan-
tity of gas adsorbed per gram
of solid expressed as cubic centimeters of gas at 0°C and 1
atm (a convenient unit if the
quantity adsorbed is deduced
by volumetric gas analysis);
the abscissa is pressure in mm
Hg. In spite of considerable
differences in the conditions
governing their investigations,
the plotted data of Richardson
and of Titoff for ammonia are
in remarkable agreement.

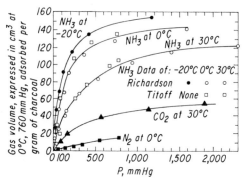

Fig. 21.15. *Gas volume (expressed in cm^3 at 0°C, 760 mm Hg) adsorbed per gram of charcoal as a function of the gas pressure.*

For small adsorbed amounts, the adsorption varies nearly linearly with the pressure, but for greater amounts the adsorption is relatively less. This linearity is observed for all gases illustrated at sufficiently low pressures. For gases which are poorly adsorbed, approximate linearity is noted over a wide range of pressures (as for H_2 at 0°C), but even in such cases some falling off is noted as the pressure is increased. This suggests a possible saturation effect.

Where several different isotherms are given for the same gas (hydro-gen, krypton, and ammonia), it is noted that at constant pressure the adsorption increases with decreasing temperature. This indicates it to be an exothermic process.

Langmuir's basic ideas were that in such cases molecules were sig-nificantly attracted only to given sites on bare solid surface, and were not attracted at all to other parts of the surface or to sites already cov-ered with a molecular monolayer. An expression for the equilibrium number at a particular gas pressure is obtained by equating the number of molecules striking and becoming adsorbed on uncovered parts of the surface to the number of molecules returning to the gas by desorption from the areas of the surface covered by adsorbed gas.

From kinetic theory the number of gas molecules striking unit surface in unit time is proportional to the gas pressure P, and some fraction of those striking the surface (depending on temperature, the species of gas, and the type of surface) is assumed to become attached if the surface is free of adsorbed molecules. Let θ be the fraction of the total area A which is covered at a given moment and hence unavailable; the rate of dN_a/dt at which molecules are adsorbed can then be written

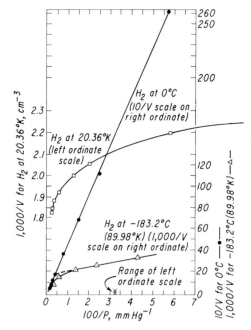

$$\frac{dN_a}{dt} = k_a(A - \theta A)P$$

$$= k_a AP - k_a \theta AP$$

where the parameter k_a will depend on the temperature, kind of gas, and the kind of surface, but not on the pressure or fraction θ. The rate dN_a/dt at which molecules are desorbed will also depend on the temperature, kind of gas, and specific surface factors; if these are kept constant, only the total number of molecules attached to the surface should

Fig. 21.16. *Adsorption of hydrogen under varying conditions of pressure and temperature.*

affect the number leaving from a given area in a given time. This total number is proportional to the surface covered, θA. Hence the rate can be written

$$\frac{dN_d}{dt} = k_d \theta A$$

where k_d is a rate constant for the desorption independent of surface covered and pressure of gas, with an exponential term involving the heat of adsorption.

Equating the rates of adsorption and desorption gives for equilibrium

$$k_a AP - k_a \theta AP = k_d \theta A \qquad (21.44)$$

The amount of surface covered, θA, will be proportional to the number of molecules adsorbed N_a if each molecule occupies a definite area or becomes attached only at certain sites regularly spaced on the surface.

This number N_a can then be written $N_a = K\theta A$, and taking θA in terms of P from Eq. 21.44 permits us to write

$$N_a = K\theta A = \frac{(Kk_a)P}{k_d + k_aP} \qquad (21.45)$$

This is one form of the Langmuir adsorption isotherm. At low pressure the term k_aP in the denominator can be neglected, giving $N_a = K(k_a/k_d)P$—that is, initial linear variation of adsorption with pressure. At extremely high pressures k_d can be neglected, giving $N_a = K$, corresponding to complete surface coverage. Equation 21.45 thus qualitatively reproduces the observed behavior. To test it more quantitatively, rearrangement conveniently gives

$$\frac{1}{N_a} = \left(\frac{k_a}{k_aK}\right)\frac{1}{P} + \frac{1}{K} \qquad (21.46)$$

This can be tested by plotting $1/V$ versus $1/P$, since N_a is proportional to V, the volume of gas adsorbed. The data of Fig. 21.14 are thus plotted in Figs. 21.16 and 21.17, and those of Fig. 21.15 in Fig. 21.18.

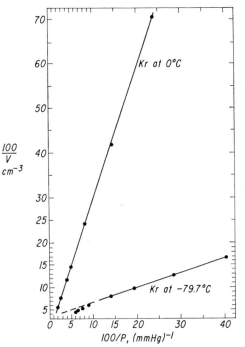

Fig. 21.17. *Adsorption of krypton under varying conditions of pressure and temperature*

The data for krypton and hydrogen at 0°C, where the amounts adsorbed are small, meet this test for the Langmuir isotherm as expressed in Eq. 21.46 over their entire range. Other data give linear $1/V$ versus $1/P$ plots over limited portions of the range of data, as for krypton at -79.7°C. In some instances it appears that the data can be divided into several different linear portions, each with a different slope. This might indicate a change in the nature of the adsorption process or of the structure of adsorbing surface, with change in pressure or fraction of surface saturated. Variations in the heat of adsorption (which enters the k_d term) have been observed. In the case of hydrogen at 20°K,

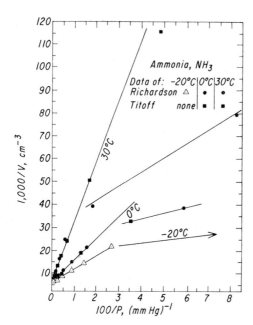

Fig. 21.18. *Adsorption of ammonia under varying conditions of pressure and temperature.*

where no linearity is observed, there could be a continuous change of the value of the heat of adsorption as the extent of charcoal surface covered varies, corresponding to interaction of adsorbed molecules in such a way that the energy of adsorbing a molecule varies with the surface coverage. This kind of explanation is supported by measurements of heats of adsorption for different coverages, either directly or by application of Clapeyron's equation; these show a considerable change with amount of coverage.

A variety of other effects have been observed in adsorption. A chemical effect occurs for hydrogen on tungsten at 1000°K, as shown by a rapid production of hydrogen *atoms* at a rate which varies as the square root of pressure and increases markedly at high temperatures. The adsorption and desorption at the surface clearly involves atoms, indicating that the reaction $H_2(gas) = 2H(adsorbed)$ is involved.

A frequently observed effect is indicated schematically in Fig. 21.19. The quantity of gas or other species adsorbed rises at first rapidly, then more slowly, and then more rapidly again with increasing pressure or concentration of adsorbent in contact with the surface. This has been attributed by Brunauer, Emmett, and Teller to multimolecular (or multilayer) adsorption: at first the bare surface becomes increasingly covered with a strongly

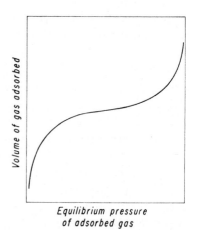

Fig. 21.19. *Typical BET isotherm based on the theory of multimolecular adsorption.*

adsorbed monomolecular layer, but at later stages further less strongly adsorbed layers begin to build up. The analysis is too lengthy to be given here, but the resulting *BET isotherm* (from the author's initials) predicts the S-shaped curves capable of representing the behavior indicated by Fig. 21.19.

Problems

21.1. From known values of surface tension and density for water at 25°C calculate the capillary rise in a tube 0.6 mm in diameter.

21.2. At 20°C the variation of surface tension with concentration of a 0.05 M aqueous solution of phenol is $d\gamma/dc = -165$ erg cm^{-2} mole^{-1} liter. What is the surface concentration of phenol adsorbed?

21.3. At 90°K a sample of mica adsorbed the quantities of nitrogen indicated for the following pressures:

Volume (cm³ at 20°C, 760 torr) × 10²	2.55	2.16	1.70	1.51	1.20
Pressure (atm)		12.8	7.3	4.9	3.9	2.8

Graph these data to determine whether or not they may be represented by one of the classical adsorption isotherms. If so, evaluate the constants.

21.4. (a) Derive the expression for surface area per unit mass of a solid subdivided as small spheres of radius r. (b) What is the area per unit mass x of a given substance present as spheres of radius $r = 1000$ Å, as compared with spheres of $r = 1$ mm?

21.5. Give examples of phase discontinuities, including two that involve but a single state of matter.

21.6. What is the surface area occupied per hydrocarbon chain for a fatty acid if the monolayer film as formed from 0.25 ml of 0.005 M alcoholic solution occupies an area on a water surface of 1,500 cm²? What molecular dimension could this represent?

21.7. What is the basis for calling surface tension the surface free energy?

21.8. A suspension of spherical particles of uniform radius of 10^{-7} cm is prepared from a solid of density 2.3 g/cm³. Estimate the total surface area.

21.9. Derive the Gibbs adsorption isotherm from considerations of free energy.

21.10. What assumptions are involved in deriving the expression

$$\gamma = \tfrac{1}{2}hdrg$$

for the surface free energy of a liquid in contact with its vapor, as determined by capillary rise?

21.11. Can the data given below for the adsorption of nitrogen on 1 g of activated carbon be fitted by the Langmuir adsorption isotherm?

Pressure of nitrogen (torr)	0.43	1.21	3.93	12.98	22.94	34.01	56.23	77.46
Volume adsorbed (ml at STP)	0.111	0.298	0.987	3.043	5.082	7.047	10.310	13.053

21.12. If a capillary tube has a diameter of 10^{-4} mm, at 18°C how much pressure would be required to blow a column of water out of it? of CH_3OH at 20°C?

21.13. From measurements by Ramsey and Shields of the surface tension of carbon tetrachloride in equilibrium with its vapor, the following expression is obtained:

$$\gamma = 62.99 - 1.301 \times 10^{-1}T - 1.276 \times 10^{-5}T^2 + 7.33 \times 10^{-8}T^3$$

(a) From this calculate the surface entropy and the surface enthalpy at 25°C. (b) Five grams of finely divided powder with surface area of 220 m^2/g has its surface covered with a thin layer of CCl_4 at 20°C, and is dropped into a large volume of liquid CCl_4 at the same temperature. How much heat will be evolved?

21.14. The bottoms of two capillary tubes of approximately $\frac{1}{2}$-mm bore are immersed in water at 25°C. The capillary rise in tube *A* was 1.2 mm greater than that in tube *B*. To what difference in diameters does this correspond?

21.15. Calculate the surface entropy and surface enthalpy for benzene at 30°C from the following data:

Temperature (°C)	20	25	30	35	40
Surface free energy (dynes/cm)	28.86	28.19	27.61	26.62	26.21

21.16. What is the surface tension of a liquid of density 1.4 g/cm^3 if for a capillary of 1.8-mm diameter 1.5 mm below the surface of the liquid a maximum bubble pressure equal to 1450 torr can be achieved?

Suggested Readings

The classic reference for this subject is N. K. Adam, *The Physics and Chemistry of Surfaces* (2nd ed., Oxford, 1944). Another useful book with a variety of illustrations is S. Brunauer, *The Adsorption of Gases and Vapors* (Princeton University Press, 1943).

Much of electrochemistry is concerned with reactions and properties of surfaces; these aspects are discussed in several of the references for Chapter 17.

Chapter 22

Chemical Kinetics

IN PREVIOUS CHAPTERS, chemical properties of substances have been discussed in relation to structure, the physical properties of states of matter have been examined, and necessary conditions for equilibrium have been deduced from general laws and applied to a variety of problems. Only occasionally and incidentally in these developments have we considered how rapidly or slowly chemical reactions actually occur under various conditions. This is a subject of major importance, but it is one about which conventional thermodynamics can give no information, because the element of time nowhere appears in the fundamental laws. Thus thermodynamics leads to useful statements about possible directions of chemical change and to valuable relations between measurable quantities in changes between equilibrium states, but thermodynamics cannot help determine whether changes will occur in seconds or years nor can it indicate *how* the changes occur within a given period of time.

Chemical kinetics, or reaction kinetics, is first of all concerned with quantitative treatment of rates of reactions, the factors influencing reaction rates, and the prediction of reaction rates. Of equal importance and more fundamental interest is the possibility that from such knowledge hypotheses can be put forward and tested with regard to the mechanism by which atoms and molecules undergo reactions of combination, rearrangement, or decomposition. At present, in all candor, it must be recognized that the mechanisms of many common reactions still elude explanation, in spite of the great effort and able attention of competent scientists using the most modern tools of research. The difficulties are suggested by the fact that the simplest tenable explanations of superficially simple reactions frequently involve several kinds of molecules different from either reactants or products, and a sequence of intermediate reactions.

The determination of reaction rates is for the most part essentially empirical, and the determination of mechanisms still needs further sound theoretical treatment on the basis of statistical and quantum mechanics. The ultimate goal of chemical kinetics is to predict absolute rates of reaction from the fundamental physical constants of the atoms and molecules, and from the nature of their quantum and thermodynamic properties and exchanges. Much work remains to be done before this goal is realized.

Not only is the study or reaction kinetics invaluable in leading to an understanding of the reaction processes themselves, but it is also of immense practical importance, both in the laboratory and out. The organic chemist wants to know how *fast* a given reaction may go, and what *conditions* will make it go faster or slow it down. The industrial process chemist must have information concerning reaction velocities, in order to determine whether feasible conditions exist for a contemplated process. The designer of piston engines must know how to prevent fast oxidation reactions from becoming explosions; the jet engine designer, the conditions of pressure and temperature to give the proper oxidation rate for optimum engine performance. Fundamental to all of these is the knowledge of reaction rates and the understanding of mechanisms.

22.1. Factors Affecting Rate of Reaction

The rate of chemical reactions is dependent upon many factors, most important of which are the nature of the reacting substances and the temperature of the reaction. Reactions between ionic substances are usually too fast for easy measurement; reactions between organic substances often proceed at practical measurable rates. The student in elementary chemistry is aware of the difference in the rates of reactions of potassium with water, and of calcium with water. He also knows that reactions go more rapidly at higher temperatures and the rule of thumb that the speed of a reaction is approximately doubled for an increase of 10°C in the temperature of the reactants. (Thus reaction of calcium with water is extremely slow at room temperature, but occurs at an easily observable rate when the water is at 100°C.)

Reaction rates also vary with the concentrations: in the case of gases these are usually stated in terms of the partial pressures, and in liquid solutions according to defined concentration units. It is thus obvious that as the reactants are consumed by the reaction, the diminution in concentrations will cause the *instantaneous rate of reaction* to diminish as the reaction proceeds. *Specific rate constants*, independent of concentration, are therefore defined and evaluated in describing particular reactions. Reactions involving but a single phase are called *homogeneous reactions*, and are not subject to the additional rate controlling factors involved in *heterogeneous reactions* (reactions involving more than one phase), such as extent of interfacial contact (extent of surface or state of subdivision), and the nature of the surface. Intimacy of mixing, or degree of agitation, can also be significant factors.

Parallel with, and somewhat analogous to, the effect of temperature on reaction rates is the availability of a source of energy for "activating" the reaction. Various theories invoke the concept of an energy required for activation, and for many reactions already known to the reader, the necessity of an energy "boost" to get a reaction started is apparent. This energy can be in the form of thermal energy, recognized by Arrhenius in defining an energy of activation (to be discussed in Section 22.11). It can be in the form of photons or light quanta ($h\nu$), in which case it is usually discussed under the heading *photochemistry*. It can equally well be in other forms, such as high-energy particles: α particles, β particles, γ-rays, high-voltage electrical discharge (as in ozone formation), electron bombardment, or high-energy particles from cyclotron or other accelerators. Processes thus activated are usually classified under the title *radiation chemistry*. (Phenomena such as luminescence and phosphorescence are often discussed under these last two somewhat arbitrary categories, although usually no chemical reaction in the ordinary sense is involved. Chemiluminescence and bioluminescence do involve chemical processes, however.)

The phenomenon of *catalysis* by some "foreign" substance present in relatively small amount, and not consumed by the process, can increase or decrease reaction rates, sometimes by several powers of ten. While no general theory of catalysis is universally applicable, the understanding of the phenomenon has not only been of practical importance but has helped in the more general understanding of reaction mechanisms.

The rates of many chemical reactions are remarkably dependent upon environmental factors. In addition to their sensitivity to temperature and other forms of "absorbable" energy, and to the pressure or concentration of reactants and their state of subdivision, reactions may also be dependent upon the dimensions and nature of the reacting vessel. Thus a reaction occurring within a vessel with a large wall area will often have a different rate than in a vessel of small wall area, and the rate in a glass-walled vessel will differ from that in a vessel with platinum walls.

22.2. Rate Equations

As in so many physical and chemical problems, equations of chemical kinetics are found to be simpler and of more fundamental significance when they are written in terms of rates of change with time rather than in terms of amounts present as a function of time. The rates of reaction are simply the time rates of change of concentration of one or more of the reactants or products. Thus in a reaction $A + B \longrightarrow$ products, with species A and B present in concentrations C_A and C_B, the rate at any particular time t can be expressed by either of the derivatives dC_A/dt and dC_B/dt, these rates depending on the concentrations of the species involved. It is often found that the dependence is quite simple, involving products of concentrations, each raised to some power. An equation of this form for the rate of disappearance of A is

$$-\frac{dC_A}{dt} = kC_A^p C_B^q \qquad (22.1)$$

where the powers p and q and the specific rate constant k do not depend on concentrations or time.

There is no general necessary reason for a rate to depend on concentrations in this way, nor are equations of this form always obeyed by the overall reaction. The reasons for trying this form of rate equation are two. First, the rates of reactions, or of individual steps in a complex reaction, frequently do satisfy such a relation, and when they do, the coefficients p, q are usually small integers (0, 1, 2) or simple fractions $(\frac{1}{3}, \frac{1}{2}, \frac{3}{2})$.

The second reason for considering Eq. 22.1 is because simple arguments concerning elementary molecular combinations lead to expressions of this form. Thus if the reaction $A + B \longrightarrow$ products actually takes place by direct combination of one molecule of A with one of B, the number of such combinations in unit time should be directly proportional to the numbers of molecules present, both of A and B, in the reaction volume, and hence to the concentrations. For such a process then, one expects the relation

$$-\frac{dC_A}{dt} = kC_A C_B \qquad\qquad (22.2)$$

which is of the form of Eq. 22.1 with $p = q = 1$.

In case A and B are identical—that is, the reaction $2A \longrightarrow$ products occurs by combination of two molecules A—the rate equation is

$$-\frac{dC_A}{dt} = kC_A^2$$

again of the form of Eq. 22.1 with $p = 2$. As another example, the reaction $A + 2B \longrightarrow$ products, occurring by direct combination of one A and two B molecules, gives

$$-\frac{dC_A}{dt} = kC_A C_B^2$$

corresponding to $p = 1$ and $q = 2$ in Eq. 22.1.

At this point, an important caution and warning is necessary. This is the fact that the coefficients p, q appearing in the rate equation need not be, and frequently are not, the same as the stoichiometric coefficients of the overall reaction. A few examples of actual rate laws deduced from experiment (by methods soon to be discussed) illustrate the point sufficiently for the present; others will be encountered later.

EXAMPLES

(a) The gas reaction $2NO + 2H_2 \longrightarrow 2H_2O + N_2$ obeys the rate equation

$$-\frac{d[NO]}{dt} = k[NO]^2[H_2]$$

where the brackets indicate concentrations as usual. The powers in the rate equation obviously do not match the coefficients in the reaction equation, however written.

(b) The gas reaction $CO + Cl_2 = COCl_2$ obeys the equation

$$-\frac{d[CO]}{dt} = k[CO][Cl_2]^{3/2}$$

(c) The reaction between acetone and iodine in acid aqueous solution, $CH_3COCH_3 + I_2 \xrightarrow{H^+} CH_3COCH_2I + HI$, is found to be proportional to concentration of acetone, but *independent* of iodine concentration over a wide range and proportional to hydrogen ion concentration. The empirical rate law is thus

$$-\frac{d[\text{CH}_3\text{COCH}_3]}{dt} = k[\text{CH}_3\text{COCH}_3][\text{H}^+]$$

(d) As an extreme example, the reaction $\text{H}_2 + \text{I}_2 \longrightarrow 2\text{HI}$ has the much simpler rate law,

$$-\frac{d[\text{H}_2]}{dt} = k[\text{H}_2][\text{I}_2]$$

(Even this is complicated by the opposing reaction, $2\text{HI} \longleftarrow \text{H}_2 + \text{I}_2$, however. See Section 22.8.)

_____

Many other examples could be cited to show that the rate equation need have no simple correspondence to the stoichiometry, and must therefore be determined by other means. The fact that the molecular picture which we discussed to make more plausible the *form* of the rate equation gives such a correspondence indicates that the picture is often unrealistic and the molecular processes are different than assumed for the picture. They may be either more complex, as in example (b) or simpler, as in example (d).

22.3. Order and Molecularity

Reactions may be classified according to the particular form of the equation which represents the rate at which they take place. For a reaction in which A, B, and C are reactants, with respective concentrations C_A, C_B, and C_C, the rate of reaction may be expressed as the differential of one concentration with respect to time:

$$-\frac{dC_A}{dt} = kC_A^p C_B^q C_C^r \tag{22.3}$$

(In order that k will be positive for decreasing concentration of A, the differential carries the negative sign.) The *overall order* of the reaction is given by the sum of the exponents:

$$\text{order} = p + q + r \tag{22.4}$$

The order may be zero (in which case the reaction rate is independent of concentration), or any integer (usually small), or it may be fractional (usually simple). Thus there are reactions of zero order, first order, second order, $\frac{3}{2}$ order, and so on. If we were concerned primarily with a particular reactant, such as B, and the value for y happened to be 2, we could describe the reaction as of second order with respect to B. (The *overall* order would still be the sum of the individual exponents.)

The term *molecularity* has been variously defined; in the interests of clarity, it will not be used extensively in this volume, and might well be dropped from the vocabulary of reaction kinetics. Initially, it was erroneously taken to be synonymous with *order of reaction:* a unimolecular reaction was said to be of first order and vice versa, bimolecular second order, and so on. In actuality there are probably more exceptions to this definition than examples in agreement with it.

At present, the definition of molecularity is usually begged, at best. One text, in discussing molecularity of reaction, giving no definition, merely states that "they [reactions] can be classed also as unimolecular, bimolecular, or trimolecular, depending on the number of molecules involved in the reaction." When any but the simplest reactions are considered, this leads to ambiguity and confusion.

Molecularity is less ambiguously defined in another text as "the number of molecules involved in the step leading to reaction," to which confusion is added by the succeeding sentence which states: ". . . reactions are unimolecular, bimolecular, and so on, depending on whether one, two, or more molecules are involved in the rate determining step." The "step leading to reaction" and the "rate determining step" will often be quite different. Another author differently but more precisely defines molecularity to be "equal to the number of molecules of reactants that are used to form the activated complex." (The activated complex is a high-energy intermediate in an overall reaction, to be discussed in Section 22.13.)

Use of the term molecularity is best confined to the simplest of processes of known mechanism, which can correctly and unambiguously be called unimolecular, bimolecular, and so on. Further extension of its use cannot be justified in any simple terms.

22.4. Measurement of Reaction Velocity

The study of reaction kinetics involves first of all the measurement of the velocity at which reactions take place. Since reaction velocities are affected by many factors, it is necessary to control as many of them as possible. The temperature of reaction is always a factor and usually must be controlled by thermostating the reacting systems. If the reaction is light-sensitive, the light striking the mixture is carefully controlled. Preliminary studies may be necessary to indicate the size and shape of the containing chamber which will have least effect on the speed of reaction, and the wall material which will have minimum effect. Once the factors affecting the reaction are established, usually they may be adequately controlled.

In almost all instances (save the special case of zero-order reactions), the velocity of reactions decreases as the concentrations of the reactants decrease. It is therefore necessary to determine the instantaneous velocity of the reaction at any given time, t, after it has begun, which may be done if the course of the reaction is known as a function of time. This requires that the amount of reactants consumed or products formed by the reaction be determined at known times during its course. Since reactions, once started, ordinarily continue to "completion" at equilibrium, the mere removal of a sample of the reaction mixture at a given instant does not arrest the reaction. If the subsequent analysis of the sample requires a finite time, this leads to an uncertainty in fixing the time of observation, with consequent loss of precision in the rate determination.

This error may be minimized if the reaction is quenched: by chilling the sample removed to a temperature low enough to reduce the reaction velocity materially; or by dilution of the sample to slow the rate. This can sometimes be accomplished in combination for reactions in aqueous solutions by quickly mixing a small measured amount of sample with a large known quantity of chilled water. Quenching can also be accomplished in some cases by adding a reagent to the sample which stops the reaction. Thus addition of acid or base can be employed to remove one of the reactants, leaving unaffected other reactants or products to be analyzed. Examples of this technique may be found in rate studies of the hydrolysis of simple esters, such as methyl acetate.

Analysis by means of some physical property which can be measured continuously without the removal of samples from the reaction chamber minimizes the lack of precision in time measurement, discussed above. Fortunately there are many such properties available for measurement. Some of the more commonly used continuous methods of analysis are described briefly below.

(a) *Optical rotatory power.* The degree of rotation of plane-polarized light passing through a solution (measured by a polarimeter) depends upon the substances in solution, their concentrations, and the length of path through the solution. When the specific rotation of the reactants differs from that of the products, the course of a reaction may be followed in this way. This method was used by L. Wilhelmy in 1850 in his classic experiment to determine the rate of inversion of sucrose,

$$\underset{\text{sucrose}}{C_{12}H_{22}O_{11}} + H_2O \longrightarrow \underset{\text{fructose}}{C_6H_{12}O_6} + \underset{\text{glucose}}{C_6H_{12}O_6}$$

(b) *Colorimetry*. If there is a difference in color between reactants, or if some indicator is present with color dependent upon the concentration of a reactant or product, a reaction can be followed colorimetrically, provided the presence of other colored substances does not obscure the color change. The reaction between bromophenol blue and hydroxyl ion in various solvents has been followed by means of colorimetry.

(c) *Spectroscopic methods*. As an extension and refinement of colorimetric methods, reactions can be followed by spectroscopic measurements, not necessarily limited to the visible, and often in the presence of other colored substances. An absorption line or band with frequency characteristic of a reactant or product is continuously observed, and is related to the velocity of reaction. This technique is useful particularly for hydrocarbons, where a distinguishing band in the infrared can often be employed.

(d) *Index of refraction*. A reaction may be followed by index of refraction measurements, and for continuous determination by a dipping refractometer, for example.

(e) *Manometric measurements*. Gas phase reactions, or reactions in which a gas is consumed or produced, can often be followed by observing pressure changes. Caution must be exercised in the use of manometric methods with complex reactions, particularly those involving gaseous intermediates, for errors in interpretation of data are easy to make.

(f) *Dilatometric measurements*. Volume changes, frequently minute, which accompany a reaction in solution can be continuously followed by means of a dilatometer. In essence, this consists of a large closed chamber connected to a capillary tube; small changes in volume cause proportionately larger changes of level in the tube, which can be measured more readily.

(g) *Dielectric constant*. Reactions with significant differences in reactant and product dielectric constant may be carried out within a capacitance cell, or condenser plates may be inserted in the reaction chamber itself and the changes in dielectric constant observed.

(h) *Electrolytic conductivity and electromotive force measurements* have been used effectively in reaction rate studies, as have measurements of many other physical properties, as they may be applicable and convenient.

22.5. Fast Reactions

Reactions more rapid than those which can be easily controlled and followed in the usual reaction vessel can be studied by special techniques. One such is the *flow tube* technique, which involves a system in motion, as opposed to the static systems in the foregoing cases. A schematic plan

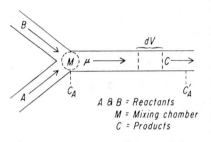

Fig. 22.1. *Schematic diagram of flow method for reaction rate measurements.*

for a flow system is shown in Fig. 22.1. Two gaseous reactants, A and B, are fed at determined steady rates of flow through separate tubes into a mixing chamber M, where (it will be assumed for this discussion) the mixing is perfect and instantaneous. The mixed reactants then flow from M along the tube with volume flow velocity μ, with products C forming by the reaction. (Complications of design of the mixing chamber, imperfect mixing, tempera-ture and volume changes will be neglected here.) Evidently, points further along the common tube contain solution at progressively later times after initiation of the reaction in the chamber M; hence the changes with time can be deduced from the differences in solution properties at different points along the tube.

The flow method is obviously limited in application to fluid systems consisting of gases, liquids, or solutions. For these it has been most useful, and has permitted the measurement of reaction rates for re-actions taking place in but a few milliseconds. (See F. J. W. Roughton and Britton Chance, *Rapid Reactions,* in Weissberger's compendium in references on p. 781.

Techniques for measurement of even faster reactions are being developed or refined. The shock tube is one such development, in which a shock wave or a detonation wave is propagated axially along a tube filled with the mixed reactants, the reaction taking place in the wave front. Observation is by optical and spectrographic techniques, permit-ting measurement of reaction rates of the order of microseconds.

Recently another class of techniques has been developed; these are characterized by observing the effects of periodic changes in the condi-tion of the system. In photochemical reactions, the light intensity can be turned on and off periodically by a rotating shutter or other device, and the changes in chemical composition studied as a function of the

rate of switching. Fast ionic reactions can be induced by rapidly alternating or pulsed electric fields, and changes in conductivity or dielectric
constant produced by reaction followed by electronic methods. Conclusions about the chemical changes corresponding to the observed effects
often require complicated reasoning and may involve dubious assumptions, but the methods provide tools for study of processes much too fast
to be examined in less sophisticated ways.

22.6. Rates of Reaction

When data are available describing the course of a reaction as a
function of time, concentration of reactants, and other factors, suitable
means of reducing these results to recognizable laws and theories must
be developed and applied.

First-order Reactions

A reaction of the first order is represented by the equation for the
reaction,

$$A \longrightarrow \text{products}$$

with a rate equation of the form

$$\frac{-dC_A}{dt} = k_1 C_A \tag{22.5}$$

where k_1 is the *specific reaction rate constant*. If a is taken as the initial
concentration of A before reaction, and x is the concentration which
reacted in time t, then $C_A = a - x$ and

$$-\frac{d(a - x)}{dt} = \frac{dx}{dt} = k_1(a - x) \tag{22.6}$$

This can be integrated (by separation of variables) between the limits
$x = 0$ to $x = x$, and $t = 0$ to $t = t$, with the result (which the reader
should verify) that

$$k_1 = \frac{1}{t} \ln \frac{a}{a - x} \tag{22.7}$$

For reactions of the first order at constant temperature the substitution
of measured values of a, x, and t will result in a constant. Note that the
constant is independent of the initial concentration, and of the units of
concentration, having only units of t^{-1}.

The equation can also be written in the exponential form

$$C_A = ae^{-k_1t} \qquad (22.8)$$

recalling that C_A is the concentration of A at time t. This shows clearly that the concentration falls off exponentially during the reaction.

Half-life. A useful concept for giving a quick indication of the rate of a reaction is the reaction's half-life. This is the time required for half the amount of reactant initially present to react, or in the above case, the time $t_{1/2}$ at which $x = a/2$. Substituting in Eq. 22.7, $k_1 = (1/t_{1/2}) \ln 2$, or

$$t_{1/2} = \frac{\ln 2}{k_1} \qquad (22.9)$$

This, too, is independent of the initial concentration, as might be expected from the exponential form of the rate equation. The time required for an initial concentration of 5 moles liter^{-1} to be reduced to 2.5 moles liter^{-1} is the same as for 0.01 mole liter^{-1} to be reduced to 0.005 mole liter^{-1}. In fact, this is one test by which one can determine whether or not a reaction is of first order.

An example of a first-order reaction is the decomposition of gaseous nitrogen pentoxide at 45°C:

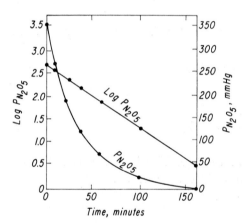

Fig. 22.2. *Decomposition of nitrogen pentoxide; temperature 45°C.*

$$N_2O_5 \longrightarrow N_2O_4 + \tfrac{1}{2}O_2$$

Measurements are complicated because of the further reaction $N_2O_4 \longrightarrow 2NO_2$, but by giving this consideration one can obtain the concentration of N_2O_5 in terms of its partial pressure $(P_{N_2O_5})$ for the times (t) after initiation of the reaction. The data given in Table 22.1 are plotted in Fig. 22.2.

To make the above calculations of values for k_1, Eq. 22.7 was integrated between the limit t_1 and t_2, and x_1 and x_2, yielding

$$k_1 = \frac{1}{t_2 - t_1} \ln \frac{a - x_1}{a - x_2}$$

TABLE 22.1. *Decomposition of Nitrogen Pentoxide. Temperature 45°C.*

Time (minutes)	$P_{N_2O_5}$ (mm Hg)	$k_1 \times 10^4$ (sec^{-1})
0	(348)*	—
10	247	—
20	185	4.81
40	105	4.78
60	58	4.84
100	18	4.51
160	3	4.67

From F. Daniels and E. H. Johnston, *J. Am. Chem. Soc.*, **43**:53 (1921).

* By extrapolation, since precise determination of zero time is not feasible. For reference only; not used in calculation of k_1.

The half-life for this decomposition is

$$t_{1/2} = \frac{\ln 2}{4.8 \times 10^{-4} \text{ sec}^{-1}} = 1.44 \times 10^{-3} \text{ sec} = 24 \text{ minutes}$$

Another example of a reaction following a first-order equation is the classic inversion of sucrose in aqueous solution, already mentioned:

$$C_{12}H_{22}O_{11} + H_2O \rightleftharpoons 2C_6H_{12}O_6$$

Since water is present in such excess, its concentration is essentially constant, and the reaction is of first order with respect to sucrose concentration. (This is sometimes called a pseudo first-order reaction, because this order results by the concentration of one of the two reactants being essentially constant.)

Another example of a first-order reaction is the isomerization of *N*-chloracetanilide to *p*-chloracetanilide. The reaction is followed by adding excess of potassium iodide solution to the reaction mixture, from which *N*-chloracetanilide liberates iodine, no reaction occurring with *p*-chloracetanilide. The free iodine is then titrated against standardized thiosulfate solution.

Second-order Reactions

A second-order reaction,

$$A + B \longrightarrow \text{products}$$

with initial concentrations a and b, respectively, is represented by the rate equation

$$-\frac{dC_A}{dt} = -\frac{d(a-x)}{dt} = \frac{dx}{dt} = k_2(a-x)(b-x) \qquad (22.10)$$

where x is the number of moles per liter reacting in time t. (The concentration of reactant B obviously could be used in place of A to indicate the rate.) Integrating between the limits $x = 0$ at $t = 0$, and $x = x$ at $t = t$, will yield

$$k_2 = \frac{1}{t(a-b)} \ln \frac{b(a-x)}{a(b-x)} \qquad (22.11)$$

Inspection shows that if the two original concentrations were equal ($a = b$), this equation is indeterminate. This special case corresponds with a special type of second-order reaction,

$$2A \longrightarrow \text{products}$$

The differential rate expression for this special case becomes

$$\frac{dx}{dt} = k_2(a-x)^2 \qquad (22.12)$$

which upon integrating yields for the specific reaction rate constant

$$k_2 = \frac{1}{t}\left(\frac{1}{a-x} - \frac{1}{a}\right) = \frac{1}{ta}\left(\frac{x}{a-x}\right) \qquad (22.13)$$

Examples of reactions following the second-order rate law are numerous: the hydroxyl ion hydrolysis of esters or amines, the combination of hydrogen and iodine, and the dissociation of hydrogen iodide:

$$H_2 + I_2 \longrightarrow 2HI$$

Another example of a reaction which follows the second-order rate law is the formation of propylene by treatment of propylene bromide with potassium iodide in 99% methanol solution:

$$CH_3CHBrCH_2Br + 3KI \longrightarrow CH_3CH{=}CH_2 + 2KBr + KI_3$$

The rate equation is found to be

$$\frac{d[CH_3CH{=}CH_2]}{dt} = k_2[CH_3CHBrCH_2Br][KI]$$

or

$$\frac{dx}{dt} = k_2[a-x][b-3x] \qquad (22.14)$$

Here a is the initial concentration of dibromide, b that of potassium iodide, and x the amount of dibromide which has reacted at time t.

The determination that the reaction is in fact described by this equation was made by employing the integrated form

$$k_2 = \frac{1}{t(3a - b)} \ln \frac{b(a - x)}{a(b - 3x)} \qquad (22.15)$$

The reaction is followed by a thiosulfate titration of free iodine: $KI_3 = KI + I_2$, whence $x = [I_2]$. Table 22.2 summarizes the data under different conditions of concentration and temperature from which the rate expression is computed. The second column gives the iodine concentration at the listed times after the initiation of the reaction, the third column the quantity which should from Eq. 22.15 be linearly dependent on the time (plotted in Fig. 22.3), and the fourth the calculated values for the specific reaction rate constant k_2. These are satisfactorily constant and average value at 59.7°C is 3.1×10^{-6} liter moles^{-1} sec^{-1}. (The other data of Table 22.2 will be further discussed in Sections 22.7 and 22.11.)

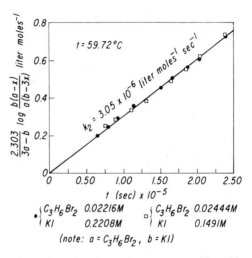

$$• \begin{cases} C_3H_6Br_2 & 0.02216M \\ KI & 0.2208M \end{cases} \quad \square \begin{cases} C_3H_6Br_2 & 0.02444M \\ KI & 0.1491M \end{cases}$$

(note: $a = C_3H_6Br_2$, $b = KI$)

Fig. 22.3. *Reaction of propylene dibromide with potassium iodide:*

$$CH_3CHBrCH_2Br + 3KI \longrightarrow$$
$$CH_3CHCH_2 + 2KBr + KI_3$$

$$\frac{1}{3a - b} \ln \frac{b(a - x)}{a(b - 3x)} = k_2t.$$

Third-order Reactions

Reactions of the third order may be represented by

$$3A \longrightarrow \text{products}$$
$$2A + B \longrightarrow \text{products}$$

or

$$A + B + C \longrightarrow \text{products}$$

In the simplest case, where the initial concentrations of reactants are all equal, the differential rate equation is

$$\frac{dx}{dt} = k_3(a - x)^3 \qquad (22.16)$$

TABLE 22.2.   *Reaction of Propylene Bromide and Potassium Iodide in 99% Methanol.*

$$C_3H_6Br_2 + 3KI \rightleftharpoons CH_3CH{=}CH_2 + 2KBr + KI_3$$

Time (sec × 10⁻⁶)	$x = [I]$ (mol/liter × 10³)	$\dfrac{1}{(3a-b)}\ln\dfrac{b(a-x)}{a(b-3x)}$	k_2 (liter mol⁻¹ sec⁻¹)	$\dfrac{1}{(3a-b)^2}\left[\dfrac{3x(3a-b)}{b(b-3x)} - \ln\dfrac{b(a-x)}{a(b-3x)}\right]$	k_3 (liter² mol⁻² sec⁻¹)	
0.630	0.967	0.204	3.24×10^{-6}	0.933	1.48×10^{-5}	$a = 0.02216M$
0.795	1.192	0.251	3.16	1.144	1.44	$b = 0.2208M$
0.918	1.368	0.299	3.25	1.379	1.50	$T = 59.72°C$
1.116	1.619	0.360	3.22	1.672	1.50	
1.503	2.090	0.456	3.04	2.100	1.40	
1.668	2.285	0.505	3.03	2.335	1.40	
1.857	2.511	0.562	3.02	2.604	1.37	
2.037	2.721	0.604	2.97	2.789	1.40	
2.376	3.193	0.719	3.03	3.331	1.40	
			av: 3.11×10^{-6}		av: 1.43×10^{-5}	
0.756	0.892	0.2530	3.34×10^{-6}	1.720	2.28×10^{-5}	$a = 0.02444M$
0.900	1.013	0.2935	3.26	2.031	2.26	$b = 0.1491M$
1.110	1.188	0.3342	3.01	2.240	2.02	$T = 59.72°C$
1.290	1.353	0.3883	3.01	2.645	2.05	
1.629	1.689	0.4836	2.97	3.266	2.00	
1.836	1.875	0.5524	3.01	3.817	2.08	
2.052	2.080	0.6214	3.03	4.332	2.11	
2.376	2.486	0.7326	3.08	5.002	2.11	
			av: 3.08×10^{-6}		av: 2.11×10^{-5}	
0.643	4.693	1.035	1.61×10^{-5}			$a = 0.02404M$
0.738	5.238	1.179	1.60			$b = 0.2170M$
0.939	6.462	1.513	1.61			$T = 74.93°C$
1.116	7.464	1.812	1.62			
1.514	9.392	2.458	1.62			
2.043	11.54	3.318	1.62			
			av: 1.61×10^{-5}			

Data from R. T. Dillon, *J. Am. Chem. Soc.*, **54**:952 (1932).
Energy of activation was 25,100 calories.

and, upon integrating, the expression for the constant is

$$k_3 = \frac{1}{2t}\frac{2ax - x^2}{a^2(a-x)^2} = \frac{1}{2t}\frac{2x(a-x)}{a^2(a-x)^2} = \frac{1}{2t}\frac{2x}{a^2(a-x)} \qquad (22.17)$$

The formation of nitrosyl bromide from nitric oxide and bromine is an example of a third-order reaction:

$$2NO + Br_2 \rightleftharpoons 2NOBr$$

The rate expression may be in terms of either reactant or of the product, with necessary stoichiometric adjustment:

$$-\frac{d[NO]}{dt} = -2\frac{d[Br]}{dt} = \frac{d[NOBr]}{dt}$$

For the first, $-d[NO]/dt = k_{3,NO}[NO]^2[Br_2]$ and the other two expressions may be written similarly. It will be recognized that the specific reaction rate constant will have a value in this case dependent both on the concentration and the substance to which it refers:

$$k_{3,NO} = k_{3,NOBr} = 2k_{3,Br_2}$$

In general, for a reaction of the order n, for which

$$\frac{dx}{dt} = k_n(a-x)^n \qquad (22.18)$$

$$k_n = \frac{1}{t(n-1)}\left[\frac{1}{(a-x)^{n-1}} - \frac{1}{a^{n-1}}\right] \qquad (22.19)$$

(It is observed that this solution is indeterminate for $n = 1$.)

Zero-order Reactions

Some reactions proceed at rates apparently independent of reactant concentrations, and are called zero-order reactions. In general, there are special conditions attending such reactions. An example is the decomposition of ammonia on a hot tungsten surface, at pressures sufficient to ensure saturation adsorption of the gas on the tungsten surface, and hence an essentially constant surface concentration of ammonia. Even though the "true" order of the reaction rate may be other than zero, the zero-order equation represents the experimental data. Other examples may be found in certain enzyme-catalyzed reactions.

A summary of the rate equations, specific reaction rate constants and their units, and half-life expressions is given in Table 22.3. (Half-life expressions are found by setting $x = a/2$ at $t = t_{1/2}$ as shown in Section

22.6.) For $n = 1$, the generalized equation for the rate constant and half-life is indeterminate, and these must be found by solution of the differential rate equation.

For reactions of fractional order (such as $n = \frac{1}{2}$ or $n = \frac{3}{2}$), the generalized expression will give valid expressions for the rate equation, rate constant, and half-life. An interesting example of a reaction of order $\frac{3}{2}$ is the conversion of ortho to para-hydrogen, or vice versa,

$$o\text{-}H_2 \rightleftharpoons p\text{-}H_2$$

(These two forms are nuclear isotopes, the nuclear spins being parallel in o—H_2 and antiparallel in p–H_2.) The observed rates and half-time are represented among the general equations of Table 22.3. This fractional order can be explained by assuming a dissociation ($H_2 \rightleftharpoons 2H$) and reaction to take place between a hydrogen atom and a hydrogen molecule:

$$H + o\text{-}H_2 \longrightarrow p\text{-}H_2 + H$$

nuclear spins

Assuming that atomic and molecular hydrogen are in equilibrium, $[H] = K[H_2]^{1/2}$, which gives the rate equation

$$\frac{dx}{dt} = k[H][H_2] = kK[H_2]^{1/2}[H_2] = k_{3/2}H_2^{3/2} \qquad (22.20)$$

(Study of this reaction, by considering the concentration of atomic hydrogen independently of molecular hydrogen, yields a second-order rate constant, as might be expected.) Fractional order rate laws usually are explained by the assumption of free atoms or radicals in equilibrium with molecules. As in the case of any proposed mechanism, it is impor-

TABLE 22.3. *Rate Equations, Rate Constant Expressions, and Units, and Half-lives for Reactions of Different Orders.*

Order	Half-life $(t_{1/2})$	Rate Equation	Specific Rate Constant	Units
0	$t_{1/2} = \dfrac{a}{2k_0}$	$\dfrac{dx}{dt} = k_0$	$k_0 = \dfrac{x}{t}$	mol liter^{-1} sec^{-1}
1	$t_{1/2} = \dfrac{\ln 2}{k_1}$	$\dfrac{dx}{dt} = k_1(a - x)$	$k_1 = \dfrac{1}{t}\ln\dfrac{a}{a - x}$	sec^{-1}
2	$t_{1/2} = \dfrac{1}{ak_2}$	$\dfrac{dx}{dt} = k_2(a - x)^2$	$k_2 = \dfrac{1}{t}\dfrac{x}{a(a - x)}$	liter mol^{-1} sec^{-1}
3	$t_{1/2} = \dfrac{3}{2a^2 k_3^2}$	$\dfrac{dx}{dt} = k_3(a - x)^3$	$k_3 = \dfrac{1}{2t}\dfrac{2x}{a^2(a - x)}$	liter^2 mol^{-2} sec^{-1}
n	$t_{1/2} = \dfrac{2^{n-1} - 1}{a^{n-1}k_n n^{-1}}$	$\dfrac{dx}{dt} = k_n(a - x)^n$	$k_n = \dfrac{1}{t(n - 1)}\left[\dfrac{1}{(a - x)^{n-1}} - \dfrac{1}{a^{n-1}}\right]$	liter^{n-1} mol$^{-(n-1)}$ sec^{-1}

tant to obtain independent supporting evidence for any key assumptions. For this reason, much recent research has been directed at study of the properties of atoms and free radicals in reaction systems. The problems can be difficult, because such species are usually unstable and present only in very low concentrations.

22.7. Determination of Order of Reaction

Essentially, the order of a reaction is determined by finding a rate expression which fits observed data over a wide range of conditions. This is a simple enough statement, but carrying out the procedure is not always easy or obvious. Several special procedures used in deter-mining such consistency are very much worth mentioning explicitly, as are some pitfalls of which to be aware.

Integral Rate Expression Method

Experimental rate data are substituted into the integrated forms of the rate expression obtained by assuming a given order for the reaction, such as Eq. 22.15. If the calculated value for the specific reaction rate constant is constant within experimental error, the order assumed in writing the rate ex-pression is obviously capable of representing the reaction under the conditions of the experi-ment. The method can be illus-trated using data for the reac-

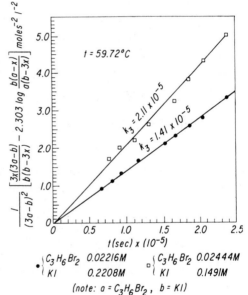

Fig. 22.4. *Reaction of propylene dibromide with potassium iodide. Test of third-order rate expression. (99% methanol solvent.)*

tion of propylene dibromide with potassium iodide in 99% methanol to give propylene, the calculated rate constants being given in Table 22.2 and plotted in Figs. 22.3 and 22.4. Note that the calculated values for k_2 are quite constant, being close to 3.1×10^{-6} liter moles^{-1} sec^{-1} for the temperature 59.72°C. But note also that substitution

of data from the first run tabulated for initial concentrations of
0.02216M and 0.2208M for the dibromide and potassium iodide,
respectively, into the integrated third-order expression yields consistent
values for $k_3 = 1.43 \times 10^{-5}$ liter moles^{-2} sec^{-1}. Thus, no choice between
the two rate expressions can be made on the basis of these data alone.

The use of further data to resolve such ambiguities can be illustrated
as follows. When the initial concentration of one of the reactants is
significantly altered, as in the second run tabulated, the values calculated for k_3, while consistent within themselves ($k_3 = 2.11 \times 10^{-5}$ liter
moles^{-2} sec^{-1}), differ significantly from the first run. (See Fig. 22.4.)
Values for k_2, on the other hand, are essentially the same for both, as
indicated in Fig. 22.3. Determining a reaction rate order by restricting
the independent variable to time will not lead uniquely to the proper
value. This integrated expression method also has the tendency to force
data to fit a reaction rate order of integral, or simple fractional, value,
even when the actual course of the reaction in time cannot be described
by a simple rate equation.

Differential Rate Expression Methods

For a general reaction such as

$$A + B + C \longrightarrow \text{products}$$

where the initial concentrations of reactants are a, b, and c, and the
amount reacted at time t is x, the rate is written

$$-\frac{dC_A}{dt} = \frac{dx}{dt} = k(a-x)^p (b-x)^q (c-x)^r \qquad (22.21)$$

with the order of the reaction $= p + q + r$. Several possibilities exist
for evaluating p, q, and r for a given reaction.

For reactions which are not too rapid, the *initial reaction rate*,
$(-dc_A/dt)_{t=0}$ can often be determined, and will depend upon the initial
concentrations of the reactants. If the initial concentration of one
reactant is varied, keeping all others fixed, from the determination of
the initial rates the order with respect to this reactant may be determined by comparing these rates. Thus, measuring $-dC_A/dt$ for different
values of a, holding b and c constant, will permit evaluation of p:

$$\left(-\frac{dC_A}{dt}\right)_{x=0} = (kb^q c^r)a^p = \text{constant } (a^p)$$

The value of p required to fit the data can then be found from a plot of

$\log \left(-dC_A/dt\right)_{x=0} \left[= p \log a\right]$ against $\log a$. If this is a straight line, the slope is p. Similar procedures can obviously be used for q and r. This method is particularly advantageous in studying complex reactions, where the products of the reaction may affect the overall measured rate (see Sections 22.8 and 22.9).

Isolation Method

The dependence of the reaction rate upon the concentration of a single reactant (A) may be determined by an "isolation method," in which the concentrations of the remaining reactants $(B$ and $C)$ are such relatively high values that they may be considered constant during the reaction ($a \ll$ both b and c). In this case,

$$\frac{-dC_A}{dt} = (kb^q c^r)(a - x)^p$$

from which p can be evaluated. When the reaction can take place in a solution in which one reactant can serve as solvent, this method is particularly appropriate, as for the alcoholysis of benzohydryl chloride by ethanol:

$$(C_6H_5)_2CHCl + C_2H_5OH \longrightarrow (C_6H_5)_2CHOC_2H_5 + H^+ + Cl^-$$

In this case, the concentration of ethanol can change very little if the initial solution is dilute. In some instances it is possible to hold the concentration of a reactant constant by maintaining an equilibrium with a condensed or nonreactive phase or form of the reactant.

Half-life Method

Reference to the generalized expression for *reaction half-life* in Table 22.3 indicates another method for determining the order n. If we take the logarithm of the equation for $t_{1/2}$,

$$t_{1/2} = \left[\frac{2^{n-1} - 1}{k_n(n - 1)}\right] a^{1-n}$$

then $\log t_{1/2} = \log [\text{constants}] + (1 - n) \log a$. Hence n can be determined from the slope $(1 - n)$ of a plot of $\log t_{1/2}$ versus $\log a$. The classic illustration of this, already mentioned, is the ortho-parahydrogen conversion at 650°C, where the half-lives for initial total hydrogen pressures of 50, 100, 200, and 400 mm Hg were determined to be 10.8, 7.5, 5.3, and 3.7 minutes, respectively. The log-log plot is shown in Fig. 22.5, from which the slope $(1 - n) = -0.51$ and $n = 1.51$, corresponding to a reaction order of $\frac{3}{2}$.

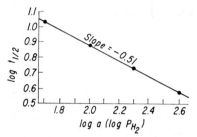

The caution necessary in reaching definite conclusions from the integral method applies in whole or in part to others, and just as much care must be taken. Combinations of the methods given, and others as well, may often be required. In some cases no method, or combination of methods, gives a satisfactory representation of the reaction as being of any simple order. If the difficulty cannot be traced to experimental error, it is indicative of complicating factors in the reaction, which will now be considered.

Fig. 22.5. *Half-life versus initial hydrogen concentration for ortho-para hydrogen conversion.*

22.8. Opposing Reactions

A common complication is failure of the reaction to go to completion, equilibrium being reached when reactants are still present. This can only be because there is a reverse reaction, in which the products react, directly or indirectly, to reform the reactants. The simplest case is first-order in both directions, and may be represented as

$$A \underset{k_{-1}}{\overset{k_1}{\rightleftharpoons}} B$$

where k_1 is the specific reaction rate constant for the forward reaction, and k_{-1} is the constant for the reverse direction. The forward rate

$$\left(-\frac{dC_A}{dt}\right)_f = \left(\frac{dC_B}{dt}\right)_f = \left(\frac{dx}{dt}\right)_f = k_1 C_A = k_1(a - x) \qquad (22.22)$$

The reverse rate, if B is present in concentration b before reaction, is

$$\left(-\frac{dC_B}{dt}\right)_r = \left(\frac{dC_A}{dt}\right)_r = \left(-\frac{dx}{dt}\right)_r = k_{-1} C_B = k_{-1}(b + x) \qquad (22.23)$$

If B is not present initially,

$$\left(-\frac{dC_B}{dt}\right)_r = k_{-1} C_B = k_{-1} x \qquad (22.24)$$

The net rate of reaction (in the forward direction) as a result of both concurrent processes, is

$$\frac{dx}{dt} = \left[\left(\frac{-dC_A}{dt}\right)_f - \left(-\frac{dC_B}{dt}\right)_r\right] = k_1(a - x) - k_{-1}(b + x) \quad (22.25)$$

When the reaction has reached equilibrium, $dx/dt = 0$, and

$$\frac{(a - x)}{(b + x)} = \frac{k_{-1}}{k_1} = K_{equil}$$

(Compare with the thermodynamic derivation of K_{equil} of Chapter 15.) To assume from this that reaction rate expressions can be derived from the equilibrium expression is incorrect. For example, the equilibrium constant expression for the reaction

$$CO + H_2O \rightleftharpoons CO_2 + H_2$$

is

$$K_{equil} = \frac{[CO_2][H_2]}{[CO][H_2O]}$$

and the opposing rate constants are related to it by $K_{equil} = k_1/k_{-1}$. The actual rate expressions are, however, $k_1[CO][H_2O]^y/[H_2]^{1-x}$ and $k_{-1}[CO_2][H_2]^x/[H_2O]^{1-y}$, *not* $k_1[CO][H_2O]$ and $k_{-1}[CO_2][H_2]$. Quite obviously, any of an infinite number of pairs of rate equations would satisfy the relation $K_{equil} = k_1/k_{-1}$. For K_{equil}, directly related to ΔF, is fundamentally a thermodynamic quantity, dependent upon the initial and final states only, and independent of intermediate paths.

Examples of first-order opposing reactions are found in internal molecular rearrangements, racemizations, and isomerizations.

Opposing reactions of other orders are numerous, such as second order–second order, second order–first order, first order–second order, second order–third order, and so on. The reaction and net rate equations for the first three types are the following.

(a) Second order–second order:

$$A + B \underset{k_{-2}}{\overset{k_2}{\rightleftharpoons}} C + D$$

$$\frac{dx}{dt} = k_2(a - x)(b - x) - k_{-2}(c + x)(d + x)$$

(b) Second order–first order:

$$A + B \underset{k_{-1}}{\overset{k_2}{\rightleftharpoons}} C$$

$$\frac{dx}{dt} = k_2(a - x)(b + x) - k_{-1}(c + x)$$

(c) First order–second order:

$$A \underset{k_{-2}}{\overset{k_1}{\rightleftharpoons}} C + D$$

$$\frac{dx}{dt} = k_1(a - x) - k_{-2}(c + x)(d + x)$$

Many other types could be written, but the ones above are the most common. A classic example of opposing reactions is the dissociation and formation of hydrogen iodide.

$$2\ HI \underset{k_{-2}}{\overset{k_2}{\rightleftharpoons}} H_2 + I_2$$

a	b	c	(initial concentrations)
$a - 2x$	$b + x$	$c + x$	(concentrations at time t)

$$\frac{dx}{dt} = k_2(a - 2x)^2 - k_{-2}(b + x)(c + x)$$

At equilibrium, $dx/dt = 0$, and

$$K_{\text{equil}} = \frac{k_{-2}}{k_2} = \frac{(a - 2x)^2}{(b + x)(c + x)}$$

22.9. Consecutive Reactions

Many reactions take place "stepwise," the products of the first reaction in turn reacting to form further products, which may or may not be followed by further processes. A special but important sequence of consecutive reactions is a *chain reaction*, in which one or more intermediate products react with an initial species to form other intermediates and provide further possibilities for subsequent reaction.

When two or more reactions take place consecutively, the variations of rates with concentrations and time can become complicated and difficult to analyze. Certain characteristic features often appear, however, which if present and understood help to elucidate the molecular processes. Also, simplifying approximations can sometimes be made which greatly facilitate the analysis. Both kinds of aids to the study of complex reactions are illustrated in the two following examples.

Two Successive First-order Reactions

Because this represents the simplest case, even though it is not often encountered in the laboratory, it will be considered first. The type reaction is

$$A \xrightarrow{k_1} B \xrightarrow{k_1'} C$$

and the rate equations for concentrations C_A, C_B, and C_C are

$$-\frac{d}{dt} C_A = k_1 C_A$$

$$-\frac{d}{dt} C_B = -k_1 C_A + k_1' C_B \qquad (22.26)$$

$$\frac{d}{dt} C_C = k_1' C_B$$

The first equation can be integrated; the result for the initial condition $C_A = a$, when $t = 0$, is

$$C_A = a \exp(-k_1 t)$$

Inserting this in the rate equation for C_B gives

$$-\frac{d}{dt} C_B = -k_1 a \exp(-k_1 t) + k_1' C_B$$

Solving this linear first-order differential equation for the initial condition that $C_B = 0$ at $t = 0$,

$$C_B = \frac{k_1}{k_1 - k_1'} a [\exp(-k_1' t) - \exp(-k_1 t)] \qquad (22.27)$$

unless $k_1 = k_1'$. (Deriving the result for this unlikely case is left to the reader.)

The rate equation for C_C can be integrated by substituting the solution for C_B, and assuming the initial condition $C_C = 0$ at $t = 0$:

$$C_C = \frac{k_1}{k_1 - k_1'} a [1 - \exp(-k_1' t)] - \frac{k_1'}{k_1 - k_1'} a [1 - \exp(-k_1 t)] \qquad (22.28)$$

From the three solutions, one easily verifies that the sum $C_A + C_B + C_C = a$ at all times. That they are solutions can be checked by substitution in the rate Equations 22.26.

Some characteristic features of the reaction sequence become apparent from the solutions. If the second step is much slower than the first ($k_1 \gg k_1'$), the solution for C_C is given to a good approximation by

$$C_C \cong a[1 - \exp(-k_1' t)]$$

because the ratio $k_1/(k_1 - k_1')$ becomes nearly unity and the ratio $k_1'/(k_1 - k_1')$ becomes much smaller than unity. [Also, the exponential $\exp(-k_1 t)$ goes to zero much more rapidly than $\exp(-k_1' t)$.] For the other extreme, where $k_1 \ll k_1'$, we have

$$C_C \cong a[1 - \exp(-k_1 t)]$$

Thus in either extreme, the rate at which C is formed approaches the rate for the slower reaction; this is accordingly a *rate-limiting step* or "bottleneck" for the sequence of reactions. This is likewise a common feature of complex reactions composed of steps of orders other than first order. It is important to keep this in mind when considering them.

The behavior of the above type reaction for intermediate situations when k_1 and k_1' do not differ widely is illustrated in Fig. 22.6, where

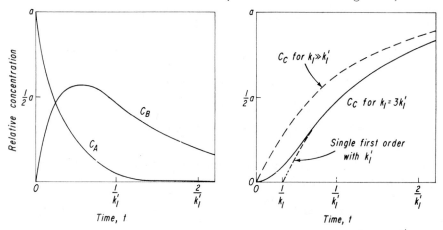

Fig. 22.6. *Concentration changes in time for the first order sequence* $A \xrightarrow{k_1} B \xrightarrow{k_1'} C$

$k_1 = 3k_1'$—that is, the rate for the first step is three times that for the second. The concentration of the intermediate, C_B, rises at first as it is formed by the reaction of A, then falls off as appreciable quantities of C are formed. The concentration C_C rises very slowly at the beginning, actually with zero initial rate, since no B has yet formed at $t = 0$. As B becomes available, the concentration C_C then increases with time to the final value a, much in the manner of a single first-order process with rate constant k_1', which is delayed until time $t = 1/k_1$, as indicated by the broken line originating at $t = 1/k_1$ in the right diagram of Fig. 22.6. It is interesting to compare the curve for C_C in this same diagram with the upper broken curve representing the extreme case of $k_1 \gg k_1'$.

A time lag before appreciable product is formed is called an *induction period* and, like the bottleneck effect, is also found in more complicated reaction sequences.

Formation of Hydrogen Bromide

The classic example of a chain-reaction sequence is the homogeneous gas-phase reaction of hydrogen and bromine to form hydrogen bromide.

Bodenstein found that this reaction, $H_2(g) + Br_2(g) = 2HBr(g)$, did not follow a simple second-order rate law, as would have been expected for a simple bimolecular combination, and which he did find for the seemingly similar reaction of hydrogen with iodine to form hydrogen iodide.

By studying initial reaction rates for various concentrations of the reactants and by varying the conditions under which the reaction took place, Bodenstein was able to deduce a quite different rate law, which provided a good fit for the experimentally measured rates:

$$\frac{d}{dt} [HBr] = \frac{A[H_2][Br_2]^{1/2}}{1 + B\frac{[HBr]}{[Br_2]}} \qquad (22.29)$$

This purely empirical law was obtained in 1907. Although Bodenstein suspected that atomic bromine played an essential role (note the factor $[Br_2]^{1/2}$ and compare with the discussion in Section 22.6), it was not until 1919 that this rate law could be explained by a possible reaction mechanism, given independently by Christiansen, by Herzfeld, and by Polanyi. They proposed that the bromine atoms from the dissociation of Br_2 react to form HBr, both by direct attack on H_2 and by the subsequent reaction of other bromine atoms with the hydrogen atoms formed:

$$Br_2 \xrightarrow{k_1} Br + Br$$
$$Br + H_2 \xrightarrow{k_2} HBr + H \qquad (22.30)$$
$$H + Br_2 \xrightarrow{k_3} HBr + Br$$

This sequence regenerates Br atoms as long as reactants are available, and in the absence of competing processes could produce explosive rates. Since the reaction does not proceed with an explosive rate, two *chain-breaking reactions* are postulated:

$$H + HBr \xrightarrow{k_4} H_2 + Br \qquad (22.31)$$
$$Br + Br \xrightarrow{k_{-1}} Br_2$$

Assuming these step reactions, the rate of formation of HBr is given by

$$\frac{d}{dt} [HBr] = k_2[H_2][Br] + k_3[H][Br_2] - k_4[H][HBr]$$

This expression involves the concentrations [Br] and [H] of reactive atoms which must satisfy the rate equations:

$$\frac{d}{dt}[\text{Br}] = k_1[\text{Br}_2] - k_2[\text{Br}][\text{H}_2] + k_3[\text{H}][\text{Br}_2] + k_4[\text{H}][\text{HBr}] - k_{-1}[\text{Br}]^2$$

$$\frac{d}{dt}[\text{H}] = k_2[\text{Br}][\text{H}_2] - k_3[\text{H}][\text{Br}_2] - k_4[\text{H}][\text{HBr}]$$

The rate equations governing $[\text{H}_2]$ and $[\text{Br}_2]$ could be added to the above, and the entire set manipulated to obtain a rate equation for any one of the five species alone. The results are quite unmanageable, and simplifying approximations must be introduced to permit a solution. These approximations recognize that the reactive atoms, although essential to the sequence of reactions, are not expected to be present in large amounts at any time, nor will the concentrations of these reactive atoms present change rapidly. It can therefore be assumed that the net rates for $[\text{H}]$ and $[\text{Br}]$ are both zero to a good approximation (the so-called *steady state approximation*). During the period of significant reaction of the reactive intermediates in a complex sequence, this is often a good approximation, even though it fails in the initial and final stages of the reaction.

Making this assumption for $[\text{H}]$ and $[\text{Br}]$, a rate equation for $[\text{HBr}]$ in terms of reactant and product concentrations is readily obtained. If $d[\text{H}]/dt$ is set equal to zero, and substituted in the expression for $d[\text{Br}]/dt$, also set equal to zero, then

$$[\text{Br}]^2 = \frac{k_1}{k_{-1}}[\text{Br}_2] \qquad (22.32)$$

which when substituted back into the expression for $d[\text{H}]/dt = 0$ gives

$$[\text{H}] = \frac{k_2[\text{H}_2](k_1/k_{-1})^{1/2}[\text{Br}_2]^{1/2}}{k_3[\text{Br}_2] + k_4[\text{HBr}]} \qquad (22.33)$$

Using these results, the rate equation for $[\text{HBr}]$ can be written as

$$\frac{d}{dt}[\text{HBr}] = \frac{k_2(k_1/k_{-1})^{1/2}[\text{H}_2][\text{Br}_2]^{1/2}}{1 + (k_4/k_3)\dfrac{[\text{HBr}]}{[\text{H}_2]}}$$

This corresponds exactly with Bodenstein's experimentally determined rate expression, Eq. 22.29, if his empirical constants A and B are given the values $A = k_2(k_1/k_{-1})^{1/2}$ and $B = k_4/k_3$.

This reaction sequence and the reasoning used to analyze its consequences are worth careful study. Note that the steady-state concentration of $[\text{Br}]$, given by $[\text{Br}]^2 = (k_1/k_{-1})[\text{Br}_2]$, is precisely that for the equilibrium of the opposing reactions $\text{Br}_2 \underset{k_{-1}}{\overset{k_1}{\rightleftarrows}} 2\text{Br}$, the ratio k_1/k_{-1} being the equilibrium constant. A similar situation does not exist for $[\text{H}]$, as the reactions $H_2 \rightleftarrows 2H$ have not been included. These omissions can be justified by independent evidence that they are much slower than the postulated reactions which form and remove hydrogen atoms.

To be considered whenever reactions forming atoms A by dissociation or removing them by combination are postulated is the requirement of the presence of a third body to absorb the energy evolved in the collisions resulting in forming A_2 according to the reaction $A + A \longrightarrow A_2$, and to supply the energy for the dissociation $A_2 \longrightarrow A + A$. This is discussed in Section 22.12.

The inference from the observed rate law that the direct reaction $H_2 + Br_2 \longrightarrow 2HBr$ is not important is supported by evidence from other sources, as is the neglect of the reaction $HBr + Br \longrightarrow H + Br_2$. Altogether, direct and indirect evidence from a variety of measurements has established the chain-reaction sequence for the formation of hydrogen bromide more firmly than the molecular mechanism of any other complex gas reaction. In spite of this, one must always remember that this mechanism has not been uniquely established; until it is, there is always the possibility, however remote, that some alternate mechanism might provide equally good agreement.

22.10. Competing Reactions

If, from a given set of reactants, more than one reaction can take place, the reactions are said to be *competing* for the reactants required in them. (These are also sometimes called parallel reactions, and sometimes side reactions.) In generalized notation, a system of competing reactions may be represented by

where k_1 and k_2 are the specific reaction rates of the two competing reactions consuming reactants represented by A, and forming the sets of products represented by B and by C. (Obviously, there could be additional reactions competing which could in turn have reaction rate constants k_3, k_4, $\cdots$, and the products D, E, $\cdots$.) The corresponding reaction rates would be

$$\frac{dx}{dt} = k_1 C_A$$

$$(22.34)$$

$$\frac{dy}{dt} = k_2 C_A$$

where x and y will indicate the amounts of the respective products B and C formed from A in time t. The individual rates are:

$$\frac{dx}{dt} = k_1(a - x - y)$$

$$\frac{dy}{dt} = k_2(a - x - y)$$

$$(22.35)$$

The rate at which the reactant is consumed is the sum of the rates of the two reactions:

$$-\frac{dC_A}{dt} = \frac{dx}{dt} + \frac{dy}{dt} = k_1 C_A + k_2 C_A$$

$$= (k_1 + k_2)C_A = (k_1 + k_2)(a - x - y) \qquad (22.36)$$

If $k_1 \gg k_2$, then $x \gg y$, and

$$-\frac{dC_A}{dt} \cong k_1(a - x) \cong \frac{dx}{dt} \qquad (22.37)$$

and

$$\frac{dy}{dt} \cong k_2(a - x) \qquad (22.38)$$

In this case, the overall rate at which reactant is consumed will be governed by the faster reaction, which predominates, in contrast with the situation for consecutive reactions just discussed. The reaction with the greater rate constant will form the greater amount of product and consume the greater amount of reactant.

Competing reactions are frequently found in organic chemistry, and from a given set of reactants it may be possible to form many products. The "reaction" is said to "go" in the direction of the product formed with greatest yield, which will generally be that resulting from the fastest reaction. This is evident from the ratio

$$\frac{(dx/dt)}{(dy/dt)} = \frac{k_1(a - x - y)}{k_2(a - x - y)} = \frac{k_1}{k_2} \qquad (22.39)$$

Among the reactions first studied was the nitration of benzoic acid, to yield the ortho-, meta-, or para-isomers, in amounts proportional to the specific reaction rates.

22.11. Variation of Reaction Rates with Temperature

With few exceptions, chemical reactions take place more rapidly at higher temperatures. A useful rule of thumb already mentioned is that rates of reactions near room temperature increase by a factor two to three with a 10°C rise in temperature. Such simple propositions are useful but neither, even if free from exception, is adequate for quantitative statements or predictions; for these, a more detailed analytical expression of the facts is needed.

An important equation which is often found to fit the temperature dependence of reaction rate constants is the Arrhenius equation

$$\frac{d \ln k}{dT} = \frac{E_A}{RT^2} \qquad (22.40)$$

where k is the specific rate constant, T the absolute temperature, and the quantity E_A, called the *activation energy*, is often assumed to be a constant independent of temperature. Arrhenius proposed this equation in 1889, partly by analogy with the Van't Hoff equation for the temperature dependence of equilibrium constants,

$$\frac{d \ln K}{dT} = \frac{q}{RT^2} \qquad (22.41)$$

where, as defined in Chapter 12, q is the heat absorbed per mole of reaction (equal to ΔH if at constant pressure, and to ΔE if at constant volume). This equation for *equilibrium*, supplemented by the mass action concept of rates proportional to concentration products of reacting species, makes plausible a similar form of equation for rate constant, but there is no direct thermodynamic justification for the kinetic equation.

If the activation energy E_A is taken to be independent of temperature, integration yields the equation

$$\ln k = -\frac{E_A}{RT} + \text{constant}$$

or

$$k = A \exp\left(-\frac{E_A}{RT}\right) \qquad (22.42)$$

where the constant of the first form of the equation appears as $\ln A$ in the second form. This equation for k also has a suggestive form, as $\exp(-E_A/RT)$ has the appearance of a Boltzmann factor, found so frequently in earlier chapters.

The obvious way of testing the integrated form of the Arrhenius equation graphically is by a plot of $\ln k$ or $\log k (= \ln k/2.303)$ against reciprocal absolute temperature, $1/T$. This can be illustrated by the classic example of bimolecular reaction, $2HI \longrightarrow H_2 + I_2$. Logarithms

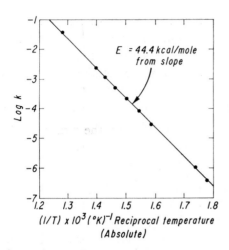

Fig. 22.7. *Log k versus* $1/T$ *for the decomposition of hydrogen iodide. Test of Arrhenius equation.*

of measured second-order rate constants over the range 560° to 780°K are plotted against $1/T \times 10^3$ in Fig. 22.7 and are seen to lie close to the straight line. The activation energy from the slope of the line is 44.0 kcal/mole.

A second example from the reaction in 99% methanol solution of propylene dibromide with potassium iodide is shown in Table 22.2 and Fig. 22.8. The energy of activation can be calculated from the values at any two temperatures T_1 and T_2 by the equation, easily derived from Eq. 22.42,

$$\frac{k_{T_2}}{k_{T_1}} = \frac{E_A}{2.303R}\left(\frac{1}{T_2} - \frac{1}{T_1}\right). \qquad (22.43)$$

From values at 74.9°C and 59.7°C, $E_A = 25.3$ kcal/mole.

Many other data could be cited which conform within their accuracy to an equation of the Arrhenius form over the temperature range of the measurements. There is little doubt that this form is adequate over moderate temperature ranges for a great many reactions; nor does the equation have any successful competitor of comparably simple form.

A number of examples are known for which the Arrhenius equation does not hold in the integrated form, and many data represented by the equation have been taken over such

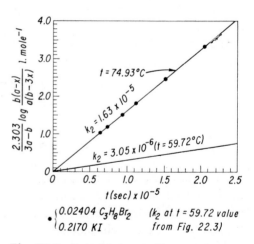

$\bullet \begin{cases} 0.02404\ C_3H_8Br_2 \\ 0.2170\ KI \end{cases}$ (k_2 at t = 59.72 value from Fig. 22.3)

Fig. 22.8. *Second-order specific rate constants at 74.93°C and 59.72°C for reaction of propylene dibromide with potassium iodide. (99% methanol as solvent.)*

a narrow range of temperatures that other simple equations could be used equally well to fit the measurements. In the latter case, it could well be that a somewhat wider range would favor the Arrhenius expression, and it might be that very accurate data or a very wide temperature range would show deviations from the Arrhenius equation. Despite these reservations, the popularity of the equation is largely deserved so far as its success in fitting data is concerned, and an important problem of chemical kinetic theory is the explanation of this form of equation and of the "activation energy" appearing in it.

22.12. Molecular Collisions

So far in our discussion of reaction rates, little attention has been paid to the magnitudes of the specific rate constants of reactions or to the properties of molecular interactions which determine those rates. A logical starting point is to consider the kinetics of reaction of molecules in dilute gases, as in this case the free motions of molecules are quite simply described and well understood in terms of the kinetic theory of gases discussed in Chapter 9.

Collision Frequencies

For a simple bimolecular reaction—such as $A + B \longrightarrow C$—to occur in a gas, a clearly necessary minimum requirement is that a pair of molecules, one A and one B, approach more closely than some collision distance, which cannot reasonably be very much larger than the sum of the molecular radii. As shown in Section 9.3, the number of times per second that *one* molecule comes within a distance $2r$ of a second one of the same kind is given by the reciprocal of Eq. 9.6a:

$$\text{collision frequency per molecule} = 4\sqrt{\pi}r^2 \left(\frac{4RT}{M}\right)^{1/2} \frac{N}{V}$$

where N/V is the number of molecules in volume V and M the molecular weight. An extension of the kinetic theory argument giving this result shows that the frequency of collision of a molecule A with one from among N_B molecules of kind B in volume V is

$$\text{collision frequency} = \sqrt{\pi}(r_A + r_B)^2 \left[4RT\left(\frac{1}{M_A} + \frac{1}{M_B}\right)\right]^{1/2} \frac{N_B}{V} \quad (22.44)$$
(one A molecule
with any B mol-
ecule)

where $r_A + r_B$ is the collision separation of molecules with radii r_A and r_B, and M_A and M_B are their molecular weights. If there are N_A molecules of A in volume V, the total number of collisions of A and B molecules is then

collisions of A and B per second

$$= \sqrt{\pi}(r_A + r_B)^2 \left[4RT \left(\frac{1}{M_A} + \frac{1}{M_B} \right) \right]^{1/2} \frac{N_A}{V} \frac{N_B}{V} \quad (22.45)$$

If every such collision led to a reaction decreasing the number of A and B molecules each by one, the rate of reaction would be

$$-\frac{d}{dt}\left(\frac{N_A}{V}\right) = \sqrt{\pi}(r_A + r_B)^2 \left[4RT \left(\frac{1}{M_A} + \frac{1}{M_B} \right) \right]^{1/2} \frac{N_A}{N} \frac{N_B}{V} \quad (22.46)$$

Introducing molar concentrations

$$C_A = \frac{1000}{N_0} \left(\frac{N_A}{V} \right) \qquad C_B = \frac{1000}{N_0} \left(\frac{N_B}{V} \right)$$

where N_0 is Avogadro's number, and the factor 1000 converts from cm^3 to liters, a second-order rate equation results:

$$-\frac{dC_A}{dt} = k_2 C_A C_B \quad (22.47)$$

where, for the assumptions made in the collision model, k_2 should have the value

k_2 (all collisions)

$$= \sqrt{\pi}\, \frac{N_0}{1000}\, (r_A + r_B)^2 \left[4RT \left(\frac{1}{M_A} + \frac{1}{M_B} \right) \right]^{1/2} \quad (22.48)$$

The fact that the collision-reaction assumption leads to second-order kinetics is to be expected; a more significant test is whether observed rate constants agree with values predicted by Eq. 22.48. The predicted values are very large: for molecular weights $M_A = M_B = 100$, a collision distance $r_A + r_B = 7$ Å, and $T = 600°K$, k_2 from Eq. 22.48 has the value 3.3×10^{11} liters mole^{-1} sec^{-1}. How large this figure is can be appreciated by calculating the half-life for representative pressures of the gases. For equal concentrations, $C_A = C_B = 0.042$ moles liter^{-1} (partial pressures 0.50 atm each), using the half-life expression for a second-order reaction given in Table 22.3,

$$t_{1/2} = \frac{1}{k_2 C_A} = \frac{1}{3.3 \times 10^{11} \times 4.2 \times 10^{-2}} = 7.2 \times 10^{-11} \text{ sec}$$

The reaction would thus be explosively rapid. Many much, much slower reactions are known, with measured rate constants commonly in the range 10^{-7} to 10^{-2} liters mole^{-1} sec^{-1}, and thus many times smaller.

The only reasonable deduction from such comparisons is that in many reactions only a minute fraction of molecular collisions occurring in gases at ordinary temperatures result in products. Two general kinds of restrictive effects have been proposed to account for the differences: steric factors and energy limitations.

Steric Factors

It is only reasonable to suppose that molecules will not form products by collision if they approach each other with unfavorable relative orientations. As an example, hydrogen and iodine molecules can meet on a collision course with a variety of inclinations of their molecular axes to each other and to the line of centers. Some of the possibilities are shown in Fig. 22.9, and of these only a configuration sim- ilar to (c) looks very promising for the process of simulta- neously breaking H—H and I—I bonds while forming two H—I bonds as in the reaction $H_2 + I_2 \longrightarrow 2HI$. (To assume that reaction can occur only by this mechanism would be

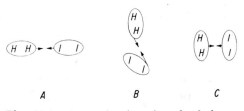

Fig. 22.9. *Approach orientations for hydrogen and iodine molecules.*

incorrect on the basis of available data. In fact, other mechanisms can be hypothesized.)

One can thus very plausibly assume that only a small fraction of all possible collisions bring the molecules together in sterically favorable conditions for molecular rearrangements to occur. With more complex molecules and reactions involving attack on a particular bond or functional group, the possibilities for the proper orientation upon each collision could well be even more drastically limited, and result in only a very small fraction of collisions being effective with respect to reaction.

Atom Recombinations

Consideration of the mechanics of collisions and the stability of molecules shows why atoms, such as hydrogen and chlorine, do not react to form molecules in the gas phase without the intervention of some third body.

Energies of the order 10 to 100 or more kilocalories are required to dissociate diatomic molecules, and corresponding amounts of energy must be absorbed from the two colliding atoms if they are to unite to form the stable molecule. Without some other body present to take up this energy in sufficient amounts, the two atoms will rebound without forming a bond, much as in the impact of two billiard balls.

Atom recombinations can, however, occur when some third body is available. This can be a third atom or otherwise neutral molecule, or it can be the container wall at which the collision takes place, thus accounting for the dependence of rates of atom recombination on concentrations of added inert gases and surface areas available to them.

The union of two bromine atoms, $Br + Br \longrightarrow Br_2$, is catalyzed by adding helium, argon, and other gases, the rate law being of the form

$$-\frac{d[Br]}{dt} = k_3[Br]^2[X]$$

where $[X]$ is the concentration of the added gas. Interestingly, the rate constant k_3 has approximately the value calculated from kinetic theory collision frequencies for three atoms; such reactions are among the few cases where this simple kind of treatment contains most of the essential features required to interpret the observed facts.

When one or both members of the colliding pair is a molecule, the requirement that a third body be present no longer exists, as molecules may take up excess energy in internal forms of motion—vibration and rotation—not possible for atoms. Just how the energy transfer takes place, and how efficient the process is, will depend on the specific molecules involved, and may become very complicated for molecules with several atoms and a correspondingly large number of internal degrees of freedom. Arguments which have been advanced for simpler molecules will be considered in the next sections, after considering implications of the observed temperature dependences of rate constants.

22.13. Activation Energy

A second significant discrepancy between collision frequencies and measured rate constants is found on examining the effect of temperature. From Eq. 22.48, a variation as $T^{1/2}$ is predicted if all collisions were to lead to reaction. Thus an increase of absolute temperature from 300°K to 600°K, for example, would increase the rate only by a factor $(600/300)^{1/2} = 1.41$. By contrast, observed rates often increase by several powers of ten on raising the temperature 50–100°, and the variation with temperature is at least approximately described by the Arrhenius equation with the exponential factor $\exp(-E_A/RT)$.

The pronounced difference thus implies that for many reactions the fraction of collisions leading to reaction, although minute at ordinary temperatures, increases rapidly with temperature. The striking similarity of the Arrhenius exponential to the Boltzmann factor found in gas kinetic theory and to the equilibrium constant expression $K_p = \exp(-\Delta F^0/RT)$ has doubtless influenced the many attempts to account for rate constants by models in which a characteristic activation energy E_A is an essential element.

Energetic Colliding Molecules

Interpretations of activation energy in terms of kinetic theory concepts have been made by supposing that only those collisions are effective in which the colliding pair of molecules possesses a minimum kinetic energy of their relative velocity of approach along the line of centers. From kinetic theory the frequency of collisions between molecules A and B in a gas with velocity lying between U and $U + dU$ is found to be

$$df = \sqrt{\pi}(r_A + r_B)^2 \left[\frac{\mu}{2RT}\right]^{1/2} \exp(-\mu U_0^2/2RT)\, U\, dU\, \frac{N_A}{V}\frac{N_B}{V} \quad (22.49)$$

where N_A/V and N_B/V are the concentrations in molecules cm^{-3}, $r_A + r_B$ is the collision distance, and μ is the reduced molecular weight of the pair defined by $1/\mu = 1/M_A + 1/M_B$. (Derivations of the equation will be found in texts on kinetic theory listed in references at the end of the chapter.) The number of collisions with velocity greater than a minimum value U_0, and hence kinetic energy E_0 greater than $\frac{1}{2}\mu U_0^2$, is found by integrating from $U = U_0$ to $U = \infty$; this gives

$$f(U > U_0)$$

$$= \sqrt{\pi}(r_A + r_B)^2 \left(\frac{4RT}{\mu}\right)^{1/2} \exp(-\mu U_0^2/2RT)\, \frac{N_A}{V}\frac{N_B}{V} \quad (22.50)$$

The corresponding rate constant k_2 is

$$k_2(U > U_0) = \sqrt{\pi}\,\frac{N_0}{1000}(r_A + r_B)^2 \left(\frac{4RT}{\mu}\right)^{1/2} \exp(-E_0/RT) \quad (22.51)$$

The expression of Eq. 22.50 thus differs from Eq. 22.45 for the frequency of all collisions by the factor

$$\exp(-\mu N_0^2/2RT) = \exp(-E_0/RT).$$

For some gas reactions, the modified kinetic theory rate constant of Eq. 22.51 agrees reasonably well with measured rates when E_0 is taken to be equal to the experimental activation energy. This is so for the reaction $2HI = H_2 + I_2$, for which Bodenstein found $E_A = 44$ kcal mole^{-1}; use of this value for E_0 and the estimate $r_A + r_B = 7 \times 10^{-8}$ cm in Eq. 22.51 gives $k_2 = 5.2 \times 10^{-7}$ liter mole^{-1} sec^{-1} at 556°K, in good agreement with the observed value $k_2 = 3.5 \times 10^{-7}$ liters mole^{-1} sec^{-1}.

In many cases, however, any simple models based on assumptions of minimum kinetic energy in collsions are in poor agreement with experiment. The importance of such considerations is generally accepted, but other factors must even so be involved, and in any case the molecular significance of an activation energy remains to be explained. Theories directed to elucidation of this last point are still in development; as a preliminary to introducing some of the concepts, a simplified schematic representation of molecular changes as a collision state is approached will next be outlined.

Energy Changes in Collisions

Consider the reaction of a molecule AB with an atom C to form atom A plus molecule BC: $AB + C \longrightarrow A + BC$. This transfer of atom B from bonding with A to bonding with C requires disruption of the AB bond and formation of the bond BC, whether in sequence or simultaneously.

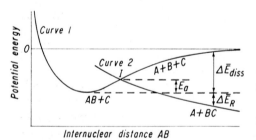

Fig. 22.10. *Energy as function of internuclear distance for reaction $AB + C \longrightarrow A + CB$.*

As a function of the internuclear distance (bond length) of molecule AB, the potential energies of the systems $AB + C$ and $A + BC$ can be represented as shown in Fig. 22.10.

The minimum of curve 1, marked "$AB + C$," corresponds to the stable state of molecule AB with C far away; the abscissa for zero potential energy corresponds to the three separated atoms $A + B + C$; and the energy difference between the two corresponds to the energy of dissociation $\Delta \bar{E}_{diss}$. Curve 2 represents potential energy of A plus molecule BC, which decreases with greater separation of AB. A possible course of reaction is the stretching of the AB bond until point I is reached, followed by further separation of atoms A and B along the second curve with atom B increasingly firmly attached to C and separated from A until, at large A and B distances, the system is the atom A plus stable molecule BC.

For this or similar processes to occur, an amount of energy E_a corresponding to the height of I above the minimum of curve 1 must be supplied, and this represents an activation energy $\bar{E}_A$. This energy clearly need not be the same as either $\bar{E}_{\text{diss}}$ or the final net change $\Delta \bar{E}_R$ in the overall reaction from stable reactants to stable products. From the scheme as pictured, it is reasonable to infer that $\bar{E}_A$ will be less than the dissociation energy of either AB or BC, but further consideration of molecular energies is necessary to obtain the relation to the potential energy change in the reaction.

A gas reaction of this type which has been studied experimentally is $H_2 + Br \longrightarrow H + HBr$. The dissociation energies of H_2 and HBr are known to be 103 and 86.5 kcal/mole, while the measured second-order rate constants at different temperatures give an activation energy of 18 kcal/mole, and the energy change of reaction is $\Delta \bar{E}_R = 16.5$ kcal/mole. The values are evidently consistent with the model of the activation process. More detailed considerations of the transition process are discussed in Section 22.13.

22.14. Collision Theory and First-order Reactions

If it is assumed that a first-order reaction is unimolecular, one may well ask how the collision theory can explain first-order reactions at all. The difficulty arises because a process in which a molecule acquires the necessary energy to react by collision with a second molecule should presumably result in a second-order rate law.

A way out of the impasse is as follows. If the reacting molecule after collision requires a finite time for the activating energy to be concentrated in the mode which will result in decomposition, some activated molecules can instead lose this energy through subsequent collision and thus fail to react. The frequency of decomposition will therefore be less than the frequency of activating collision, and the rate will depend directly on the concentration of reacting molecules. This is represented by

$$A + A \underset{k_{-2}}{\overset{k_2}{\rightleftharpoons}} A^- + A^*$$
$$\downarrow k_1$$
$$\text{products}$$

where A^* represents an activated molecule, and A^- an energy-deficient molecule. Rate equations can be written for each of the reactions involved, and for appropriate values the rate of formation of products is found to be proportional to the concentration of A. (The student should demonstrate this as an exercise.) This theory, first proposed by Lindemann in 1922, seems valid for some first-order reactions. A simple check on the theory, by studying a given "unimolecular" reaction as the pressure is lowered, indicates that it fails to follow the first-order law at sufficiently low pressure, where the time between collisions is so long that the rate of deactivation is no longer sufficiently large relative to $k_1 C_{A*}$, where C_{A*} is the concentration of activated molecules, and the activation step involving C_A^2 becomes rate-controlling. Data from the thermal decomposition of azomethane confirm this. Actually, however, the number of reactions not susceptible to quantitative interpretation by simple collision theory is sufficient that this kind of theory cannot be considered generally satisfactory. It will be noted also that no attempt has been made to apply it to reactions in solution, or elsewhere than in a homogeneous gaseous system.

22.15. Absolute Reaction Rates

A theory of "absolute rates" of reactions has been developed, from quantum and statistical mechanics, notably by Eyring and his co-workers, with the hope of overcoming the shortcomings of the collision theory and to define more adequately the nature of the activation process. Because of the complexity of the calculations, it has so far only been possible to consider the simplest of systems, for which the quantum equations are least intractable. The reaction of the hydrogen atom with the hydrogen molecule has been studied, first in terms of conversion of ortho- to parahydrogen already discussed in Section 22.4, and later by use of the deuterium isotope:

$$\text{H} + \text{O-H}_2 \rightleftharpoons p\text{-H}_2 + \text{H}, \qquad E_A = 7.0 \text{ kcal}$$

$$\text{D} + \text{H}_2 \rightleftharpoons \text{DH} + \text{H}, \qquad E_A = 8.5 \text{ kcal}$$

Potential energy contour surfaces for different relative atom positions can be calculated approximately and plotted, as Eyring has done for the latter system, shown in Fig. 22.11. The two coordinates represent the distance along the linear axis $\text{H}_B\text{—H}_A\text{—D}$ between D and $\text{H}_A(r_1)$ and H_B and $\text{H}_A(r_2)$. (The two coordinates are not at right angles in order to represent the conversion of energy of translation to energy of

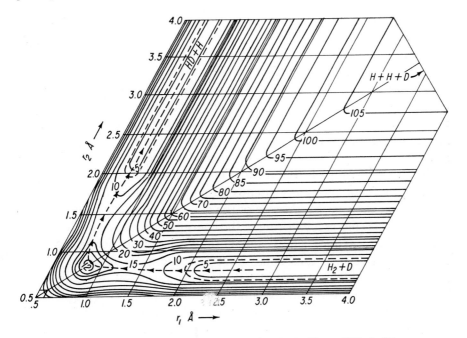

Fig. 22.11. *Potential energy surface for the reaction $D + H_2 = HD + H$.*

vibration by the motion of a frictionless object moving under gravity on the potential energy surface.) For r_1 large enough so that there is no change in energy with r_1, the profile through the surface will correspond with the potential energy diagram for the hydrogen molecule shown in Figs. 6.1 and 6.2. The course of reaction requiring least energy proceeds by a path along the valley minimum parallel with the r_1 coordinate toward lower values of r_1, over the top of the saddle at the minimum energy for $r_1 = r_2$, and then out along the valley parallel to the r_2 coordinate. The equidistant configuration D—H—H occurs for $r_1 = r_2 = 0.95$ Å; this distance is thus somewhat greater than the internuclear distance, 0.74 Å, for the normal molecule. The energy required to reach the lowest point of the saddle or pass from the valley is 7.8 kcal/mole, which agrees well with the measured activation energy of 8.5 kcal/mole.

The construction of such potential energy surfaces for more complex molecules can be imagined to give quantitatively similar results, but the necessary calculations are usually unmanageable or so approximate if manageable with present methods that their quantitative value is dubious.

22.16. Catalysis

A catalyst has already been defined as a substance which will change the rate of a chemical reaction without itself being consumed or produced by the reaction. Frequently this is accomplished even when the catalyst is present in very small amounts relative to the gross mass of reactants. While most catalysts are positive—that is, they accelerate the reaction rate—negative catalysts are possible; here a catalyst will be assumed to be positive unless specifically stated otherwise. Catalysis deals with the study of catalysts and catalytic action.

The process of catalysis evidently provides an easier and faster path for reaction than in the absence of the catalyst. In many cases catalysis can be interpreted as a lowering of the energy of activation or the energy barrier of a reaction. The reaction thus is made easier in both the forward and reverse directions, since less energy is required for the reactants to achieve the activated state or surmount the barrier. A catalyst cannot, by thermodynamics, shift the position of equilibrium of a reaction, and the reason, according to the present model, is that the lowering of the energy barrier is as effective in easing the reverse reaction as it is the forward reaction.

Catalysts are classified as homogeneous, heterogeneous, gas phase, contact, acid-base, enzymatic, and so on. Regardless of their classification, in general a catalyst is involved in the formation of a reaction intermediate which, upon forming the final reaction products, releases the catalyst in its original form. This is almost inherent in considering homogeneous catalysis, and may be easily understood in the case of heterogeneous catalysis. *Homogeneous catalysis* involves the catalyst in the same phase as the reacting substances. An example from the study of elementary chemistry is the reaction involved in the production of sulfuric acid by the chamber process. The oxidation

$$2SO_2 + O_2 \longrightarrow 2SO_3$$

is very slow at ordinary temperatures. However, in the presence of nitric oxide it is much faster. The catalytic action involves the formation of intermediate nitric oxide, and its oxidation of sulfur dioxide:

$$2NO + O_2 \longrightarrow 2NO_2$$

$$2SO_2 + 2NO_2 \longrightarrow 2SO_3 + 2NO$$

Nitrosylsulfuric acid [$SO_2(OH)ONO$] is observed in the actual process, in which water vapor is present.

Another example of gas phase catalysis is the effect of iodine vapor upon the decomposition of aldehydes and ethers. The thermal decomposition of gaseous acetaldehyde to methane and carbon monoxide has a measured energy of activation of 45.5 kcals, but in the presence of iodine vapor it is but 32.5 kcals, and the rate constant is increased by a factor 10^4. The intermediate reactions

$$CH_3CHO + I_2 \longrightarrow CH_3I + HI + CO$$

$$CH_3I + HI \longrightarrow CH_4 + I_2$$

have been proposed to account for the observations.

In liquid solution, examples of homogeneous catalysts are found in acid-base catalysis. The inversion of sucrose catalyzed by the presence of hydrogen ion is already familiar, as are hydrolysis reactions of various organic compounds. Generalized acid-base catalysis is similar, with acids and bases defined in the Brönsted sense as proton donors or proton acceptors. Table 22.4 gives numerous examples.

Heterogeneous catalysis will occur when the catalyst is in a different phase than the reactants. Usually it is present as a solid—possibly the wall of the reacting vessel—or finely divided to increase the extent of surface. Special treatment will sometimes produce more effective "activated" surfaces. Surface catalysis is sometimes called contact catalysis. The catalytic process is complicated and may involve such factors as diffusion of reactants toward the catalytic surface, adsorption on the surface, reaction, desorption from the surface, and diffusion of products away from the surface. Any one of these processes may be rate-controlling, although the first and last are usually rapid relative to the others, and generally the second and fourth are faster than the third. Adsorption processes as discussed in Sections 21.11 and 21.17 are pertinent. It should be emphasized that in being adsorbed on a surface, a molecule may form a chemical bond with the solid of which the surface is composed at a point described as an "active center." This intermediate compound by "chemisorption" is then available for reaction with a molecule of a second kind, with less energy required than for the direct combination.

In the contact process for sulfuric acid, sulfur dioxide is oxidized to the trioxide in the presence of platinum or vanadium pentoxide. Hydrogenation of unsaturated organic substances by means of nickel or metallic oxide contact catalysts, and the dehydrogenation of alcohols by metallic catalysts are other examples. Glass will catalyze the bromination of ethylene. An interesting case is the decomposition of formic acid, either

TABLE 22.4.   *Homogeneously Catalyzed Reactions in Solution.*

Reaction	Catalyst	Solvent
Decomposition of H_2O_2	HBr, HCl, HI	water
Oxidation of persulfates	Ag^+	water
$Ce^{4+} + S_2O_3^{--}$	I^-	water
Inversion of menthone	$C_2H_5O^-$	C_2H_5OH
Inversion of sucrose	H^+	water
Hydrolysis of esters, amides, acetals	H^+	water
Decomposition of diazoacetic acid	H^+	water
Hydrolysis of sulfamic acid	H^+	water
Hydrolysis of pyrophosphates	H^+	water
Decomposition of nitroso-triacetone-amine	OH^-	water
Decomposition of triacetone alcohol	OH^-	water
Conversion of acetone to triacetone alcohol	OH^-	water
Hydrolysis of ethyl orthocarbonate, ortho-acetate, and orthopropionate	Generalized acid	water
Oxidation of phosphorus and hypophosphorus acids by iodine	Generalized acid	water
Rearrangement of N-bromacetanilide	Generalized acid	C_6H_6, C_6H_5Cl
Decomposition of nitramide	Generalized base	water, isoamyl alcohol, m-cresol
Isomerization of nitromethane	Generalized base	water
Mutarotation of glucose	Generalized acid-base	water
Enolization of acetone	Generalized acid-base	water
Acetylation of β-naphthol	Generalized acid-base	CH_3COOH

From Maron and Prutton, *Principles of Physical Chemistry* (Macmillan, New York, 1958).

(1) to water and carbon monoxide, or (2) to hydrogen and carbon dioxide. In the presence of a glass surface, neither reaction predominates; on alumina the first does, and on zinc oxide the second. It is thus possible to control the course of reaction by suitable choice of the catalyst.

Other examples are given in Table 22.5, which compares the activation energies for reactions without and with a catalyst.

Enzymatic catalysts are of extreme importance in life processes. Reactions which ordinarily proceed at measurable rates only at high temperatures will in the presence of enzymes proceed at temperatures of living

TABLE 22.5. *Activation Energies for Homogeneous and Heterogeneous Reactions. (Units are cal/mole.)*

Decomposition of Gas	E_A^* Homogeneous	E_A^* Heterogeneous
HI	44,000	25,000 (gold)
N_2O	58,500	29,000 (gold)
N_2O	58,500	32,500 (platinum)
NH_3	80,000 (est.)	39,000 (tungsten)

From Maron and Prutton, *Principles of Physical Chemistry* (Macmillan, New York, 1958).

TABLE 22.6. *Activation Energies for Some Catalyzed Reactions (cal/mole).*

Reaction	Catalyst	E_A
The decomposition of hydrogen peroxide in aqueous solution	None	18,000
	Iodide ion	13,500
	Colloidal platinum	11,700
	Liver catalase	5,500
The decomposition of acetone-dicarboxylic acid in aqueous solution	None	23,200
	Aniline	13,900
The hydrolysis of sucrose in aqueous solution	Hydrogen ion	25,560
	Saccharase	8,700
The hydrolysis of casein in aqueous solution	Hydrochloric acid	20,600
	Trypsin-kinase	14,400
The decomposition of triethylsulphonium bromide in acetone solution	None	33,500
	4% water	30,700
The decomposition of trinitrobenzoic acid in nitrobenzene solution	None	35,000
	Adventitious impurity (probably water)	21,700
The decomposition of trichloracetic acid	Water (solvent)	37,050
	Aniline (solvent)	28,350
The Beckmann rearrangement of the picryl ether of benzophenone oxime in carbon tetrachloride solution	None	30,250
	Nitromethane	23,800
The decomposition of ethylene iodide in the gas phase and in carbon tetrachloride solution	None	37,000
	Iodine (atomic)	12,500
The decomposition of diethylether in the gas phase	None	53,500
	Iodine (molecular)	34,300

tissues. (Enzymes are chemical compounds of high molecular weight, which seem almost intermediate between nonliving and living systems.) Examples are the *amylases*, a series of enzymes which break down carbohydrates, and *proteases*, a series which break down proteins. *Zymase* is present in yeast and catalyzes the formation of carbon dioxide and alcohol from dextroses. *Urease* will cause urea to hydrolyze to ammonium carbonate.

Numerous other examples of various types of catalytic processes and the corresponding activation energies are listed in Table 22.6.

Catalytic Poisons and Promoters

Certain substances will inhibit or stop catalytic action, and thus are said to "poison" a catalyst. This action seems to involve a preferential compound formation of the catalyst with the poison. Arsenic, for example, will poison the platinum catalyst of the contact process for sulfuric acid, apparently by being adsorbed irreversibly (with high energy) upon the active centers of the platinum surface, thus leaving none available for the SO_2 molecules.

Other substances promote or enhance the action of a catalyst. Copper ion in trace quantity will cause a significant increase in the rate of the ferrous ion catalyzed reaction

$$2I^- + S_2O_8^{2-} \rightleftharpoons I_2 + 2SO_4^{2-}$$

although it has little catalytic effect by itself.

Autocatalysis

Occasionally a reaction will be catalyzed by one of the products of the reaction, and it is said to be autocatalytic. Such reactions are distinguished by a slow initial and rapidly accelerating reaction rate.

Obviously it has been impossible here to do more than give the briefest introduction to the subject of reaction kinetics. Much more is known of the subject than could be encompassed in an entire course, but much remains to be learned and better understood through further research. The study of the mechanism of chemical reaction is one of today's most interesting and important areas for further work.

Problems

22.1. Ethyl bromide reacts with solvent ethanol to form hydrogen bromide. A 0.100 molar solution at 55°C contained the following concentrations of HBr at times t after the reaction began:

t (hours)	0	19.9	29.8	44.0	49
[HBr] (moles/liter)	0	0.0016	0.0024	0.0036	0.0039

Show that either zero or first-order rate expressions are consistent with the data. What are the rate constants in each case?

22.2. The gas phase decomposition of ethylene oxide into methane and carbon dioxide was followed by measurements of the pressure, with the following results at 400°C:

Time (min)	0	6.00	10.8	14.4	21.6
P (mm Hg)	98.55	102.70	107.6	111.6	118.4

(a) Calculate the partial pressures of undissociated ethylene oxide. (b) Plot the logarithms and reciprocals of these pressures against time. From your plots, what can you say about the order of reaction?

22.3. Uranium X_1, formed from the natural uranium isotope of mass number 238 by α-particle emission, itself decays quite rapidly with emission of electrons. Measurement of this emission gives the following concentrations of the isotope at different times after chemical separation from uranium:

Time (days)	0	10	20	30	40	60	80
Fraction of original amount	1.00	0.70	0.51	0.39	0.28	0.17	0.10

Show by a suitable plot that the decay obeys the equation of first-order reactions, and calculate the half-life and rate constant.

22.4. The thermal decomposition of acetone vapor at 600°C has been studied by the times $t_{1/4}$, $t_{1/2}$, $t_{3/4}$ in seconds for one-quarter, one-half, and three-quarters of the original concentration of acetone to be decomposed. The results for different initial pressures P of acetone were:

P (mm Hg)	360	300	190	100
$t_{1/4}$	26	27	20	30
$t_{1/2}$	77	80	78	85
$t_{3/4}$	152	160	155	165

Within the accuracy of the data, what is the order and the rate constant?

22.5. The decomposition of acetaldehyde to methane and carbon monoxide can be followed by the increase in pressure of the gas mixture. For an initial pressure of 360 mm Hg at 800°K the following pressures were observed at times t (in seconds):

t (sec)	42	105	242	480	840	1440
P (mm Hg)	394	434	494	554	604	644

Determine the order of the reaction under these conditions and calculate the rate constant.

22.6. The overall reaction between acetone and iodine in acid solution is

$$CH_3COCH_3 + I_2 = CH_3COH_2I + HI$$

Initial rates (in arbitrary units) of disappearance of acetone for a series of experiments with varying concentrations were as follows:

$[CH_3COCH_3]$	$[I_2]$	$[H^+]$	Rate
0.27	0.01	0.01	1.30
0.45	0.01	0.01	2.15
0.45	0.01	0.005	1.15
0.27	0.005	0.005	0.64

(a) What are the orders with respect to CH_3COCH_3, I_2, and H^+? (b) Discuss the rate law on the basis that the initial and slow step is enolization of acetone to CH_3COHCH_2, followed by reaction with iodine.

22.7. The reaction $2NO + 2H_2 = N_2 + 2H_2O$ was studied by Hinshelwood and Green by following the pressure change. When concentrations of NO were varied, the initial rates of pressure change were as follows:

P_{NO} (mm Hg)	360	300	150
dP/dt (mm/sec)	1.50	1.03	0.25

From these data, determine the order of the reaction with respect to NO.

22.8. At high temperatures, decomposition of dimethyl ether occurs by the reaction $(CH_3)_2O \longrightarrow CH_4 + H_2 + CO$, which is found to be first order with a specific rate constant 4.4×10^{-4} sec^{-1}. Calculate the time for 10% and half reaction with an initial pressure of 500 mm Hg.

22.9. The reaction of *n*-propyl bromide with thiosulfate ion in a mixed alcohol-water solvent, $C_3H_7Br + S_2O_3^{2-} \longrightarrow C_3H_7S_2O_3^- + Br^-$, is second order with specific rate constant $k_2 = 1.64 \times 10^{-3}$ liter/mole sec at 37°C. (a) If the initial concentrations are $[C_3H_7Br] = 0.100$ mole/liter and $[S_2O_3^{2-}] = 0.040$ mole/liter, what is the initial rate of disappearance of C_3H_7Br? (b) Calculate and plot the concentrations of C_3H_7Br and $S_2O_3^{2-}$ for times until reaction is about 80% complete. (c) Devise a rearranged form of the integrated rate equation involving amount of $S_2O_3^{2-}$ reacted and time, which should give a straight line. Test your answer by using your values calculated in part (b).

22.10. The gas reaction $2NO + Br_2 = 2NOBr$ is third order with a specific rate constant $k_3 = 2.7 \times 10^3$ (liter/mole)^2 sec^{-1} at 15°C. (a) What is the initial rate of disappearance of NO if the pressures of NO and Br_2 are 100 and 200 mm Hg? (b) Assuming equal initial concentrations (C) of NO and Br_2, obtain by integration of the rate equation an expression for the amount of NOBr formed at different times t. If $C = 0.01$ mole/liter, how long will it take to form 0.01 mole/liter of NOBr?

22.11. The reaction $2HI \longrightarrow H_2 + I_2$ and the reverse reaction $H_2 + I_2 \longrightarrow 2HI$ are both second order. Rate constants k_2 and k_{-2} for the respective reactions were determined by Bodenstein before 1900; some of the results are:

$T°K$	556	629	666	716	781
k_2 (liter/mole^{-1} sec^{-1})	3.52×10^{-7}	3.02×10^{-5}	2.20×10^{-4}	2.50×10^{-3}	3.95×10^{-2}
k_{-2} (liter/mole^{-1} sec^{-1})	4.45×10^{-5}	2.52×10^{-3}	1.42×10^{-2}	1.40×10^{-1}	1.34

(a) Calculate the equilibrium constant K at these temperatures and compare with directly determined values (see Problem 15.16). (b) Make plots of log k_2 and log k_{-2} against $1/T$. How do the slopes compare with the value of $\Delta H/2.3R$ for the equilibrium constant plot (of log K against $1/T$)? Discuss the differences. (c) Compare the activation energy determined in (b) with the energy necessary to break two HI bonds inferred from thermochemical data (Section 13.10).

22.12. Make plots like those of Fig. 22.6 for the reaction sequence

$$A \xrightarrow{k_1} B \xrightarrow{k_2} C$$

when $k_2 = 3k_1$. (Suggestion: Calculate $[A]/a$, $[B]/a$, and $[C]/a$ for values of k_1t from 0 to 3 and plot against k_1t.) Do the plots show the rate-limiting and induction-period features discussed in Section 22.9?

22.13. Describe experiments you would perform to confirm or disprove Bodenstein's rate law for the formation of HBr (Eq. 22.29 of Section 22.9), assuming that the concentration of Br_2 can be measured photometrically.

22.14. Some dissociation and combination reactions are written for a purpose in the forms

$$X_2 + M \longrightarrow 2X + M$$
$$2X + M \longrightarrow X_2 + M$$

Why should M be included when it appears on both sides, and what do X and M stand for?

22.15. The reaction $2NO + O_2 \longrightarrow 2NO_2$ is third order, experimentally, and also has the exceptional behavior that its rate decreases with increasing temperature in the range 80°K to 600°K. [At 80°K, $k_3 = 98 \times 10^5$ (liter/mole)^2 sec^{-1}; at 600°K, $k_3 = 6.6 \times 10^5$ (liter/mole)^2 sec^{-1}.] (a) One possible explanation is based on the assumption that there are two steps: the equilibrium $2NO = (NO)_2$ provides a supply of $(NO)_2$ molecules with which O_2 reacts,

$(NO)_2 + O_2 \longrightarrow 2NO_2$ with second-order rate constant k_2. Show that this gives a third-order reaction with $k_3 = Kk_2$, where K is the equilibrium constant of the dimerization. (b) From the result in (a), suggest a possible reason for the slower rate at higher temperatures, which does not violate the usual fact that true molecular rate constants increase with temperature. (c) Discuss the possibility of the equilibrium $NO + O_2 = NO_3$, followed by $NO_3 + NO \longrightarrow 2NO_2$, by obtaining the rate equation, and by considering the stability of the molecules concerned.

22.16. The gas phase reaction between hydrogen and iodine chloride, $H_2 + 2ICl \longrightarrow 2HCl + I_2$, is found experimentally to be second order in formations of HCl or I_2 rather than third order. Show that this can be explained by assuming that there is first a slow reaction

$$H_2 + ICl \longrightarrow HI + HCl$$

followed by a fast reaction

$$HI + ICl \longrightarrow HCl + I_2$$

22.17. The overall reaction for decomposition of sodium hypochlorite, NaClO, is $3NaClO \longrightarrow 2NaCl + NaClO_3$, but the reaction is found to be second order. Show that this can be accounted for by assuming the successive reactions

$$2NaClO \longrightarrow NaCl + NaClO_2$$
$$NaClO_2 + NaClO \longrightarrow NaClO_3 + NaCl$$

if the rate constant for the second reaction is much larger than that for the first.

22.18. The photochemical gas reaction of chloroform with chlorine, $CHCl_3 + Cl_2 + I \longrightarrow CCl_4 + HCl$, obeys the rate law

$$\frac{d}{dt}[CCl_4] = k[CHCl_3][Cl_2]^{1/2}I^{1/2}$$

where I is the light intensity. Devise a sequence of reactions that can explain the observations, assuming that the initial step is formation of chlorine radicals Cl, and that the stationary state approximation can be applied to reactive intermediates.

22.19. The reaction of stilbene $(C_6H_5CH = HCC_6H_5)$ with bromine in methanol is believed to proceed by bromine attack on the double bond to form the brominated ion $C_6H_5CHBrHCC_6H_5^+$ plus the bromide ion, followed by reaction of the positive ion with Br^- or solvent. Write out the reaction scheme and obtain a rate equation for loss of stilbene.

22.20. The thermal decomposition of ozone is found to be catalyzed by chlorine, the rate of decomposition following the rate expression

$$\frac{d}{dt}[O_3] = -k[O_3]^{3/2}[Cl_2]^{1/2}$$

Show that this can be explained by a chain reaction with the initial steps

$$O_3 + Cl_2 = ClO_2 + ClO$$
$$ClO_2 + O_3 = ClO_3 + O_2$$

followed by reaction of ClO_3 with O_3 to give ClO_2 and thus propagate the sequence; the chain-breaking step is the combination of ClO_3 to form Cl_2 and O_2 by the reaction $2ClO_3 = Cl_2 + 3O_2$. (Hint: Apply the steady-state treatment to concentrations of ClO_2 and ClO_3, and assume that the combination reaction is slow—i.e., the chains are long.)

22.21. Many reactions with readily measurable rates at room temperature are found to double or triple in rate for $10°C$ rise in temperature. (a) What is the range of activation energies corresponding to these changes? (b) If a reaction doubles in rate between $25°C$ and $35°C$, how much faster would you estimate it to be at $70°C$?

22.22. Boiling an egg denatures a protein which has an activation energy of about 130 kcal/mole. At sea level and $100°C$ a favored time is 3 min. How long is required for the same stage to be reached at an altitude of approximately 8000 feet and a boiling point of $95°C$ for water?

22.23. (a) The dimerization of liquid cyclopentadiene has a specific rate constant varying with temperature according to $k = Ae^{-E/RT}$, where $\log A = 5.7$ and $E = 16.0$ kcal/mole. Calculate k at $25°C$. (b) The reaction in the gas phase is represented by $A = 6.1$ and $E = 16.7$ kcal/mole. Calculate the rate constant at $25°C$ and compare with the answer to (a).

22.24. Second-order rate constants for the reaction $C_2H_5I + OH^- \longrightarrow C_2H_5OH + I^-$ have been measured over the range $16°C$ to $90°C$; some values are:

t, °C	16	32	60	90
k_2 (liter mole^{-1} sec^{-1})	5.0×10^{-5}	3.7×10^{-4}	6.7×10^{-3}	1.2×10^{-1}

(a) Plot $\log k_2$ against $1/T$ and obtain the activation energy. (b) If initial concentrations of ethyl iodide and OH^- are 10^{-2} moles/liter and 10^{-4} moles/liter, find the initial rate of disappearance and the half-life of C_2H_5I at $32°C$.

22.26. Nitramide is a very weak acid and decomposes in water to N_2O and water. The reaction is first order in nitramide and is base catalyzed; the rate expression with OH^- in solution is

$$\frac{d}{dt} [NH_2NO_2] = -k[NH_2NO_2][OH^-]$$

Show that this can be explained by a reaction sequence in which $NHNO_2^- \longrightarrow N_2O + OH^-$ is the slow step, using the fact that the ionization reaction $H^+ + OH^- \longrightarrow H_2O$ reaches equilibrium rapidly.

22.27. The photobromination of methane around 200°C yields principally HBr and CH_3Br, and the rate of formation of methyl bromide has been found to follow the equation

$$\frac{d}{dt}[CH_3Br] = \frac{k'\mathbf{I}^{1/2}[CH_4][Br_2]^{1/2}}{P^{1/2}\left(1 + k''\dfrac{[HBr]}{[Br_2]}\right)}$$

where $\mathbf{I}$ is the light intensity, k' and k'' are constants (involving molecular rate constants), and P is the total gas pressure. The reaction steps proposed for the process are

$$Br_2 + \mathbf{I} \longrightarrow Br + Br$$
$$Br + CH_4 \longrightarrow CH_3 + HBr$$
$$CH_3 + Br_2 \longrightarrow CH_3Br + Br$$
$$CH_3 + HBr \longrightarrow CH_4 + Br$$
$$Br + Br \longrightarrow Br_2$$

Show that the observed rate expression can be obtained by applying the steady-state approximation to concentrations of CH_3 and Br and taking account of the fact that the rate of recombination of bromine atoms, which requires a third body, is expected to be proportional to the total pressure.

22.28. The reaction $A + B \longrightarrow C$ with bimolecular rate constant k_1 does not go to completion, but reaches equilibrium with the back reaction $C \longrightarrow A + B$, with first-order constant k_{-1}. (a) Show for equal initial amounts (a) of A and B that the amount (x) of C formed follows the rate equation

$$\frac{dx}{dt} = k_1(a - x)^2 - k_{-1}x$$

(b) If the amount of C at equilibrium is C_{eq}, show that the integrated expression for x at different times t is

$$\left(\frac{C_{eq}}{a^2 - C_{eq}^2}\right)\ln\frac{C_{eq}(a^2 - C_{eq}x)}{a^2(C_{eq} - x)} = k_1 t$$

(Hint: Express the rate equation in terms of $a - x$ as a new variable z and use the condition that $dx/dt = 0$ when $x = C_{eq}$ to eliminate k_{-1}.)

22.29. (a) If the reaction sequence

$$A \xrightarrow{k_1} B \xrightarrow{k_2} C$$

starts with pure A at concentration a for time zero, show that the maximum concentration of B is reached at the time $t_m = (k_1 - k_2)^{-1}\ln(k_1/k_2)$ and that this concentration is $[B]_m = (k_1/k_2)a \exp(-k_1 t_m)$. (b) If the rates k_1 and k_2 of the sequence are the same, show that the solutions for $[B]$ and $[C]$ are

$$[B] = ak_1 t e^{-k_1 t}$$
$$[C] = a(1 - e^{-k_1 t})t - ak_1 t e^{-k_1 t}$$

(c) Show that for $k_1 = k_2$ the maximum value of $[B]$ is $[B]_m = a/e$ ($e = 2.7183$) and is reached at time $t_m = 1/k_1$.

22.30. (a) On the basis of collision theory, what basis can you give for writing the rate of formation of A_2 by the reaction $A + A \xrightarrow{k} A_2$ as $(d/dt)[A_2] = \frac{1}{2}k[A]^2$, rather than $(d/dt)[A_2] = k[A]^2$? (b) How does this differ from the reaction $A + B \longrightarrow AB$ when A and B are present in the same amount? (c) Are there any similar considerations in writing the reverse reactions? Explain.

22.31. The rate equation for the formation of addition polymers A_n by the series of reactions $A + A \longrightarrow A_2$, $A + A_2 \longrightarrow A_3$, and all other reactions $A_i + A_{n-i} \longrightarrow A_n$ can be solved if the rate constant k is the same for all reaction. (a) Write rate equations for each A_n and manipulate these equations to obtain an equation for the rate of disappearance of A. If the initial concentration of monomer is a, the integrated equation for remaining amount of A at time t is found to be

$$[A] = \frac{a}{(1 + \frac{1}{2}akt)^2}$$

(The factor $\frac{1}{2}$ appears essentially because the reactions $A + A \longrightarrow A_2$, $A_2 + A_2 \longrightarrow A_4$ remove two molecules to form one.) (b) Calculate $d[A]/dt$. What apparent order would be inferred from the initial variation of A with time? (c) What order would be inferred from the variation of initial rate with a?

22.32. Show for the preceding problem that the total concentration C of polymer molecules is

$$C = [A_2] + [A_3] + [A_4] + \cdots = a \frac{\frac{1}{2}akt}{(1 + \frac{1}{2}akt)^2}$$

and the total amount x of monomer molecules used up in forming polymers is

$$x = 2[A_2] + 3[A_3] + 4[A_4] + \cdots = a \frac{akt(1 + \frac{1}{4}akt)}{(1 + \frac{1}{2}akt)^2}$$

22.33. The decomposition of dimethyl ether has been studied to provide a test of the Lindeman mechanism for first-order gas reactions. (a) If the decomposition goes by the sequence

$$2(CH_3)_2O \underset{k_2}{\overset{k_1}{\rightleftharpoons}} (CH_3)_2O + (CH_3)_2O^*$$

$$(CH_3)_2O^* \xrightarrow{k_3} products$$

where $(CH_3)_2O^*$ indicates activated molecules, show that the rate law is

$$\frac{d}{dt}[(CH_3)_2O] = -\frac{k_1[(CH_3)_2O]^2}{1 + \frac{k_2}{k_3}[(CH_3)_2O]}$$

(b) Show that the initial rate (i.e., before much concentration change has occurred) will appear to be first order with an apparent rate

$$\frac{1}{k_{app}} = \frac{k_2}{k_1 k_3} + \frac{1}{k_1 C_0}$$

where C_0 is the initial ether concentration. (c) Values of apparent rates k_{app} for various initial concentrations C_0 of ether at 500°C are:

C_0 (moles/liter)	.020	.013	.010	.005	.003	.0012
$k_{app} \times 10^4$ (sec^{-1})	7.6	7.0	6.7	5.4	4.2	2.5

Test the equation for k_{app} derived in (b) by a suitable graphical plot of the data, and derive values for k_1 and k_2/k_3.

22.34. The decomposition of N_2O_5 has become a classic in chemical kinetics, because the results of Daniels and Johnston (discussed in Section 22.6) were the first example of a homogeneous first-order gas reaction and because of difficulties in explaining the order. Daniels and Johnston proposed an initial step $N_2O_5 \longrightarrow N_2O_3 + O_2$, which has since been ruled out because of the changes in molecular symmetry required, and the change in order predicted from the Lindeman mechanism (see the preceding problem) does not occur at the pressure required by this mechanism. The most satisfactory explanation is Ogg's proposal that an initial decomposition

$$N_2O_5 \xrightarrow{k_1} NO_3 + NO_2$$

is followed by the reaction steps

$$NO_3 + NO_2 \xrightarrow{k_2} NO_2 + O_2 + NO$$
$$NO + N_2O_5 \xrightarrow{k_3} 3NO_2$$

and the equilibrium $2NO_2 = N_2O_4$, or by the recombination

$$NO_3 + NO_2 \xrightarrow{k_{-1}} N_2O_5$$

Show that this gives the first-order rate expression

$$\frac{d}{dt}[N_2O_5] = -2\frac{k_1 k_2}{k_{-1} + k_2}[N_2O_5]$$

if the stationary-state approximation is applied to $[NO_3]$ and $[NO]$.

22.35. Some enzyme action in formation of proteins from reactant species (substrate) can be represented by the reaction scheme

$$\text{Substrate} + \text{enzyme} \underset{k_2}{\overset{k_1}{\rightleftharpoons}} \text{complex}$$

$$\text{Complex} \xrightarrow{k_3} \text{products}$$

(a) Assuming that the complex is never present in large amounts, derive a rate law for the reaction. (b) Show that the reaction is first order if the enzyme is a catalyst fixed in amount, and second order for experiments varying the enzyme concentration if the concentration of substrate is low.

22.36. The rate constants of ionic reactions may change considerably with ion concentrations, and in dilute solutions the logarithms of specific rate constants often vary approximately in proportion to the square root of ionic strength, I. Brönsted and Livingston studied the reaction

$$[Co(NH_3)_5Br]^{2+} + NaOH \longrightarrow [Co(NH_3)_5OH]^{2+} + NaBr$$

varying ionic strength by reactant concentrations and by adding NaCl and BaCl$_2$. Some of their data for the second-order rate constant k in liters-mole^{-1} sec^{-1} as a function of I are as follows:

I	.0022	.0031	.0041	.0125	.0175	.0235	.0325
k	1.48	1.48	1.40	1.27	1.13	1.10	0.97

Test the dependence described above by a plot of $\log k$ against $I^{1/2}$ and obtain a value for k at zero ionic strength.

22.37. Brönsted and Bjerrum have suggested an explanation for the kinetic salt effect, illustrated by the preceding example, in terms of an initial equilibrium complex which then decomposes slowly to products. (a) Show that the rate is governed by the concentration of the complex, and that from the Debye-Hückel theory this concentration will be increased relative to ion concentrations if the reacting ions have the same sign of charge, but will be decreased if they are oppositely charged. (b) On this basis, discuss the nature of the ions and complex in the reaction in the preceding problem.

22.38. Predict the dependence on ionic strength of the rates of the reactions

$$NH_4^+ + CNO^- \longrightarrow CO(NH_2)_2$$
$$S_2O_8^{2-} + 2I^- \longrightarrow I_2 + 2SO_4^{2-}$$
$$CH_2ICOOH + CNS^- \longrightarrow CH_2CNSCOOH + I^-$$
$$CH_3COONa + H_2O \longrightarrow CH_3COOH + NaOH$$

Suggested Readings

An excellent introduction to the subject is given in the paperback *How Chemical Reactions Occur* by E. L. King (Benjamin, New York, 1963). Also to be recommended is the discussion in *Physical Chemistry* by E. A. Moelwyn-Hughes (Pergamon, New York, 1957).

Two comprehensive treatises with a wealth of examples are *Chemical Kinetics* by K. J. Laidler (McGraw-Hill, New York, 1950) and *The Foundations of Chemical Kinetics* by S. W. Benson (McGraw-Hill, New York, 1960).

An introductory discussion of absolute rate theory is presented by H. and E. M. Eyring in the paperback *Modern Chemical Kinetics* (Reinhold, New York, 1963). Experimental methods are discussed by various authors in the compendium *Investigations of Rates and Mechanisms of Reactions* (2nd ed.), Volume 8, Part 2 of *Techniques of Organic Chemistry*, edited by A. Weissberger (Interscience, New York, in press 1964).

Index

Absolute temperature, 182, 188
Absolute zero, 182, 396
Absorption spectra, 130
Acid, ionization of, 611 ff.
Acid-base catalysis, 768
Activation energies: effect of catalyst, 770; Table, 771
Activation energy, 757, 758, 759, 763, 765
"Active center," 689, 769
Activity, 495 ff.; ionic, 545, 608; of solids, 632
Activity coefficient: defined, 495 ff.; and solubility, 633; see also Mean ionic activity coefficient
Adiabatic changes, 116
Adiabatic flame temperatures, 368
Adiabatic process: change in entropy, 393; defined, 333; ideal gas, 331 ff.; speed of sound, 335
Adsorbents, 719
Adsorption: and catalysis, 769; defined, 689, 707; on liquids, 707; molecular theory of, 720; physical, 720; on solids, 719
Adsorption isotherm: for liquids, 707; for solids, 719
"Aging" of precipitates, 698
Allotropes, heat of formation, 357
Alloys: binary, 164; structure, 164
Alpha particles, 29 ff.
Amalgam electrodes, 549
Amorphous solids, 145
Andrews, Thomas, 198
Angle of contact, surface tension, 693, 695
Angular momentum: quantization, 57; quantum number, 76–82
Anisotropic crystals, 144
Anode, definition, 517
Antiparallel magnetic moments, 82
Antisymmetric function, 104, 107
Arrhenius, Svante, 487, 729
Arrhenius exponential, 763
Arrhenius rate equation, 757
Atmosphere, standard, 180
Atom recombinations, 761

Atomic crystal, 264
Atomic heats, 16
Atomic nucleus, 29
Atomic number, 95
Atomic orbital, 77; method, 103–106; in molecular structure, 8, 57 ff.
Atomic weight: C^{12} scale, 3; chemical and physical scales, 3, 17; from X-ray data, 18
Attractive force: between gas molecules, 202, 343; between unlike ions, 554
Autocatalysis, 772
Average speed, 239
Avogadro, Amedeo, 186
Avogadro's hypothesis, 5
Avogadro's number, 9
Azeotropic mixture, 658 ff.

Balmer, Johann, 55
Balmer series, 55
Band model, 160–166
Band spectra, 126
"Barn," 34
Bases, 611
Beattie-Bridgman equation, 210
Bending vibrations, 134, 137
Berthelot, Pierre, 384, 464
Berthelot's equation, 210
Berzelius, Jöns, 5
BET isotherm, 724
Beta particles, 30
Beta rays, 29
Bimolecular reaction, 733
Binary alloys, 164
Binding energy, 104
Bioluminescence, 729
Bjerrum, Nils, 600
Black-body radiation, 44
Blood, pH of, 629
Bodenstein, Ernst, 753, 764
Body-centered cubic structure, 149, 154
Bohr, Niels, 57, 62
Bohr atom, 57
Bohr radius, 93

Boiling point: diagrams, 654 ff.; elevation, 476; of gases, Table, 199; immiscible liquids, 666; rule, 282

Bolometers, 43

Boltzmann constant, 45, 222

Boltzmann distribution factor, 235 ff., 261 ff., 387, 555

Bond angle, 114

Bond energies: determination of, 370–372; Table, 374

Bond lengths, 132

"Bonding" electrons, 110

Bonds: carbon, 116; covalent, 110, 111, 156; crystalline, 156, 160; ionic, 109 ff.; metallic, 156–163, 199; polyatomic molecules, 110 ff.

Born, Max, 65

Born-Oppenheimer approximation, 127

Bottleneck effect, 752

Boundary method, Hittorf moving, 587

Boyle's law, 6, 183 ff., 221

Brackett series, 56

Bragg equation, 150, 154

Bravais, 149

Bridgman, P. W., 290, 650

Brillouin, L., 163

Brillouin zones, 163

Brittleness in solids, 159

Brönsted, Johannes N., 558, 611

Brönsted acid, 611–616, 769

Brownian motion, 719

Brunauer, Stephen, 724

Buffer solutions, 627–630

Calomel electrode, 515, 534, 546

Calorie, defined, 247

Calorimeter, bomb, 368

Camera, cylindrical X-ray, 152

Capacitance cell, 735

Capillary effects, 692

Carnot, Nicolas, 386, 396

Carnot cycle, 396, 397

Catalysis: acid base, 638, 769; auto-, 772; defined, 729; homogeneous, 768, 769

Catalytic poisons, 772

Catalytic properties, metals, 159

Catalyzed reactions: activation energies, 771; Table, 770, 771

Cathode, defined, 517

Cathode ray tube, 24

Cation, 572

Cavitate (cavitation), 206

Cell conventions, 517

Cell potentials, 516

Cell reaction: defined, 519; and free energy, 526; types of, 548

Celsius scale, 181

Centigrade scale, 181

Chadwick, James, 32

Chain reactions, 750–753

Chance, Britton, 736

Change of state, 324, 325, 403

Characteristic X-rays, 32, 96

Charge density: electrolyte solutions, 555; surface potential, 715

Charge distributions: atomic, 90 ff.; symmetry of, 111

Charge to mass ratio, 25

Charles' law, 6

Chemical equilibrium: and chemical potential, 403; electrolyte solutions, 623; and phase rule, 644

Chemical potential: and adsorption, 707; and chemical equilibrium, 410; defined, 405; and equilibrium constants, 427 ff.; and freezing point depression, 471; ideal gas, 418; and ionic activity, 501; ionic equilibria, 487; and physical equilibrium, 403, 406; pressure, effect of, 439; and solution equilibria, 462 ff.

Chemical species and phase rule, 645

Chemisorption, 720, 769

Christiansen, C., 753

Clapeyron equation, 408, 724

Clapp, L. B., 607

Clausius, Rudolf, 386

Clausius-Clapeyron equation, 409, 441

Coagulating agent, 717

Colligative properties, 475, 495

Collins cryostat, 343

Collision frequency, 226, 759

Collision theory: and first-order reactions, 765; of reaction rates, 760 ff.

Colloids: chemistry of, 717; physical properties, 718; types, 716

Colorimetry, 734

Combustion, heat of, 356

Common ion effect, 492, 609, 633

Competing reactions, 755

Complex ions, 125, 634

Components, phase rule, 646–648

Composition from chemical formula, 14

Composition variables, phase rule, 645 ff.

Compressibility coefficient, 291

Compressibility factor: critical region, 198; defined, 196; Hougen-Watson charts, 207; surface films, 712; van der Waals' equation, 203

Compression, ideal gas, 393

Concentration, units: for gases, 183; for liquid solutions, 304

Concentration cells: EMF, 548 ff.; with transference, 549; without transference, 550, 589

Concentration dependence, Debye-Hückel theory, 555

Condensation of liquids, 278
Condensation nuclei, vapor, 697
Condensed films, surface, 710, 713
Condensed phase, and gas equilibria, 439
Conductance: concentration dependence,
    580; equivalent, 578 ff.; and ion mobility,
    592; of ionic solutions, 571 ff.; limiting
    values, 582; measurement, 576; metallic,
    159, 571; specific, 580; in strong electro-
    lytes, 597; in weak electrolytes, 595 ff.
Conduction: electrical, in gases, 572; ionic,
    and Faraday's law, 573
Conductivity, ionic, 582, 583
Conductors, types of, 162, 571, 580
Congruent melting point, 671
Conjugate acid-base pair: defined, 611; equi-
    libria, 612 ff.
Consecutive reactions, 750
Conservation of energy, 71
Consolute points, 662
Constant boiling mixture, 659
Contact angle θ at interface, 693, 695
Contact catalyst, 768
Coolidge, A.S., 109
Cooling curves, 652–656, 669–672
Coordination number, 635
Coplanarity, sp^2 hybridization, 120
Correspondence principle, 62
Coulomb forces: ionic crystals, 167; ionic
    solutions, 553, 574, 599
Covalence, 101
Critical constants of gases, Table, 199
Critical point: law of corresponding states,
    208; and phase law, 649; solid-fluid, 275
Critical region: general, 197; and van der
    Waals' equation, 204
Critical solution pressure, 662
Critical temperature: boiling point rule, 282;
    surface tension, 704
Crookes, William, 24
Cryostat, 343
Crystal: atomic, 264; faces, 146; symmetry
    axes, 144; systems, 147; units, 154
Crystalline solids, characteristics of, 143, 581
Crystallization, fractional, 656
Cubic crystal, 146–156
Current: density, 577; flow in cells, 520
Current-voltage relationship, 576
Cyclic process, 396

d wave function, 77
Dalton, John, 2
Daniell cell, 520
Dative bond, 126
Davisson, C. J., 64
de Broglie, Louis, 63, 64
de Broglie's relation, 63, 233
Debye, Peter, 266, 719

Debye temperature, 267
Debye unit, 112
Debye-Hückel theory, ionic solutions, 552–
    562, 597
"Degraded" energy, heat, 399
Degree of dissociation: and conductance,
    596; and equilibrium constants, 609; in
    gases, 195
Degrees of freedom: and energy transfer,
    762; equipartition of energy, 256; and
    phase rule, 647–675
Delocalization of electrons, 121, 160
Democritus, 2
Desorption, 721, 769
Detergents, 708
Detonation wave, 736
Deviation from ideality in gases, 199
Diabetic coma, 629
Diatomic molecules: bond energies, 370;
    bonding in, 102–114; dipole moments,
    Table, 113; heat capacity, 251–259; mo-
    lecular spectra, 129–133
Dielectric constant: and dipole moment,
    291–296; and solubility, 482; of solvent,
    554, 636; and surface effects, 715; Table,
    300
Dieterici's equation, 210
Differential rate, method, 746
Diffusion, 228, 231, 287
Digonal hybridization, 121
Dilatometry, 735
Dilution law, 609
Dimerization, 485
Dipole forces, 170
Dipole moments: defined, 111; and ionic
    character, 115; measurement of, 293;
    Tables, 113, 296
Dirac, Paul, 82
Dispersed systems, types of, 716
Dispersion in colloidal solution, 716
Dissociation: and conductance, 595; of a gas,
    370; in ionic solutions, 608
Dissociation constant: complex ions, Table,
    635; of water, 616
Dissociation energies, 372, 765
Distillation, 661
Distribution: of energies, 234, 387; of solute
    between solvents, 483
Divalent elements, conductivity, 162
Double bond: electronic structure, 119; vi-
    bration frequencies, 137
Double layer, surface, 716
Double molecule, 485
Doublets, 62, 95
"Dry ice," 217
Dualistic nature of light, 63
Dühring's rule, 281
Du Nöuy tensiometer, 700

Efficiency, thermodynamic, 398
Effusion of a gas, 392
8-n rule, 163
Einstein equation, 3, 34
Einstein hypothesis, photoelectric effect, 49
Einstein theory of heat capacity, 266
Electric charge, the faraday, 524
Electric moments: see Dipole moments
Electrical changes, 512 ff.
Electrical conductivity: see Conductivity
Electrical effects at interfaces, 715
Electrical potential, and Debye-Hückel theory, 555
Electrochemical processes, 512–562
Electrode polarization, 578
Electrode potentials: and cell EMF, 533; defined, 532; Table of standard, 536; uses of, 537–542
Electrolysis, 520–524
Electrolyte solutions, 487, 512–638
Electrolytic cell: compartments of, 584; voltaic pile, 512
Electromagnetic waves, velocity of, 40
Electromotive force: see EMF
Electron: existence of, 23; mass of, 28; properties of, 25; size of, 29
Electron alloys, 163
Electron beams, 64
Electron bombardment of surfaces, 720
Electron compounds, 164
Electron configurations, 90
Electron density: in atoms, 91; in bonds, 107
Electron diffraction: and molecular structure, 154; and the wave nature of the electron, 7, 64
Electron microscope, 8
Electron repulsion, 84
Electron spin, 79–83
Electronegative elements, 167
Electronic charge, 27, 28
Electronic energy and heat capacity, 256
Electronic states: classifications, 78; hydrogenlike, 72–79; symmetry, 91
Electronic structures: heavy elements, 87–89; light elements, 84–86
Electronic transitions, 128
Electroosmosis, 719
Electrophoresis, 719
Electroplating, 523
Electropositive elements, 167
Elementary particles, 23
EMF: concentration dependence, 527, 590; defined, 522; and entropy of reaction, 542; and free energy change, 525; and heat of reaction, 542; pH measurement, 544, 618; temperature dependence, 542; in terms of electrode potentials, 533
EMF cells: see Concentration cells

Emission spectra, 59
Emissivity, 45
Emmett, P. H., 724
Emulsions, 716
Endothermic reactions: defined, 355; spontaneous, 385
Energy: of activation, 754 ff.; of dissociation, 370; and equilibrium, 403; of ionization, hydrogen, 59; and Schrödinger equation, 69
Energy band, 161
Energy conversion, efficiency, 398
Energy distribution (statistical), 234, 387
Energy level diagram: hydrogen, 61; sodium, 61
Energy levels: and heat capacity, 255–263; hydrogenlike, 72; molecular, 126; rotational, 130–132; vibrational, 132–137
Energy radiation, black-body, 44
Energy states: density of, 233; and the Third Law, 451
Energy transfer, collisions, 763
Engines, heat, 398
Enthalpy: defined, 344; heat of atomization, 370; heats of ionization, 362; heats of reaction, 354; and Joule-Thomson experiment, 344; partial molar, 361; standard heat of formation, 357
Enthalpy change, temperature dependence of, 366
Enthalpy-time plots, 669
Entropies, of reaction, 542; spectroscopic, and Third Law, Table, 454
Entropy: calculation of absolute, 452; and Carnot cycle, 396; change and heat of transition, 408; defined, 389; and free expansion, 392; spectroscopic, 455; surface, 702; and temperature scale, 390, 394; and thermal equilibrium, 391; and thermodynamic equilibrium, 400; Third Law, 451, 454
Enzyme, 770
Eötvös, Roland, 703
Eötvös "constant," 704
Equations of state: films, 709; gases, 178–211
Equilibria in ionic solutions, 608
Equilibrium: catalysts, effect of, 768; condition for, 405, 411; at constant temperature, 401; electrolyte solutions 525 ff.; gas phase and chemical potential, 419–427; ionic, 487; liquid-vapor, 475, 497; measurement of, 449; phase rule, 645; potential difference, 525; process, 393; properties of a gas, 226; solid-liquid, 471; solubility, 481; solution-vapor, 463; steady-state, 749; surface energy, 692; "surface vapor pressure," 714; temperature dependence, 432–438; thermal, 391; thermodynamic requirements for, 645

Equilibrium constant, K_P, 421
Equilibrium constants: complex ions, Table, 635; chemical, 466; and conductance, 596; hydrolysis, 619–622; indicators, 630; non-aqueous solvents, 637; pressure dependence, 429; solubility product, 632; and standard free energies, 442, 450; temperature dependence, 280; Third Law entropies, 451
Equipartition of energy, 256
Equivalent conductance, 578 ff.; at infinite dilution, 581
Equivalent ion conductance, 593
Equivalent weight, 16, 524
Eutectic halt, 668–671
Eutectic point, 667 ff.
Eutectic points, lead-tin-bismuth system, Table, 675
Exchange energy, 106
Excited electronic states, 59, 117
Exclusion principle, 79, 80, 167
Exothermic reaction: defined, 355; effect of temperature, 384
Expansion: coefficient of thermal, 289; work, 328
Explosion, 347
Extensive property, 390
Extraction, 483
Eyring, Henry, 766

f orbitals, 79
Face-centered cubic, 149,154
Fahrenheit scale, 181
Falling drop method, surface tension, 699
Faraday, unit of electrical charge, 524
Faraday's laws of electrolysis, 5, 523
Fermi-Dirac statistics, 269
Filled band, 162
Films, surface, classification, 710
Fine structure, 62
First Law of thermodynamics, 323–348; electrical work, 525; limitations of, 385; statement of, 327; thermochemistry, 354
First-order reactions, 737, 738; collision theory, 765
Flame temperatures, 369
Flow method, rate of reaction, 736
Fluidity, 274
Foams, 716
Fogs, 697, 716
Forbidden transitions, 136
Force between ions, 554
Formality, solution, 305
Fourfold coordination complexes, 124
Fourfold symmetry axis, 146
Fractional crystallization, 656, 669
Fractional distillation, 656
Franklin, Benjamin, 512

Free electron model, heat capacity, 268
Free energy: and condition for equilibrium, 402, 410; defined, 402; electrochemical cells, 525; of formation, determination of, 448; of formation, Table, 446; of ions, 555, 637; partial molar, 405; and the phase rule, 644; pressure dependence, 420; solution equilibrium, 463–503; surface, 689–695; temperature dependence, 432
Free energy changes: and EMF, 527, 542; junction potential, 552; standard, 442
Free particle, 69
Freezing point curve, 654–656, 666–680
Freezing point depression: electrolytes, 493; nonelectrolytes, 471–474
Frequency, electromagnetic radiation, 40
Frequency of collisions: expression for, 226; and rate constant, 763
Frequency condition, 57
Fugacity, 430, 532
Fuoss, Raymond M., 600

Galileo, 2
Galvani, Luigi, 512
Galvanic cell, 512; conventions, 517, 518; spontaneous reaction, 523
$\gamma_\pm$: see Mean ionic activity coefficient
Gamma rays, 29
Gas constant, 187, 192
Gas reactions, equilibria, 418–449
Gaseous films, 710
Gases: concentration units, 183; deviations from ideality, 199; equations of state, 203, 210; ideal, 191; kinetic theory of, 218; liquefication of, 197; mixtures of, 178; permanent, 197; properties of, 178; real, 194, 199 ff.; transport properties, 227
Gay-Lussac, Joseph Louis, 5
Geiger counters, 43
Germer, Lester H., 64
Gibbs, Willard, 242, 644
Gibbs' adsorption isotherm, 707
Gibbs' function, 402; see also Free energy
Gibbs' phase rule, 406, 645 ff.
Gibbs-Helmholtz equation, 543
Gilliam, O. R., 131
Glass, catalytic effect, 769
Glass electrode, 546
Globulins, separation of, 719
Goniometer, 145
Gordy, W., 131
Goudsmit, Samuel A., 82
Graham, Thomas, 717
Graham's law, 6
Gram equivalent weight: see Equivalent weight
Gram molecular weight, 182

Ground state: carbon atom, 117; hydrogen atom, 73
Guthrie, G. B., 308

Haber process, 437
Half-cell potentials, 536
Half-life: determination of reaction order, 743, 747; first-order reaction, 738
Halogen molecules, bonding, 111
Halt, eutectic, 656
Hardness, 143, 159
Harkins, W.D., 716
Heat: of adsorption, 723; of atomization, bond energies, 371–374; of combustion, 356; conduction of, 159; of dilution, 359; of dissociation, 371; of fusion, 408, 472; of hydration, 362; of hydrogenation, 357; of ionization, 362; of mixing, 361; of neutralization, 362; of solution, 359, 361; statement of First Law, 327, 385; of vaporization, Trouton's rule, 282
Heat capacities: of gases, Table, 251; polyatomic crystals, Table, 268
Heat capacity: constant pressure, C_p, 248; constant volume, C_v, 248; Debye theory of, 266; defined, 247; difference in general case, 340; difference in ideal gas, 250; Einstein theory of, 266; electronic, 261; and heat of reaction, 367; metals, 268; rotational, 257; solids, 264; temperature dependence, 253; Third Law entropy, 453; translational, 252; vibrational, 259
Heat capacity ratio, 335; velocity of sound, 337
Heat content: see Enthalpy
Heat equilivalent of work, 324
Heat of formation: and equilibrium constants, 454; of ions, Table, 365; standard, 357; Table, 359
Heat of reaction: concept, 355; at constant pressure, 357; and EMF, 542; temperature dependence, 366
Heat to work conversion, 396
Heisenberg, Werner, 62
Heisenberg uncertainty principle, 67
Heitler, W., 104
Heitler-London atomic orbital, 109, 111, 115
Helmholtz, Hermann von, 24, 715
Helmholtz double layer, 717
Helmholtz function, 401
Henry's law, 316, 466
Hertz, Heinrich, 48
Hertzian waves, 42
Herzfeld, K. F., 753
Hess' law of constant heat summation, 355
Heterogeneous catalysis, 768

Heterogeneous equilibria: gases, 438; solutions, 462
Heterogeneous reactions, defined, 404
Hexagonal layer structure, 158
Hexagonal system crystal, 148
Higgins, William, 2
High-energy particles, 729
Hindered rotation, 135
Hittorf method (transport numbers), 584–587
Hodgkin, Dorothy, 173
Hofmeister's series, 718
"Hole theory" of liquids, 284
Homogeneous catalysis, 768
Homogeneous gas reactions, 418–437
Hougen, O. A., 207
Hougen-Watson charts, 207
Hückel, E., 597
Hume-Rothery, W., 165
Hund's rules, 90
Hybridization, 116–126
Hydration, 612, 619
Hydrogen atom spectrum and energy levels, 54–57
Hydrogen bond, 172, 199, 301
Hydrogen electrode, 519; effect of pressure on, 531
Hydrogen ion: Brönsted acid, 611; mobility, 591; solvation of, 575
Hydrogen ion concentration: buffered solutions, 627; indicators, 630; pH, 544
Hydrogen molecule, electronic wave function, 106–108
Hydrogenation: heat of, 367; unsaturated organic compounds, 769
Hydrogenlike wave functions, 72
Hydrolysis, 619–622
Hydronium ion, 675, 612
Hydrosols, 717
Hydroxonium ion, 612
Hydroxyl ion proton affinity, 614

Ice, high-pressure forms of, 650
"Ice point," 181, 191
Ideal efficiency, 398
Ideal gas: chemical potential changes, 418; collision frequencies, 326; expansion work, 330; reaction equilibria, 420
Ideal gas law, 191; deviations from, 202; and kinetic theory, 281 ff.
Ideal gas temperature scale, 181, 190, 394
Ideal solutions: chemical potential of, 463; deviations from, 495, 552; Raoult's law, 310
Ideality in gases, deviation from, 199
Immiscible liquids, steam distillation, 665
Incomplete shells, 159

Incongruent melting point, 671
Independent variables, 647
Indeterminacy, position and momentum, 66
Indicators, acid-base, 629–631
Induced dipole forces, 170
Induced polarization, 295
Induction period, 752
Infrared spectra, 126–129, 137
Inhibition, 772
Initial rate, 746
Instability constants, complex ions, Table, 635
Insulators, electrical, 158, 162
Interatomic distances, 132
Interfaces: see Surface
Interfaces, electrical effects at, 715
Interfacial tension: see Surface tension
Interionic forces, 501, 597, 637
Intermolecular repulsive forces, 200
Internal coordinates, 136
Internal energy: concept of, 325; and conditions for equilibrium, 400; First Law of thermodynamics, 327, 346; as a function of state, 338; ideal gas, 332; and Second Law of thermodynamics, 385–388
Internal kinetic energy, 255
Internal pressure, 203
Internuclear distance, bimolecular reaction, 764
Interplanar distance, 151
Invariant systems, 649
Inversion of sucrose, 739
Inversion point, Joule-Thomson, 342
Ion: association, 597 ff.; atmosphere, 555; complexes, 634; conductances, limiting, 591; interactions, strong electrolytes, 597; mobility, 592; pair effects, 600; potentials, 490; product constant temperature dependence, 616; sizes, in crystals, 168; speeds, 593; transport, 589; triplets, 600
Ionic activity, 556; coefficient, 558
Ionic charge and activity, 560
Ionic conduction and Faraday's law, 573
Ionic conductivity, 574 ff.
Ionic dipole moments, Table, 113
Ionic equilibria, 608; and chemical potential, 487
Ionic equilibrium, solution of problems, 622
Ionic interactions, and the Debye-Hückel theory, 552 ff.
Ionic radii, Table, 94
Ionic reactions, 607–638; cell conventions, 517; kinetics of, 737; in nonaqueous systems, 636
Ionic solutions, freezing point depressions, 493
Ionic term, bond orbitals, 111, 123

Ionization: of an acid, 610 ff.; buffer solutions, 623; complete, 554; constant, 608; dilute solutions, 488; indicators, 630; potential, electronic spectra, 59
Ionization constants: acids, Table, 612; bases, Table, 615
Ionized fraction, 609
Ions: complex, 125, 634; with single electron, 60
Isobaric planes, phase diagrams, 662
Isoelectronic anion relative size, 93
Isolation method, 747
Isomerizations, kinetics of, 749
Isomorphism, law of, 17
Isopleth, 663
Isothermal projections, 678
Isotherms: for adsorption of gases on charcoal, 721; ideal gas, 335; surface films, 714
Isotropic abundances, 34
Isotropic crystals, 144

James, H. M., 109
Jellies, 716
Johnson, R. S., 131
Joule, James P., 247, 324
Joule (energy unit), 247
Joule experiment, 331
Joule-Thomson coefficient, 342, 344
Joule-Thomson experiment, 340
Junction potential effect, 589
Junction potentials, 551, 552

K lines, 95
Kamerlingh-Onnes, H., 197
Katayama, S., 704
Kékulé structure, 375
Kelvin, Lord, 182, 340, 386
Kelvin equation, 697
Kelvin temperature scale, 182
Kieselguhr, 719
Kinetic energy: average, in gases, 223, 239; translational, quantization of, 232
Kinetic theory: of gases, 6, 219 ff.; rate constant, 763
Kinetics, chemical, 727–772
Kirkwood, J. G., 302
Kohlrausch, Friedrich, 513, 581
Kohlrausch's law, 583
Kraus, C. A., 600
Kundt's tube, 336

Λ: see Conductivity, ionic
LaMer, Victor K., 558
Langmuir, Irving, 720
Langmuir adsorption isotherm, 723
Langmuir surface balance, 709
Laplace, Pierre Simon, 354

Latent heat: of fusion, 408; of vaporization, 407
Laue patterns, 151
Lavoisier, Antoine, 354
Law of combining volumes, 4, 14
Law of combining weights, 4, 13
Law of conservation of mass, 3
Law of corresponding states, 209
"Law of constancy of interfacial angles," 145
Law of constant heat summation, 355
Law of definite proportions, 3, 11
Law of Dulong and Petit, 16
Law of Lavoisier and Laplace, 354
Law of mass action, 418
Law of multiple proportions, 4, 12
"Law of rational indices," 146
Laws of electrolysis, 512
Laws of thermochemistry, 354
Le Châtelier's principle, 383; effect of concentration, 424; effect of pressure, 425; effect of temperature, 432
Lenard, P. E. A., 30
Leucippus, 2
Lewis, G. N., 430, 556
Limiting behavior, dilute solutions, 466
Lindemann, F. A., 766
Linear molecule, molecular spectra of, 127
Linearity of thermometers, 190
Liquid mixtures with limited miscibility, 662
Liquid state, 273–317
Liquid-solid equilibria, 654
Liquid-vapor equilibria, 653; steam distillation, 655
Liquid-vapor interface, 695
Liquids: completely miscible, 666; equation of state, 288; structure of, 276; viscosities of, 284
Localized atomic orbitals, 110
London, F., 104
London dispersion forces, 170
Long-range order, 145, 277
Lubricating properties, graphite, 157
Lyman series, 56, 59
Lyophilic sols, 718
Lyophobic sols, 718
Lyotropic series, 718

Magnetic moment, oxygen, 114
Magnetic moments, antiparallel, 82
Magnetic quantum number, 76, 79
Malleability, 159
Manometric measurements, 735
Mass: of electron, 25; hydrogen atom, 33
Mass action expression, 428
Mass spectrometer, 7, 33
Mass/charge ratio, 25

Matter, states of, comparison, 274
Maximum boiling mixtures, 660
Maximum bubble method, 698
Maximum electrical work, 525
Maximum reversible work, 329, 398
Maxwell, James C., 225, 229, 256, 298
Maxwell distribution, 237–241
McLeod equation, 704
Mean free path, 224
Mean ionic activity coefficient: defined, 500; and EMF, 527, 535; and Debye-Hückel theory, 556 ff.
Mechanism and kinetics, 755
Melting: entropy change, 407; physical equilibria, 403
Melting point: amorphous solids, 145; curve, 656; depression of, 471; diagram, 666–670; index of purity, 669; pressure dependence, 409; three-component system, 673; unstable, 651
Membrane, solvent-permeable, 478
Mesons, 8
Metal electrodes, 514
Metallic bonding, 156
Metallic properties, 159
Metals, heat capacity of, 268
Metastable equilibrium, 651
Mho, 576
Micelle, 717
Michelson, Albert, 40
Microwave spectroscopy, 129
Migration, 550, 586 ff.
Miller indices, 147
Millikan, R. A., 27
Millikan oil drop experiment, 27, 719
Minimum boiling point, 658
Miscibility gap, 662, 664
Mixed melting point, 669
Mixing chamber, 736
Mixtures of gases, 193
Mobility, ionic, 588 ff.
Modes of vibration, 134
Molality, 305, 307
Molarity, 305, 307
Mole, 183
Mole fraction, 306, 307
Molecular collisions, 224
Molecular crystals, 169
Molecular energies, 102, 255; of gases, 246
Molecular orbital method, 106–109
Molecular properties of matter, 390
Molecular refractions, 299
Molecular spectra, 126–137
Molecular structure, 102
Molecular vibrations, 134
Molecular volume, 202
Molecular weights, determination of, 719
Molecularity, 732

Molecules, concept, 2
Moment of inertia, 130, 131
Momentum change: pressure, 219; viscosity, 229
Monatomic gas, heat capacity, 252
Monoclinic crystal system, 148
Monolayer (or unimolecular) films, 709
Monomer, 485
Moseley's law, 95
Moving boundary method, 587
Multi-electron atoms, 61
Multilayer adsorption, 724

Natural process, entropy change, 391
Negative deviation, monolayer films, 713
Negative ions, anions, 572
Negative pressure, 206
Neutralization, Brönsted definition, 613
Neutrino, 8
Neutron, 8
Newton, Isaac, 2
Newton's Second Law, 336
Nonaqueous systems, 636
Noncoherent film, 710
Nonequilibrium condition, 399, 420
Nonideal behavior, gas phase, 199ff., 331, 429
Nonlinear triatomic molecules, 134
Nonmetallic elements, 163
Nonpolar gases, dielectric constant, Table, 294
Nonpolar liquids, dielectric constant, 297
Normality, 305
Normalization condition, 72
Noyes, A. A., 490
Nuclear charge: and electron distribution, 92; X-ray diffraction, 95
Nuclear mass, 33
Nuclear resonance experiments, 302
Nuclear size, 34

Ohm's law, 521, 576
One-electron atoms, 60, 92
Onsager, Lars, 302, 598
Oppenheimer, Robert J., 127
Optical isomer, melting point of, 670
Optical microscope, resolution, 8
Optical properties, colloids, 718
Optical rotatory power, 734; crystals, 144
Orbit, Bohr, 57, 62
Orbital: atomic, 77; atomic, molecular structure, 110; hybrid, 116; molecular, 108, 111; unoccupied, 159
Order: degree of, in crystals, 145; of reaction, determination of, 744–748; and reaction mechanism, 732, 733; of reflection, 155
Ortho-para hydrogen conversion, 747

Orthorhombic system, crystal, 147
Osomotic pressure, 477–480
Ostwald, William, 2, 513
Ostwald dilution law, 596
Overvoltage at electrodes, 523
Oxidation: defined, 517; ease of, 537; potential, 532; potentials, Table, 536
Oxidation-reduction: indicator, 630; reactions, 539
Oxide hydrosols, 717
Oxonium ion, 575; see also Hydronium ion

p function, 75
p orbitals, 77
p type semiconductors, 166
"p" values, 618
Pairing, electron, 105, 110
Parachor, 704, 705
Parallel spins, 114
Paramagnetism, 114
Partial miscibility, 662
Partial molar quantities, 361, 405–407
Partial pressure, 193, 420
Particle in a box, 70
Paschen series, 56
Passive electrodes, 516
Pauli exclusion principle, 79; and the bond model, 161; heat capacity of metals, 268; and molecular bonds, 105, 110; and the periodic table, 84
Pauling, Linus, 117, 163
Pauling's rule, 168
Penicillin, 173
Perfect gas: see Ideal gas
Periodic table, 9, 83
Peritectic, 671
"Perpetual motion," 382
pH: blood, 629; measurement, 544–548; scale, 617
Phase, defined, 645
Phase diagram, 274; carbon dioxide, 275; water, 650
Phase discontinuities, 688
Phase equilibrium, condition for, 405, 463
Phase rule: derivation of, 645–648; one-component system, 649; three-component system, 673; two-component system, 653 ff.
Photochemical reactions, 736
Photochemistry, 729
Photoelectric effect, 48
Physical atomic weight scale, 3, 17
Physical equilibria, 403
Physical process, 343
π bond, 114, 119
Piezoelectric effect, 144
pK, defined, 618
Planar square structure, 125

Planck, Max, 46
Planck radiation law, 47
Planck's constant, 47
Planetary electron, 54
Poise, (unit), 285
Poiseuille's method, 284
Poison, catalytic, 772
Polanyi, Michael, 753
Polarimeter, 734
Polarity: see Dipole moments
Polarizability of neutral molecules, 294–300
Polarization: and conductance measurements, 578; induced dipoles, 170; in ionic solutions, 554
Polishing, and surfaces of solids, 690
Polyatomic crystals, heat capacity, Table, 268
Polyatomic molecules, energy levels, 255
Polybasic oxy-acid, ionization of, 613
Polythermal projection, 676, 678
Positive adsorption, 709
Positive ions (cations), 572
Positron, 8
Potential, junction, 516, 554
Potential difference: electrolysis, 521; at an interface, 715; Ohm's law, 576
Potential energy surface, absolute rate theory, 766
Potentiometer, 522
Powder diagram, 152
Precipitates, aging of, 698
Precipitation, 717
Pressure: defined, 179; effect on equilibrium, 424; ideal gas, 222
"Pressure" of films, 712
Price, C. C., 467
Primary ionization, 614
Principal quantum number, n, 57, 72, 78
Probability: and entropy, 389; quantum mechanical, 66, 73
Promoters, catalytic, 772
Properties of liquids, 273
Protease, 772
"Protein error," 631
Proton, 8; acceptor, 611; donor, 611; transfer, 595, 613, 619
Pseudo first-order reaction, 739
Pseudoequilibrium, 672
ψ function, 66
Pulsed electric fields, 737
PVT charts, 207

Quantity, and concentration, 182
Quantization: of rotational energy, 130; of translational energy, 232; of vibrational energy, 132
Quantum, energy, 48, 49
Quantum mechanics, development of, 62

Quantum numbers, 55, 78, 130, 132
Quantum theory, and heat capacity, 261
Quenching of reactions, 734
Quinhydrone electrode, 544, 546, 618

R, gas constant, 192
Radiant energy, distribution of, 44 ff.
Radiation: black-body, 44; electromagnetic, 39
Radii of atoms and ions, 94
Radio waves, 42
Radioactivity, 29
Radius: Bohr, 73; molecular, 225; nuclear, 34
Radius ratio of ions, 168
Raman effect, 136
Ramsay-Shields equation, 704
Randall, M., 430
Raoult's law, 310–316; and chemical potential of solutions, 463–475
Rate of adsorption, 722
Rate constant, dimensions of, 744
Rate of deactivation, 766
Rate of desorption, 722
Rate of reaction: absolute theory of, 763–767; competing reactions, 755; consecutive reactions, 750; determination of order, 745–748; fast reactions, 736; first-order reaction, 737–739; influencing factors, 727; measurement of, 733–737; opposing reactions, 748; order and molecularity, 732; rate equation, 730, 731; second-order reaction, 739; steady-state approximation, 754; temperature dependence, 280, 756; and thermodynamics, 448; third-order reaction, 741–743; zero-order reaction, 743
Rate-limiting step, 750
Ratio of mass to charge, 25
Ratios of interplanar distances in crystals, 155
Rayleigh-Jeans law, 46
Reaction: equilibria, 410; intermediate, 768; of order n, 743
Reaction rate: see Rate of reaction
Reaction velocity: see Rate of reaction
Reactions: competing, 755; consecutive, 750; at electrodes, 512; first-order, 737–739; kinetics, 727 ff.; opposing, 748; second-order, 739; in solutions, 462 ff.; third-order, 741; zero-order, 743
Real gas, deviation from ideality, 195
Recombination, atomic, 761
Rectilinear diameters, rule of, 283
Reduced mass, 58
Reduced pressure, 207
Reduced temperature, 207
Reduction, defined, 517

Reference axes, crystal systems, 146
Reference electrode, 515
Reflection order, 155
Refractions: additivity of, 299; atomic and group, 299; molar, 298
Refractive index, 298
Reid, A., 65
Repulsive force: crystals, 171; gases, 342
Resistance, Ohm's law, 576
Resonance, 107; energy, 121, 375; of valence bond structures, 121
Restrictions, and the phase rule, 646
Retarding potential, 49
Reverse reaction, 748
Reversibility, 330, 570
Reversible cell reactions, 535
Rhombohedral system, crystal, 148
Richardson, O. W., 721
RMS speed, 223
Root mean square speed, 223
Rotational energy levels, 130
Rotational spectra, 129–134
Roughton, F. J. W., 736
Rumford, Benjamin, 324
Rutherford, Ernest, 30
Rutile structure, 169
Rydberg constant, 55, 58
Rydberg equation: general, 55; X-rays, 96

s orbitals, 77
St. Gilles, P. de 464
Salt, molten, 572
Salt bridge, 516, 552
Salt effect, 493
Salt error, 631
Salting-out, 718
Saturated hydrocarbons, bond energies, 372
Saturation effect, gaseous adsorption, 721
Scattering power, 156
Schrödinger, Erwin, 62
Schrödinger equation, 69
Screening by electrons, 97
Second Law of thermochemistry, 355
Second Law of thermodynamics, 382–411; Carnot cycle, 396; statement of, 390; tests of, 391–394
Secondary ionization, 613, 614
Second-order rate law, 740; and first-order reactions, 765
Second-order reaction, collision theory, 759
Second-order reactions, 739
Second-order reflection, 156
Sedimentation-equilibrium, ultracentrifuge, 719
Sedimentation-velocity, ultracentrifuge, 719
Selection rule: electronic transitions, 61;

rotational transitions, 130; vibrational transitions, 133, 135
Self-diffusion, 287
Semiconductors, 163–166
Semipermeable membranes, 478
Series, electronic transitions, 56
Series limit, electronic transitions, 59
Sequester, 673
Shear flow, 284, 285
Shielding: of the nucleus, 84; by solvent molecules, 554
Shock tube, 736
σ bonds, 111, 119
Silica gel, adsorption by, 719
Simple cubic structure, 149
Single-component system, 649 ff.
Size effects, 560
Smith, R. Angus, 8
Smokes, 716
Soaps, 30
Soddy, Frederick, 145
Softening point, 145
Solid solutions, 670
Solid state, 142–143
Solidified foams, 716
Solid-liquid equilibria, 654, 660
Solids: amorphous, 145; crystalline, 143
Sols, 717
Solubility: and activity coefficients, 558; dependence on total ion concentration, 492; from EMF measurements, 541; thermodynamic requirements, 481
Solubility product, 492, 541, 631–634; constant, Table, 632
Solute, defined, 303
Solute associations, 485
Solution boundary, electrolytic cell, 549
Solution composition, 306
Solution concentration, units, 304
Solution equilibria: condition for, 462; the phase rule, 644
Solution laws, 314
Solutions: buffer, 622–630; concepts, 302; solid, 670
Solvated protons, 611
Solvation, 574
Solvent: defined, 303; role in solution equilibrium, 468
Solvent drag, 598
Solvent molecules, shielding effect, 554
Solvent power, 303
Sorensen, S. P. L., 548
Sorption, 689
sp hybridization, 121
sp^2 hybridization, 119
sp^3 hybridization, 117
sp^2d hybridization, 125
sp^3d^2 hybridization, 126

Species, defined, 645
Specific conductance: defined, 577; of electrolyte solutions, 578–580
Specific heat: *see* Heat capacity
Specific rate constants, 729, 737; temperature dependence, 757; theory of, 759
Specific volume, liquids, Table, 289
Spectra: atomic, 57; molecular, 126; rotational, 129 ff.; vibrational, 132 ff.
Spectroscopic entropies, Table, 454
Speed, RMS, 223
Speed of electromagnetic radiation, 40
Speed of gas molecules, 223
Speed of ions in solution, 592
Spin, electron, 81–83
Spontaneous process: entropy change, 389; internal energy change, 400
Square planar structure, 125
Stalagmometer, 699
Standard atmosphere, 180
Standard chemical potential, 419
Standard electrode potential: defined, 535; Table, 536
Standard EMF, 528, 534
Standard entropies, Table, 454
Standard entropy change, 450; electrolytic cell, 543
Standard free energies of formation, determination of, 449
Standard free energy, 420; of formation, Table, 446
Standard free energy change, electrolytic cell, 527
Standard heat of reaction, 434; electrolytic cell, 543
Standard heats of formation, 357
Standard state, pure liquid, 463
State: change of, 324, 325, 403; function, 389; of a system, 328
States of matter, comparison, 274
Statistical mechanics, 235, 388
Statistical nature of heat, 386
Statistics, and the Third Law, 451
Steady-state approximation, 754
Steam distillation, 665
Steam point, 181
Stefan-Boltzmann law, 44
Steric factors, 761
Stoke's law, 594
Stoney, G. J., 24
Stretching vibrations, 134–137
Strong electrolytes: conductivity of, 574–595; ion interactions in, 597
Structure of molecules, 101–137
Sublimation, 179; pressure curve, 649
Sugden, Samuel, 704
Supercooled liquid, 651
Superheating, 477

Supermolecular orbital, 268
Superperitectic temperatures, 672
Supersatured gas, 206
Surface, molar properties, 702
Surface active agents, 708
Surface catalysis, 769
Surface concentration, defined, 706
Surface double layer, 716
Surface effect on vapor pressure, 695
Surface energy, 689–695
Surface enthalpy, 695, 704
Surface entropy, 704
Surface equation of state, 721
Surface film, analogue for, 711
Surface free energy, 689–707
Surface potential measurements, 710
Surface pressure, 710
Surface tension, 691–710; composition dependence, 705; temperature dependence, 704; values, Table, 701–702
Surface work, 692
Surfaces, nature of, 688
Symmetric function: atomic orbital, 104; valence bond orbital, 109
Symmetry properties, crystal systems, 146
System: closed, 404; defined, 646

T^3 law, 267, 453
Temperature: flames, 368; and kinetic energy, 221; and phase law, 646; scale, 181, 188; and the Second Law of thermodynamics, 390
Temperature-composition diagram, 662
Temperature-enthalpy graphs, 669
Teller, E., 724
Ternary eutectic, Table, 675
Ternary mixture, 673
Tetragonal systems, crystal, 147, 148
Tetrahedral bonding, 117, 156, 157
Thermal analysis, 652–655, 671, 672
Thermal conductivity: of gases, 230; metal, 162
Thermal expansion, 288
Thermistors, 43
Thermochemistry, laws of, 354
Thermocouples, 43
Thermodynamic conductions for equilibrium, 400
Thermodynamic scale of temperature, 181, 394
Thermodynamics: First Law of, 323; Second Law of, 389; Third Law of, 462
Thermometry, 188
Third body, 762
Third Law entropies, Tables, 454
Third Law of thermodynamics, 451
Third-order reactions, 741
Thomsen, J., 384

Thomson, G. P., 65
Thomson, J. J., 8, 24
Thomson, William, 340
Three-component system, 673
Threefold axes, crystal, 146
Tie line: three-component system, 679; two-component system, 665
Titoff, A., 721
Titration curve, calculation of, 625
Tobacco mosaic virus, 717
Torsional vibration, 135, 137
Transfer of matter, electrolytic cell, 548
Transference, 550, 551
Transference numbers, 584, 590
Transition elements, 85, 159
Transition halt, 673
Translational energy: distribution of, 239; heat capacity, 252; quantization of, 233
Transport: of energy, 228; of mass, 228, 231; of momentum, 228
Transport numbers: determination of, 583; of ions, 590
Transport properties of gases, 226
Triclinic systems, crystal, 148
Trigonal bonding, 119
Triple bond, 121
Triple point, 647, 649
Trouton's rule, 282
True equilibrium constant, 501
Two-component systems, 653–673
Two-dimensional surface pressure, 709
Twofold axes, 146
Tyndall effect, 718

Uhlenbeck, George E., 82
Ultracentrifuge, 719
Uncertainty principle, 65
Unimolecular films, 709
Unimolecular reaction: collision theory, 765; molecularity, 733
Unit cell, 148, 154
Units: of concentration, 304; of heat, 246; of pressure, 180; of rate constants, 744; of volume, 179; of work, 246
Unstable equilibrium, thermodynamic, 651

Valence bond orbital, 104, 109
Valence crystals, 158
Valence type, effect on activity, 558
van der Waals, Johannes D., 201, 203
van der Waals' attraction, 301
van der Waals' constant a, 203
van der Waals' constant b, 226
van der Waals' constants, 206; Table, 199
van der Waals' equation, 203, 204
van der Waals' forces, 169, 202
van der Waals' surface tension equation, 704

Van't Hoff, Jacobus H., 474, 513
Van't Hoff equation, 757
Vapor pressure, 197, 278; curve, and phase rule, 649; curved surfaces, 695; deviations, 658, 660; lowering, 475; of solutions, 308; temperature dependence, 407
Variables, thermodynamic, 646
Variance, phase rule, 647, 649
Velocity distribution, 239
Velocity of electromagnetic radiation, 40
Velocity of migration: see Mobility, ionic
Velocity of reaction: see Rate of reaction
Vibration of molecules, 127
Vibrational energy levels, 132–137
Vibrational heat capacity, 259–263
Vibrational spectra and bond energies, 370
Vibration-rotation spectra, 129
"Violet catastrophe," 46
Virial coefficients, 211, 429
Virial equations, 210, 211
Viscosities of liquids, Table, 286
Viscosity: approximate temperature dependence, 280; of colloids, 719; and ion speeds, 593; kinetic theory of, 227–230; measurement of, 284
Volta, Alessandro, 512
Voltaic pile, 512
Volume: specific, of liquids, 289; units of, 179
Volume changes, measurement of reaction rates, 735
Von Laue, Max T. F., 95

Walden's rule, 595
Water gas reaction, 437
Water molecule, electronic structure, 123
Watson, K. M., 207
Wave equation, 69, 70
Wave function, 65; atomic orbital method, 103 ff.; boundary conditions, 67; molecular orbital method, 102; statistical nature, 68
Wave nature of the electron, 62
Wave number, 41
Wave property of matter, 63
Wavelength, 40
Weak electrolyte: conductance of, 580, 595; ionization of, 611, 613
Weight formality, 305
Weight fraction, 304, 306
Weight molarity, 305
Weight normality, 305
Weight percent, 304
Weight ratio, 304
"Weiss notation," 147
Wein, Max, 47
Wilhelmy, L., 734

Work: conversion of heat to, 396; defined, 327; electrical, 525; expansion, 250, 328; heat equivalent, 324; isothermal, 217, 330; and kinetic energy, 346; surface, 692
Work function, defined, 401

X-ray diffraction, 6, 96
X-ray patterns, 143

X-ray scattering, liquids, 276
X-ray series, 95
X-ray structures, 171, 301
X-rays, 32, 95, 96

Zartman, I. F., 241
Zero-order reactions, 743
Zymase, 772